Birds of the Czech Republic

Birds of the Czech Republic

Josef Kren

CHRISTOPHER HELM
A & C BLACK · LONDON

DEDICATION

To my grandfather, the late Frantisek Vasat, who taught me how to be a patient and humble observer of Nature.

Line drawings by Pavel Prochazka

Christopher Helm (Publishers) Ltd., a subsidiary of A & C Black (Publishers) Ltd., 35 Bedford Row, London WC1R 4JH

0-7136-4784-1

A CIP catalogue record for this book is available from the British Library

Printed and bound by Biddles Ltd, Guildford, Surrey in Great Britain

CONTENTS

Preface 6
Foreword by Professor Paul Johnsgard 7
Acknowledgements 8
Introduction 9
Format of the book 11
Geographical and ecological background 16
Bird protection, Ramsar sites, and Important Bird Areas 23
Photographs of habitats in the Czech Republic 43
Species accounts 61
- Gaviiformes 61
- Podicipediformes 63
- Pelecaniformes 66
- Ciconiiformes 68
- Phoenicopteriformes 75
- Anseriformes 76
- Accipitriformes 94
- Falconiformes 107
- Galliformes 111
- Gruiformes 115
- Charadriiformes 122
- Pteroclidiformes 151
- Columbiformes 152
- Cuculiformes 156
- Strigiformes 157
- Caprimulgiformes 164
- Apodiformes 165
- Coraciiformes 166
- Piciformes 169
- Passeriformes 177
- Accidentals 260

Where to watch birds 286
Bibliography 310
Place names 313
Checklists 317
Appendix A: Species which may be hunted in the Czech Republic 329
Appendix B: Plant names 330
Appendix C: Useful addresses 331
Index of species 332

PREFACE

It is early in the morning and I am sitting in the backyard of my parents' house. I love this part of the day, when the chorus of singing birds is not yet disturbed by all the surrounding noises. It is the same backyard where 30 years ago my grandfather, the late Frantisek Vasat, introduced me to an activity which became my love and a part of my life. The backyard is almost the same and has not changed too much since my early days of birdwatching. There are probably the same species here today that my grandfather showed me in my early childhood. At the time I did not keep a record of birds I had seen because I was not even in my first grade and was unable to write. However, I memorized the names, many of them folk names given to birds by laymen. My grandfather passed away before I was able to show him my serious interest in studying nature, and particularly birds. As the years passed by, I became more and more involved in ornithology, one of the most fascinating subjects within zoology. During my undergraduate and graduate studies in the 1980s, several foreign ornithologists became my correspondents, and I quickly realized the lack of information on Czech birds for non-natives. It was mostly due to the language barrier, since almost all the papers on birds were published in Czech with brief German or, rarely, English summaries. The exchange of scientific information between the West and East was not flourishing at the time because of the many government restrictions on communication. After the positive changes in the Czech political climate in 1989, the door opened for foreigners travelling to the Czech Republic as well as Czechs 'discovering' the West. I was lucky enough. After a brief research period at Ben-Gurion University in Israel, I came to the United States of America. At the University of Nebraska-Lincoln I met my future Ph.D. advisor, Professor Paul Johnsgard. Spending 7 days a week with a person who has written almost 40 books on birds encouraged me in my idea to bring coherent information on the Czech avifauna to an English-speaking audience in the form of a book. After Gerald Gorman's book, *The Birds of Hungary*, was published in 1996, my decision to complete a similar book was irreversible.

This book is aimed at birdwatchers travelling to the Czech Republic and seeking information on the status and distribution of birds in the country and the areas in which they may be found. It is also aimed at professional ornithologists looking for more detailed information on distribution, which is not provided in the large-scale maps in monographs on birds within large geographical areas, as well as more detail on migration, habitats, vertical distribution etc. The data provided on breeding and non-breeding densities may be of interest to them as well. Everyone who needs quick access to basic data on the birds of the Czech Republic need look no further!

Josef Kren
Podoli, Czech Republic

FOREWORD by Professor Paul Johnsgard

It is with great pleasure that I write this introductory piece to Dr Josef Kren's welcome volume, the first English-language book on the birds of the Czech Republic. In reviewing earlier drafts of the manuscript I was amazed to learn how much distributional information is available on the avifauna of this relatively small European country, and its notable diversity of both habitats and bird species. I would never have imagined that such wonderfully diverse and spectacular species as Barred Warbler, Golden Oriole, Bearded Tit, White-backed and Syrian Woodpeckers, Ural Owl and White-tailed Eagle might be seen there. Nearly 400 species are documented, each with an associated range map and appropriate county-level symbols indicating seasonal or breeding status. Information on population trends and seasonal timing is also provided for every species.

One of the most welcome and remarkable aspects of this book is the high degree of detail as to locational information that is available for each species, either in terms of their associated range maps or described in narrative form. There is not only a listing of the most important bird areas of the country, with associated maps, descriptions of these areas and their associated species, but also detailed information on obtaining access to them. The same is true of the major birdwatching areas of the Czech Republic, with additional suggestions for planning birding trips.

I congratulate Dr Kren on providing this valuable addition to our knowledge of the central European avifauna, and also the publisher A & C Black for producing it and gambling on its economic success. There can be no doubt that it will be a major scientific achievement.

Paul A. Johnsgard, Foundation Professor
University of Nebraska-Lincoln

ACKNOWLEDGEMENTS

One author alone could not have collected all of the information provided in this book. Several of my colleagues in the Czech Republic welcomed my decision to gather the most recent knowledge of some aspects of the country's avifauna and helped me in numerous ways. I would like to thank Kvetoslav Frystak, David Horal, Martin Hrouzek, Petr Pavelcik, Zdenek Polasek, Libor Schöpfer and Petr Simcik. My special thanks to Martin Hrouzek, Jaroslav Klapste and Pavel Vasak whose field expertise and all-round knowledge greatly improved this book.

Information on Slovak bird names, and the status and population of birds within that country, was provided by Bohumil Murin and Ludovit Kocian. My friend and birding partner on several trips in the Czech Republic, Germany and Slovakia, Hans Grünwald, kindly checked the German names and allowed me to use his photographs in this book. I was also kindly provided with photographs of various habitats by Borek Seehak, who made special trips to take the pictures I needed. The line drawings are by Pavel Prochazka, who produced them within a short space of time, and they were paid for by my parents, Irena and Jiri Matousek.

Last but not least I want to thank to my friends, without whose help and support I would not have even begun work on this book. My advisor, not only in academic matters, Paul Johnsgard, was always willing to provide any information on writing, English grammar, preparing a typescript, and other issues during the writing as well. Several desks and chairs in Linda Brown's residence were occupied by various books, journals and photocopies of articles. Linda also helped to correct my English. During the final stage of preparing this typescript, Hana Barova patiently helped with a variety of tasks.

I would like to express my thanks to Robert Kirk, and to all those at Christopher Helm (Publishers) Ltd involved in this project, for their continuous support and encouragement.

I would not be able to present all this information without the indirect help of unnamed field ornithologists, many of whom provided invaluable data in several Czech ornithological journals.

INTRODUCTION

The Czech Republic, a small central European country, has a rich diversity of birds. Out of the 394 species recorded in the country since 1800, 19 are endangered, and 55 vulnerable according to Tucker and Heath (1994). Among the endangered breeding species are birds such as Eurasian Spoonbill, Saker Falcon and Eastern Imperial Eagle, while endangered visiting or migrating species include Barrow's Goldeneye, White-headed Duck, Pallid Harrier, Bonelli's Eagle and Aquatic Warbler. Various habitats in the Czech Republic provide breeding opportunities for species such as Great Bittern, Little Bittern, Night Heron, Purple Heron, Greylag Goose, Red Kite, Montagu's Harrier, Hazel Grouse, Black Grouse, Capercaillie, Corn Crake, Black Tern, Pygmy Owl, Tengmalm's Owl and White-backed Woodpecker, although some of these breed in low numbers. The variety of habitat, ranging from remnant natural wetlands to alpine meadows, supports a high diversity of birds in an area of less than 80,000 km^2. Owing to its geographical position in Europe, species from both north and south breed in the Czech Republic, and stragglers from Asia and North America are occasionally recorded in the country.

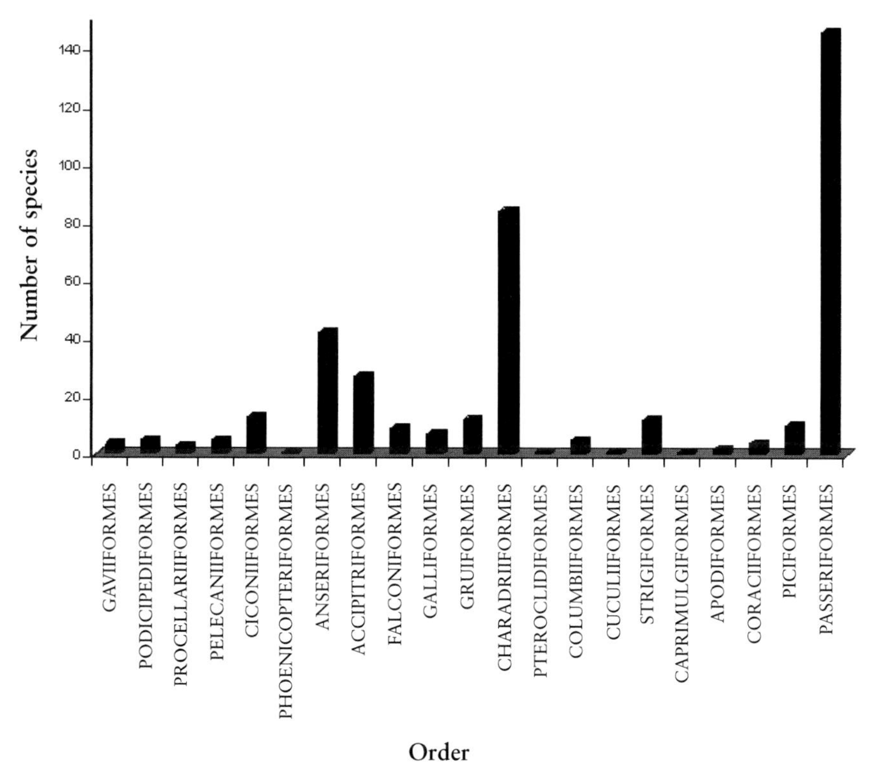

The number of species in each order recorded in the Czech Republic (total = 394).

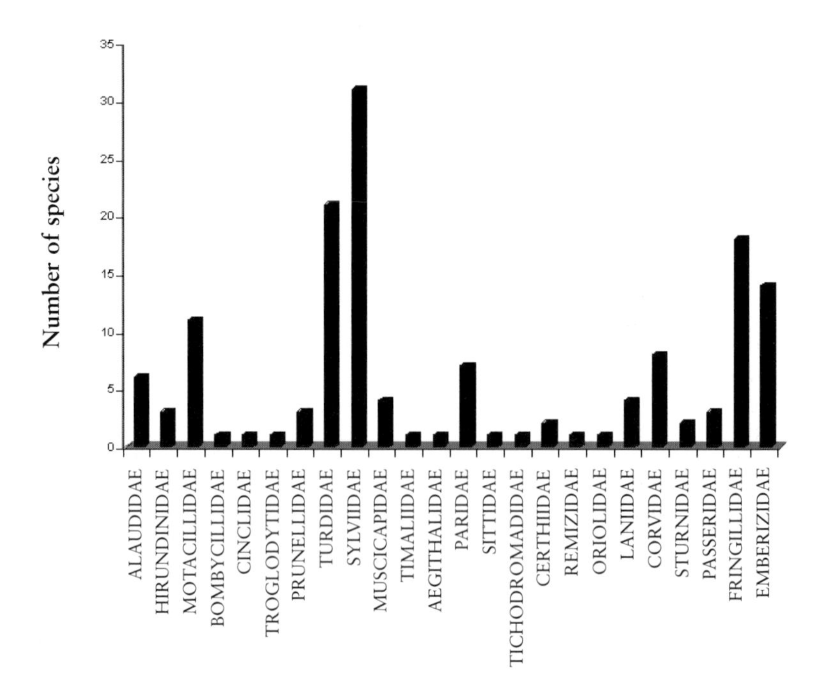

The number of species in each family of passeriforme recorded in the Czech Republic (total = 146).

FORMAT OF THE BOOK

The species accounts

The species described in this book are placed in 2 categories. The first deals with birds regularly occurring in the Czech Republic, and includes 310 species. Birds included in the 'Accidentals' category have each been recorded fewer than 10 times (with the exception of Alpine Swift: 11 times) since 1800, and total 83 species.

The checklist of the birds of the Czech Republic as recognized by the Czech Faunistic Committee at 31 December, 1998 includes 396 species (Hudec *et al.* 1999). The species accounts in this book, however, treat in detail only 393 species. The difference is due to the exclusion of 3 species: Wood Duck *Aix sponsa*, Mandarin Duck *Aix galericulata* and Monk Parakeet *Myiopsitta monachus*, which are included in the category of 'escapes from captivity'. Although the occurrence of Blue-winged Teal in the Czech Republic was recognized by the Czech Faunistic Committee (Chytil 1998), it is omitted from the current list (Hudec *et al.* 1999). I include this species in the category of 'accidentals'. Even though Rock Pipit *Anthus petrosus* is included in the checklist of birds of the Czech Republic (Hudec *et al.* 1999), as well as in the checklist in this book, I was refused additional observational data by the Czech Faunistic Committee, and hence am unable to treat this species in detail.

Additional species not included in this book were omitted for a number of reasons. Published records, mostly from the 19th and beginning of the 20th centuries, which are not accepted by the Czech Faunistic Committee because of a lack of sufficient evidence have been omitted. The 17 species in the latter category include: Southern Giant Petrel *Macronectes giganteus*, Manx Shearwater *Puffinus puffinus*, Falcated Duck *Anas falcata*, Harlequin Duck *Histrionicus histrionicus*, Bufflehead *Bucephala albeola*, Lammergeier *Gypaetus barbatus*, Ivory Gull *Pagophila eburnea*, Brünnich's Guillemot *Uria lomvia*, Yellow-billed Cuckoo *Coccyzus americanus*, Blue Rock Trush *Monticola solitarius*, White's Trush *Zoothera dauma*, Siberian Trush *Zoothera sibirica*, Subalpine Warbler *Sylvia cantillans*, Arctic Warbler *Phylloscopus borealis*, Siberian Jay *Perisoreus infaustus*, Red-billed Chough *Pyrrhocorax pyrrhocorax*, and Rock Sparrow *Petronia petronia*. Details about observation and specimen evidence for these species can be found in Hudec *et al.* (1995).

The following category includes species observed in the wild but which are, without doubt, escapes from captivity. The Czech Faunistic Committee (Hudec *et al.* 1995, Chytil 1997) listed 15 species in this category, however, I include the 3 additional species already mentioned above. These species are: Brown Pelican *Pelecanus occidentalis*, Chilean Flamingo *Phoenicopterus chilensis*, African Spoonbill *Platalea alba*, Black Swan *Cygnus atratus*, Bar-headed Goose *Anser indicus*, Egyptian Goose *Alopochen aegyptiacus*, Wood Duck *Aix sponsa*, Mandarin Duck *Aix galericulata*, Chiloe Wigeon *Anas sibilatrix*, White-faced Whistling-Duck *Dendrocygna viduata*, Willow Ptarmigan *Lagopus lagopus*, Rock Ptarmigan *Lagopus mutus*, Rock Partridge *Alectoris graeca*, Red-legged Partridge *Alectoris rufa*, Sarus Crane *Grus antigone*, Wild Turkey *Meleagris gallopavo*, Budgerigar *Melopsittacus undulatus*, and Monk Parakeet *Myiopsitta monachus*. It is likely that this list is incomplete because other species which have escaped from breeders have not been reported. The English names used for this group of species follows the nomenclature provided by Sibley and Monroe (1990).

Nomenclature

English names

With one exception, namely Carrion Crow, the sequence and scientific nomenclature follows the 'List of Birds of the Western Palearctic' (*British Birds* 1997). Instead of using the name Carrion Crow for *Corvus corone*, I use Crow; Carrion Crow is *Corvus corone corone*; and Hooded Crow is *Corvus corone cornix*. The English names in the 'List of Birds of the Western Palearctic', are those adopted by *British Birds* in 1993 (*British Birds* 86:1–2).

English vernacular names

Many species have multiple English names. These names are used in various field guides or reference books. The vernacular names should help to cross-reference other works to this title. I decided to provide the other English names used in *The Handbook of Bird Identification for*

Europe and the Western Palearctic (Beaman and Madge 1998). This work treats all species recorded, up to the point of publication, in the Western Palearctic, and is available to a wide audience.

Scientific names
The scientific names and sequence used in the 'List of Birds of the Western Palearctic' (*British Birds* 1997), and in this book, follow those used in the concise edition of *The Birds of the Western Palearctic* (Snow and Perrins 1998).

Czech names
Czech names are those used in *The EBCC Atlas of European Breeding Birds: their distribution and abundance* (Hagemeijer and Blair 1997).

Slovak names
Slovak names are those used by Ferianc (1977–1979) and modified by Matousek (1994). The list of names, and explanations of their modification, were kindly provided by Bohumil Murin.

German names
German names are those used in the concise edition of *The Birds of the Western Palearctic.*

ALTITUDINAL DISTRIBUTION, NAMES OF PLACES

For the majority of species, details of altitudinal distribution are provided. I adapted the data from Hudec (1983, 1994), Hudec and Cerny (1977), and Stastny *et al.* (1987, 1996). My own data are mostly from the Bile Karpaty mountains (HO, UH, ZL). The name of the place is followed by the name of the county in which it is located (in parentheses). If the same place name is used more than once in the species account, the name of the relevant county is used only once. Czech geographical names are followed by a habitat description of the site, e.g. a pond, a gravel pit, mountains etc.

Czech frequently uses diacritical marks above vowels. While typing the names of places, I faced a dilemma: whether to use these marks or not. After consulting with native English-speaking colleagues, I decided against this. For the English-speaking audience, I was told, these diacritical marks make no sense. Besides, the marks do not change the proper spelling of geographical names and, if using Czech maps, one will have no problem in finding the correct place.

HABITATS

Basic information on habitat utilization within the Czech Repubic is provided for all species. Usually, preferred habitats are listed, as well as those generally avoided. However, it does not necessarily mean that any species, particularly a migrant, cannot be found in any type of habitat. 'Preferred' therefore refers to a habitat where a given species will most likely be found. If nesting has been recorded in unusual habitat for the species treated, information is given.

NEST SITES

These data strictly refer to nest sites in the Czech Republic. The names of trees and bushes in which nests were found are listed in descending order of occurrence. This information is from Hudec (1983, 1994), Hudec and Cerny (1977), and my own findings, mostly from UH and HO counties.

BREEDING DENSITIES

It is necessary for everyone considering the breeding densities provided in this book to keep in mind that these data came from studies usually conducted in small areas. These densities are therefore 'localized' and nor for larger areas such as a certain county or mountain complex. However, for a given species, where available, I provide data from different parts of the country, as well as from different habitats. In many of the studies the data are usually given for the number of pairs or individuals per hectare. For consistency, I converted all densities into 'per km^2'. Densities per km^2 were in original papers usually provided for birds of prey and the larger owls. I realize that the numbers expressed as densities per km^2 may look enormous, especially in species breeding in loose colonies, on islets, in strips of reedbed etc. If playback was used to find the density of breeding species, then the number of males per km^2 is given.

If not otherwise stated, all data on breeding densities are from Stastny *et al.* (1987, 1996). My own data were collected in UH and HO counties between the end of the 1970s and the beginning of the 1990s, and those from around Nesyt pond (BV) at the end of the 1980s.

WINTER DENSITIES

Winter densities, either from various published sources or unpublished correspondence, are summarized in Bejcek *et al.* (1995). If not otherwise stated, all data on winter densities are from this work. My own data were collected in UH and HO counties between the end of the 1970s and beginning of the 1990s. Information on size of flocks during migration or in winter is from reports in *Zpravy MOS*, *Zpravy CSO* and *Ptaci kolem nas*, and covers the past 20 years.

RACES

In some species certain populations can be recognized at the subspecies level. Where appropriate, races recorded in the Czech Republic are listed. Sufficient documentary evidence for this racial identification was usually provided by a netted or banded individual, or a bird collected as a specimen. The races listed in this book basically follow those given by Hudec *et al.* (1999).

STATUS

Terms such as 'resident', 'vagrant', 'spring or autumn migrant', or 'winter visitor' are self-explanatory. The terms 'common', 'uncommon', 'rare', and 'local' used in this section, as well throughout the text, are more or less subjective. In most instances I did follow an 'occurrence status' given by Hudec *et al.* (1999).

Based on conservation concern, breeding species (including species with at least one breeding record) were placed in the following categories: extinct, extinct in the wild, critically endangered, endangered, vulnerable, conservation-dependent, near-threatened, least concern, data deficient, and not evaluated (Hudec *et al.* 1999).

POPULATION TRENDS

The data on numbers of individuals or pairs provided in this section are from Stastny *et al.* (1987), Hudec *et al.* (1995), and Bejcek *et al.* (1995). Data on birds of prey and owls are also from Danko *et al.* (1994). Data regarding sightings of a larger flock at a particular site during a certain time are from the 'Rare and Uncommon Records of Birds', published in *Zpravy MOS*, *Zpravy CSO* and *Ptaci kolem nas*.

It was impossible to provide information on population trends for many species, particularly those included in the category of accidentals. However, many rare visitors have been recorded in higher numbers during the past 20 years. Statements concerning increasing numbers of sightings and therefore total numbers for these species should be treated with some caution. Increasing records may reflect a growing interest in birdwatching, more attention paid to rarities, and also the better field skills of observers.

DISTRIBUTION

Although each species account is accompanied by a map, in this section I provide a more detailed description of distribution. For example, the maps say nothing about a density of a species in a given county. Where information is available on the distribution of breeding and/or wintering birds it is included here. Also, this section lists certain sites where a given species occurs frequently, information extracted from about 20 years' of records published in *Zpravy MOS*, *Zpravy CSO* and *Ptaci kolem nas*, from personal correspondence with colleagues, and from my own observations, particularly in s. Moravia.

TIMING

Information regarding timing of migration is partly taken from Hudec (1983, 1994), and Hudec and Cerny (1977) and spans most of this century. The most recent data on migration are from 'Rare and Uncommon Records of Birds' published in *Zpravy MOS*, *Zpravy CSO* and *Ptaci kolem nas*, and span about the last 20 years. My own data cover the period from the mid-1970s to the end of the 1980s. Information on breeding seasons is mostly from Hudec (1983, 1994), Hudec and Cerny (1977), and my own data covering the same period as for migration.

ABBREVIATIONS

CFC	= Czech Faunistic Committee: a committee of several ornithologists evaluating records of rare species in the Czech Republic
m	= metres
km	= kilometres
km^2	= square kilometres
n.	= north
s.	= south
e.	= east
w.	= west

1 km	= 1000 m = 0.621 miles
1 km^2	= 100 ha (hectares) = 247 acres

THE DISTRIBUTION MAPS

The Czech Republic is divided into 76 counties. During the process of working on this book, a new, seventy-seventh county, called Jesenik, was established in n. Moravia. It covers parts of Sumperk (SU) and Bruntal (BR) counties. However, the distribution maps do not reflect this change.

The maps are based on data from Stastny *et al.* (1987, 1996), Bejcek *et al.* (1995) and the 'Rare and Uncommon Records of Birds' published in *Zpravy MOS*, *Zpravy CSO* and *Ptaci kolem nas*. Several colleagues of mine also provided unpublished data, and I used my own records as well. These maps are as up-to-date as possible. However, in the case of winter visitors or migrants, there could be a record of an individual that is not shown for a given county.

These maps do not indicate whether a species occurs across a whole county, has a patchy distribution, or is recorded only at certain sites. Considering the variety of habitat within some counties and specific habitat requirements of many species, it was impossible to adjust the maps in such a way.

Distribution of many species has been changing rapidly over the past decade. This is due to significant modifications in agriculture after the economic changes in the country at the end of the 1980s. There has also been a growing interest in field ornithology, reflected in the increasing skill of observers. These factors have contributed to a greater knowledge of bird distribution in the Czech Republic.

KEY TO THE MAPS

There are 4 key symbols indicating occurrence of a species in each county. If a county is left blank, the species has not been recorded there.

 All year round (resident)

 Non-breeding record (spring and autumn migration, wintering record)

 Breeding and wintering record for a typically migratory species

 Breeding record only

THE CHECKLISTS

The 'Checklist of Birds of the Czech Republic' (see p.317) lists all species which are treated in this book, including Rock Pipit (mentioned but not treated in detail in this book). The layout of the *Checklist* could be helpful in recording one's own observations.

The 'Checklist of Birds of Slovakia' (see p.325) is based on data from Murin *et al.* (1994). I decided to include this checklist for Slovakia since many ornithologists and birdwatchers travel to both countries.

Abbreviations used in the 'Checklist of the Birds of Slovakia'
RB = regularly breeding species; IB = irregularly breeding species; RNO = regularly occurring non-breeding species (usually refers to migrants); INO = irregularly occurring non-breeding species (usually refers to migrants); RR = rarely occurring species (fewer than 10 records since 1980)

Bibliography

The Bibliography (see p.310) lists books and articles cited in this work. The complete bibliography of Czech ornithology up to 1992 has been summarized in the following 4 books.

Hudec, K. and O. Kokes. 1981. *Czech Ornithological Bibliography 1. Before 1933*. SZN, Praha.
Hudec, K. and O. Kokes. 1982. *Czech Ornithological Bibliography 2. From 1934 till 1960.* SZN, Praha.
Kozena, I., K. Hudec, O. Kokes, B. Matousek. 1983. *Czech Ornithological Bibliography 1961–1980*. SZN, Praha.
Kozena, I., K. Hudec and M. Saniga. 1994. *Czech and Slovak Ornithological Bibliography 1981–1992*. UEK, AVCR, Brno.

The citation for these 4 titles is provided here and not in the Bibliography.

Since 1992, the Czech ornithological bibliography has been published bi-annually in the journal *Zpravy MOS*. The titles are as follows.

Hudec, K. and I. Kozena. 1994. Czech Ornithological Bibliography 1993–1994. *Zpravy MOS* 52: 113–145.
Hudec, K. and I. Kozena. 1997. Czech Ornithological Bibliography 1995–1996. *Zpravy MOS* 55: 147–202.

GEOGRAPHICAL AND ECOLOGICAL BACKGROUND

Location and description of the Czech Republic

In January 2000, the Czech Republic was divided into 14 administrative regions. However, it does not change the fact that there is still Central Bohemia, Eastern Bohemia etc. These administrative changes will have no effect on finding places mentioned in this book, communication with people regarding geographical locations, or travelling through the country.

The total population of the Czech Republic is about 10.5 million. The maximum altitudinal difference is 1487 m, with the highest point being Mt Snezka at 1602 m (Krkonose mountains; SE, TU), and the lowest point on the Labe river near Hrensko (DC), at 115 m.

The limit coordinates of the country are as follows:

Limit coordinates	Southern	Northern	Western	Eastern
Extreme points	Lat. 48° 33' 09''N	Lat. 51° 03' 22''N	Long. 12° 05' 33''E	Long. 18° 51' 40''E
County	Cesky Krumlov	Decin	Cheb	Frydek-Mistek

Upland dominates the country. The Czech Republic has 4.9% of lowland up to 200 m, 15.7% of lowland up to 300 m, 71% of upland up to 750 m, and 8.4% of land above 750 m. The total land area can be divided into the following categories: arable (32,934 km^2 – 41.7%); gardens and orchards (2045 km^2 – 2.6%); meadows (5776 km^2 – 7.3%); pastures (2732 km^2 – 3.5%); woodland/forest (26,244 km^2 – 33.3%); fishponds and other open water (973 km^2 – 1.2%); and others (built-up areas etc.) (7937 km^2 – 10.1%).

Regions

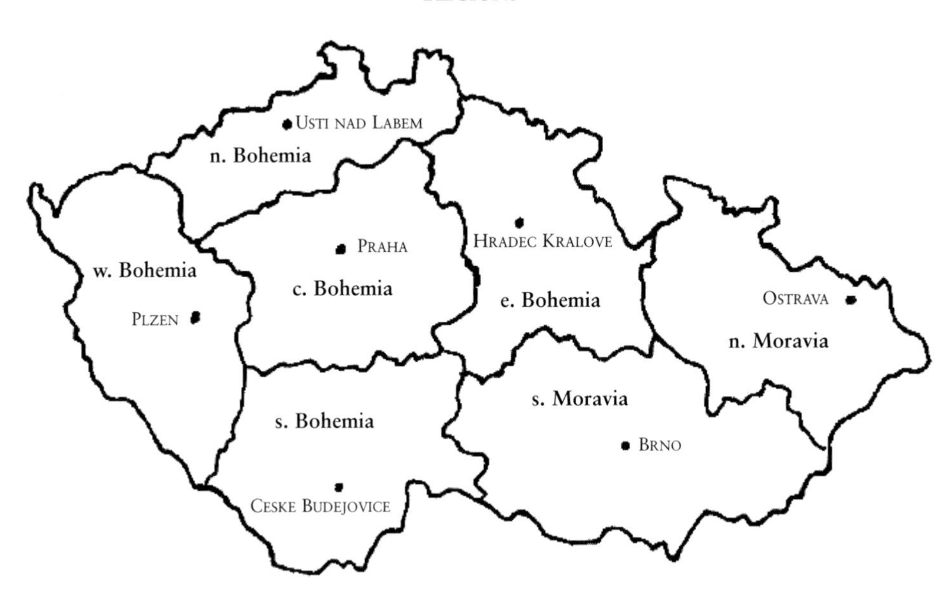

Central Bohemia

Covers 11,004 km^2, plus the area of the Czech capital, Praha, which occupies 497 km^2. Land usage (does not include Praha): arable land 52.6%; hop-gardens and vineyards 0.3%; orchards and gardens 3.4%; meadows 4.5%; pastures 1.9%; woodland 26.7%; fishponds 0.4%; other areas of water 1.3%; built-up area 8.9%. This is one of the warmest and driest regions of the country, the annual average temperature being 8–10°C. The average temperature in July is 17–18°C; in January it is –2°C. The average annual precipitation is between 500 and 600 mm. There are 40–50 days with snow cover annually.

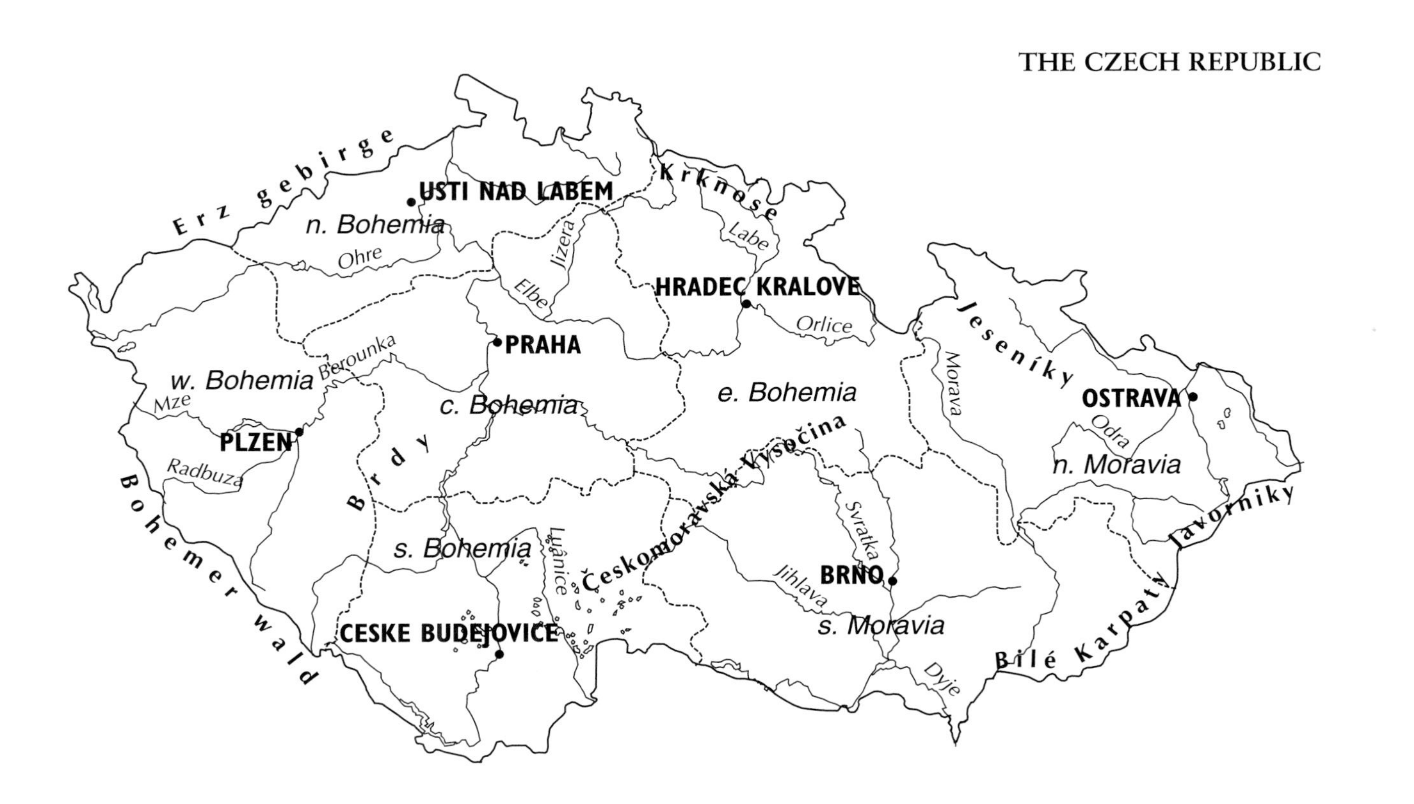

THE CZECH REPUBLIC

Eastern Bohemia

Covers 11,240 km^2. Land usage: arable land 43.1%; hop-gardens and vineyards 0%; orchards and gardens 2.9%; meadows 10.3%; pastures 2.8%; woodland 31.5%; fishponds 0.6%; other areas of water 0.9%; built-up area 7.9%. The average annual temperature is 7–8°C. The average temperature in July is 17–18°C; in January it is –2°C to –4°C. The coldest site is Mt Snezka in the Krkonose mountains (SE, TU) with an annual average temperature of 0.2°C. The average annual precipitation is 600–800 mm in most areas of the region, and 1300–1500 mm in the Krkonose and Orlicke hory (RK) mountains. Days with snow cover number 40–50 annually in most areas of the region, 60–80 days in the Ceskomoravska vysocina highlands (HB, JI, PE, ZR), and 120–180 days in the Krkonose and Orlicke hory mountains.

Northern Bohemia

Covers 7810 km^2. Land usage: arable land 35.5%; hop-gardens and vineyards 0.8%; orchards and gardens 2.9%; meadows 6.9%; pastures 4.5%; woodland 35.1%; fishponds 0.1%; other areas of water 1.4%; built-up area 12.8%. The average annual temperature is 3–9°C. The average temperature in July is 13°C in the Jizerske hory mountains (LB, JN), and 19°C in the Krusne hory mountains (KV, CV, MO, TP). The average temperature in January ranges from –2°C to –5°C. Average annual precipitation is between 500 and 700 mm, locally below 450 mm, and in the Jizerske hory mountains around 1600 mm.

Western Bohemia

Covers 10,876 km^2.

Land usage: arable land 33.4%; hop-gardens and vineyards 0%; orchards and gardens 1.6%; meadows 9.1%; pastures 4.5%; woodland 40.2%; fishponds 0.5%; other areas of water 1.1%; built-up area 9.6%. The majority of the region has upland with an average altitude of 500 m. The average temperature in July at various places across the region is around 18°C; in January it is –2°C to –4°C. Average annual precipitation is between 500 and 650 mm, locally below 500 mm, and in the mountains around 1500 mm, for example in the Sumava mountains (CK, PT, KT); and 1200 mm in the Krusne hory mountains (KV, CV, MO, TP). Days with snow cover range from 10 (around Plzen; PM) to 80 (the Sumava and Krusne hory mountains) annually.

Southern Bohemia

Covers 11,344 km^2. Land usage: arable land 37.4%; hop-gardens and vineyards 0%; orchards and gardens 1.4%; meadows 11.3%; pastures 2.8%; woodland 35.1%; fishponds 2.2%; other areas of water 1.7%; built-up area 8.1%. The average annual temperature ranges from 3.2°C (the Sumava mountains; CK, PT, KT) to 9°C (Ceske Budejovice; CB). The average temperature in July ranges from 12°C (the Sumava and Novohradske hory mountains; CB, CK) to 18°C (areas around Ceske Budejovice; Trebon; JH). The average temperature in January ranges from –1°C (altitudes below 500 m) to –4°C (the Sumava and Novohradske hory mountains). Average annual precipitation is 700–1500 mm. Days with snow cover range from 40 (areas around Ceske Budejovice and Trebon) to 220 days (Sumava mountains) annually.

Southern Moravia

Covers 15,028 km^2. Land usage: arable land 49.3%; hop-gardens and vineyards 1.0%; orchards and gardens 2.8%; meadows 4.7%; pastures 2.7%; woodland 29.5%; fishponds 0.6%; other areas of water 1.0%; built-up area 8.4%. The average annual temperature ranges from 5.8°C (Ceskomoravska vysocina highlands; HB, JI, PE, ZR) to 9.5°C (Dolnomoravsky uval valley). The average temperature in July ranges from 16°C (around 500 m) to 19.8°C; in January from –1°C to –2°C, and around –4°C in the Ceskomoravska vysocina highlands. Average annual precipitation is 500–950 mm. Days with snow cover number 30–40 annually.

Northern Moravia

Covers 11,067 km^2. Land usage: arable land 36.9%; hop-gardens and vineyards 0.1%; orchards and gardens 2.8%; meadows 5.3%; pastures 5.6%; woodland 37.6%; fishponds

0.2%; other areas of water 1.2%; built-up area 10.3%. The average annual temperature ranges from 1.2°C (mountains) to 8.6°C (Olomouc). Average annual precipitation is 570–1500 mm.

Abbreviations for counties

AA Praha city
BE Beroun
BK Blansko
BM Brno city
BN Benesov
BO Brno
BR Bruntal
BV Breclav
CB Ceske Budejovice
CH Cheb
CK Cesky Krumlov
CL Ceska Lipa
CR Chrudim
CV Chomutov
DC Decin
DO Domazlice
FM Frydek Mistek
HB Havlickuv Brod
HK Hradec Kralove
HO Hodonin
JC Jicin
JH Jindrichuv Hradec
JI Jihlava
JN Jablonec nad Nisou
KH Kutna Hora
KI Karvina
KL Kladno
KM Kromeriz
KO Kolin
KT Klatovy
KV Karlovy Vary
LB Liberec
LN Louny
LT Litomerice
MB Mlada Boleslav
ME Melnik
MO Most
NA Nachod
NB Nymburk
NJ Novy Jicin
OL Olomouc
OP Opava
OV Ostrava
PB Pribram
PE Pelhrimov
PH Praha east
PI Pisek
PJ Plzen south
PM Plzen city
PR Prerov
PS Plzen north
PT Prachatice
PU Pardubice
PV Prostejov
PZ Praha west
RA Rakovnik
RK Rychnov nad Kneznou
RO Rokycany
SE Semily
SO Sokolov
ST Strakonice
SU Sumperk
SY Svitavy
TA Tabor
TC Tachov
TP Teplice
TR Trebic
TU Trutnov
UH Uherske Hradiste
UL Usti nad Labem
UO Usti nad Orlici
VS Vsetin
VY Vyskov
ZL Zlin
ZN Znojmo
ZR Zdar nad Sazavou

Counties

Bird habitats in the Czech Republic

The altitudinal range within the country is reflected in its flora. The Czech Republic includes lowland with thermophilic flora and intensive agriculture, forest-steppe with deciduous woods, low mountains with recent spruce monocultures, mountains with beech and spruce, and a lower alpine range with dwarf pine. Three types of flora can be recognized in the country: central European, Pannonian, and Carpathian. These can be further subdivided into subregions and districts.

The Czech Republic has a variety of habitats suitable for birds, as well as other animals, with specific ecological requirements. Composition of habitats is specific for each of the 7 major regions of the country. The Czech Republic is an agrarian country, and arable land is dominant in each of the regions.

Aquatic habitats make up only a small portion of habitats across the country. Although rivers can be found in all 7 regions of the country, fishponds and marshes are not distributed equally. Most of the larger rivers have been controlled, but some parts are still unregulated with surrounding floodplain woodland. The majority of fishponds are found in s. Bohemia and s. Moravia, and the Czech Republic has the greatest area of fishponds of any country in Europe. Many of these ponds are used for breeding domestic ducks and geese. Most marshes have been drained or converted into meadows. Natural lakes, mostly located in mountains, are rare in the country, and are mainly small. Dams and gravel pits are distributed throughout the country, and vary in size from several hectares to several square kilometres. Industrial complexes with substantial areas of water are usually found in close proximity to power plants. Fishponds remain the most important areas of water for breeding herons, waterfowl and gulls.

Farmland is the dominant habitat in the Czech Republic, mostly in s. Moravia, central Bohemia, e. Bohemia, and n. Bohemia. The majority of the land is arable, with smaller areas of meadow and pasture. This type of habitat is important for several breeding non-passerine species, for example Grey Partridge, Common Pheasant and Northern Lapwing, as well as passerine species such as Sky Lark and Common Stonechat. Migrating and wintering flocks of Bean Geese, Greylag Geese, Turtle Doves, Eurasian Jackdaws, Rooks and other species use mixed farmland. Vineyards, orchards and gardens are a significant part of the area of farmland in some counties, for example LN, LT, ME, RA, HO, BV and ZN.

Forest covers a significant part of the country, especially along the border. Although the majority of forest comprises spruce plantations growing at any altitude from lowland up to the mountains, native forest, such as beech, can still be found in the mountains. Besides spruce, pine monocultures are also found, particularly at lower altitudes. Oak-dominated forest is mainly confined to the highlands, but willow and poplar grow along rivers at most altitudes. Remnants of riverine, mostly broadleaved, forest line the banks of the larger rivers such as the Morava (OL, PR, KM, UH, HO), Becva (VS, PR), Dyje (BV, ZN), Labe (HK, PU, KO, LT, ME, NB), Ohre (LN, LT) and Vltava (CB, CK). Poplar-dominated windbreaks are common in farmland, primarily in lowland areas. Other types of growth such as woods, hedges and scattered groups of trees are found throughout the country.

Mountains dominate the border areas, and are mainly forest-clad. Some mountain areas form the best preserved habitats in the Czech Republic, even though acid-rain has had a detrimental effect on forest. The forests comprise spruce, beech-spruce, fir-beech, and beech at higher altitudes, with dwarf pine at the very highest. There are only a few birds which can be classified as truly montane, but many other species extend their range up to the alpine zone in the Krkonose and Jeseniky mountains. There are few montane sites with significant rocky gorges or cliffs, and none of dolomitic or limestone origin.

Urban habitats provide breeding opportunities for a surprisingly large number of passerine as well as non-passerine species. Within urban habitats, quite unique places suitable for breeding of various species can be found. Among such places are old cemeteries with mature growths of trees, old parks around castles, and mature gardens. For example, tall chimneys around factories serve as nest sites for White Storks; barns around farms and church towers as nest sites for Barn Owls.

Climate and geography

The Czech Republic is a continental country, located on the main western European watershed. It has northern hemisphere mild belt climate conditions determined by the position of the country. The continental and oceanic climate therefore both influence weather in the Czech Republic. The coastal influence affects mainly the western part of the country: the range of day and night temperatures is smaller in the west than in the east of the country. However, precipitation is higher in the west. The east is more influenced by the continental climate. Winters here are colder, summers warmer, the range of day and night temperatures is wider, and precipitation is lower than in the west. The climate in the Czech Republic is influenced by altitude: as altitude increases, temperature drops and precipitation increases. Daily weather in the country is changeable, caused primarily by variable air pressures resulting from the effect of the changes in the 3 major pressure systems affecting Europe: over Iceland, the Azores, and conditions over Asia.

The main rainfall ranges in the Czech Republic are in the highlands (the Czech Massif) which cover most of the country, concentrated in the west, and in the Carpathians to the east. Both mountain systems are separated by a belt of depressions. Most agricultural lands has medium-heavy soil, while podzol soil is an important element in the makeup of the earth in forests.

The 3 tables below show long-term climatic means: air temperature, total precipitation, and sunshine hours for the period from 1961 to 1990.

Mean air temperature in °C

Place	Month											
	1	2	3	4	5	6	7	8	9	10	11	12
Brno-Turany (BM)	-2.5	-0.3	3.8	9.0	13.9	17.0	18.5	18.1	14.3	9.1	3.5	-0.6
Ceske Budejovice (CB)	-1.8	-0.3	3.4	8.1	13.0	16.2	17.7	17.1	13.5	8.4	3.3	-0.3
Hradec Kralove (HK)	-2.1	-0.2	3.5	8.4	13.5	16.7	18.1	17.6	13.9	9.1	3.6	-0.3
Klatovy (KT)	-2.0	-0.5	3.2	7.6	12.5	15.9	17.6	17.0	13.4	8.3	3.1	-0.5
Liberec (LB)	-2.5	-1.2	2.3	6.6	11.7	14.8	16.2	15.8	12.4	8.3	2.9	-0.8
Olomouc (OL)	-2.4	-0.2	3.8	9.1	14.2	17.1	18.6	18.0	14.3	9.1	3.7	-0.4
Praha-Ruzyne (AA)	-2.4	-0.9	3.0	7.7	12.7	15.9	17.5	17.0	13.3	8.3	2.9	-0.6

Total precipitation (mm)

Place	Month											
	1	2	3	4	5	6	7	8	9	10	11	12
Brno-Turany (BM)	24.6	23.8	24.1	31.5	61.0	72.2	63.7	56.2	37.6	30.7	37.4	27.1
Ceske Budejovice (CB)	22.6	23.4	32.0	46.5	70.1	93.0	77.8	78.8	47.5	32.0	34.7	24.5
Hradec Kralove (HK)	36.3	31.8	33.8	38.8	72.1	75.0	71.1	83.1	50.0	39.2	43.0	42.6
Klatovy (KT)	29.3	29.8	36.7	46.1	67.4	72.7	79.0	78.6	53.3	37.1	37.3	32.6
Liberec (LB)	53.3	46.2	48.9	58.2	80.2	84.9	87.9	88.4	65.4	59.6	63.1	67.3
Olomouc (OL)	27.5	25.5	27.2	37.8	73.3	78.4	76.4	68.8	44.5	40.0	40.4	30.3
Praha-Ruzyne (AA)	23.5	22.6	28.1	38.2	77.2	72.7	66.2	69.6	40.0	30.5	31.9	25.3

Sunshine (h)

Place	Month											
	1	2	3	4	5	6	7	8	9	10	11	12
Brno-Turany (BM)	45.3	71.6	121.5	169.1	219.1	221.0	234.9	217.9	161.9	124.0	51.3	40.1
Ceske Budejovice (CB)	47.0	63.3	116.3	151.1	184.6	204.8	219.1	201.8	162.3	114.1	56.8	43.1
Hradec Kralove (HK)	48.6	71.0	118.1	164.9	210.9	214.0	216.9	209.5	153.9	123.3	48.4	42.5
Klatovy (KT)	43.3	66.8	110.8	149.8	197.0	205.9	218.5	204.1	152.1	111.5	50.4	38.7
Liberec (LB)	36.0	60.3	102.0	139.1	182.5	178.8	183.4	183.6	139.9	112.0	41.3	29.2
Olomouc (OL)	38.7	65.8	113.4	166.2	215.9	213.9	228.5	216.9	159.2	118.8	46.3	33.2
Praha-Ruzyne (AA)	50.0	72.4	124.7	167.6	214.0	218.6	226.7	212.3	161.0	120.8	53.6	46.7

BIRD PROTECTION, RAMSAR SITES, AND IMPORTANT BIRD AREAS

Bird protection

Bird protection has a long tradition in the Czech Republic. One of the first protected areas of ornithological importance in Europe was riverine forest near Veltrusy (ME). This breeding area for Rooks was established as a protected site in 1826. Two protected areas, mostly for breeding montane birds, were established in the Novohradske hory mountains (CB, CK) in 1838. Twenty years later, another important site for the protection of montane species, Boubinsky prales primeval forest, was established in the Sumava mountains (CK, PT, KT). Over 100 protected sites, preserving bird diversity, had been established by the end of 1930s. This trend of establishing protected sites, mostly for breeding populations, has continued to the present day. There are about 1,000 protected areas in the country, varying in importance. Bird protection in the country is currently regulated by The Czech National Council Act No.114/1992 on the Protection of Nature and Landscape, and the Decree of the Ministry of Agriculture of the Czech Republic No. 512/1992 and No. 134/1996.

Problems relating to bird protection in the country centre on several main issues. Large-scale changes in land use have occurred, mainly between 1950 and 1990. Small fields have been converted into large fields, and hedges, avenues, growths along brooks and rivers, and patches of shrub and trees have been destroyed. As a consequence, the diversity in habitats has decreased. Fishpond management has changed, resulting in the partial or complete destruction of littoral vegetation. Such changes have affected mainly breeding populations of waterfowl, and some passerines. Natural forest has mostly been replaced by spruce monocultures, and the logging of mature trees has been extensive. In addition to this, air pollution due to industrial emissions and 'acid-rain' has affected not only forest but other types of woodland as well. This problem is most severe in the Krusne hory (CV, KV, MO, TP), Krkonose (SE, TU), Jeseniky (BR, SU) and Beskydy (FM, VS) mountains. The result of forest destruction is a reduction in forests birds and their replacement by open-land species. Moreover, the contamination of farmland by pesticides has had a severe impact on numerous species, primarily by destroying suitable food resources. Pollution of surface water is threatening various breeding species, as well as wintering waterfowl. Unsuitable or inappropriate installation of power lines has caused injuries to or killed large birds, mostly hawks, eagles and White Storks. Agriculture has generally had a negative effect on many ground-breeding species, both passerines and non-passerines. Although current law protects the majority of birds occurring in the Czech Republic, direct harassment of breeding, wintering or passage birds is still common. Particularly affected are birds of prey, either persecuted by hunters who shoot nests with clutches and incubating females, or by people robbing the nests of hatchlings (used in various commercial enterprises). Birds such as hawks, egrets, gulls and corvids are killed regularly, all year round, at pheasantries and fish hatcheries.

Active protection of birds in the Czech Republic takes several forms. The most common is direct nest protection and the installation of artificial nests for various species. Breeding stations, mostly for endangered species of birds of prey and galliformes have been established, and reintroduction programs run in several counties. Many injured birds are rehabilitated in special hospitals located across the country.

Ramsar sites in the Czech Republic

The Ramsar Convention focuses on wetlands of international importance, especially as waterfowl habitats. The aim of the convention is to ensure the protection of wetlands. The Czech Republic (former Czechoslovakia) signed the convention in 1990. There are 9 areas which have been recognized as Ramsar sites in the country. Some of the Ramsar sites are described in detail below in the category of IBAs. Ramsar sites in the Czech Republic are:

Krkonosska raseliniste – peatboags in the Krkonose mountains (SE, TU), see below in the IBAs section.
Lednicke ponds – (BV) see below in the IBAs section.
Litovelske Pomoravi – (OL) see 'Where to Watch Birds (p.286).

Mokrady dolniho toku Dyje – (BV); marshes along the Dyje and Morava rivers (total area 115 km^2). Part of this wetland area is formed by the lower and middle section of Nove Mlyny reservoir and Soutok (see below in the IBAs section).
Novozamecky and **Brehynsky pond** – (CL) see below in the IBAs section.
Poodri (FM, NJ, OV) – see below in the IBAs section.
Sumavska raseliniste – peatbogs in the Sumava mountains (CK, PT, KT) (total area 63.7 km^2).
Trebonske ponds – ponds around Trebon (JH) (total area 101.5 km^2, area of ponds is 53 km^2).
Trebonska raseliniste – peatbogs at higher elevations around Trebon (JH) (total area 11 km^2). Mostly without large areas of open water.

Some information on Ramsar sites is from Chytil (1996).

Important Bird Areas

Important Bird Areas (IBAs) are sites of particular value for breeding birds. These sites also have a great value because their ecosystems contain a variety of other animals and plants. There are 20 sites in the Czech Republic recognized as Important Bird Areas.

The scale of the maps in this section is 1:200,000 except for the map of the Beskydy and Sumava mountains, where it is 1:800,000.

IBAs

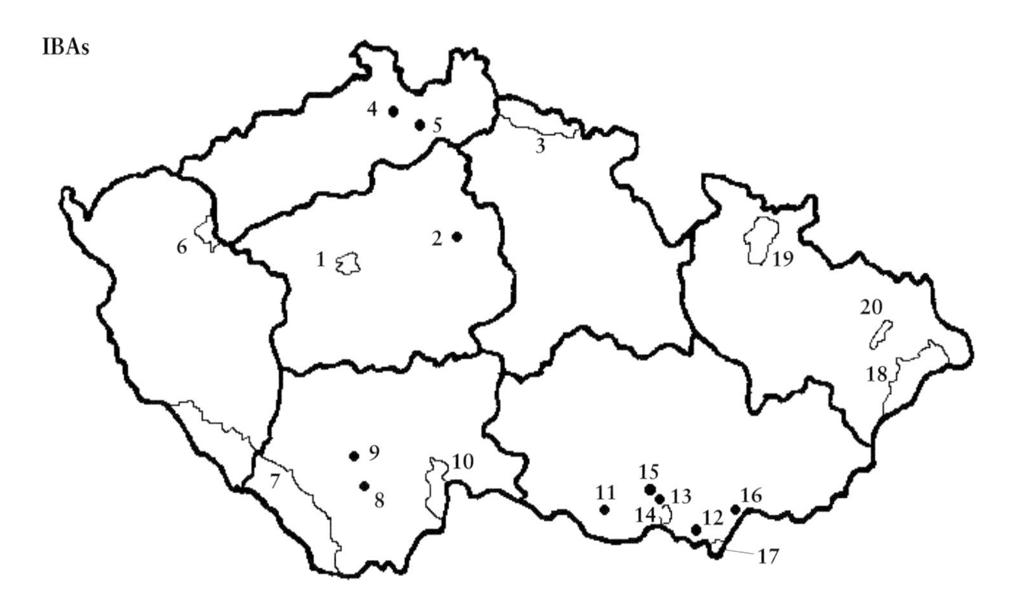

CENTRAL BOHEMIA

(1) Krivoklatsko (BE, KL, RA)

General characteristics

49°59'–50°05'N 13°46'–13°50'E

Krivoklatsko is a wooded area of 630 km^2, lying about 30 km southwest of Praha, with the towns of Beroun and Zdice to the east, Zbiroh to the south, Rakovnik to the west, and Nove Straseci to the north. The whole area is hilly, along a river valley, with an elevation ranging from 230 to 615 m. The main river is the Berounka, joined by numerous brooks and streams. The main biotopes are mixed forest and growths of deciduous trees along the rivers and brooks. Rocky cliffs are prominent along the Berounka.

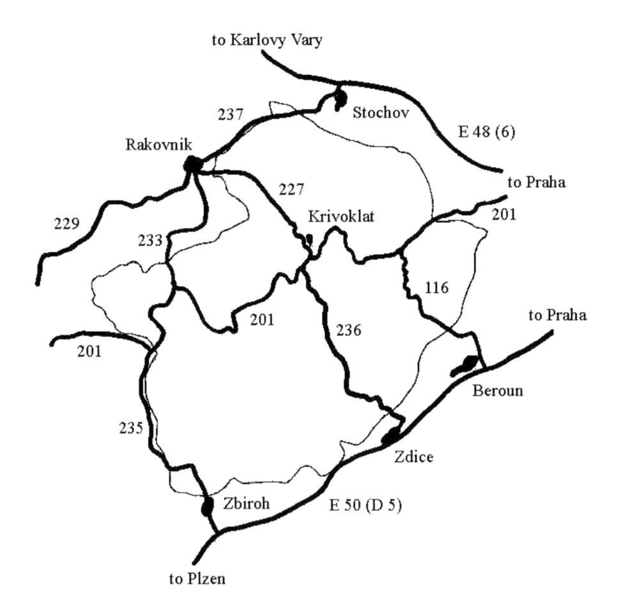

Species

Regularly breeding species include up to 10 pairs of Black Stork and Red Kite, dozens of pairs of European Honey-buzzard, Northern Goshawk, Eurasian Sparrowhawk and Common Buzzard. Among other commonly breeding species are Woodcock, Stock Dove, Eagle Owl, Tawny Owl, Common Kingfisher, Wryneck, Grey-headed Woodpecker, Black Woodpecker, Middle Spotted Woodpecker, Lesser Spotted Woodpecker, Grey Wagtail, Spotted Flycatcher, Red-breasted Flycatcher, Collared Flycatcher, and Pied Flycatcher. Less common or occasional nesters include Barn Owl, Pygmy Owl, Tengmalm's Owl, Hoopoe, Yellow Wagtail, Northern Wheatear, Barred Warbler, Great Grey Shrike, Nutcracker, and Common Raven. There are about 120 breeding species recorded, mostly those preferring broadleaved forest.

Access

Various routes can be used to access the area. The E50 road connects Praha and Plzen. From the E50, highway 116 crosses the area in the north, and highway 235 runs along the southern boundary of the area. The E48 runs from Praha along the northern boundary of Krivoklatsko. From the E48, highway 201 can be taken, and this crosses the area from north to southwest, running along the scenic rocky cliffs near the Berounka river.

(2) Zehunsky pond (NB)

General characteristics

50°10'N 15°19'E

This pond, located on the Cidlina river, at 250 m, is about 2.58 km^2. It is surrounded by rich emergent vegetation, and wet meadows lie close to the pond as well as the river. The pond is mainly used for fish-farming, as a source of water for irrigation, and for water sports.

Species

Among regular and occasional breeding species are Great Bittern, Black Kite, Marsh Harrier, Montagu's Harrier, Common Quail, Spotted Crake, Little Crake, Corn Crake, Common Kingfisher, *Locustella* and *Acrocephalus* species, Barred Warbler, Bearded Tit, and Reed Bunting. Passage or wintering species include Red-throated Diver, Black-throated Diver, Red-necked Grebe, Slavonian Grebe (rare), Great Cormorant, Great White Egret, Black Stork, Bean Goose, White-fronted Goose, Greylag Goose, Common Shelduck, Eurasian Wigeon,

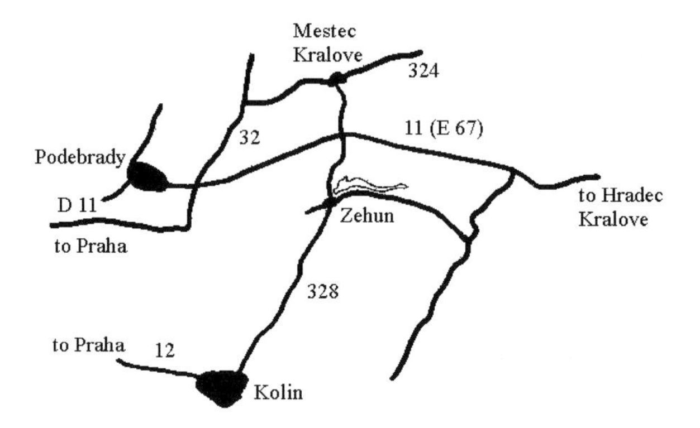

Pintail, Red-crested Pochard, Greater Scaup, Common Goldeneye, Smew, Goosander, White-tailed Eagle, Hen Harrier, Osprey, Oystercatcher, European Golden Plover, Grey Plover, Jack Snipe, Eurasian Curlew, Little Gull, Gull-billed Tern (rare), Caspian Tern, Little Tern, Whiskered Tern, Black Tern, White-winged Black Tern, Short-eared Owl, Aquatic Warbler (rare but often overlooked), Twite, Common Rosefinch and Snow Bunting. Geese can number in the hundreds, and there are several thousand ducks, either individuals of 1 species or a mixture of the species listed above. A total of 237 species had been recorded at Zehunsky pond and in its environs by 1996.

Access

The pond lies about 0.5 km northeast of the village of Zehun, east of highway 328, which

EASTERN BOHEMIA

(3) Krkonose mountains (SE,TU)

General characteristics

50°37'–50°47'N 15°23'–15°53'E

The Krkonose mountains, with a maximum elevation of 1602 m (Mt Snezka), are situated on the border between the Czech Republic and Poland. The region covers about 547 km^2 and is divided into 4 zones: the alpine and partly subalpine zone (44 km^2), the subalpine and upper

montane zone (40 km^2), the montane and submontane zone (279 km^2), and the submontane zone (184 km^2). Habitats include mountain spruce and mixed forest, subalpine meadows, subarctic peatbogs, glacial corries and dwarf pine. These habitats support a specialized flora and fauna. Within the Krkonose mountains lie another 2 IBAs: the **Pancavska and Labska louka peatbogs** (at 1300–1360 m), and **Upska raselina peatbog** (at about 1400 m).

Species

Among regular breeding species are Black Stork, European Honey-buzzard, Black Grouse, Capercaillie, Corn Crake, Eagle Owl, Pygmy Owl, Tengmalm's Owl, Common Kingfisher, Grey-headed Woodpecker, Black Woodpecker, Three-toed Woodpecker, Wood Lark, Water Pipit, Alpine Accentor, Bluethroat (*L.s. svecica;* Pancavska and Labska louka peatbogs, and Upska raselina peatbog), Ring Ouzel, Greenish Warbler, Red-breasted Flycatcher, Crested Tit, Red-backed Shrike, Nutcracker, Common Raven, Common Redpoll, Common Crossbill and Common Rosefinch. Occasional breeding of Lesser Spotted Eagle, Merlin, Peregrine Falcon and Dotterel may occur.

Access

From Praha, the E65 runs along the western border of the area, continuing to Poland. From the E65, a road extends to Harrachov. Highway 295 connects Vrchlabi and Spindleruv Mlyn in the central part of the mountains. The eastern part of the Krkonose mountains can be reached via highway 296 and 296A from Trutnov. Well-marked paths cross the mountains in every direction.

NORTHERN BOHEMIA

(4) Novozamecky pond (CL)

General characteristics

50°40'N 14°30'E

Although this is a large fishpond (at 300 m), the area of open water covers only about 0.38 km^2, and most of the remaining area (about 2 km^2) is reedbed. The extensive reedbeds are surrounded by conifers and wet meadows.

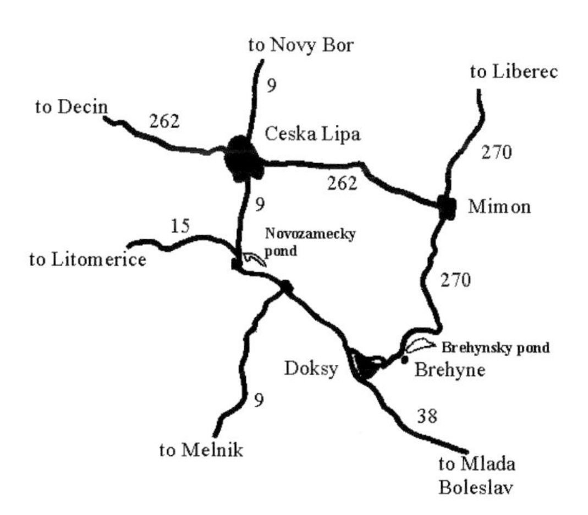

Species

Regular breeding species include Great Bittern, Little Bittern, Marsh Harrier, Common Crane, Spotted Crake, *Acrocephalus* and *Locustella* species, Penduline Tit, and Reed Bunting. Passage or wintering birds include Great Cormorant, Bean Goose, Greylag Goose, numerous species of duck (up to several thousand individuals), White-tailed Eagle, Osprey, Common Tern, Black Tern, and Red-throated Pipit.

Access

The pond lies east of highway 9, which connects Ceska Lipa and Melnik. It is 6 km south of Ceska Lipa, and within several hundred metres of Zahradky village. There are several other ponds within close distance.

(5) Brehynsky pond (CL)

General characteristics

50°35'N 14°42'E

The main feature of this highly eutrophic 0.92-km^2 fish-pond is the diversity of its surrounding habitats. A mosaic of reedbeds, peatbogs, conifers and boggy forest provides a suitable environment for various breeding and migrant birds. This pond (at about 320 m) is used for fish-farming.

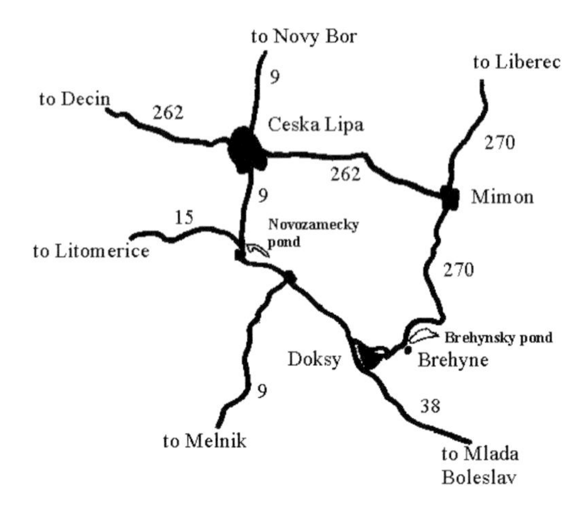

Species

Among numerous breeding species are Great Bittern, Little Bittern, Black Stork, White-tailed Eagle, Marsh Harrier, Common Crane, *Acrocephalus* and *Locustella* species, Penduline Tit, and Reed Bunting. Passage or wintering birds include Black-throated Diver, Great Cormorant, Mute Swan, various species of duck (thousands of individuals), Osprey and Black Tern.

Access

Take highway 38 from Mlada Boleslav to Doksy (via the E65 from Praha), or 9 and then 38 from Ceska Lipa (Novozamecky pond) to Doksy. Brehyne village is the closest settlement. Brehynsky pond lies on the east side of highway 270, about 3 km northeast of Doksy. Close to Doksy is another large area of water called Machovo jezero, a water-sports centre.

WESTERN BOHEMIA

(6) The Doupovske hory mountains (KV)

General characteristics

50°14'–50°15'N 12°56'–12°59'E

The geomorphology of these mountains has been determined by their volcanic origin. Numerous shallow brooks with rocks can be found across this 600-km^2 area, lying on the right bank of the Ohre river. Beech forest of varying size, and forest steppe-like habitats with brush and hedgerows are typical in these mountains. There are several large areas of open water situated towards the periphery of the area. The highest point is at 930 m. Owing to the range in elevation, average annual temperature ranges from 5°C to 8°C, and precipitation from 500 to 700 mm. At the end of the 1980s, over 220 breeding and non-breeding species had been recorded in the area.

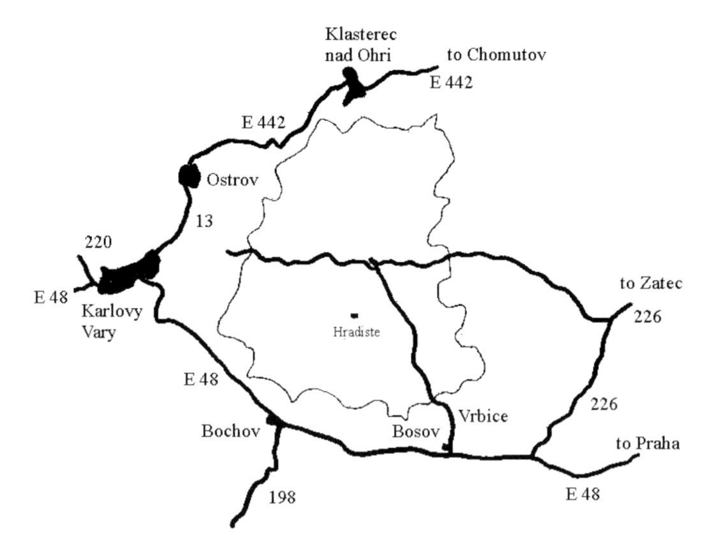

Species

Among the breeding species are Great Bittern (2–3 pairs), Black Stork (12–14 pairs), European Honey-buzzard (15–18 pairs), Red Kite (3–5 pairs), Montagu's Harrier (1–2 pairs), Hobby (8–10 pairs), Black Grouse (about 200 individuals), Common Quil (40–50 pairs), Woodcock (40–60 pairs), Stock Dove (hundreds of pairs), Barn Owl (5–8 pairs), Eagle Owl (25–30 pairs), Little Owl (8–10 pairs), European Nightjar (10–15 pairs), Hoopoe (1–2 pairs), Wryneck (80–100 pairs), Wood Lark (20–30 pairs), Tawny Pipit (up to 5 pairs), Yellow Wagtail (20–30 pairs), Bluethroat (*L. s. cyanecula*; 3–5 pairs), Rufous Nightingale (50–70 pairs), Whinchat (hundreds of pairs), Barred Warbler (hundreds of pairs), Red-breasted Flycatcher (50–70 pairs), Golden Oriole (20–25 pairs), Red-backed Shrike (hundreds of pairs), Common Raven (3–5 pairs), Common Rosefinch (10–20 pairs), Ortolan Bunting (5–10 pairs) and Corn Bunting (50–70 pairs). Non-breeding species occurring on migration or in winter include Ferruginous Duck, Black Kite, White-tailed Eagle, Lesser Spotted Eagle, Common Crane and Avocet.

Access

The E48 connecting Praha and Karlovy Vary runs along the south border of the Doupovske hory mountains. Because the whole area was used for army training until 1990, the roads within it are not marked. One of the best ways to access the mountains is by using a county road running from Bosov village (on the E48) via Vrbice.

(7) The Sumava mountains (CK, KT, PT)

General characteristics

48°40'–49°20'N 13°15'–14°10'E

This is a wooded region along the border with Germany and Austria. About 120 km long and up to 40 km wide, the Sumava mountains span 3 counties. Altitude ranges from 600 m up to 1378 m. The majority of the area is covered by primary spruce forest and plantations, and at lower altitudes by fir-beech forest. The distinctive feature of the Sumava mountains is the treeless plains, covered by numerous peatbogs, covering a total area of about 35 km^2, and extending from 800 up to 1200 m. Streams, river valleys and farmland compose a smaller area in the mountains. The climate is rather harsh, with annual average temperatures of 3.5–6.5°C, and total annual precipitation from 800 to 1600 mm. Within the Sumava mountains, **Mt Boubin** and the **Vltavsky luh floodplain** are recognized as IBAs. The total area covered by the Sumava mountains is about 1630 km^2.

Species

Among regularly breeding species are Black Stork, European Honey-buzzard, Hen Harrier, Lesser Spotted Eagle, Hazel Grouse, Black Grouse, Capercaillie, Corn Crake, Eagle Owl, Pygmy Owl, Tengmalm's Owl, Common Kingfisher, Grey-headed Woodpecker, Black Woodpecker, White-backed Woodpecker, Three-toed Woodpecker, Wood Lark, Bluethroat (*L.s. cyanecula*), Ring Ouzel, Redwing, Greenish Warbler, Red-breasted Flycatcher, Crested Tit, Red-backed Shrike, Nutcracker, Common Redpoll, Common Crossbill and Common Rosefinch. Occasional breeding of Peregrine Falcon and Ural Owl may occur. Flocks of thousands of Bramblings can be seen at lower altitudes in late autumn and in winter.

Access

There are many points of access to the mountain region. They E53 connecting Praha, Plzen-Zelezna Ruda and Deggendorf (Germany) crosses the mountains in the west. From this highway, county roads running into the mountains can be taken. Highway 4 runs across the central part of the mountains, connecting Prachatice with the German border. From Vimperk (on the road), there is access to the many county roads which cross the mountains. In the south, the E55 from Ceske Budejovice to the Austrian border can be taken; from Kamenny Ujezd it continues as highway 159 to Cesky Krumlov, and goes to the village of Cerna v Posumavi. This village lies at the edge of a large reservoir called Lipno. Paths and tracks in the mountains are clearly marked.

SOUTHERN BOHEMIA

(8) Dehtar pond (CB)

General characteristics
49°00'N 14°17'E

A fishpond of about 2.5 km^2 (with a buffer zone) which is surrounded by farmland. It lies at 420 m, and is about 15 km west of Ceske Budejovice. In the past, part of the pond was surrounded by wet meadows which provided a suitable breeding habitat for species such as Montagu's Harrier, Black-tailed Godwit and Eurasian Curlew. The meadows have been drained and replaced by farmland.

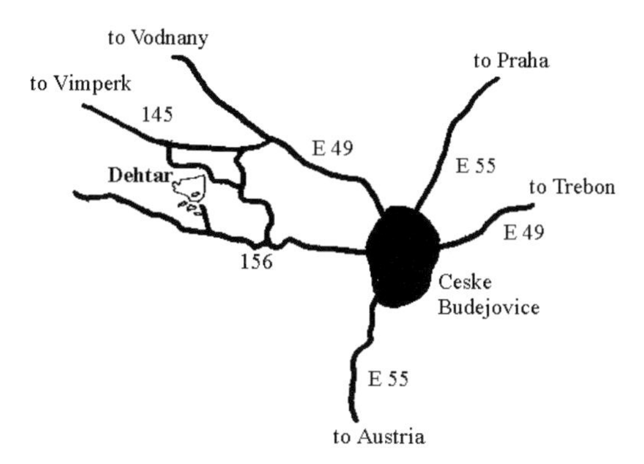

Species
The pond and adjacent areas provide suitable breeding habitat for Grey Heron, Marsh Harrier and Common Tern. Among regularly observed birds during migration, or non-breeding species in summer, are Red-throated Diver, Black-throated Diver, Red-necked Grebe, Eurasian Spoonbill, White-fronted Goose, Greylag Goose, thousands of individuals of *Anas* and *Aythya* duck, Common Shelduck, Eurasian Wigeon, Osprey, Peregrine Falcon, Common Crane, Avocet, Great Ringed Plover, European Golden Plover, Red Knot, Bar-tailed Godwit, Red-throated Pipit and Twite.

Access
Take the Ceske Budejovice road (E49) to the village of Cesnovice (about 11 km), from here, highway 145 to the village of Brehov (3 km), and from here to Dehtare village (about 3 km).

(9) Rezabinec pond (PI)

General characteristics
49°15'N 14°06'E

Rezabinec pond, which is primarily used for fish-farming, covers about 0.90 km^2, with reedbeds of about 0.4 km^2. It lies about 7 km southwest of Pisek, at 370 m. A variety of habitats such as dry and wet meadows, peatbogs, secondary growths of woods, and flooded sandpits surround the pond. A large part of the pond is covered by vegetation spreading from the edges.

Species
Regularly breeding species include Greylag Goose, Marsh Harrier, Spotted Crake, Black-headed Gull, Common Tern and Black Tern. Mediterranean Gull and Bearded Tit have bred sporadically. Passage, winter or non-breeding species include Red-necked Grebe, Great Cormorant, Great Bittern, Great White Egret, Purple Heron, Barnacle Goose, Ruddy Shelduck (rare), Common Shelduck, Pintail, Red-crested Pochard, White-tailed Eagle, Osprey, Red-footed Falcon, Peregrine Falcon, Grey Plover, Little Stint, Temminck's Stint, Curlew

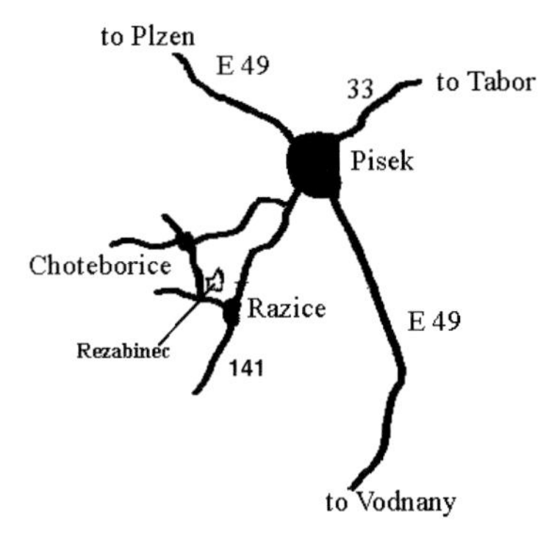

Sandpiper, Whimbrel, Wood Sandpiper, Little Gull, Common Gull, Caspian Tern, Water Pipit, Thrush Nightingale and Bluethroat. Flocks of thousands of individuals of *Anas* and *Aythya* duck and over a dozen species of shorebird occur on passage.

Access

From Pisek, take highway 141 to Razice village (about 7 km). The pond lies to the the west of highway 141, about 1 km north from Razice, and can also be accessed using county roads.

(10) Trebonsko (CB, JH, TA)

General characteristics

48°10'–49°07'N 14°39'–14°59'E

This is an area of about 700 km^2 with a diverse range of habitats. It spans 3 counties and is adjacent to the boder with Austria, at an elevation of 410–450 m. The Trebon basin is main-

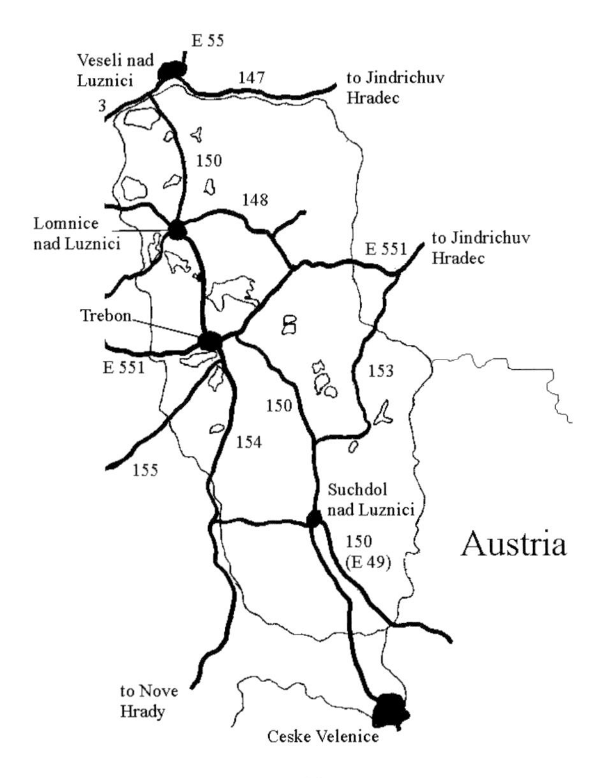

ly a flat inland plateau, surrounded by rolling hills. The area has abundant surface water (about 500 artificial fish-ponds and lakes of various sizes) as well as ground water. The habitats include various types of open water, oxbows of natural river systems, wet meadows, alluvial wetland, peatbogs, pond littoral zones, temperate broadleaf forest, conifer plantations, dry meadows, sand dunes, and farmland. The numerous fishponds are connected by chains of canals and brooks. Extensive littoral zones and wet meadows surround the majority of ponds. Clusters of ancient oaks grow around many of these ponds and along the roads. Land usage in the area is as follows: forest 47.5%, farmland 28.1%, other 10.5%, fish-ponds 10.3%, other open water 2.8%, and urban areas 0.8%. Within this area, there are a number of IBAs: **Stara reka river** and **Novorecke mocaly marshes, Ruda peatbog, Horusicky pond**, and **Velky** and **Maly Tisy ponds**. The Trebon basin is particularly important for migrating waterfowl and shorebirds, which occur in flocks of thousands.

Species

Breeding species include Black-necked Grebe, Great Cormorant, Great Bittern, Night Heron, Grey Heron, Purple Heron, Black Stork, White Stork, Greylag Goose, Red-crested Pochard, Common Goldeneye, European Honey-buzzard, Black Kite, Red Kite, White-tailed Eagle, Marsh Harrier, Hen Harrier, Montagu's Harrier, Hobby, Hazel Grouse, Black Grouse, Capercaillie, Water Rail, Spotted Crake, Little Crake, Corn Crake, Black-tailed Godwit, Common Tern, Black Tern, Eagle Owl, Pygmy Owl, Short-eared Owl, Tengmalm's Owl, European Nightjar, Common Kingfisher, Grey-headed Woodpecker, Black Woodpecker, Middle Spotted Woodpecker, Wood Lark, Yellow Wagtail, Bluethroat (*L. s. cyanecula*), *Locustella* and *Acrocephalus* species, Barred Warbler, Red-breasted Flycatcher, Collared Flycatcher, Bearded Tit, Penduline Tit, Short-toed Treecreeper and Golden Oriole. Most of the above named non-passerines nest in dozens of pairs, and the passerines in dozens and hundreds of pairs. Among non-breeding species occurring during summer or on passage are Red-throated Diver, Black-throated Diver, Red-necked Grebe, Slavonian Grebe, Squacco Heron, Great White Egret, Glossy Ibis, Eurasian Spoonbill, Common Shelduck, Lesser Spotted Eagle and Osprey.

Access

The town of Trebon is in the centre of this area. It can be reached from the E55 running from Praha to Ceske Budejovice. At the northwest tip of the area, between Veseli nad Luznici and Horusice, take highway 150 to Trebon (22 km). On both sides of this road are many fish-ponds. From Veseli nad Luznici (on highway 150), several roads criss-cross the area. The E49 runs south from Trebon to the border with Austria (about 26 km) and may be used to reach the southern part of the Trebon basin.

SOUTHERN MORAVIA

(12) Lednicke ponds (BV)

General characteristics

48°43'–48°48'N 16°42'–16°48'E

This is a system of 5 highly eutrophic fishponds with extensive reedbeds: Nesyt pond (3.2 km^2), Hlohovecky pond (1.05 km^2), Prostredni pond (0.48 km^2), Mlynsky pond (1.07 km^2), and Zamecky pond (30 km^2). All but Nesyt and Hlohovecky have 2 or more islets; and all of them, except Nesyt, are located in parkland with mature trees. Nesyt pond, which lies at the edge of Sedlec u Mikulova village, is surrounded by farmland. The ponds are found at an elevation of about 200 m. Water-level management is an important factor influencing the diversity and number of breeding as well as migrating species. Near the Zamecky ponds, adjacent to the village of Lednice, is Pastvisko, an extensive marsh and meadow area with reedbed.

Species

Among regular or irregular breeding species are Great Bittern, Little Bittern, Night Heron, Grey Heron, Purple Heron, White Stork, Greylag Goose, Red-crested Pochard, European Honey-buzzard, Black Kite, Marsh Harrier, Hobby, Water Rail, Spotted Crake, Little Crake,

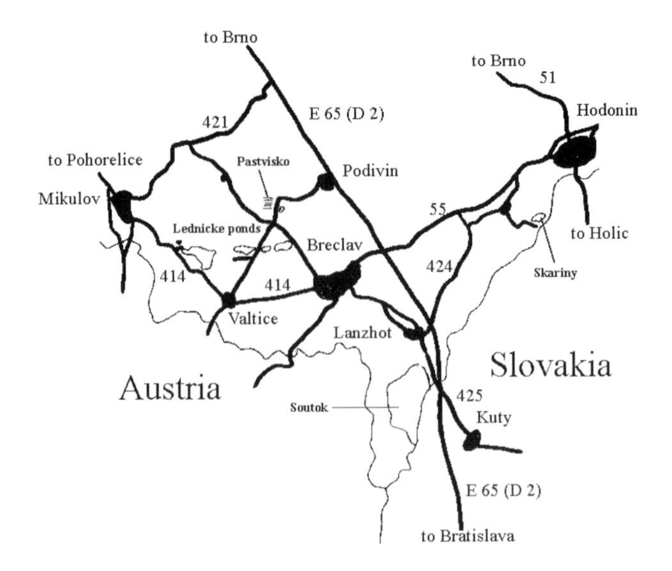

Corn Crake, Little Ringed Plover, Common Redshank, European Nightjar, Common Kingfisher, Grey-headed Woodpecker, Green Woodpecker, Black Woodpecker, Syrian Woodpecker, Middle Spotted Woodpecker, Lesser Spotted Woodpecker, Wood Lark, Yellow Wagtail, Bluethroat (*L. s. cyanecula*), *Locustella* and *Acrocephalus* species, Barred Warbler, Collared Flycatcher, Bearded Tit, Penduline Tit, Short-toed Treecreeper and Golden Oriole. The Lednicke ponds are important for migrating waterfowl, shorebirds, gulls and terns, and virtually all the possible species which could occur in the Czech Republic from these groups have been recorded. Among other migrating, wintering or non-breeding species are Red-throated Diver, Black-throated Diver, Red-necked Grebe, Slavonian Grebe, Great Cormorant, Squacco Heron, Little Egret, Great White Egret, Glossy Ibis, Eurasian Spoonbill, Common Shelduck, White-headed Duck, White-tailed Eagle, Osprey, Black-winged Stilt, and Avocet.

Access

From Brno, take the D2 to Bratislava. At the Podivin exit, highway 422 takes you to Lednice village. From here, Zamecky pond and Pastvisko are within walking distance. Continue on highway 422 to about 2.5 km south off Lednice. This road runs between Mlynsky and the Prostredni ponds. Continue on highway 422 to Valtice, and from here take the 414 to Sedlec u Mikulova. The 414 runs along the southern edge of Nesyt pond. From Mikulov (and Vienna after crossing the border with Austria), use highway 414 to Sedlec u Mikulova.

(13) Nove Mlyny reservoir (BV)

General characteristics

48°52'–48°55'N 16°36'–16°39'E

This is a man-made reservoir in an old area of riverine forest, marshes, meadows and oxbows along the Dyje river. It comprises 3 sections; however, only the middle part is significant for breeding and migrant birds. The reservoir was built during the 1970s and 1980s to control flooding from the Dyje, Svratka and Jihlava rivers, and to provide water for irrigation. The whole area is surrounded by farmland. Remnants of riverine forest can be found around the lower section of the reservoir. The upper section is 5.3 km^2; the middle section, which covers about 10.8 km^2, has several sandy islets with a total area of 0.18 km^2; and the lower section covers 16.5 km^2. The islets in the middle section have some sparse vegetation with bushes, while willow and reeds are scattered around this section of the reservoir.

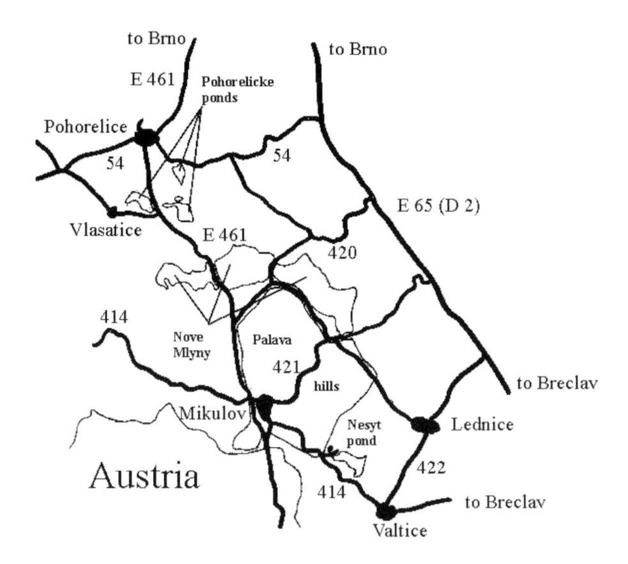

Species

Breeding species include Great Cormorant (about 200 pairs, but varies from year to year), Purple Heron, Eurasian Spoonbill (up to 1988), Greylag Goose (up to 200 pairs), Red-crested Pochard, Marsh Harrier, Little Ringed Plover, Mediterranean Gull (2–3 pairs), Common Gull (1–3 pairs), Yellow-legged Gull (accidental nesting), Common Tern (about 200 pairs) and Black Tern, Bluethroat (*L. s. cyanecula*), *Locustella* and *Acrocephalus* species, Bearded Tit and Penduline Tit. For migrating species, Nove Mlyny reservoir holds the same birds as the Lednicke ponds. Almost all likely species of waterfowl, shorebird, gull and tern have been recorded. Among other migrating, wintering or non-breeding species are Red-throated Diver, Black-throated Diver, Red-necked Grebe, Slavonian Grebe, Squacco Heron, Little Egret, Great White Egret, Glossy Ibis, Common Shelduck, White-headed Duck, White-tailed Eagle, Osprey, Black-winged Stilt, and Avocet. The number of migrating and wintering waterfowl reaches thousands of individuals, and occasionally up to 60, but more often a dozen or so, White-tailed Eagles.

Access

The E461 from Brno to Mikulov (and the border with Austria) runs between the middle and upper section of the reservoir (about 40 km from Brno and 11 km from Mikulov). Also from Brno (or Bratislava, the capital of Slovakia) take the D2, and exit at Hustopece. From Hustopece take highway 420 to Strachotin village (about 9 km). The road continues to Dolni Vestonice and runs between the middle and lower sections of the reservoir. The reservoir lies to the west of Strachotin.

(14) Palava hills (BV)

General characteristics

48°46'–48°53'N 16°37'–16°45'E

This is an area of about 83 km^2, situated close to the border with Austria. The main geological feature of the Palava hills is the limestone outcrops, with the highest hill, Devin, at 550 m. The area is surrounded by lowlands (160–180 m) where there is extensive farming. The whole region is warm and dry with a mean temperature of 9.6°C. Over 300 days a year have a temperature above 0°C. Typical habitats are oak forest, forest-steppe and broken stone forest. Included in the Palava protected area is a game preserve called Milovicky les, which is mainly broadleaved forest, and Krive jezero lake (part of Mokrady dolniho toku Dyje Ramsar site), which is an oxbow lying in the Dyje river floodplain.

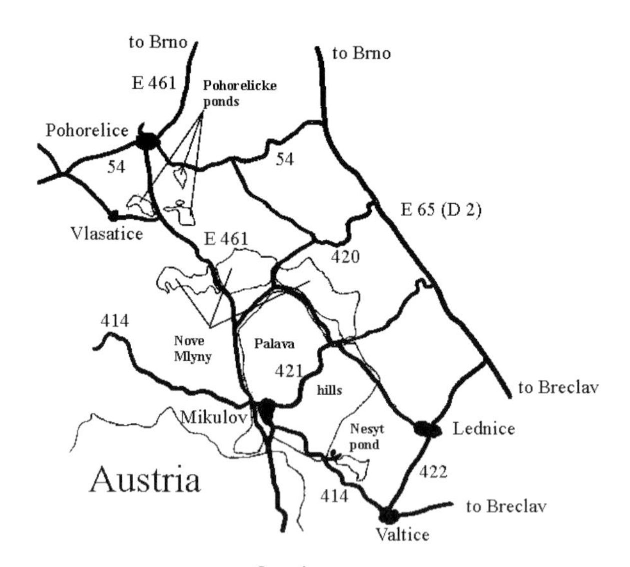

Species

Breeding species include Black Stork, White Stork, Greylag Goose, European Honey-buzzard, Red Kite, Black Kite, White-tailed Eagle (several attempts but no records so far), Marsh Harrier, Northern Goshawk, Common Buzzard, Saker Falcon (bred for the first time in 1998), Eagle Owl, Common Kingfisher, Hoopoe, Grey-headed Woodpecker, Green Woodpecker, Black Woodpecker, Syrian Woodpecker, Middle Spotted Woodpecker, Rufous Nightingale, Northern Wheatear, Barred Warbler, Collared Flycatcher, Bearded Tit, and Golden Oriole. Regularly observed non-breeding species include Eastern Imperial Eagle and Wallcreeper.

Access

The Palava hills lie about 4 km north of the border with Austria, and 46 km south of Brno, along the E461. From Mikulov, take a county road to Klentnice. On the same road you can also reach Perna and Pavlov. Highway 421 runs from Mikulov to Milovice, and from this road you can also get to Milovicky les and Krive jezero. There are well-marked trails in the Palava hills and throughout the whole area.

(15) Pohorelicke ponds (BV)

General characteristics

48°50'–48°59'N 16°30'–16°34'E

The Pohorelicke ponds embrace a system of 3 large (Novovesky pond (1.38 km^2), Vrkoc pond (1.56 km^2), Stary pond (1.3 km^2)) and several small ponds surrounded by farmland. Extensive littoral vegetation, dense shrub and trees along the banks provide favourable nesting sites for various species. The ponds, which are used for fish-farming, lie at an elevation of about 200 m. The total area covers about 5 km^2.

Species

Among regular breeding species are Great Bittern (rare), Little Bittern, Purple Heron, White Stork, Greylag Goose, Red-crested Pochard, Marsh Harrier, Water Rail, Spotted Crake, Common Tern, Grey-headed Woodpecker, Syrian Woodpecker, Middle Spotted Woodpecker, *Locustella* and *Acrocephalus* species, Barred Warbler, Collared Flycatcher, Bearded Tit, Penduline Tit, Red-backed Shrike, and Golden Oriole. Non-breeding species and species on migration include Squacco Heron, Bean Goose, White-fronted Goose, Barnacle Goose, Red-breasted Goose (very rare), and White-tailed Eagle. Almost all the species of duck and shorebird occurring in the Czech Republic have been recorded at the Pohorelicke ponds.

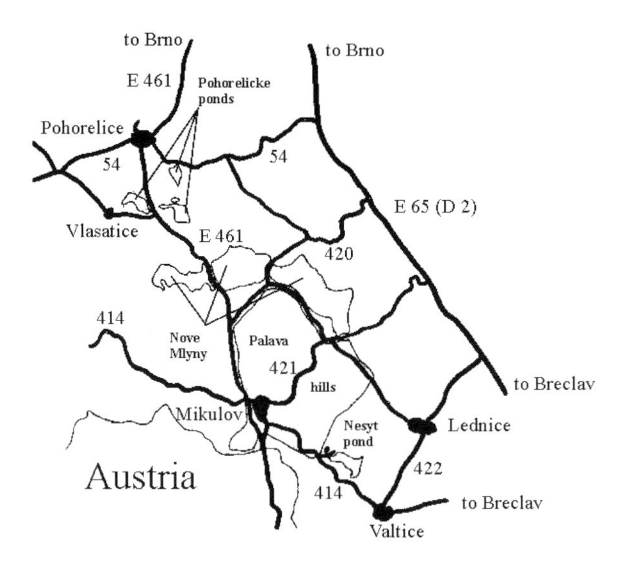

Access

The ponds lie about 27 km south of Brno. Take the E461 from Brno to Pohorelice. This road runs between Novovesky and Vrkoc ponds, and continues to Nove Mlyny reservoir. From Pohorelice, take highway 54 to access Stary pond.

(16) Skariny (HO)

General characteristics

48°48'N 17°05'E

Skariny is a mature riverine forest lining a stretch of the Morava river about 3 km east of the village of Mikulcice. The protected area covers about 0.135 km^2, and is regularly flooded during the spring. The dominant trees are oak, willow, elm, poplar and ash, and there is a rich brush undergrowth.

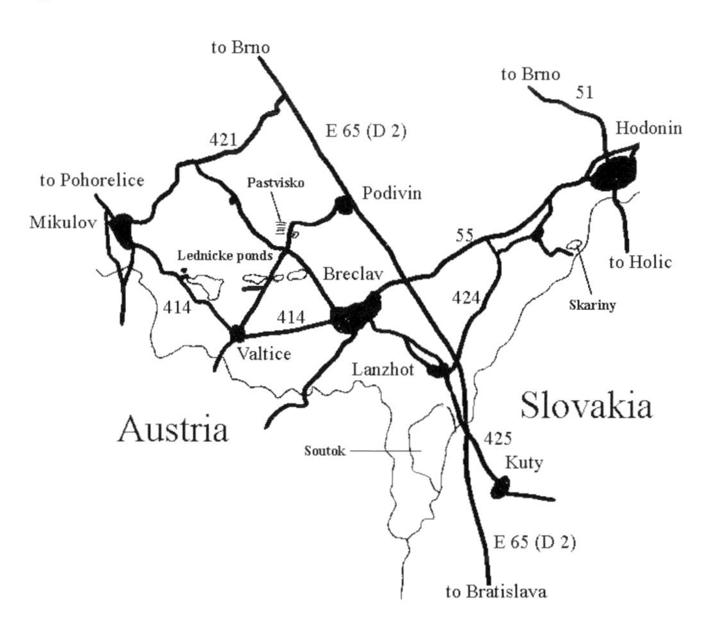

Species

Among the breeding species are Grey Heron, Black Stork, White Stork, European Honey-buzzard, Black Kite, Grey-headed Woodpecker, Green Woodpecker, Black Woodpecker, Syrian Woodpecker, Middle Spotted Woodpecker, and Collared Flycatcher. On the Morava river various species of duck, and White-tailed Eagle, can be seen in winter.

Access

The village of Mikulcice lies 5 km south of Hodonin and 18 km from Breclav on highway 55. The reserve can be accessed using a county road from Mikulcice.

(17) Soutok (BV)

General characteristics

48°37'–48°44'N 16°53'–17°02'E

This is an area of 50 km² in the southeastern tip of the Czech Republic, near the border with Slovakia and Austria. Soutok is a unique area, dominated by riverine forest (about 40 km²) with wet meadows, solitary oaks, marshes, and numerous canals, oxbows, brooks and small pools. The forest comprises mainly ancient oak, willow, elm, poplar and ash, with a rich brush undergrowth. The average elevation is about 150 m.

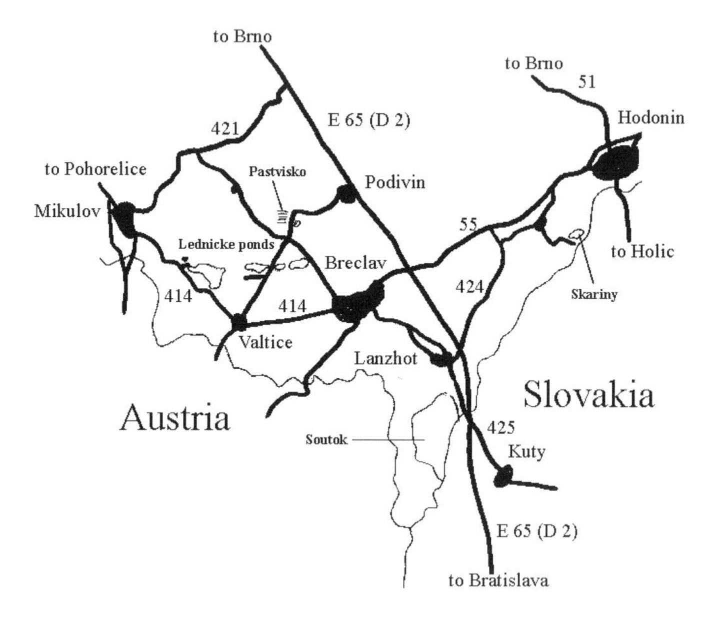

Species

Breeding species include Grey Heron, Black Stork, White Stork, European Honey-buzzard, Black Kite, Red Kite, Saker Falcon, Corn Crake, Common Kingfisher, Wryneck, Grey-headed Woodpecker, Green Woodpecker, Black Woodpecker, Syrian Woodpecker, Middle Spotted Woodpecker, Lesser Spotted Woodpecker, Barred Warbler, Collared Flycatcher, Short-toed Treecreeper and Golden Oriole. A pair of Eastern Imperial Eagles successfully nested in 1998 and 1999. Among passage or wintering birds are White-tailed Eagle, Eurasian Wigeon, Pintail, Horned Lark and Thrush Nightingale.

Access

The area lies about 5 km south of the village of Lanzhot. From Lanzhot, take highway 425 (about 3 km) to access the area. However, Soutok is closed to motor vehicles. Numerous forestry roads are available, although these are not marked. Lanzhot lies about 8 km southeast of Breclav, and can be accessed using the interstate D2 from Brno to Bratislava (Slovakia).

(11) Znojemsko (ZN)

General characteristics

48°47'–48°51'N 16°10'–16°16'E

Znojemsko is an area of about 75 km², composed mostly of arable land, orchards, windbreaks, and remnants of dry grassland, originally the main habitat. A few sandpits serve as breeding sites for several species. The area, which is contained by the villages of Bozice, Hodonice, Hradek and Lechovice, lies about 8 km east of Znojmo. The area is primarily farmland, mainly maize, alfalfa, winter wheat, sugar-beets, sunflowers and cereals being grown. Znojemsko is at an elevation of 200–240 m.

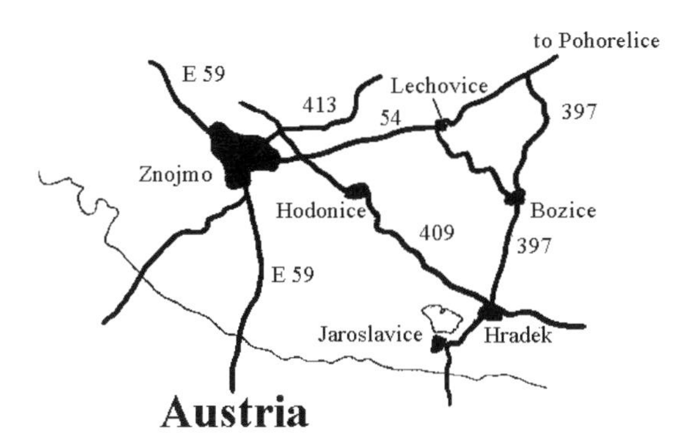

Species

Occasional or regular breeding species include Red Kite, Great Bustard (individuals from Austria?), Stone-curlew, European Bee-eater, Syrian Woodpecker, Sand Martin, Tawny Pipit (its only known breeding site in s. Moravia), Northern Wheatear, Barred Warbler, Red-backed Shrike, Rook and Corn Bunting. In winter, Saker Falcon, Sky Lark and numerous flocks of Reed Buntings can be seen.

Access

Highway 54, connecting Znojmo and Pohorelice, can be considered the northwest boundary of the area. From the village of Lechovice, highway 414 runs to Bozice village. This village, and the village of Hradek, are connected by highway 397, and the villages of Hradek and Hodonice by highway 408. From Brno, the E461 goes to Pohorelice, and highway 54 to Lechovice village.

NORTHERN MORAVIA

(18) Beskydy mountains (FM, VS)

General characteristics

49°06'–49°46'N 17°58'–18°46'E

The Beskydy mountains cover 1160 km² and are found in the northeast of the country. Although the majority of the area is covered by spruce plantations, there are also remnants of the primary broadleaved forest, preserved in nature reserves such as Mionsi, Salajka and Razula. In some areas, primeval beech forest is mixed with fir stands, and there is a rich undergrowth. Pastures and meadows cover about 20% of the area. Numerous streams and brooks criss-cross the region. Altitude ranges from about 400 m up to 1323 m. The climate is generally cold and wet. The range in annual average temperatures as well as precipitation is wide: temperatures vary from 2.7 to 7.6°C, and precipitation from 972 to 1540 mm. Almost the whole area, particularly the ancient primeval forest, has been damaged by pollution from the industrial region of Ostrava. Within the Beskydy mountains there is another IBA, called **Mionsi**. This is a 1.56-km² area of primeval fir-beech forest at about 950 m.

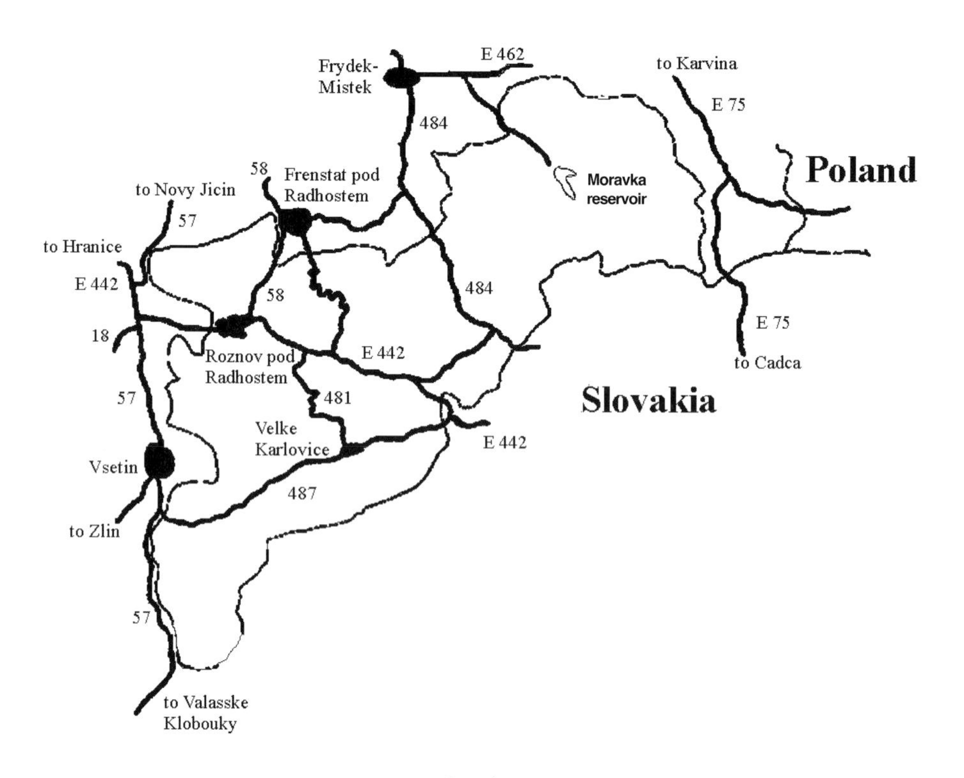

Species

Breeding birds include Black Stork, European Honey-buzzard, Hobby, Hazel Grouse, Capercaillie, Corn Crake, Stock Dove, Eagle Owl, Pygmy Owl, Ural Owl, Tengmalm's Owl, European Nightjar, Common Kingfisher, Grey-headed Woodpecker, Black Woodpecker, White-backed Woodpecker, Three-toed Woodpecker, Meadow Pipit, Ring Ouzel, Redwing, Barred Warbler, Firecrest, Red-breasted Flycatcher, Collared Flycatcher, Crested Tit, Red-backed Shrike, Nutcracker, Rook, Common Crossbill and Common Rosefinch.

Access

From Brno, take the D1 to Vyskov and from here highway 47 to Prerov and Hranice. From Hranice, take the E442 to Valasske Mezirici and Roznov pod Radhostem. This road continues to the border with Slovakia. From the E442 you can access the southern and central areas of the mountains. From Ostrava, take highway 56 to Frydek-Mistek, and from here highway 484 to Frydlant nad Ostravici. This road continues toward the central part of the mountains, and joins the E442. The distance from Brno to Roznov pod Radhostem is about 150 km, and from Ostrava to the mountains about 35 km.

(19) Jeseniky mountains (BR, SU)

General characteristics

49°54'–50°18'N 17°01'–17°27'E

Jeseniky is a mountain region in the northern part of Moravia, covering about 730 km^2. The highest peak, **Praded**, which is part of an IBA, reaches 1492 m. The tree-line extends up to 1300 m. Although the majority of the woodland is spruce, remnants of fir-beech forest are spread across the area. Other habitats found in the mountains include upland grassland, peat-bogs, pastures and meadows. Numerous streams and brooks flow down from the mountains. The climate is cold and damp.

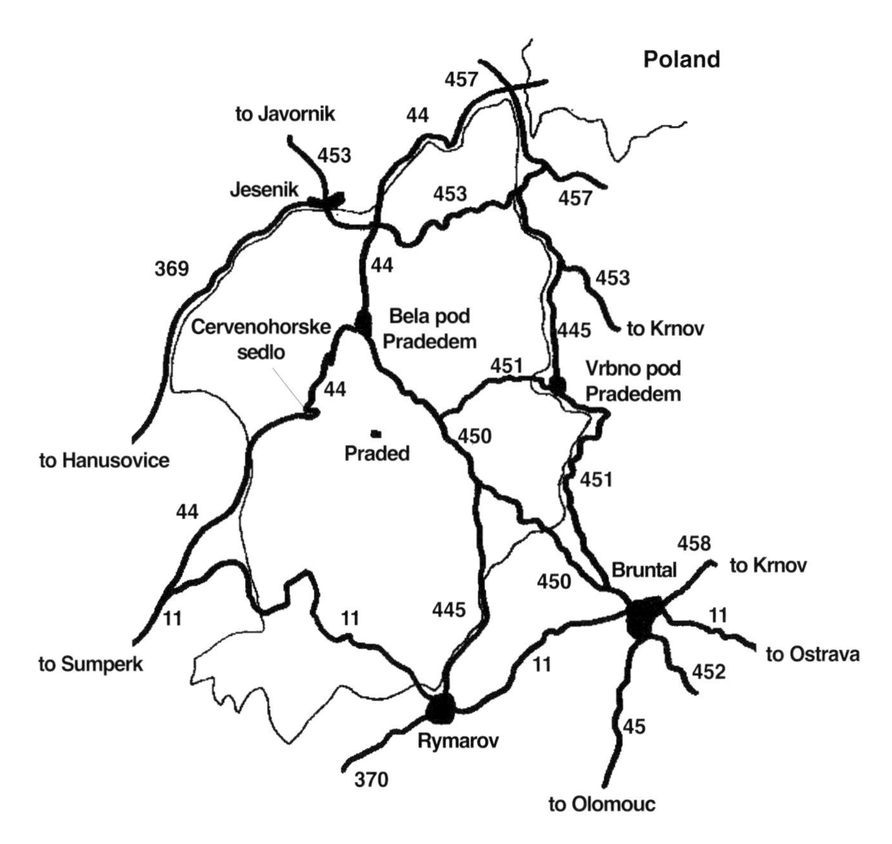

Species

Breeding birds include Black Stork, European Honey-buzzard, Hen Harrier, Hazel Grouse, Black Grouse, Capercaillie, Corn Crake, Stock Dove, Eagle Owl, Tengmalm's Owl, European Nightjar, Common Kingfisher, Grey-headed Woodpecker, Black Woodpecker, Three-toed Woodpecker, Water Pipit, Alpine Accentor, Ring Ouzel, Firecrest, Red-breasted Flycatcher, Collared Flycatcher, Crested Tit, Red-backed Shrike, Nutcracker, Rook, Common Redpoll, Common Crossbill and Common Rosefinch. Among possible or occasional breeding species are Peregrine Falcon and Dotterel (the latest breeding for the latter being in 1985).

Access

From Ostrava, highway 11 goes through Opava to Bruntal (about 65 km). From Bruntal, take either highway 450, which runs across the mountains to Jesenik (about 40 km), or continue on highway 11 through the southern area to Sumperk (51 km). From Brno to Olomouc take the E462 (76 km); from here to Mohelnice travel on the E442 (33 km); and from Mohelnice to Sumperk on highway 44 (27 km). There are well-marked trails across the mountains.

(20) Poodri (FM, NJ, OV)

General characteristics

49°36'–49°47'N 17°54'–18°14'E

Poodri is a system of lakes, ponds and backwaters around the Odra river, between the towns of Ostrava and Mankovice. The area of water covers about 15 km^2, and the total area about 81.5 km^2. The habitats include oxbows, canals, wetland, alluvial meadow with solitary trees, and floodplain forest. The ponds are surrounded by rich growths of reeds. The drier forests are dominated by maple, lime, oak and hornbeam. At many places there are steep slopes with lime- and maple-dominated forest. The altitude of the region ranges from 214 to 298 m.

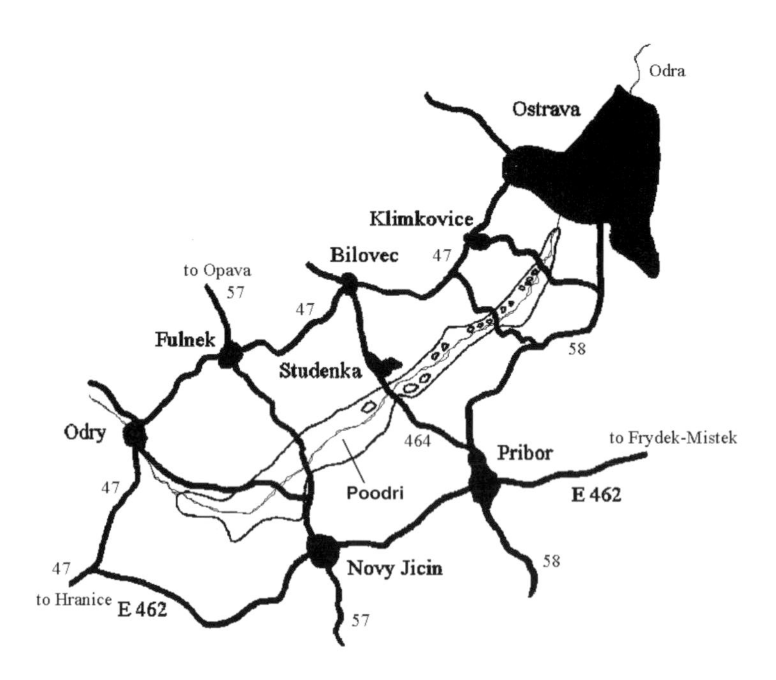

Species

Breeding species include Red-necked Grebe, Black-necked Grebe, Little Bittern, Grey Heron, Black Stork, White Stork, Common Teal, Garganey, Northern Shoveler, Common Goldeneye, Marsh Harrier, Water Rail, Spotted Crake, Common Snipe, Black-tailed Godwit, Common Redshank, Grey-headed Woodpecker, Green Woodpecker, Black Woodpecker, Middle Spotted Woodpecker, Lesser Spotted Woodpecker, *Locustella* and *Acrocephalus* species, Barred Warbler, Collared Flycatcher and Penduline Tit. Passage species include Great White Egret, Osprey, Common Crane and various species of waterfowl, shorebird and gull.

Access

The area lies between highways 47 and 58. Either one can be taken from Ostrava to the south. Many smaller roads connect these 2 highways. From Brno, on the E462 to Vyskov, and from here highway 47 to Prerov, Hranice and Fulnek (a total distance of about 140 km).

1 Tree-lined banks along the Morava river (UH). Photo: Borek Seehak.

2 Brooks surrounded by peatbogs are typical at lower altitudes in the Sumava mountains (CK, KT, PT). Photo: Hans Grünwald.

3 A brook in mountain foothills (CK). Photo: Hans Grünwald.

4 Canals in farmland provide breeding opportunities for a number of species (HO). Photo: Josef Kren.

5 Steep banks along rivers provide suitable breeding conditions for European Kingfishers (here along the Olsava river (UH)). Photo: Josef Kren.

6 and 7 Fishponds are numerous, particularly in the lowlands. Photos: Josef Kren.

8 Lednicke ponds (BV). Photo: Borek Seehak.

9 The flooded area below the lower section of the Nove Mlyny reservoir (BV).
Photo: Josef Kren.

10 and 11 Oxbows on the Morava river (UH). Photos: Borek Seehak.

12 Lipno reservoir (CK). Photo: Hans Grünwald.

13 Wintering waterfowl prefer larger rivers: the Labe in Nymburk (NB). Photo: Hans Grünwald.

14 The Vltava river in Praha (AA) is one of the best sites for wintering waterfowl. Photo: Hans Grünwald.

15 Typical lowland farmland (HO). Photo: Josef Kren.

16 (left) Extensive meadows in the foothills of the Ceskomoravska vysocina highlands (HB, JI, PE, ZR). Photo: Josef Kren.

17 (right) A mosaic of meadows, trees and bushes along a brook in the foothills of the Bile Karpaty mountains (HO, UH, ZL). Photo: Kvetoslav Frystak.

18 Pastures with solitary trees, mostly oaks, in the Bile Karpaty mountains (HO, UH, ZL). Photo: Hans Grünwald.

19 Decidous lowland forest (UH). Photo: Josef Kren.

20 Remnant beech forest is found throughout the country, particularly in highlands and mountains in the east (ZL). Photo: Borek Seehak.

21 and 22 Pine forest on sandy soil (HO). Photos: Borek Seehak.

23 Spring in riverine forest along the Morava river (UH). Photo: Borek Seehak.

24 (left) Primeval forest at 940 m in the Bile Karpaty mountains (HO, UH, ZL).
Photo: Josef Kren.
25 (right) Many cities around the country have large parks with mature trees, here for example in Luhacovice (ZL). Photo: Hans Grünwald.

26 Orchards in villages (UH). Photo: Josef Kren.

27 Farmland, orchards and scattered trees surrounding villages (UH). Photo: Josef Kren.

28 (left) Ruins of castles in the Chriby hills (KM). Photo: Josef Kren.
29 (right) Brooks are numerous in the Beskydy mountains (FM, VS). Photo: Josef Kren.

30 Fishponds surrounded by meadows and trees, mostly willows (BV). Photo: Borek Seehak.

31 (left) Spruce forest in the Bile Karpaty mountains (HO, UH, ZL). Photo: Josef Kren.
32 (right) Meadows with solitary and small stands of trees at about 600 m in the Bile Karpaty mountains (HO, UH, ZL). Photo: Josef Kren.

33 Limestone outcrops in the Palava hills (BV). Photo: Borek Seehak.

34 Clearings in spruce-domintated forest in the Jeseniky mountains (BR, SU).
Photo: Borek Seehak.

35 (left) A pool surrounded by peatbogs in the Jeseniky mountains (BR, SU).
Photo: Josef Kren.
36 (right) Growths of dwarf pine in the Krkonose mountains (SE, TU). Photo: Josef Kren.

37 Acid-rain has a severe impact on spruce forest in the Krkonose mountains (SE, TU).

38 (left) Alpine meadows at about 1500 m in the Krkonose mountains (SE, TU).
Photo: Josef Kren.
39 (right) Pines at higher elevations in the Krusne hory mountains (CV, KV, MO, TP).
Photo: Josef Kren.

40 Mixed forest, mainly spruce, can be found throughout the country (PT county). Photo: Hans Grünwald.

41 Pastures in the Sumava mountains (CK, PT, KT). Photo: Hans Grünwald.

42 Meadows with bushes and trees in the Sumava mountains (CK, PT, KT).
Photo: Hans Grünwald.

43 A mosaic of meadows, forest and other growths along a brook in the foothills of the Sumava mountains (CK, PT, KT). Photo: Hans Grünwald.

GAVIIFORMES

Includes the family **Gaviidae** with 4 species breeding in the w. palearctic. All 4 species have been recorded in the Czech Republic: 3 regularly, White-billed Diver as an accidental. None of the species breeds in the country.

Red-throated Diver *Gavia stellata*

Red-throated Loon   Potaplice mala   Potaplica mala   Sterntaucher

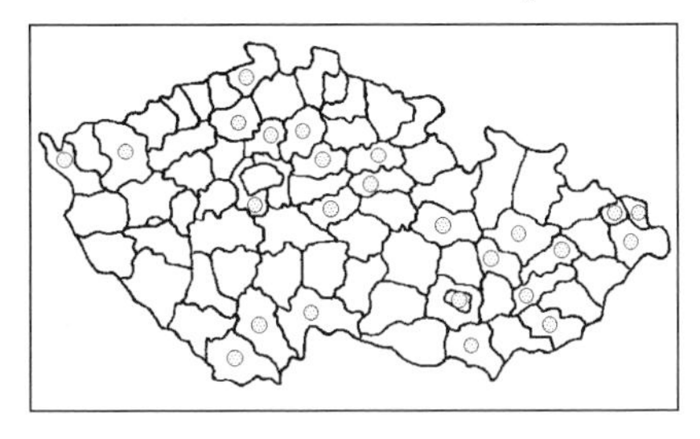

Red-throated Diver is a regular but scarce migrant in the Czech Republic. It occurs almost always as a solitary bird, although occasionally several birds may be seen together, and exceptionally as many as several dozen individuals. It is normally found with Black-throated Divers at the same sites. However, Red-throated is rarer than Black-throated Diver, and usually stays for only a few days at a site, rarely longer, before leaving. It prefers large dams, reservoirs, fishponds, gravel pits and rivers.

Status: Migrant and winter visitor. **Breeding season**: rare. **Winter**: uncommon/local. **Migration**: uncommon/local. Protected.

Population trends: The number of wintering and passage birds is usually up to 10, exceptionally up to 40 individuals.

Distribution: During migration or in winter, individuals are scattered nationwide. Some of the places where it occurs regularly include Zehunsky pond (NB), Vavrinecky pond (KH), Lipno reservoir (CK), Zabakor pond (MB), Dehtar pond (CB), Vysatov (CB), Mnissky pond (JH), Koclirov pond (JH), Hvezda pond (SY), Velky Kosir pond (SY), Naklo gravel pit (OL), Tovacovske ponds (PR), Donbas gravel pit (PR), Hulin gravel pit (KM), Ostrozska Nova Ves gravel pit (UH), Brnenska dam (BM), Lednicke ponds (BV) and Nove Mlyny (BV); also on rivers such as the Labe (HK, PU, NB, ME, LT, DC) and Vltava (CB, PZ, ME).

Timing: First birds may appear at the end of September, with increasing numbers during October and November. Most observations are from November onwards. During spring migration, most individuals occur in March, and rarely later. There have been only a few records from after the end of May.

Black-throated Diver *Gavia arctica*

Black-throated Loon   Potaplice severni   Potaplica stredna   Prachttaucher

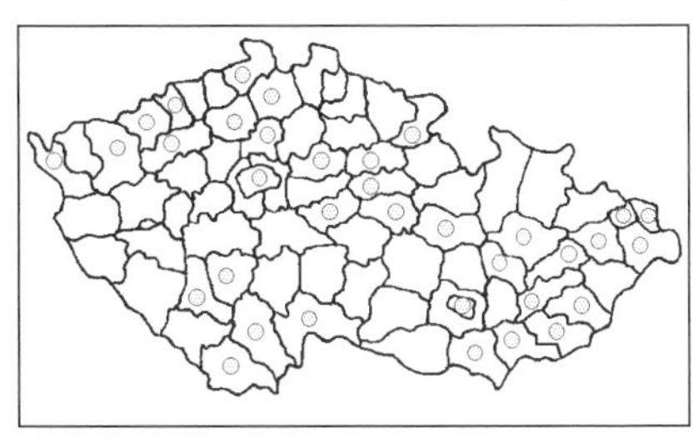

Black-throated Diver is seen in the Czech Republic more often than the other 3 species of diver. Solitary birds are most typical, but flocks of several individuals, especially during autumn migration, may be found. Early autumn and late spring migrants can be seen in breeding plumage. It prefers dams, larger and deeper fishponds, gravel pits and larger rivers.

Status: Migrant and winter visitor. **Breeding season**: rare. **Winter**: uncommon/local. **Migration**: uncommon/local. Protected.

Population trends: The number of wintering birds is lower than during migration. Usually up to 50 individuals can be recorded during winter, but the number may vary from year to year; for example, 139 individuals were recorded at a gravel pit in OL county in 1985, 110 individuals were recorded in s. Bohemia in the winter of 1987, and 27 individuals at Zelivka dam (BN) in November 1996.

Distribution: May occur nationwide, with higher concentrations in e. Bohemia, s. Bohemia and s. Moravia. Sites where it is recorded regularly include Zehunsky pond (NB), Brehynsky pond (CL), Rozkos dam (NA), Lipno dam (CK), Drazni pond (CK), Rozmberk pond (JH), Velky Tisy pond (JH), Dvoriste pond (JH), Bezdrev pond (CB), Dehtar pond (CB), Vlhlavsky

Black-throated Diver

pond (CB), Rimovska dam (CB), Velky Kosir near Litomysl pond (SY), Hvezda pond (SY), Olesna dam (FM), the Chomoutov and Naklo gravel pits (OL), Tovacovske ponds (PR), Donbas gravel pit (PR), Troubky gravel pit (PR), Plumlovska dam (PV), Hulin gravel pit (KM), Ostrozska Nova Ves gravel pit (UH), Jarohnevicky pond (HO), Lednicke ponds (BV), Nove Mlyny (BV) and the Vltava river in Praha (AA).
Timing: There are records from every month, usually from mid-October, with increasing numbers until December, and the highest numbers in November. Rarely seen before October or during spring migration.

Great Northern Diver *Gavia immer*

Great Northern Loon Potaplice ledni Potaplica velka Eistaucher

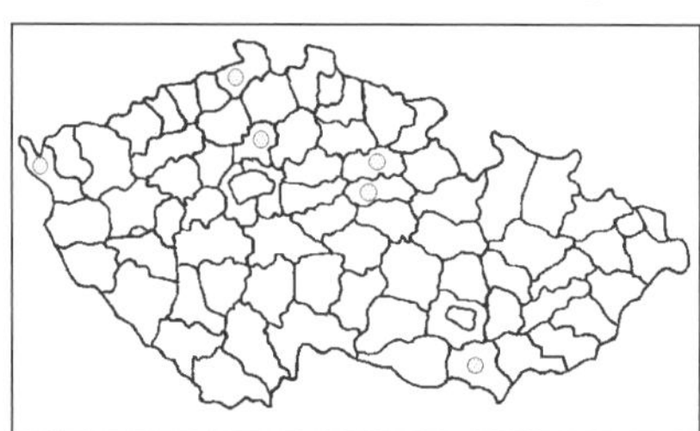

This is a rare species in the Czech Republic, and does not occur annually. The maximum number of birds recorded during winter is 2. It prefers larger dams, gravel pits, fishponds and larger rivers.
Status: Migrant and winter visitor. **Breeding season:** rare. **Winter:** uncommon. **Migration:** uncommon. Protected.
Distribution: May occur nationwide. A recent record is from Nove Mlyny (BV).
Timing: Observed usually from November until February. Occurrence before November and after February is rare, although records exist.

PODICIPEDIFORMES

In the w. Palearctic includes the family **Podicipedidae** with 3 genera. Five species of 2 genera (*Tachybaptus* and *Podiceps*) are regularly recorded in the Czech Republic. Among these, are 4 regular or irregular breeders, and 1 non-breeder.

Little Grebe *Tachybaptus ruficollis*

Potapka mala   Potapka mala   Zwergtaucher

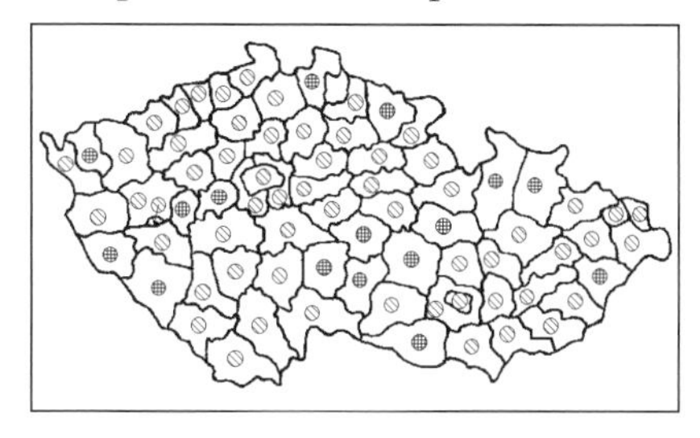

Little Grebe is found in aquatic habitats ranging from small fishponds and marshes to canals and slow stretches of river. It is often found in areas with dense submerged vegetation and little open space. Breeding occurs from lowlands up to 690 m in the Ceskomoravska vysocina highlands (HB, JI, PE, ZR), and to 730 m in the Sumava mountains (CK, PT, KT). Wintering Little Grebes, which are more common than Great Crested Grebes, stay on ice-free stretches of larger rivers where they usually associate with other waterfowl. The local decline in breeding populations recorded in several counties is probably caused by destruction of breeding habitats. In areas with undisturbed habitat, populations have remained stable. During the 1970s, breeding densities were 150–680 pairs per km^2 at Lednicke ponds (BV), 7–106 pairs per km^2 at ponds around Sedlcany (PB), 0.9 pairs per km^2 at ponds around Marianske Lazne (CH), 780 pairs per km^2 at a pond near Trebon (JH), 400 pairs per km^2 at a marsh near Havlickuv Brod (HB), 32 individuals per km^2 at a pond near Zdar nad Sazavou (ZR), 15–17 pairs per km^2 at gravel pits in Ostrozska Nova Ves (UH); and, during the 1980s, an overall spring density at about 150 ponds of varying size in s. Bohemia ranged from 3 to 6 individuals per km^2. A breeding density of 60 and 170 pairs per km^2 was recorded at 2 ponds near Vodnany (ST) at the beginning of the 1990s.

Status: Resident. **Breeding season**: local/common. **Winter**: local/common. **Migration**: common. Protected.

Population trends: The number of breeding pairs is estimated to be between 3,000 and 6,000. In the past 20 years, the breeding population has decreased locally by 20–50%.The number of wintering birds usually does not exceed 2,000 individuals.

Distribution: Nationwide. The density of breeding birds is limited by suitable aquatic habitats. Common at ponds in LT county, around Pardubice (PU), Trebon (JH), Jindrichuv Hradec (JH), Ceske Budejovice (CB), Tovacov (PR), Bartosovice (NJ), Ostrava (OV), Karvina (KI), Namest nad Oslavou (TR), Zahlinice (KM), Hodonin (HO), Lednice (BV), Pohorelice (BV) and at Nove Mlyny (BV). As a breeder, it is rather scarce in SU, VS, ZL, BK, SY, PT, KL, ME, KT, DO, SO, and FM counties. Wintering individuals prefer rivers such as the Vltava (AA, CB), Labe (PU, LT, DC), Ohre (LN), Morava (KM, HO) and Odra (OV, KI).

Timing: Spring migration starts in late March and continues through to mid-April. The breeding population departs in September, and individuals recorded after this are mostly from foreign populations. Breeding occurs in May and June, rarely at the end of April or in July.

Great Crested Grebe *Podiceps cristatus*

Potapka rohac   Potapka chochlata   Haubentaucher

This is the most common breeding grebe in the Czech Republic, occurring in similar habitats to Little Grebe. However, larger fishponds, and occasionally dams, seem more suitable than small areas of water, and it prefers more open space than Little Grebe. Nests are built in areas with sparse vegetation. Great Crested Grebes occasionally nest in small colonies at large areas of open water. It is distributed from lowlands up to about 600 m in highlands. Breeding has also been recorded at 720 m in the Ceskomoravska vysocina highlands (HB, JI, PE, ZR), and at 730 m at Lipno reservoir (CK). Breeding density may vary significantly from place to place, and from year to year. It was 39–56 pairs per km^2 at Lednicke ponds (BV) during the 1960s,

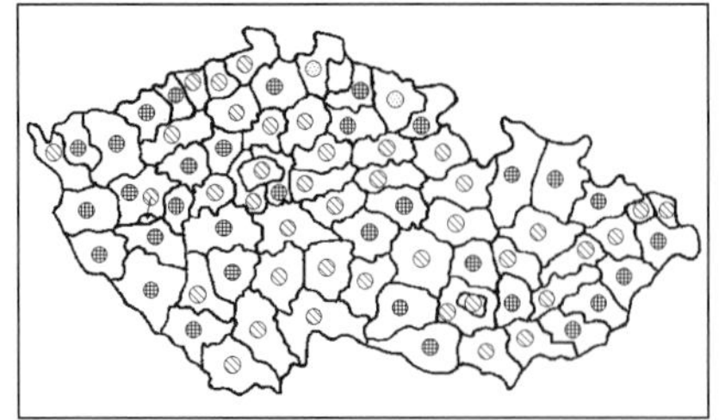

9–30 pairs per km^2 at ponds around Sedlcany (PB), and 9 pairs per km^2 at Anenske ponds (CH) during the 1970s. At Zehunsky pond (NB) it was 7–9 pairs per km^2, at Terlicka dam (KI) 8–10 pairs per km^2, at Strpsky pond (CB) 250 pairs per km^2, at gravel pits in Ostrozska Nova Ves (UH) 1–3 pairs per km^2; and, during the 1980s, the overall spring density at about 150 ponds of varying size in s. Bohemia ranged from 3 to 6 individuals per km^2. Flocks of dozens can be seen together after the breeding season. Although the majority of the breeding population is migratory, birds regularly winter at ice-free stretches of rivers such as the Vltava (AA, CB), Labe (HK, PU, LT, DC), Morava (KM, HO), Dyje (BV) and Odra (OV, KI). Wintering birds may include individuals from foreign populations. The primary cause of population decline is most likely habitat destruction, and the loss of nesting sites during reed harvesting at fishponds.

Status: Resident. **Breeding season:** local/common. **Winter:** local. **Migration:** common. Vulnerable. Protected. Not hunted all year round.

Population trends: The breeding population is between 3,500 and 7,000 pairs. It has decreased locally by 20–50% over the past 20 years. Up to 900 individuals may winter.

Distribution: Nationwide. As a breeder it is rather scarce in ZL, VS, FM, SU, BR, SY, BK, PT, BE, PE, LB, SE and TU counties. Wintering birds occur infrequently in SO, DO, PT, TC, CL, LB, SE, TU, NA, HK, PB, KH, ZN, BK, SU, BR and VS counties.

Timing: Arrives from early March, but mostly at the end of March and beginning of April. Autumn migration is mainly in September, although some birds are on passage at the end of August and in October. Breeding starts at the end of April, with a peak in May, and continues until the end of June.

Great Crested Grebe

Red-necked Grebe *Podiceps grisegena*

Potapka rudokrka Potapka cervenokrka Rothalstaucher

Red-necked Grebe, a locally common breeder at the end of the 19th century, became a rare breeding bird during the first half of the 20th century. The reasons for this sharp decline are unknown. In the past 30 years, irregular or probable breeding has been recorded in DC, CB, UL, OV, KI, VS, BV, OL, ZR and NJ counties. Nesting was recorded near Chabarovice (UL) in 1992. Breeding birds occur in lowlands, but a nest was also found at 580 m in ZR county. It is found in shallow fishponds with dense emergent vegetation, small islets and at stretches of open water. Migrating and wintering birds stay at gravel pits, dams, fishponds and on larger rivers. Usually solitary birds or sometimes flocks of a few individuals are observed.

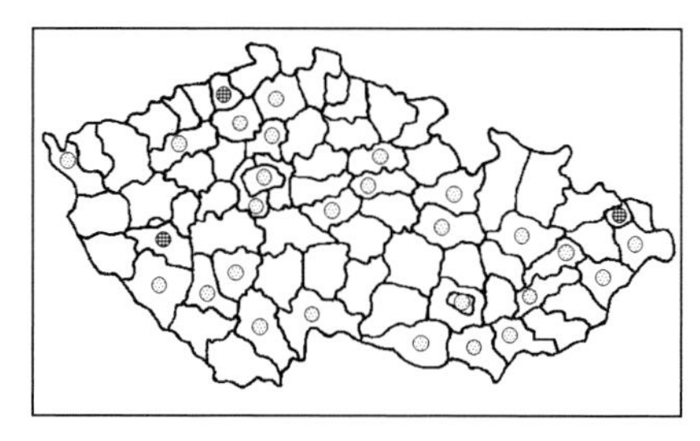

Status: Migrant and summer visitor. **Breeding season:** uncommon. **Winter:** uncommon. **Migration:** uncommon. Critically endangered. Protected.
Population trends: From 0 to 5 pairs may breed annually. Up to 20 individuals may be recorded in winter. No population trend changes in the past 20 years.
Distribution: Migrants and wintering birds may occur nationwide. Breeding may occur in the following areas: ponds around Ostrava (OV), Karvina (KI), Chlum u Trebone (JH), and ponds in TP, UL and LT counties. Places where non-breeders occur regularly include Zehunsky pond (NB), Riha pond (HK), Lenesicky pond (LN), Blatsky pond (JH), Dvoriste pond (JH), Rezabinec pond (PI), Divcicke ponds (CB), Vysatov pond (CB), Dehtar pond (CB) Bezdrev pond (CB), ponds around Trebon (JH), Skrin pond (PU), Velky Kosir pond (SY), Hvezda pond (SY), Donbas gravel pit (PR), Tovacovske ponds (PR), Zahlinicke ponds (KM), Hulin gravel pit (KM), Kvasice gravel pit (KM), Stolarka pond (HO), Brnenska dam (BM), Lednicke ponds (BV) and Nove Mlyny (BV).
Timing: Spring migration starts in mid-March, with increasing numbers in April, and the peak in May. Autumn migration occurs from September until November. Breeding extends from mid-May to the end of June.

Slavonian Grebe *Podiceps auritus*

Horned Grebe   Potapka zlutoroha   Potapka usata   Ohrentaucher

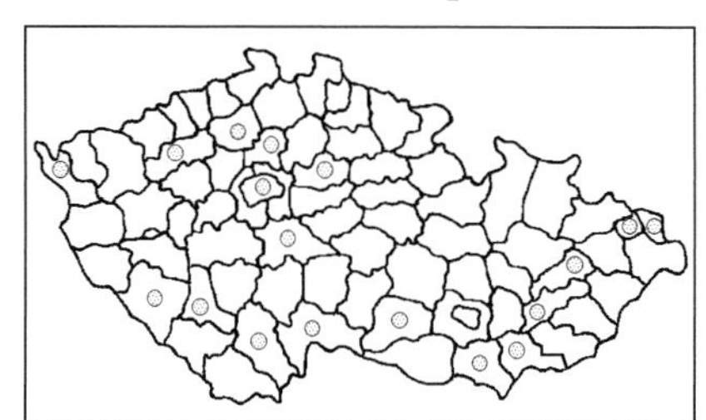

This is the rarest grebe in the Czech Republic, scattered across the country. Mostly solitary birds or flocks of a few individuals can be found at dams, gravel pits, fishponds and slow stretches of larger rivers. The number of birds observed annually may be underestimated because of confusion with Black-necked Grebe.
Status: Migrant and winter visitor. **Breeding season:** rare. **Winter:** uncommon. **Migration:** uncommon. Protected.
Population trends: The number of birds recorded annually does not seem to exceed 5 individuals.
Distribution: Nationwide. Some of the sites where it occurs regularly include the Vltava river in Praha (AA), Zehunsky pond (NB), ponds around Trebon (JH), Novy Ptacovsky pond (TR), Tovacovske ponds (PR), Zahlinicke ponds (KM), Stolarka pond (HO) and Nove Mlyny (BV).
Timing: Most records are from October, November and January, and a few from December, and February–May.

Black-necked Grebe *Podiceps nigricollis*

Potapka cernokrka   Potapka ciernokrka   Schwarzhalstaucher

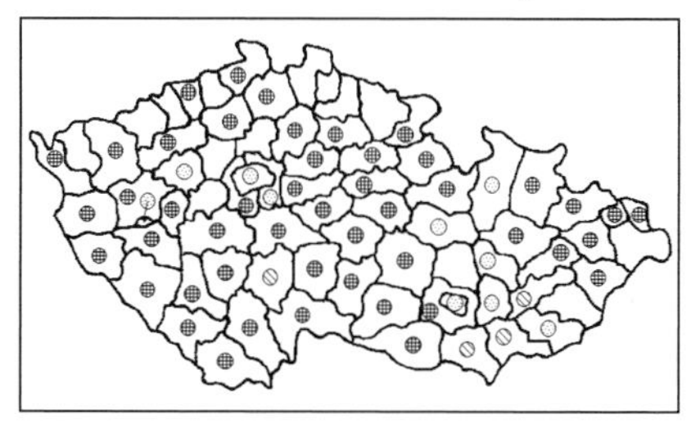

Until the end of the 19th century, Black-necked Grebe was an uncommon breeder in the Czech Republic. Since then, the population has increased, with the peak of breeding density in the early 1960s. However, during the following decades, local breeding populations have rapidly decreased for unknown reasons. The decline is well documented in studies from ponds at Namest nad Oslavou (TR): at the beginning of 1960s the breeding population was 460–470 pairs, in 1980 it was 272 pairs, in 1985 it was 76 pairs and down to only 1 pair in 1993. No significant changes had occurred in the breeding habitat. This species prefers lowlands but breeding has been recorded up to

580 m in the Ceskomoravska vysocina highlands (HB, JI, PE, ZR). This colonially nesting grebe occurs at larger shallow ponds with dense submergent vegetation and patches of open water. Colonies usually consist of up to 50 active nests; however, colonies with 50–100 nests can also be found. In the mid-1970s, breeding density at ponds around Sedlcany (PB) was 6–114 pairs per km^2, and at Anenske ponds (CH) it was 38 pairs per km^2, and 170 pairs per km^2 at a pond in Karvina (KI) in the mid-1980s; and, in the 1980s, the overall spring density at about 150 ponds of varying size in s. Bohemia was 4–14 individuals per km^2. During migration, it occurs in large flocks at dams, gravel pits and on slow stretches of rivers. Wintering individuals recorded as Black-necked Grebes may actually be misidentified Slavonian Grebes.

Status: Migrant, summer visitor and occasional winter visitor. **Breeding season:** uncommon. **Winter:** uncommon. **Migration:** common. Vulnerable. Protected.

Population trends: The breeding population is between 2,500 and 5,000 pairs, in 1994 only about 1,000–1,500 pairs. Since the 1960s, the breeding population has decreased by more than 50%. Up to 10 birds may winter.

Distribution: Migrating birds nationwide. Breeding pairs can be seen regularly at ponds in the following counties: JH, CB, TA, PI, ST, PJ, MB, JC, HK, KH, HB, PU, ZR, BV, HO, OV, KM, KI and NJ. Wintering birds have been recorded at the Vltava river (AA), Ohre river (LN), Morava river (OL, KM, UH, HO) and Dyje river (BV).

Timing: Arrives from the beginning of March, with the peak at the end of March and beginning of April. Autumn migration starts at the end of August and continues through September. Breeding occurs from mid-April, with the peak in May.

PELECANIFORMES

Includes 6 families with 17 species in the w. Palearctic. Five members of the **Sulidae**, **Phalacrocoracideae** and **Pelecanidae** families have been recorded in the Czech Republic, three as accidentals, one as a regular breeder, and one as a vagrant.

Great Cormorant *Phalacrocorax carbo*

Cormorant Kormoran velky Kormoran velky Kormoran

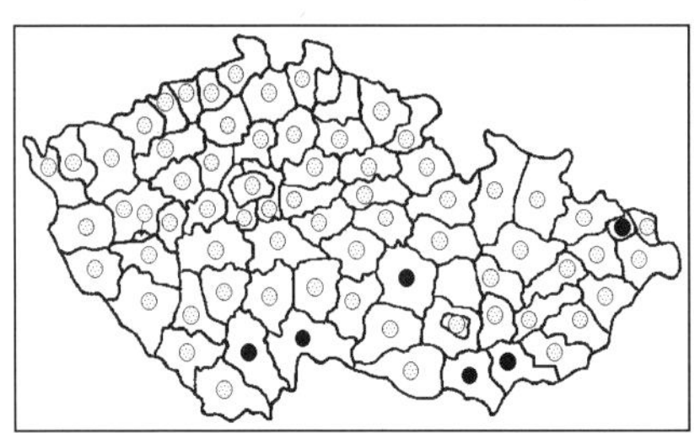

Great Cormorant's breeding attempts in the Czech Republic during the 19th and 20th centuries were usually unsuccessful because pairs were disturbed, or their clutches destroyed by fishermen and fishpond managers. The first documented successful breeding in the western part of the country occurred at Zenich pond (JH) in 1983. Breeding at Nove Mlyny (BV) in 1982 was the first successul breeding in the eastern part of the country since 1938 (Janda and Machacek 1990). Since the early 1980s, Great Cormorants have been breeding regularly but locally in s. Bohemia and s. Moravia. The first documented breeding in n. Moravia occurred in 1998. Nests are built in mature trees on islets of ponds or in other open water, or in riverine forest. Outside the breeding season, birds may be found at dams, gravel pits, fishponds and around rivers. At Zamecky pond, within the Lednicke ponds system (BV), Great Cormorants nest in mixed colonies together with Night Herons and Grey Herons. The highest numbers of Great Cormorants all year round are recorded at ponds around Trebon (JH), and at Nove Mlyny (BV), where 1,565 individuals were observed in December 1997. The breeding population belongs to the *sinensis* race.

Status: Resident. **Breeding season:** uncommon. **Winter:** local. **Migration:** local. Least concern. Hunted, with individual exceptions given by conservation authorities.

Population trends: Between 1983 and 1988, the breeding population fluctuated between 100–650 pairs, from 1989 untill 1991 it was 599–682 pairs, and in 1994 it was 319 pairs. Overall, the breeding population increased rapidly by at least 50% between 1983 and the early 1990s. The wintering population is estimated to be between 500 and 1,500 individuals.

Great Cormorant

Distribution: Strongholds of the breeding population are at ponds around Trebon (JH), Ceske Budejovice (CB), Lednicke ponds (BV), Nove Mlyny (BV) and in riverine forest along the Dyje (BV). Breeding attempts have also been reported from other counties. The successful breeding of 1 pair was recorded in ZR county in 1988. Migrating and wintering individuals occur nationwide, and are observed regularly for example at the following places: Opatovske ponds (KO), Bohdanecsky pond (PU), Velky pond (DC), Velkoholsky pond (ST), Horejsi pond (ST), Chomoutov gravel pit (OL), Tovacovske ponds (PR), Donbas gravel pit (PR), Kojetinske ponds (PR), Chorynske ponds (VS), Zahlinicke ponds (KM), Hulin gravel pit (KM), and the Vltava (CB, AA), Labe (PU, NB, LT), Dyje (BV) and Morava (KM, HO) rivers.
Timing: Spring migration starts at the end of February, more usually at the beginning of March, and continues through April. Departure from breeding grounds is at the end of August/beginning of September. The highest numbers of birds on passage are usually recorded in October and November. Breeding extends from the end of March to mid-May.

White Pelican *Pelecanus onocrotalus*

Great White Pelican Pelikan bily Pelikan ruzovy Rosapelikan

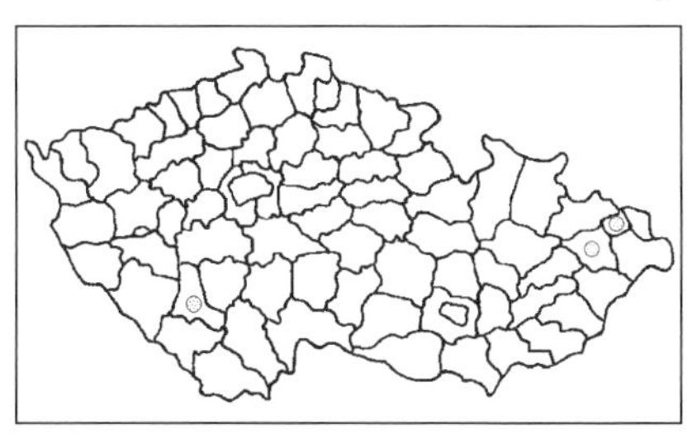

Even though it was once a breeding species in nearby Hungary, nesting was never documented in the Czech Republic, where White Pelican has been recorded about 15 times during the past 200 years. Almost always it is single birds that have been seen at large fishponds, dams, and industrial water bodies.
Status: Vagrant. **Breeding season:** rare. **Winter:** rare. **Migration:** rare. Protected.
Population trends: No data available.
Distribution: May occur nationwide. Recent observations are from Radov pond near Vrbno (ST) and Mokry pond near Sedlice (ST).
Timing: Recorded every month, except January, April, November and December.

CICONIIFORMES

Includes 3 families with 35 species in the w. Palearctic. Thirteen species have been recorded in the Czech Republic. Nine species belong to the family **Ardeidae**. Six of these are regular or irregular breeders, 2 are vagrants, and Cattle Egret is an accidental. Two regular breeders belong to the family **Ciconiidae**. Representatives of the family **Threskionithidae** include a vagrant and an irregular breeder.

Great Bittern *Botaurus stellaris*

Bittern, Eurasian Bittern   Bukac velky   Buciak velky   Rohrdommel

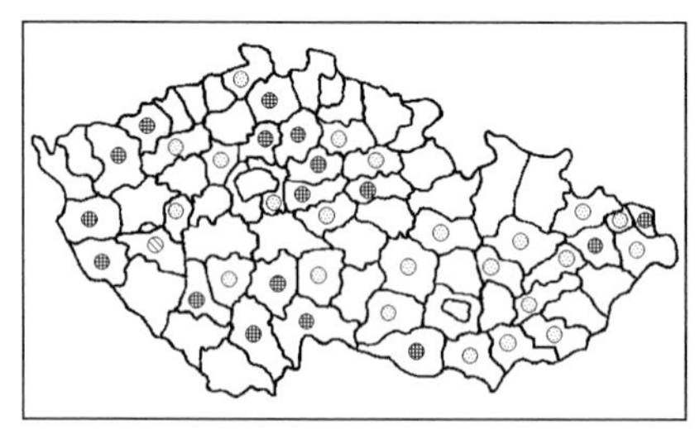

During the first half of the 20th century, Great Bittern was a regular breeding species at many fishpond areas in the Bohemian and Moravian lowlands. During the past 40 years, its numbers have declined and Great Bittern has become a rare breeder. Only a few pairs may breed from year to year in s. and e. Bohemia. It favours lowlands, but is found up to about 450 m in highlands. Males start to call during the first half of March, usually immediately after arrival at the breeding grounds. This species requires extensive reedbeds around ponds or marshes, although breeding at small areas of open water has also been recorded. Outside the breeding season, it may be observed at places with less dense vegetation, or even with no vegetation, including gravel pits, ditches, and reservoirs. Reduction of reedbeds, drainage of marshes, and disturbance by human activities are the most probable causes for its decline.

Status: Migrant, summer visitor and occasional winter visitor. **Breeding season:** uncommon. **Winter:** uncommon. **Migration:** local. Critically endangered. Protected.

Population trends: The breeding population is between 20 and 30 pairs. Since the 1950s, the breeding population has decreased by 20–50%. The number of wintering birds is estimated to be up to 5 individuals.

Distribution: More or less regular breeding occurs at Zehunsky pond (NB), Novozamecky pond (CL), Brehynsky pond (CL), ponds around Ceske Budejovice (CB), Blatec pond (CB), Strpsky pond (ST), ponds around Trebon (JH), Blatsky pond (JH), Stary pond near Sobeslav (JH), Rezabinec pond (PI), Pohorelicke ponds (BV), ponds between Jesenik nad Odrou (NJ) and Ostrava (OV), and Hermansky pond (OV). It is regularly reported during migration as well as in the breeding season at the following sites: Vinarsky pond (CV), Bohdanecsky pond (PU), Vrbenske ponds (CB), Novy pond (SY), Skucak pond (KI), Tovacovske ponds (PR), Zahlinicke ponds (KM), Pisecne ponds (HO), Mutenicke ponds (HO), Luzicke ponds (HO), Tresicky pond (HK), Cerny Nadymac pond (PU) and Lednicke ponds (BV).

Timing: Usually arrives at the end of February/beginning of March. Autumn departure from breeding grounds spreads from the end of July to September. Breeding occurs mostly from the end of April through May.

Little Bittern *Ixobrychus minutus*

Bukacek maly   Buciacik obycajny   Zwergdommel

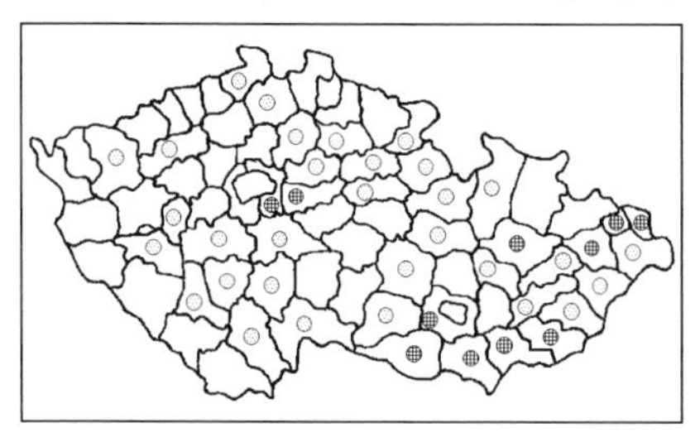

About 30 years ago, Little Bittern was the most commonly breeding Ciconiiforme in the Czech Republic. The breeding of several pairs at the same pond or small marsh was not uncommon. These days, solitary pairs are scattered across the lowlands of the country at fishponds, marshes, slow stretches of rivers, ditches, and oxbows of rivers with dense aquatic vegetation, usually reeds. During migration it also occurs at open water such as gravel pits and dams. Although this is a typical lowland species,

breeding has been recorded up to 550 m in the Ceskomoravska vysocina highlands (HB, JI, PE, ZR), and non-breeding up to 580 m in the same region. Its decline is probably due to habitat changes at its wintering grounds as well as the loss of breeding habitat in many counties.
Status: Migrant and summer visitor. **Breeding season**: uncommon. **Winter**: does not occur. **Migration**: local. Critically endangered. Protected.
Population trends: Recently, the number of breeding pairs has been estimated to be between 50 and 90. During 1973–1977, the size of the breeding population was 150–300 pairs. In the past 20 years, the breeding population has declined by 20–50%.
Distribution: During migration it may may occur in lowlands nationwide. More or less regular breeding may be observed at ponds around Ceska Lipa (CL), Pardubice (PU), Zehunsky pond (NB), ponds around Ceske Budejovice (CB), Trebon (JH), Strakonice (ST), Ostrava (OV), at Tovacovske ponds (PR), Zahlinicke ponds (KM), Lednicke ponds (BV), Nove Mlyny (BV) and Pohorelicke ponds (BV). The stronghold of the breeding population is in BV county. It is also found at oxbows of the Morava river (KM, UH, HO), and around the Labe (PU, KO, NB) and Dyje (BV) rivers.
Timing: Spring migration usually starts in mid-April and continues through to early May. Departure occurs during August and September. Breeding extends from the second half of May to the end of June, occasionally the beginning of July.

Night Heron *Nycticorax nycticorax*

Black-crowned Night Heron   Kvakos nocni   Chavkos nocny   Nachtreiher

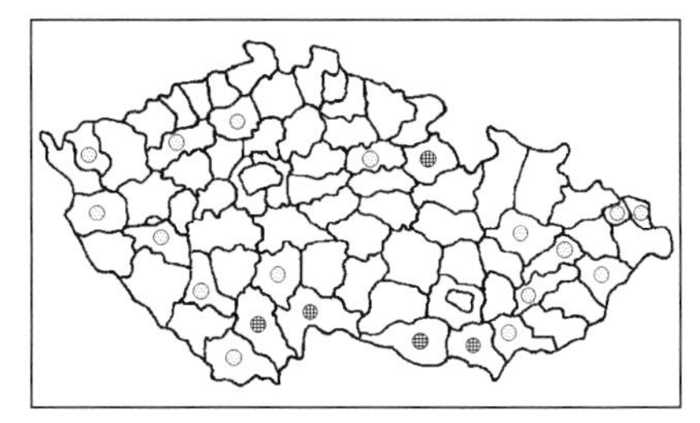

This is a colonially nesting species, with the majority of the population distributed in the lowlands of s. Moravia, and up to 450 m in s. Bohemia. Colonies are established at ponds, marshes, or in forest around rivers. The size of the colonies may reach 270 active nests, as at Zamecky pond in the Lednicke ponds system (BV). At other places, it is usually between 20 and 70 nests; however, 108 pairs nested at Zlivsky pond (CB) in 1998. Occasional nesting of solitary pairs has also been recorded in several counties. Outside the breeding season it occurs at gravel pits, dams, and larger rivers, where individual birds or flocks of several birds are observed.
Status: Migrant and summer visitor. **Breeding season**: uncommon. **Winter**: does not occur. **Migration**: uncommon/common. Endangered. Protected.
Population trends: The breeding population is between 300 and 370 pairs. During 1973–1977 it was 100–150 pairs.
Distribution: Breeding colonies are located at ponds around Ceske Budejovice (CB), and Trebon (JH). The only regular nesting site in Moravia is Zamecky pond (BV). Occasionally it may nest near Strachotin (BV), in riverine forests in BV and HO counties, and at Jaroslavicky pond (ZN). Non-breeding individuals have been regularly reported from ponds near Vodnany (ST), Chomoutov gravel pit (OL), Tovacovske ponds (PR), ponds around Karvina (KI), Zahlinicke ponds (KM), ponds around Hodonin (HO) and woodlands around the Morava river (HO). There have also been recent records from Labe, near Roudnice nad Labem (LT), and Kapelnik pond (CK) (at 860 m).
Timing: Spring migration usually occurs during late March, and autumn migration mainly in September, continuing to the end of October. Breeding extends from mid-April to the end of June.

Squacco Heron *Ardeola ralloides*

Volavka vlasata   Caplicka vlasata   Rallenreiher

This is an irregular, and quite rare visitor to the Czech Republic. It occurs mostly in fishpond areas in s. Bohemia and s. Moravia, where solitary birds, or occasionally small flocks, have been recorded. Squacco Herons are usually seen at shallow ponds or marshes.

Status: Vagrant. **Breeding season:** rare. **Winter:** does not occur. **Migration:** uncommon. Protected.
Population trends: No data available.
Distribution: There are recent records from Dobra vule pond (JH), Zahlinicke ponds (KM), Stolarka pond (HO), Breclav (BV), Lednicke ponds (BV), Pohorelicke ponds (BV) and Nove Mlyny (BV).
Timing: From April until October. Most of the observations are from May and August.

Little Egret *Egretta garzetta*

Volavka stribrita Belusa mala Seidenreiher

Little Egret is becoming a regular but not common visitor to the Czech Republic. Fifteen or so years ago it was considered a rarity. Five successful breeding attemps were recorded in the 20th century: a nest in a colony of Night Herons and Grey Herons at Zamecky pond (BV) was found in 1983 and again in 1988; 4 pairs successfully reared at least 15 juveniles at Zlivsky pond (CB) in 1997; 2 pairs were found at the same site in 1998, and in 1999 a pair with 4 young was recorded. This species is more commonly seen at ponds around Ceske Budejovice (CB) in s. Bohemia, and Lednicke ponds (BV) and Nove Mlyny (BV) in s. Moravia than in other areas of the country. Between the end of April and the beginning of September 1997, 64 individuals were observed and reported across the country.
Status: Summer visitor. **Breeding season:** rare. **Winter:** does not occur. **Migration:** uncommon. Critically endangered. Protected.
Population trends: No data available.
Distribution: Recent records are from Vavrinecky pond (KH), Cejkovy ponds (KT), Zehunsky pond (NB), Bezdrev pond (CB), Divcicke ponds (CB), Zlivsky pond (CB), Maly Bedny and Studenec ponds (NJ), Volesek pond (CB), Vysatov pond (CB), Dubovy pond (JH), Hvezda pond (SY), Bohuslavice (SU), Tovacovske ponds (PR), Hustopecske ponds (PR), Zahlinicke ponds (KM), Bzenec (HO), Moravsky Pisek (HO), Luzicke ponds (HO), Lednicke ponds (BV), Lanzhot (BV) and Nove Mlyny (BV).
Timing: From April until October. Most records are from May and August.

Great White Egret *Egretta alba*

Great Egret Volavka bila Belusa velka Silberreiher

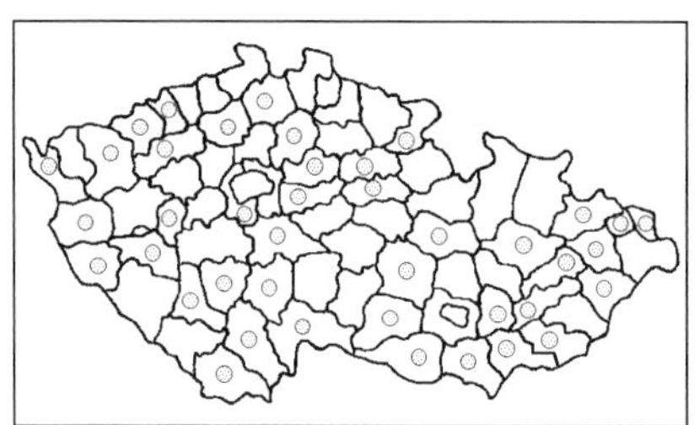

This is a regular visitor to the fishpond areas in s. Bohemia and s. Moravia, where usually solitary birds and sometimes flocks of several individuals have been observed. During the past decade, flocks of several dozens birds have been seen quite frequently. Successful breeding in the 20th century occurred at Velky Tisy pond (JH) in June 1949. This species may be seen all year round at ponds of any size, marshes, edges of industrial waters and around larger rivers. Wintering birds occur mostly in s. Moravia at Nove Mlyny (BV), and around Lednice (BV). At Nesyt pond (BV), 52 individuals were recorded in October 1997. A flock of 51 individuals was seen at Velky Tisy (JH) pond, 73 individuals at Rozmberk (JH) pond in October 1996, 65 individuals at Velky Tisy pond (JH) and 89 individuals at Cernicny pond (JH) in October 1998.
Status: Visitor. **Breeding season:** rare. **Winter:** uncommon. **Migration:** uncommon. Critically endangered. Protected.

Population trends: In 1993, there were 65 records totalling 324 individuals; in 1994, 32 with 170 individuals; and in 1995, 72 records of a total of 287 individuals (Brandl and Simek, 1995; Simek and Brandl, 1996). In 1997, 437 individuals were recorded between the end of February and the end of December.
Distribution: It has been observed regularly at Hermanicky pond (CL), Zehunsky pond (NB), ponds around Ceske Budejovice (CB) and Trebon (JH), Rezabinec pond (PI), Strpsky pond (ST), Velkoholsky pond (ST), Tovacovske ponds (PR), Chorynske ponds (VS), ponds around Karvina (KI), Zahlinicke ponds (KM), Kvasice gravel pit (KM), Tlumacov (ZL), Luzicke ponds (HO), Lanzhot (BV), Podivin (BV), Lednicke ponds (BV), Lednice-Pastvisko (BV) and Nove Mlyny (BV).
Timing: Recorded every month. Most frequently in April, May, August, September and October.

Grey Heron *Ardea cinerea*

Volavka popelava Volavka popolava Graureiher

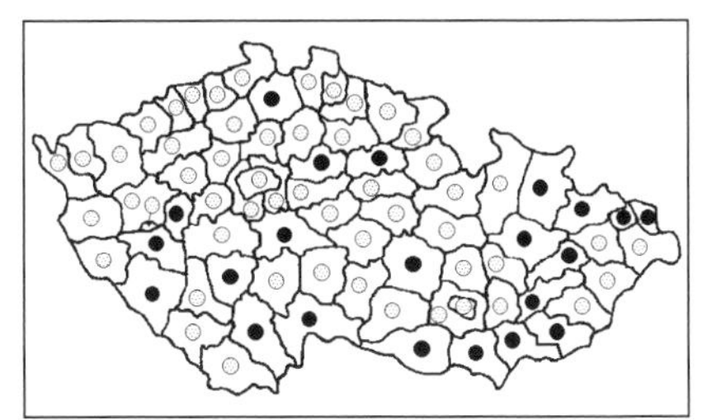

This is the most common species of heron in the country, breeding mostly in lowland areas. Breeding has also been recorded at 700 m in the 1950s. Until full protection became effective in 1975, breeding colonies of Grey Herons were regularly destroyed by fishpond managers. However, full protection status does not mean that nests are not occasionally destroyed these days. Since the mid-1970s, the number of new colonies and breeding pairs has been increasing, and Grey Heron has expanded its range into new areas where isolated pairs may now nest. It nests in fishpond areas, around marshes, at oxbows of rivers, and in riverine forest around larger and slower rivers. Nest colonies are built in high trees such as poplar, oak, willow, spruce and pine, and sometimes in close proximity to other species such as Great Cormorant (Zamecky pond; BV), Night Heron (Zamecky pond; BV) and White Stork (near Mikulcice; HO). Colonies usually contain up to 100 pairs, rarely more. For instance, in 1989 there was a colony at Zamecky pond (BV) of 260 nests, and another in riverine forest near Lanzhot (BV) with 155 nests (Hudec *et al.* 1994). The breeding population at ponds around Trebon (JH) is estimated to be between 250 and 400 pairs. Grey Herons are often seen in flocks of varying size in cultivated fields, particularly where alfalfa is grown, where they catch small rodents. The breeding population is migratory, and wintering birds perhaps belong to populations from n. and ne. Europe (Hudec *et al.* 1994).
Status: Resident. **Breeding season**: uncommon. **Winter**: local/common. **Migration**: common. Protected/not hunted all year round with exceptions.
Population trends: The breeding population is estimated to be between 1,000 and 1,200 pairs (1,400 pairs in 1993). It has increased rapidly, by at least 50% since the late 1970s when the breeding population was estimated to be between 360 and 500 pairs. The number of wintering birds may reach 6,000 individuals.
Distribution: Nationwide. Regular breeding colonies are mainly located at ponds around Hradec Kralove (HK), Ceske Budejovice (CB), Trebon (JH), Pisek (PI), Zdar nad Sazavou (ZR), Hodonin (HO) and Lednice (BV). Riverine forest around the Morava hosts breeding colonies near Mikulcice (HO), Petrov (HO) and Tovacov (PR). Solitary nests or groups of a few nests are scattered in suitable habitats elsewhere around the country. Wintering birds are found mainly in the lowlands of the following counties: BV, HO, UH, PV, PR, PU, KO, KH, NB, JH, PI, TA and CB.
Timing: All year round. The main breeding months are March and April; rarely the end of February, and May.

Purple Heron *Ardea purpurea*

Volavka cervena Volavka purpurova Purpurreiher

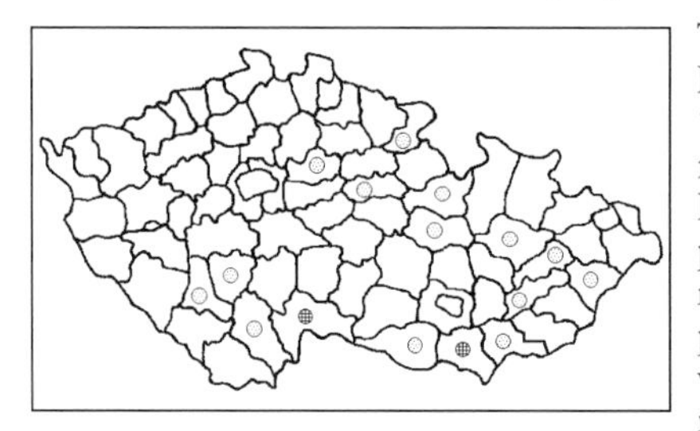

The Czech Republic is the northern limit of Purple Heron's occurrence in central Europe (Harrison 1982). Distribution of this species is mostly confined to fishpond areas in the lowlands of s. Bohemia and s. Moravia. It nests near large fishponds and in marshes with extensive and dense reedbed cover. On passage, it can be observed at ponds, gravel pits, and around other areas of open water without dense vegetation. The first breeding records for the country were at Nesyt pond (BV) in 1947, and at Velky Tisy pond (JH) in 1949. Since then, from 0–15 pairs have bred in BV county, and up to 20 pairs at Velky Tisy pond. From the 1960s, the number of breeding pairs started to decrease at both sites. The destruction of marshes and reedbeds is the most likely cause for this decline. Many breeding attempts are unsuccessful because Purple Herons are particularly sesitive to human disturbance.

Status: Migrant and summer visitor. **Breeding season:** uncommon. **Winter:** does not occur. **Migration:** local. Critically endangered. Protected.

Population trends: Between 1985 and 1989 there were 5–20 breeding pairs; from 1990–1994 only 1–5 pairs.

Distribution: More or less regular breeding may occur at Velky and Maly Tisy ponds (JH), Lednicke ponds (BV) and Nove Mlyny (BV). Occasional breeding attempts have been recorded in other parts of the country, at ponds around Pardubice (PU), and in central and n. Moravia for example. Regular reports of non-breeding individuals come from Zehunsky pond (NB), Bohdanecsky pond (PU), Strpsky pond (CB), Dvoriste pond (CB), Zenich pond (CB), Vlhlavsky pond (CB), Zahorsky pond (ST), Kalenicky pond (ST), Rezabinec pond (PI), Netrebsky pond (UO), Horky pond (SY), Hermanek pond (SY), Tovacovske ponds (PR), Zahlinicke ponds (KM), Kvasice gravel pit (KM), Pouzdransky pond (BV), Pohorelicke ponds (BV) and Lednice-Pastvisko marsh (BV).

Timing: Spring migration starts at the beginning of April, with the peak in mid-April. Departure from breeding grounds occurs in August and September. Nesting extends from mid-April to the end of June, with most nests occupied at the beginning of May. The highest number of birds are seen in May and August.

Black Stork *Ciconia nigra*

Cap cerny Bocian cierny Schwarzstorch

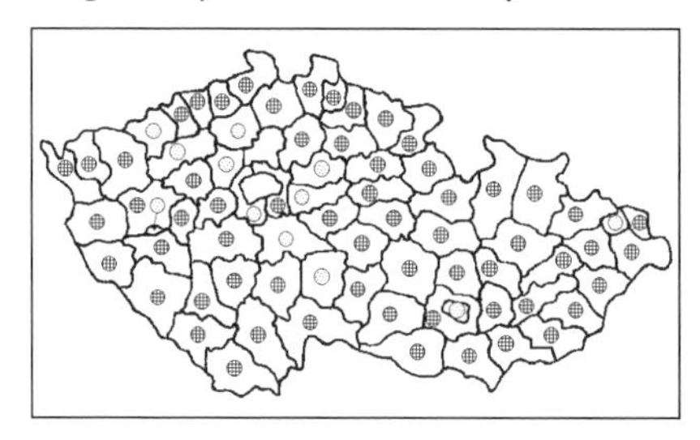

At the beginning of the 20th century, Black Stork was considered a local, irregular breeder in a few counties of the Czech Republic, and a regular breeder at Soutok (BV), where only a few pairs nested annually. During the past 50 years, it has been expanding its breeding range and now breeds from lowlands up to 1050 m in the Jeseniky mountains (BR, SU), 1090 m in the Orlicke hory mountains (RK), and 1100 m in the Sumava mountains (CK, PT, KT). In the mid-1940s, the figure had risen to 20–25 pairs, and then Black Stork started to expand its range. At the same time, the first breeding pairs were found in the Jeseniky mountains, and Oderske vrchy hills (OL, PR), in 1952 in e. Bohemia, and from the end of the 1950s in Ceskomoravska vysocina highlands (HB, JI, PE, ZR). Some of the sites with higher numbers of regularly breeding pairs include DC county with 17 pairs, LB county with 13 pairs (Vondracek 1995), the Sumava mountains with about 8–10 pairs, the area around Trebon (JH) with 5–10 pairs, the Krkonose mountains (SE, TU) with 5–7 pairs, the Doupovske hory mountains (KV) with about 12–14 pairs, riverine forest s. of Lanzhot (BV) with about 5 pairs, the Jeseniky mountains with 10–20 pairs, and

the Beskydy mountains (VS, FM) with 15–20 pairs. It breeds in large complexes of mature deciduous or mixed forest with access to nearby streams, small ponds or marshes. Black Stork occurs less frequently in coniferous plantations. Nests are usually built in beech, oak, fir and spruce, and sometimes on rocky cliffs. The same nest is often used for several consecutive years. At the end of the 1980s, breeding density was 0.008–0.17 pairs per km^2 in the Brdy mountains (RO, PB) and 0.01 pairs per km^2 in the Doupovske hory mountains. During passage, usually single birds, flocks of a few, or occasionally as many as a dozen individuals may be seen at ponds, dams, marshes and around rivers. Black Stork is sensitive to a disturbance during breeding, and nests are occasionally abandoned as a result of antipathetic forestry management. However, the population as a whole is not threatened.
Status: Migrant and summer visitor. **Breeding season**: uncommon/local. **Winter**: does not occur. **Migration**: local. Vulnerable. Protected.
Population trends: The breeding population is between 200 and 300 pairs. During 1973–1977, it was 100–150 pairs. Since the 1940s, the breeding population has increased by at least 50%.
Distribution: Nationwide in larger forests. Breeding is rather scarce in PJ, DO, ST, CL, NA, MB, TC, CR, PV and VY counties.
Timing: Birds arrive at the breeding grounds at the end of March and beginning of April, and depart in August and the first half of September. Breeding occurs from the beginning of April to mid-May.

White Stork *Ciconia ciconia*

Cap bily   Bocian biely   Weißstorch

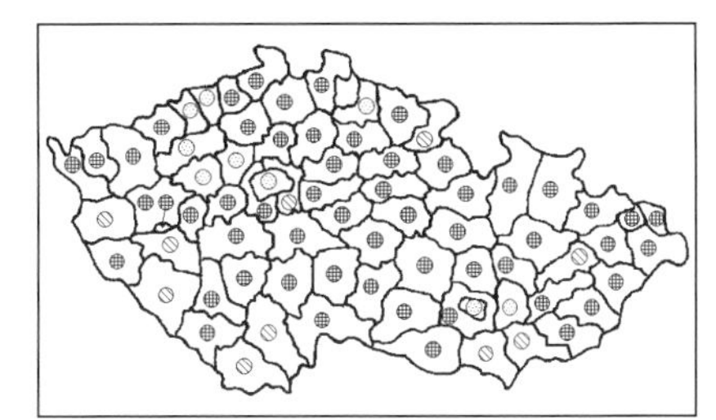

Owing to its traditional rôle in folklore, White Stork is a well known species and successfully attracted to artificial nests on human settlements. Many nests are now placed on poles, a trend observed not only in the Czech Republic but also in the Slovak Republic, Hungary and Germany (Folk and Rejman 1983). Increasing numbers of birds build nests on power lines and telegraph poles. In the Czech Republic, a survey of nesting pairs has been ongoing since 1934. In the first year, none of the 76 observed nests (in Moravia only) was placed on a pole. Fifty years later, in 1983, there were 43 nests (out of 910) on poles (Folk and Rejman 1983). In 1984, out of 944 nests, 273 were built in trees, and all the remaining on chimneys, roofs of buildings, poles, and artificially constructed nests. In 1994 and 1995, 53% of nests (out of 1,047) were built on chimneys, 21% in trees, and the rest on various artificial structures (Rejman 1997). The majority of breeding sites are in and around villages and farms. However, some sites are in flooded woodlands, such as those around the Morava river near Straznice (HO) and Mikulcice (HO), and in a parkland around the Lednicke ponds (BV). White Stork breeds from lowlands, where it is most common, up to 660 m in the Novohradske hory mountains (CB, CK), about 700 m in the Ceskomoravska vysocina highlands (HB, JI, PE, ZR), and 780 m in the Sumava mountains (CK, PT, KT). It occurs more commonly in the lowlands of e. and s. Bohemia, and s. and n. Moravia than in the remaining regions of the country. Outside the breeding season and during migration, flocks of dozens individuals can be seen in cultivated fields, meadows and around ponds; 250–300 individuals were seen near Lomnice nad Luznici (JH) in September 1996. Occasionally a few individuals may winter, but these are probably handicapped birds unable to migrate (Hudec *et al.* 1994).
Status: Migrant and summer visitor. **Breeding season**: uncommon/local. **Winter**: uncommon. **Migration**: local/common. Vulnerable. Protected.
Population trends: In 1934, there were 202 nests, in 1958 there were 469 nests, in 1974 the total had risen to 279 nests (Moravia only), and in 1984 there were 944. In 1990, 695 nests were active, in 1991, 625, in 1992, 665 nests, and 740 in 1993. In 1994 and 1995 respectively, 853 nests and 796 nests were occupied, and 2,116 young birds were successfully reared from 716, and 1,703 young birds from 635 nests respectively (Rejman 1997).

Distribution: Nationwide. Breeding is rather uncommon in VY, LB, CV, LT, PZ and BO counties.
Timing: Arrives from mid-March, the majority at the end of March and beginning of April. Departs in August, rarely at the beginning of September. Breeding extends from the beginning of April to the end of May, with the peak during the second half of April.

Glossy Ibis *Plegadis falcinellus*

Ibis hnedy Ibisovec hnedy Braunsichler

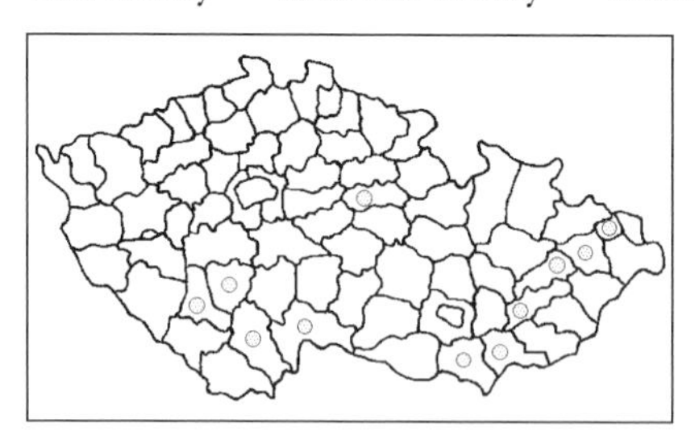

This species occurs in the Czech Republic as a vagrant, mostly in fishpond areas of s. Bohemia, e. Bohemia, s. Moravia, and central Moravia. Between 1966 and 1984 it was observed 28 times, with a total number of 57 birds (Hudec *et al.* 1994). It is found on semi-drained fishponds, at the muddy edges of ponds, shallow lakes, and in marshes. Immatures are normally the birds seen during autumn.
Status: Vagrant. **Breeding season:** rare. **Winter:** rare. **Migration:** rare. Protected.
Population trends: No data available.
Distribution: There are regular records from ponds around Pardubice (PU), Ceske Budejovice (CB), Jindrichuv Hradec (JH), Polanka nad Odrou (NJ), Zahlinice (KM), Lednice (BV) and Nove Mlyny (BV).
Timing: From March until October, with the highest numbers in May and October. It has been recorded once in December.

Eurasian Spoonbill *Platalea leucorodia*

Spoonbill Kolpik bily Lyziciar obycajny Löffler

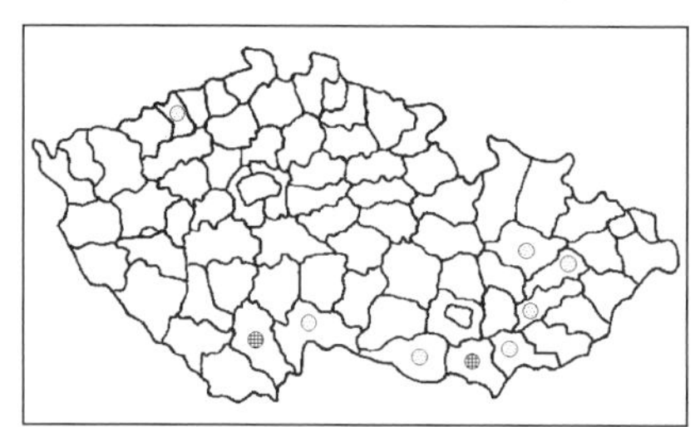

Eurasian Spoonbill's distribution in the Czech Republic is mostly limited to several fishpond areas of s. Bohemia and s. Moravia. Breeding was first recorded in the country at the Lednicke ponds (BV) in 1949. No breeding was documented between 1950 and the beginning of the 1980s. More or less regular breeding started at Nove Mlyny (BV), where flocks of up to 35 birds have been seen since 1983. In 1984, 4 pairs nested successfully; in 1985 and 1986 there were 3 and 1 unsuccessful pairs respectively; in 1987 and 1988, 4 and 1 successful pairs respectively (Martisko *et al.* 1994). Breeding was recorded in s. Bohemia in 1987, then again in 1989. Three pairs nested at Velke Nakri pond (CB) in 1998, and 2 in 1999. During the past decade or so, irregular, reasonably successful breeding has been recorded at ponds around Ceske Budejovice (CB), Lednicke ponds and Nove Mlyny. It is found at shallow ponds and lakes, semi-drained fishponds, and marshes around ponds with reedbeds and bushes. Non-breeding birds usually occur in small flocks of up to 35 individuals, rarely as singles.
Status: Summer visitor. **Breeding season:** rare. **Winter:** does not occur. **Migration:** uncommon. Protected. Critically endangered.
Population trends: There has been a breeding population of up to 4 pairs in s. Moravia since 1983, and 1–2 pairs in s. Bohemia since 1987. No available data for estimation of population trends.
Distribution: Recent records come from Dehtar pond (CB), marsh near Minkovice (MO), Zbudovsky pond (CB), Vysatov pond (CB), Zliv pond (CB), Velke Nakri pond (CB), Volesek pond (CB), Sluzebny pond (JH), Cernicny pond (JH), Zahlinicke ponds (KM), Lednicke ponds (BV), Lednice-Pastvisko (BV), Nove Mlyny (BV), Mutenicke ponds (HO) and Dubnanske ponds (HO).
Timing: From March until November, higher numbers mainly in June, July and August. Breeding starts during the first half of May.

Eurasian Spoonbill

PHOENICOPTERIFORMES

Includes the family **Phoenicopteridae** with 3 species in the w. Palearctic. Only one species, a vagrant to the country, has been recorded in the Czech Republic.

Greater Flamingo *Phoenicopterus ruber*

Plamenak ruzovy Plameniak ruzovy Flamingo

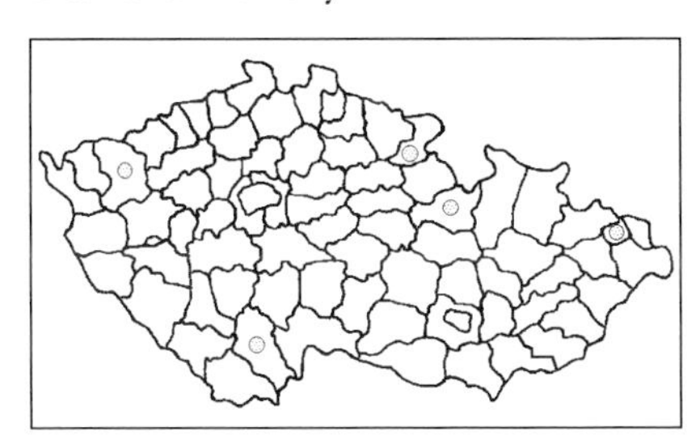

Until the early 1960s, Greater Flamingo was a rare visitor to the Czech Republic. Since 1967, birds (normally singles) have been recorded more often (Hudec *et al.* 1994). The birds seen are most likely individuals which have escaped from captive flocks throughout Europe, because they are of the *ruber* race. However, some individuals identified as of the *roseus* race could be from the breeding population in s. France. For many of the birds seen, there was no racial identification made. Several individuals were identified as *P. chilensis*, which is treated as a separate species (Monroe and Sibley 1993).

Status: Vagrant. **Breeding season:** rare. **Winter:** rare. **Migration:** rare. Protected.
Population trends: No data available.
Distribution: May occur nationwide.
Timing: It has been recorded every month, with the majority of observations in August, September and October.

ANSERIFORMES

Out of the 68 species in the family **Anatidae** recorded in the w. Palearctic, 42 have occurred in the Czech Republic. Among these are 17 regular, irregular or occasional breeders, 18 regular migrants and vagrants, and 7 accidentals.

Mute Swan *Cygnus olor*

Labut velka Labut velka Höckerschwan

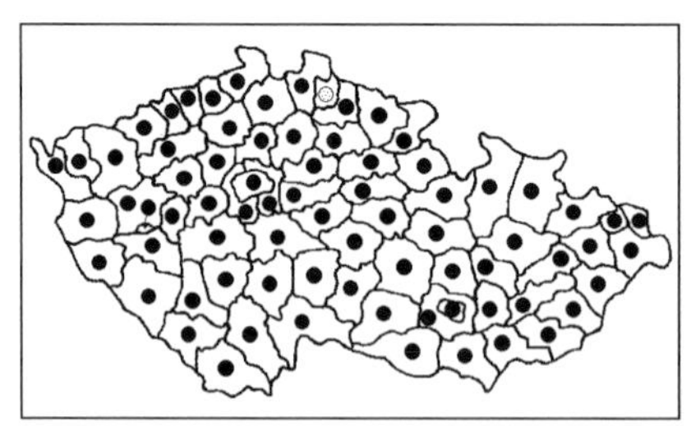

A north European species, Mute Swan was introduced in the Czech Republic as well as other central European countries. There were only sporadic nesting attempts by the introduced populations before 1940, mostly at ponds around castles. In the 1950s, Mute Swan expanded its range to ponds in s. Bohemia, in the early 1960s to central Bohemia, in the late 1960s to e. Bohemia, w. Bohemia and n. Bohemia, in the late 1950s and the early 1960s to s. Moravia, and in the late 1960s to n. Moravia. However, in the mid-1960s, the number of breeding pairs was only 24. During the 1970s, Mute Swan became widespread across the country. It occurs from lowlands, where the density is highest, up to about 570 m in RO county, 630 m in JI county, and up to 720 m, as for example at Lipno reservoir (CK). During the breeding season, preferred habitats include fishponds, oligotrophic, often man-made water bodies, small lakes in parks, gravel pits, canals and slow-running rivers. Wintering birds usually stay on ice-free stretches of larger rivers such as the Vltava (CB, AA), Dyje (BV), Svratka (BM), Morava (OL, KM, UH, HO), Ohre (LN), Odra (UO, KI), Becva (PR) and Labe (HK, PU, KO, ME, LT, DC). The winter flocks range from several dozen individuals to occasionally hundreds of birds.

Status: Resident. **Breeding season:** uncommon/local. **Winter:** local/common. **Migration:** common. Protected.

Population trends: During 1973–1977, the breeding population was about 250–300 pairs; in 1980 it was 300–350 pairs; in 1983, 556 pairs; in 1985, 528 pairs; and recently 600–700 pairs. Hundreds of non-breeding birds also occur annually during the breeding season. In the past 20 years the population has increased by at least 50%. More recently, the population growth has stopped. Up to 4,000 individuals winter regularly, and in 1994 there were 5,000.

Distribution: Nationwide. As a breeder it is rather rare in FM, VS, ZL, UH, BR and PR counties. Wintering birds occur less frequently in the following counties: ZL, VS, BR, SU, JN, JI, TU, FM and PT.

Timing: All year round. Breeding starts at the end of March, and continues until the beginning of May.

Tundra Swan *Cygnus columbianus*

Bewick's Swan Labut mala Labut mala Zwergschwan

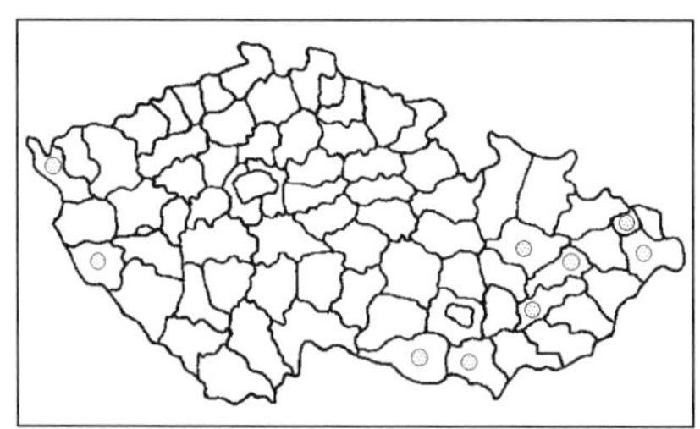

This is the rarest swan in the Czech Republic. In the past 30 years the number of birds recorded annually has increased by about 20%. Solitary birds, and rarely 2 or 3 individuals together can be seen at dams, large ponds, industrial water bodies, and less often at rivers across the country.

Status: Migrant and winter visitor. **Breeding season:** rare. **Winter:** uncommon. **Migration:** uncommon. Protected.

Population trends: The number of birds seen during autumn and spring migration is usually up to 5 individuals, and up to 3 wintering birds.

Distribution: May occur nationwide. Recent records of 1 individual are from the Odra river in Bohumin (OV), Tovacovske ponds (PR), Jarohnevicky pond (ZN) and Zahlinicke ponds (KM).

Timing: From October until April, with the highest numbers in November and March.

Whooper Swan *Cygnus cygnus*

Labut zpevna Labut spevava Singschwan

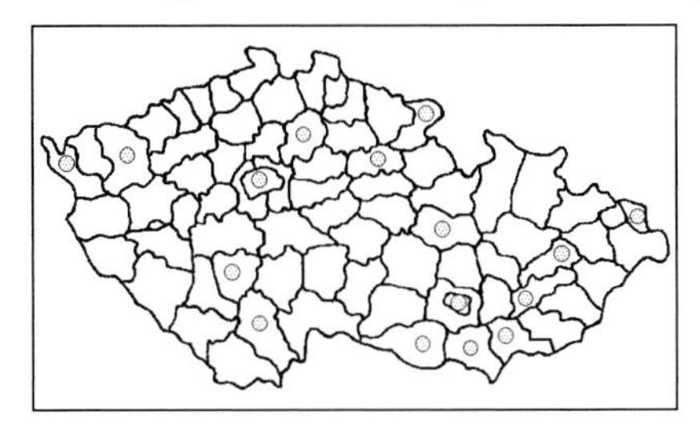

Whooper Swan is rare in the Czech Republic, although more common than Tundra Swan. In the past 15 years it has been recorded almost every winter at larger ponds, dams and rivers across the country. Usually solitary birds, occasionally flocks of a few individuals, have been recorded. It may be seen with flocks of Mute Swan.
Status: Migrant and winter visitor. **Breeding season:** rare. **Winter:** uncommon. **Migration:** uncommon. Protected.
Population trends: May occur nationwide. The annual number of migrating and wintering individuals may be up to 25. Since 1960, the number of migrating or wintering birds has increased by 15–20%.
Distribution: Recent observations are from Velky pond near Chlumec (HK), Novy pond near Mnichovo Hradiste (MB), Razicky pond (PI), Novy pond (SY), Brodsky pond (NA), Cerveny Kostelec pond (NA), the Vltava river near Hluboka nad Vltavou (CB), the Labe river in Hradec Kralove (HK), Tovacovske ponds (PR), Skasovsky pond (PR), Hulin gravel pit (KM), the Odra river in Karvina (KI), Zahlinicke ponds (KM), Brnenska dam (BM), Jarohnevicky pond (HO), Dubnanske ponds (HO), Nove Mlyny (BV) and the Morava river (UH, HO).
Timing: From October until May. Most records are from December, February and March.

Bean Goose *Anser fabalis*

Husa polni Hus siatinna Saatgans

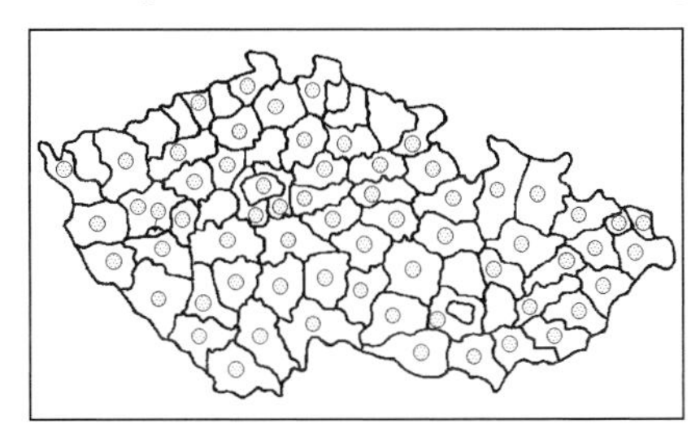

This is the most common wintering goose in the Czech Republic, with the *fabalis* and *rossicus* races both recorded. In addition to the former races, a specimen of *A. f. johanseni* was collected in e. Bohemia in 1929. The main wintering grounds are in BV county, and smaller flocks on passage can be observed across the country. This species is usually found at fishponds, dams, gravel pits, lakes, and cultivated fields close to open water; also in valleys around larger rivers. In the morning and late afternoon, Bean Geese are usually observed feeding on farmland. During most of the day, and overnight, they remain close to nearby water. The highest numbers can be seen from October until mid-November, and in February when on passage through the country. They are often in flocks with other species of goose. Bean Goose does not breed in the Czech Republic, but a few individuals are occassionally recorded during summer months.
Status: Migrant and winter visitor. **Breeding season:** rare. **Winter:** local/common. **Migration:** local/common. Hunted during fixed season.
Population trends: Until the beginning of the 1980s, 20,000–40,000 individuals were recorded annually on passage and wintering. Since then, these numbers have increased by at least 50%, and annual totals are now 80,000–100,000.
Distribution: Small flocks or solitary birds may be scattered nationwide. Flocks of thousands of individuals occur around Lednicke ponds (BV), Pohorelicke ponds (BV) and Nove Mlyny (BV). Smaller flocks are regularly observed at gravel pits and lakes in the Morava river valley (OL, PR, KM, UH, HO), until the water ices over, around the Odra river (OV, KI), and at ponds around Trebon (CB).
Timing: Mainly from the end of September until April. There have been occasional records of solitary birds or a few individuals in every month of the year.

Pink-footed Goose *Anser brachyrhynchos*

Husa kratkozoba Hus kratkozoba Kurzschnabelgans

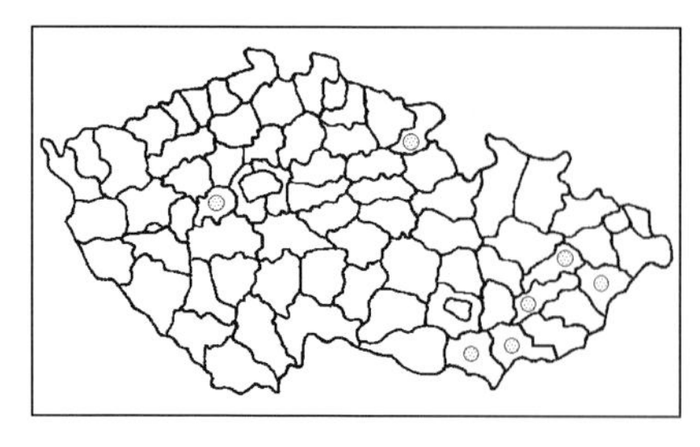

Pink-footed Goose is an irregular visitor, and is not observed annually in the Czech Republic. It may occur across the country at shallow fishponds, reservoirs, lakes, and fields surrounding open water. It is mostly recorded in autumn, with a few records from spring. Between 1965 and 1988, solitary birds or flocks of a few individuals were recorded 12 times (Hudec *et al.* 1994). The actual number may be smaller because of confusion with young Greylag Geese.

Status: Migrant and winter visitor. **Breeding season:** rare. **Winter:** uncommon. **Migration:** uncommon. Hunted during fixed season.
Population trends: During autumn migration up to 50 individuals may be seen, and up to 15 birds winter. No data for estimation of population trends.
Distribution: Recently recorded at Rozkos dam (NA), Bystrice u Benesova (BN), Tovacovske ponds (PR), Chropynsky pond (KM), Mutenicke ponds (HO) and Lednicke ponds (BV).
Timing: From September until January, with most records in October, November and December.

White-fronted Goose *Anser albifrons*

Greater White-fronted Goose Husa belocela Hus bielocela Bläßgans

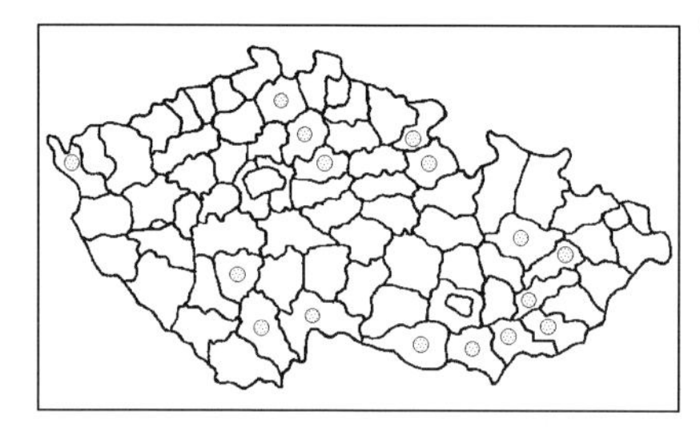

White-fronted Goose has become more numerous in the Czech Republic over the past few years. The region of s. Moravia is the only place in the Czech Republic where flocks of up to several hundred birds winter regularly. Solitary birds or smaller flocks of several dozen individuals can be seen across the country during migration, particularly in s. Bohemia. It is found on farmland and in meadows surrounding fishponds, lakes and larger rivers, usually in lowlands. On the wintering grounds, White-fronted Geese often stay in mixed flocks with Bean and Greylag Geese. Birds recorded in the Czech Republic belong to the race *albifrons*.

Status: Migrant and winter visitor. **Breeding season:** rare. **Winter:** local/common. **Migration:** local/common. Hunted during fixed season.
Population trends: During the 1980s, the wintering population was estimated to be between 400 and 800 individuals. Since then it has increased, and in 1994 the number of wintering birds was between 5,000 and 20,000; it may vary considerably from year to year.
Distribution: Regularly seen at Lednicke ponds (BV), Pohorelicke ponds (BV) and Nove Mlyny (BV). Recent records are also from Zehunsky pond (NB), Zabakor pond (MB), Blatec pond (CB), Dehtar pond (CB), Tovacovske ponds (PR), Dombas gravel pit (PR), Zahlinicke ponds (KM), Hulin gravel pit (KM) and Ostrozska Nova Ves gravel pit (UH).
Timing: Occurs from the end of September until March, with the highest numbers in October, November and March.

Lesser White-fronted Goose *Anser erythropus*

Husa mala Hus mala Zwerggans

The Czech Republic lies at the western edge of the wintering grounds of this species. Hence, Lesser White-fronted Goose is a rare visitor, mostly to s. Moravia. Wintering was recorded in that area several times at the end of the 1950s and beginning of the 1960s. Since the 1950s, there have been only 4 records from Bohemia of birds on passage (Hudec *et al.* 1994). This

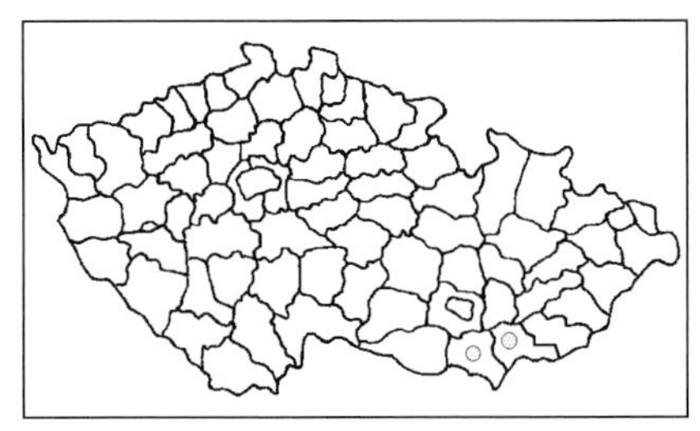

species usually stays in flocks with other geese.
Status: Winter visitor. **Breeding season:** rare. **Winter:** uncommon. **Migration:** uncommon. Hunted during fixed season.
Population trends: No data available.
Distribution: Mostly in BV county. A recent record also from HO county.
Timing: Occurs from September until April, with most records from October, November and April.

Greylag Goose *Anser anser*

Husa velka Hus diva Graugans

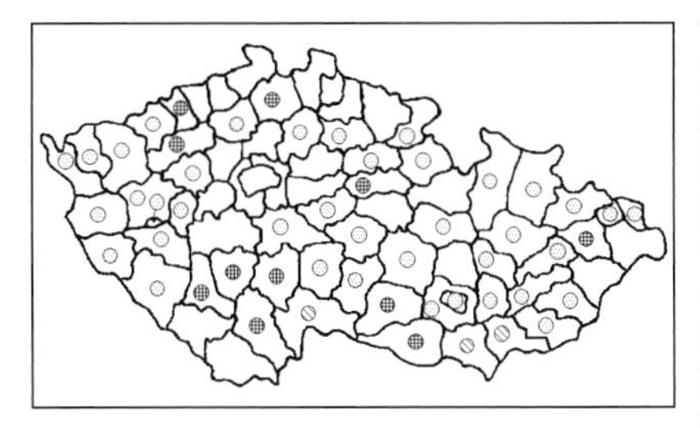

This is the only breeding goose in the Czech Republic. Until the middle of the 20th century, Greylag Goose was a less common breeding bird. From about the mid-1940s, it expanded its range to ponds in s. Bohemia and s. Moravia, while the population in n. Bohemia, which had the highest number of breeding pairs before the middle of the 20th century, has decreased. Regular breeding is confined to 2 major areas in s. Bohemia and s. Moravia. Occasional nesting may occur elsewhere, for example at Lenesicky pond (LN) in 1998 and 1999. Nests have been found up to 400 m in JH county and 460 m in TR county. Breeding habitats include large fishponds surrounded by extensive reedbeds, or flooded riverine forest where Greylag Geese nest on the tops of pollarded willows. This unusual nest placement occurs around Sakvice (BV) and Strachotin (BV), with dozens of pairs breeding annually. Breeding density was 800–1,500 pairs per km^2 in the reedbeds, and 5,000–9,000 pairs per km^2 at islets at ponds around Trebon (JH) during the 1980s, and 60–330 pairs per km^2 at 2 ponds around Vodnany (ST) at the beginning of the 1990s. Outside the breeding season, this species frequents marshes, fishponds with islets, and surrounding farmland. The breeding population leaves for the Mediterranean area, and the majority of wintering birds are from n. Europe (Hudec *et al.* 1994). Migrating and wintering flocks of thousands of birds can be seen regularly from mid-October in s. Moravia at Lednicke ponds (BV), Pohorelicke ponds (BV) and Nove Mlyny (BV). Two races, *anser* and *rubrirostris*, occur in the Czech Republic.
Status: Resident. **Breeding season:** uncommon/local. **Winter:** local. **Migration:** local/common. Endangered. Hunted during fixed season.
Population trends: At ponds around Trebon (JH) the breeding population was 32 pairs at the beginning of the 1960s, 150 pairs and 195–200 pairs at the beginning and end of 1980s respectively, 145 pairs at the beginning of the 1990s, and 150 at the end of the decade. At ponds around Ceske Budejovice (CB) it was 53 pairs at the end of the 1960s, 65–105 pairs at the beginning of the 1980s, and 250 pairs in 1999. At ponds in BV county it was 40–50 pairs at the beginning of 1950s, 100–150 pairs during the 1970s, and 300 pairs at the beginning of the 1980s. The breeding population in the whole country is now estimated to be between 580 and 670 pairs. During 1973–1977, it was 300–400 pairs, and there has been a 50% increase over the past 50 years. During migration there are thousands of individuals, while up to 1,000 birds may winter.
Distribution: On passage, there are varying numbers of birds nationwide. Regular breeding occurs at several ponds around Ceske Budejovice (CB) and Trebon (JH), with the majority of pairs at Blatec pond (CB) and Velky Tisy pond (JH). Ponds around Pohorelice (BV) and Lednice (BV), and marshes near Sakvice (BV), Strachotin (BV) and Nove Mlyny (BV) host the largest breeding population in s. Moravia. Other sites with occasional breeding include areas of open water around Most (MO), Pardubice (PU), Rezabinec pond (PI) and ponds near Hodonin (HO).
Timing: All year round. The breeding population arrives in mid-February and departs in October and November. First clutches are laid at the end of February and the beginning of March, with the majority from mid-March to mid-April.

Canada Goose *Branta canadensis*

Berneska velka   Bernikla velka   Kanadagans

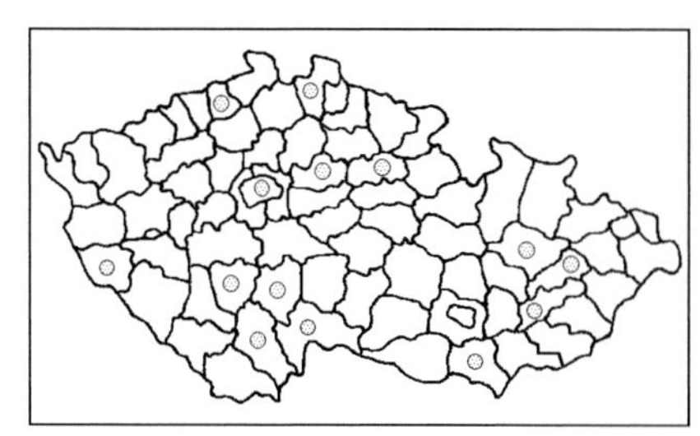

This species was observed for the first time in the Czech Republic in 1964. From then until 1986, it has been recorded 13 times (Hudec *et al.* 1994). Records have been increasing since 1986. All of the recorded individuals obviously belonged to populations introduced in n. and w. Europe, or had escaped from captivity. This species may be found at ponds, gravel pits, dams, marshes and wet meadows. Usually single birds and rarely small flocks have been recorded.

Status: Visitor. **Breeding season**: rare. **Winter**: uncommon. **Migration**: uncommon. Protected/not hunted all year round.

Population trends: Up to 25 individuals may be seen annually. Since the mid-1970s, the number of birds recorded annually has increased by 20%.

Distribution: Recent records are from Zehunsky pond (NB), Praha (AA), the pond near Ceska Kubice (DO), Nove Mesto pod Smrkem (LB), Razicky pond (PI), Nadeje pond (JH), the Labe river in Hradec Kralove (HK), Krasny les (UL), the Luznice river near Tabor (TA), Tovacovske ponds (PR) and Nove Mlyny (BV).

Timing: Recorded every month, with most observations in April and May.

Barnacle Goose *Branta leucopsis*

Berneska belolici   Bernikla bielolica   Nonnengans

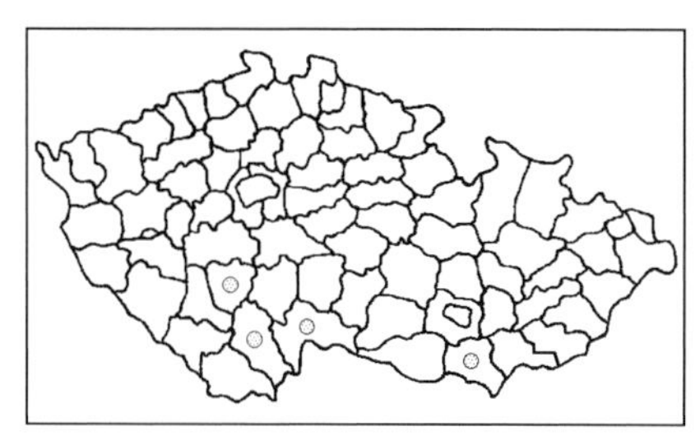

The first records of Barnacle Goose in the Czech Republic are from the middle of the 19th century. Since then, single birds have been seen irregularly across the country at fishponds and fields surrounding open water. The wintering grounds of Barnacle Goose are spread along the northwest coast of Europe, and birds observed in central Europe are probably from these areas (Hudec *et al.* 1994). However, some individuals may be escapes from captivity.

Status: Vagrant. **Breeding season**: rare. **Winter**: uncommon. **Migration**: uncommon. Protected/not hunted all year round.

Population trends: Since 1990, there have been 8 records. The number of birds to have occurred in the past 10 years is higher compared to numbers in the preceding decades.

Distribution: May occur nationwide. Recently observed at Velky Tisy pond (JH), Vrbenske ponds (CB), Novohaklovsky pond (CB), Rezabinec pond (PI), Nesvorny pond (PI), Preseka (JH), Milovice (BV), Lednicke ponds (BV), Pohorelicke ponds (BV) and Nove Mlyny (BV).

Timing: All year round. The highest numbers have been recorded in February, March, October and November.

Brent Goose *Branta bernicla*

Berneska tmava   Bernikla tmava   Ringelgans

This species is an irregular visitor to the Czech Republic. Between 1970 and 1987, when it was seen for the last time, Brent Goose was recorded 6 times, mostly in flocks of a few birds, and rarely as singles, frequenting areas of open water and their surrounding fields. Individuals observed in the Czech Republic belonged to the *bernicla* race. The *hrota* race has been recorded once.

Status: Vagrant. **Breeding season**: rare (both races). **Winter**: uncommon (*bernicla*), rare (*hrota*). **Migration**: uncommon (*bernicla*), rare (*hrota*). Protected/not hunted all year round.

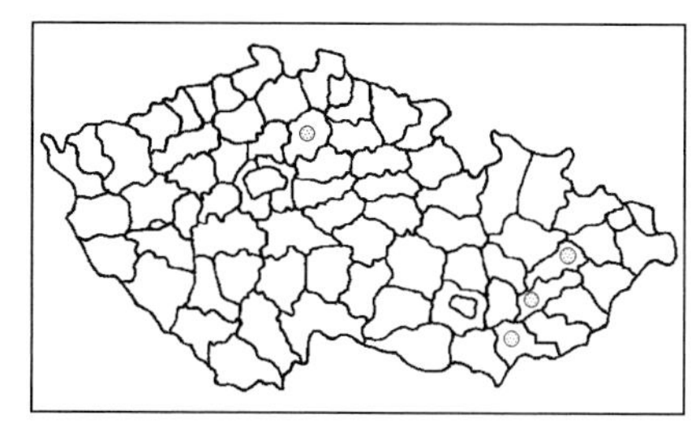

Population trends: No data available.
Distribution: Recently, mostly in the eastern part of the Czech Republic. The latest records of single birds are from Brodek pond (MB), Zahlinicke ponds (KM), Dubnanske ponds (HO) and Tovacovske ponds (PR).
Timing: Occurs from September until April, with the majority of records in December and February.

Red-breasted Goose *Branta ruficollis*

Berneska rudokrka Bernikla cervenokrka Rothalsgans

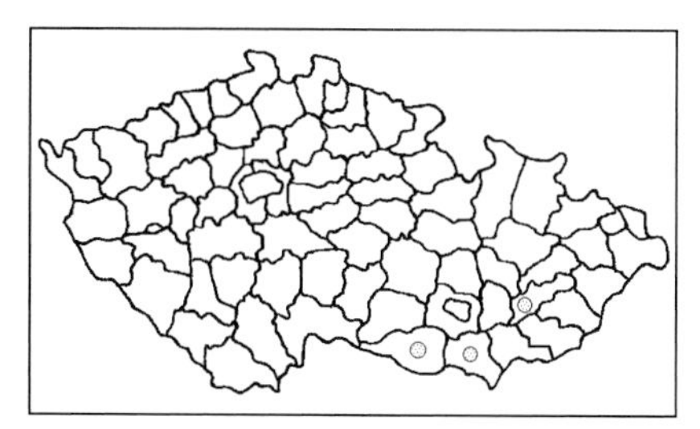

The closest regular wintering grounds of Red-breasted Goose are in the delta of the Danube river in se. Europe. Straggling solitary birds, or a flock of a few birds, may appear irregularly in the Czech Republic. A total of 10 individuals has been seen 6 times between 1980 and 1992, usually at fishponds, lakes and their environs. It is possible that some of these birds were from semi-feral stocks in w. Europe.

Status: Vagrant. **Breeding season**: rare. **Winter**: uncommon. **Migration**: uncommon. Protected/not hunted all year round.
Population trends: No data available.
Distribution: Mostly in the eastern part of country. Recent observations are from Zahlinicke ponds (KM), Milovice (BV), Pohorelicke ponds (BV) and Nove Mlyny (BV). Since 1992, 7 individuals have been recorded 5 times in BV county alone.
Timing: Recorded from November to April.

Ruddy Shelduck *Tadorna ferruginea*

Husice rezava Kazarka hrdzava Rostgans

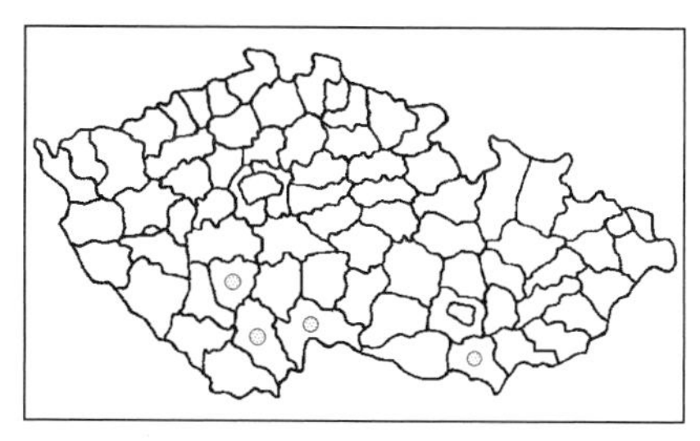

Ruddy Shelduck does not occur regularly in the Czech Republic, although the number of birds recorded has increased since 1960. In the 1970s, successful breeding was observed twice, even though in 1 case it involved a pair that had escaped from captivity. Most of the birds seen in the Czech Republic are probably from semi-feral stocks in w. Europe. Solitary birds, rarely a few birds together can usually be found, mostly in the western part of the country at fishponds, reservoirs and lakes.

Status: Vagrant. **Breeding season**: rare. **Winter**: uncommon. **Migration**: uncommon. Protected.
Population trends: Since 1960, the population has increased by at least 50%.
Distribution: Recently observed at Rezabinec pond (PI), Velky Tisy pond (JH), Volesek pond (CB) and Hodoninske ponds (HO).
Timing: Recorded every month except April, with the majority of observations in August.

Common Shelduck *Tadorna tadorna*

Shelduck Husice lisci Kazarka pestra Brandgans

Common Shelduck is an annual visitor to the Czech Republic. It normally occurs across the country in lowland areas with fishponds. Between 1990 and 1995 it was observed 10 times with

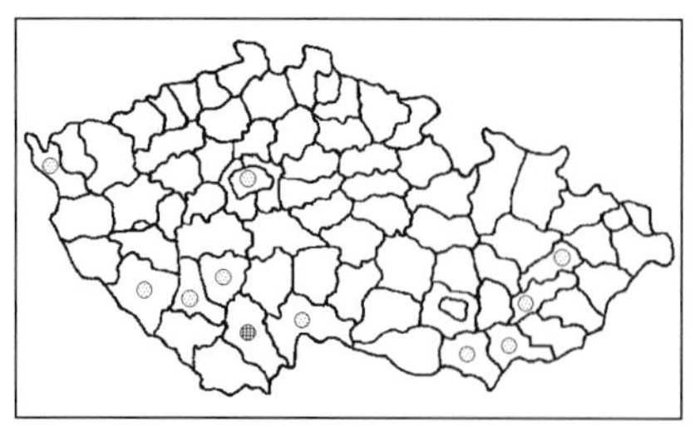

a total number of 18 birds. After 1995, observations became more frequent. The first successful breeding, of a pair which probably escaped from captivity, was recorded in KL county in 1972. The next breeding record was of a single pair near Mydlovary (CB) in 1996 and again in 1997. Five pairs were observed at industrial waters at the same site in June 1998, and breeding was recorded in 1999. It is usually found singly, less commonly flocks of a few birds can be seen at larger lakes, fishponds and rivers.

Status: Visitor. **Breeding season**: rare. **Winter**: uncommon. **Migration**: uncommon. Protected.
Population trends: No data available.
Distribution: Mostly ponds around Ceske Budejovice (CB), Trebon (JH), Zahlinicke ponds (KM), and Lednicke ponds (BV). Recent records are from the Vltava river in Praha (AA), Volesek pond (CB), Bezdrev pond (CB), Dehtar pond (CB), Mydlovary (CB), Novy pond near Cakov (CB), Nadeje pond (CB), Stary pond near Tchorovice (ST), Rezabinec pond (PI), Velky Tisy pond (JH), Zenich pond (JH), Tovacovske ponds (PR), Tlumacov (ZL), Luzicke ponds (HO), Hodoninske ponds (HO), Dubnanske ponds (HO), Lednicke ponds (BV) and Nove Mlyny (BV). A flock of 10 individuals was recorded in Bzenec-Privoz (HO) in September 1997, and up to 11 individuals have been recorded at Lednicke ponds (BV) in October and November 1997.
Timing: Recorded every month with the majority of observations in October, November and December.

Eurasian Wigeon *Anas penelope*

Wigeon Hvizdak eurasijsky Kacica hvizdarka Pfeifente

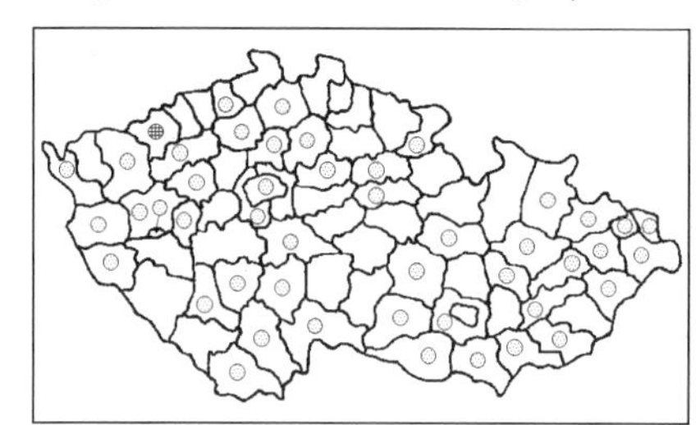

This species may be seen all year round, although it does not breed. It is distributed across the country, but usually found in the lowlands.The highest numbers turn up during migration. The only breeding record for the Czech Republic was at a marsh near Most (MO) in 1967 (Hudec *et al.* 1994). Migrating birds occur at any large area of open water such as fishponds, gravel pits, lakes and rivers. During summer, it prefers fishponds and marshes. Wintering individuals stay near ice-free sections of larger rivers such as the Vltava (CB, AA, ME), Ohre (LN), Labe (HK, PU, ME, LT), Morava (HO), Dyje (BV) and Odra (OV, KI). It is not uncommon to see small flocks of up to 20 birds, and rarely groups of several hundred on passage (Kren and Folk 1990).

Status: Migrant, summer and winter visitor. **Breeding season**: rare. **Winter**: uncommon/local. **Migration**: local/common. Critically endangered. Protected/not hunted all year round.
Population trends: No significant changes in the numbers of migrating birds over the past 20 years. Up to 50 individuals may winter.
Distribution: May occur nationwide. There are recent records of up to 75 individuals, but usually smaller flocks are seen at Zehunsky pond (NB), Novy pond near Mnichovo Hradiste (MB), Nadeje pond (CB), Dehtar pond (CB), Volesek pond (CB), Vlhlavsky pond (CB), Vysatov pond (CB), Rozmberk pond (JH), Velky Tisy pond (JH), Rozkos dam (NA), Velky Kosir near Litomysl (SY), Novy pond (SY), Hvezda pond (SY), Chomoutov gravel pit (OL), Donbas gravel pit (PR), Tovacovske ponds (PR), Kojetinske ponds (PR), Zahlinicke ponds (KM), Jarohnevicky pond (HO), Luzicke ponds (HO), Soutok (BV), Lednicke ponds (BV) and Nove Mlyny (BV); also on all large rivers.
Timing: Spring migration occurs from March to the end of April. Autumn migration is in October and November.

Gadwall *Anas strepera*

Koprivka obecna   Kacica chriplavka   Schnatterente

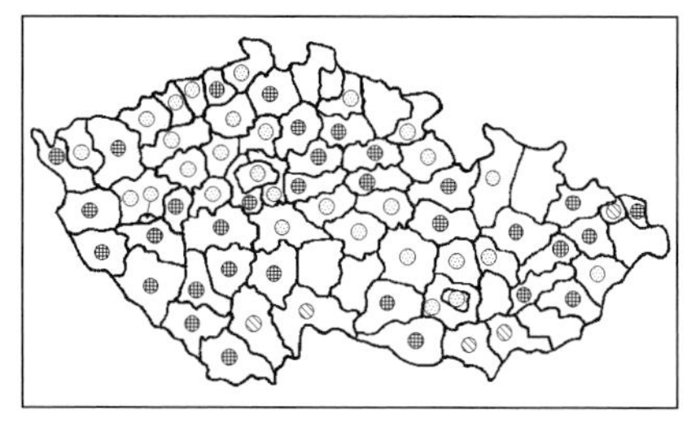

From the beginning of the 20th century to about the beginning of the 1970s, Gadwall extended its breeding range in the Czech Republic from the traditional breeding sites, mostly in the lowlands of s. Bohemia and s. Moravia, into other parts of the country. Breeding occurs from lowlands up to about 500 m in the Ceskomoravska vysocina highlands (HB, JI, PE, ZR), and to 550 m in TC county. Breeding sites include shallow and larger fishponds with patches of open water and rich emergent vegetation, autotrophic waters, and occasionally oxbows of larger rivers. During the 1970s, breeding density was 5–11 pairs per km^2 at various ponds around Blatna (ST), 2 pairs per km^2 at Anenske ponds (CH), 500–5,200 pairs per km^2 at ponds around Trebon (JH), and 20–90 pairs per km^2 at ponds around Sedlcany (PB). In the 1980s, the overall spring density at about 150 ponds of varying size in s. Bohemia was from 11 to 18 individuals per km^2. During migration, it can be found at fishponds, dams, gravel pits, industrial water bodies and larger rivers.
Status: Resident. **Breeding season:** local/common. **Winter:** uncommon. **Migration:** local/common. Least concern. Protected/not hunted all year round.
Population trends: The breeding population is between 1,500 and 3,000 pairs. From 1973–1977, it was between 570 and 1,620 pairs. Since the 1970s, the population has increased by at least 20%. The number of wintering birds is usually fewer than 100.
Distribution: On passage found nationwide up to 600 m. Regular breeding of larger numbers of pairs occurs at ponds around Pardubice (PU), Ceske Budejovice (CB), Trebon (JH), Pisek (PI), Bartosovice (NJ), Ostrava (OV), Lednice (BV) and Pohorelice (BV).
Timing: Spring migration starts in mid-March, with the peak at the end of March and the beginning of April. Autumn migration occurs in September, with lower numbers of migrating birds in October. Breeding extends from mid-April until the beginning of July, with the peak in May.

Common Teal *Anas crecca*

Teal   Cirka obecna   Kacica chrapka   Krickente

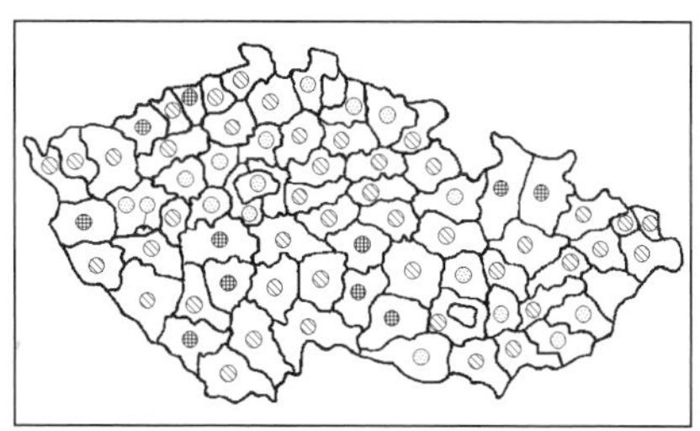

Common Teal is a regular but uncommon breeder in the Czech Republic. The breeding range extends from lowlands up to 600 m in the Ceskomoravska vysocina highlands (HB, JI, PE, ZR), to about 1050 m in the Krusne hory mountains (CV, KV, MO, TP), and up to 1200 m in the Sumava mountains (CK, PT, KT). Although breeding at higher altitudes is rare, birds on passage may occur there quite frequently. Breeding habitats include fishponds with dense emergent and peripheral vegetation, and surrounding wet meadows. During the 1970s, breeding density was about 1 pair per km^2 at various ponds around Blatna (ST), 2 pairs per km^2 at Anenske ponds (CH), and 0–20 pairs per km^2 at ponds around Sedlcany (PB). The overall spring density at about 150 ponds of varying size in s. Bohemia was from 0.9 individuals per km^2 at the beginning of the 1980s to 0.07 individuals per km^2 at the end. This species is more abundant during migration, when flocks of hundreds and rarely thousands of birds can be seen. Wintering birds can be found regularly at industrial water bodies, larger rivers and, during mild winters, also at ponds. The total number of birds recorded in December 1985, 1986 and 1987 was 1,585, and in January of the same years it was 1,119 (Folk and Kren 1987, Kren and Folk 1985, 1990). The main reason for the rapid decrease in the breeding population is the drainage of wet meadows and marshes.
Status: Resident. **Breeding season:** uncommon/local. **Winter:** local/common. **Migration:**

local/common. Critically endangered. Protected/not hunted all year round.
Population trends: The breeding population is estimated to be between 150 and 250 pairs; between 1972 and 1979 it was 430–880 pairs. Since then the population has decreased by at least 50%.
Distribution: Scattered nationwide. Regular breeding sites include ponds around Pardubice (PU), Ceska Lipa (CL), Blatna (ST), Ceske Budejovice (CB), Trebon (JH), Jindrichuv Hradec (JH) and Karvina (KI). Larger flocks of migrating birds were recently reported from the Vltava river (AA, CB), the Ohre river around Kadan (CV) and Louny (LN), Koclirov pond (JH), Velky Tisy pond (JH), Dehtar pond (CB), the Odra and Olse rivers around Karvina (KI), Tovacovske ponds (PR), the Morava river around Tovacov (PR), Kromeriz (KM), Hodonin (HO), Zahlinicke ponds (KM) and Nove Mlyny (BV).
Timing: Spring migration occurs from March until the end of April, and autumn migration from August until the beginning of October. Breeding extends from the end of April to mid-June.

Mallard *Anas platyrhynchos*

Kachna divoka Kacica diva Stockente

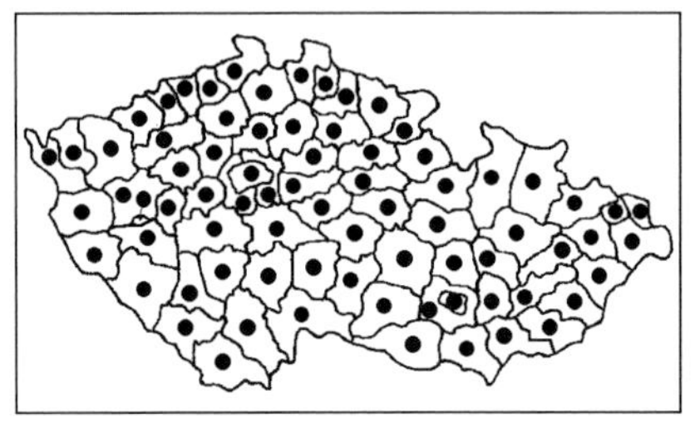

This is the most numerous duck and is widely distributed from lowlands up to 800 m in the Novohradske hory mountains (CB, CK), 950 m in the Krusne hory mountains (CV, KV, MO, TP), 1025 m in the Orlicke hory (RK), Jeseniky (BR, SU) and Jizerske hory (LB, JN) mountains, about 1100 m in the Sumava mountians (PT, CK, KT), and about 1400 m in the Krkonose mountains (SE, TU). However, regular breeding is limited up to about 1000 m. Mallard is found in a wide variety of natural and man-made habitats, ranging from lakes, ponds, ditches, the vicinity of rivers, and marshes, to industrial water bodies and small lakes in parks. Although this species is usually associated with an aquatic environment, nesting females have been found far away from water, for example in dry woodland. Individuals from semi-feral stocks occur at ponds and rivers in towns and villages. Mallard is regularly bred in captivity by hunters, and released as a game species at ponds across the country. During the 1970s, breeding density in littoral vegetation at ponds around Sedlcany (PB) was 170–530 pairs per km^2, and at Anenske ponds (CH) it was 35 pairs per km^2. During the 1980s, the overall spring density at about 150 ponds of varying size in s. Bohemia was from 22 to 45 individuals per km^2. At the end of the 1970s and the beginning of the 1980s, it was 8–13 pairs per km^2 at small ponds on farmland at about 210 m in UH county, and 21–28 pairs per km^2 around Stolarka pond (HO). At 2 ponds around Vodnany (ST), it was 170–200 pairs per km^2 at the beginning of the 1990s. The breeding population is partially migratory, and wintering birds include individuals from ne. Europe. Flocks of thousand of birds migrating and wintering in the Czech Republic may be seen, for example, at the Vltava river (AA), Zehunsky pond (NB), some parts of the Labe river (HK, PU, LT), Donbas gravel pit (PR), Zahlinicke ponds (KM), Ostrozska Nova Ves gravel pit (UH), the Morava river (HO) and Nove Mlyny (BV). Habitats at some of the traditional breeding sites have been destroyed as a result of soil reclamation, and local breeding populations have declined since the 1960s.
Status: Resident. **Breeding season:** common. **Winter:** common. **Migration:** common. Hunted in fixed season.
Population trends: The breeding population is between 30,000 and 60,000 pairs. It has declined by 20–50% over the last 20 years. The number of wintering birds ranges from 100,000 to 300,000 individuals.
Distribution: Nationwide.
Timing: All year round. Migrating populations arrive from the end of February until the beginning of April, with the peak in March, and depart in September and October. Breeding extends from mid-March to mid-May, occasionally later.

Pintail *Anas acuta*

Northern Pintail Ostralka stihla Kacica ostrochvosta Spießente

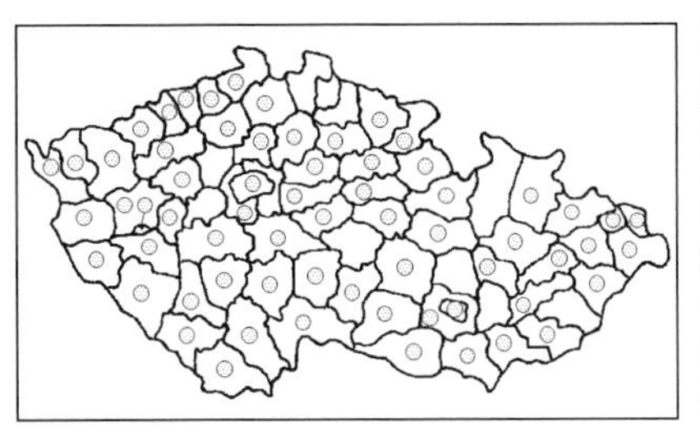

Pintail is a rare and irregular breeding bird, although it once bred quite widely. Nesting is mostly confined to lowlands in s. Bohemia and s. Moravia, and occasionally other places up to 600 m. Breeding sites include ponds with dense emergent vegetation surrounded by wet meadows. Pintail occurs in the Czech Republic more commonly during spring than autumn migration, and can be found from lowlands up to highlands at any type of water body, including rivers and flooded meadows. On passage it is usually seen in flocks of up to 40 individuals. Lowering of the water-table at nesting sites and drainage of wetlands may be the main reasons for the decline in the breeding population.

Status: Resident. **Breeding season**: rare. **Winter**: uncommon. **Migration**: local/common. Critically endangered. Protected/not hunted all year round.

Population trends: Breeding was not recorded between 1985 and 1990. After 1990, the number of breeding pairs was estimated to be no more than 3. The number of wintering individuals is up to 15.

Distribution: Breeding may irregularly occur at ponds around Divcice (CB), Trebon (JH), Namest nad Oslavou (TR), ponds near Odry (NJ) and Lednicke ponds (BV). During migration it is recorded nationwide. Recent observations, of usually small flocks, are from Zehunsky pond (NB), Semovicky pond (BN), Volesek (CB), Rezabinec pond (PI), Horusicky pond (TA), Vavrinecky pond (KH), Hvezda pond (SY), Hustopecske ponds (PR), Tovacovske ponds (PR), Donbas gravel pit (PR), Zahlinicke ponds (KM), Jarohnevicky pond (HO), Soutok (BV), Lednicke ponds (BV), Ostrozska Nova Ves gravel pit (UH) and Nove Mlyny (BV).

Timing: Spring migration starts in March and continues through to the beginning of April. Autumn migration occurs in October and November. Breeding extends from the beginning of April to mid-May.

Garganey *Anas querquedula*

Cirka modra Kacica chrapacka Knäkente

Garganey was a fairly common species in the Czech Republic about 30–40 years ago, but since then its breeding numbers have declined due to the drainage of marshes and wet meadows, and sometimes their transformation into reservoirs. This species occurs from lowlands up to about 600 m in highlands. During the 1970s, the breeding density was about 2 pairs per km^2 at Anenske ponds (CH), and 0–100 pairs per km^2 at ponds around Sedlcany (PB). In the early 1980s, the overall spring density at about 150 ponds of varying size in s. Bohemia was 1 individual per km^2, dropping to 0.4 individuals per km^2 by the end of the decade. Typical breeding habitats are shallow ponds, and oxbows of rivers with abundant emergent vegetation surrounded by marshes, and wet meadows. During migration it can be found at any type of water body, including rivers, ditches, brooks, flooded meadows and temporary pools on farmland.

Status: Resident. **Breeding season**: uncommon/local. **Winter**: uncommon. **Migration**: local/common. Critically endangered. Protected/not hunted all year round.

Population trends: The breeding population has decreased by at least 50% since the 1970s, when it was estimated to be between 290 and 600 pairs. Recently it is estimated to be between 100 and 180 pairs, with up to 10 pairs in s. Moravia, and fewer than 20 pairs in s. Bohemia. The number of individuals recorded on passage has also been declining. Up to 10 birds may be seen in winter.

Distribution: Found on passage nationwide. Breeding pairs are scattered mostly in s. Bohemia, central Bohemia, e. Bohemia, s. Moravia, central Moravia and n. Moravia.
Timing: Spring migration occurs during March, and autumn migration from August to the end of September. Breeding extends from the end of April to the end of May, and rarely occurs in mid-April and June.

Northern Shoveler *Anas clypeata*

Shoveler Lzicak pestry Kacica lyziciarka Löffelente

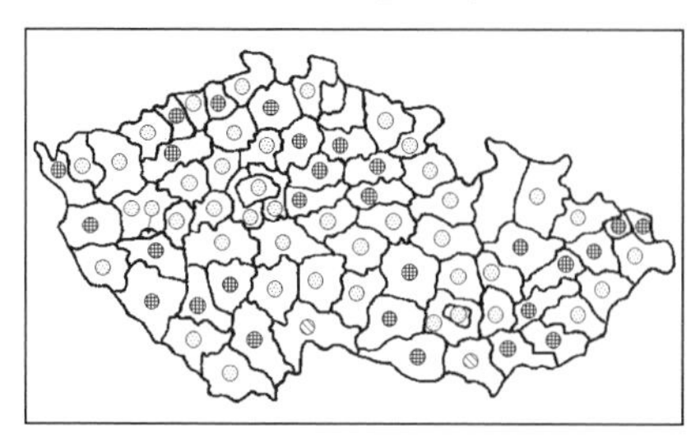

This species is most numerous during migration, when flocks of up to several hundred birds, especially in s. Moravia, are not unusual. As a breeder, Northern Shoveler occurs regularly but not commonly from lowlands up to about 450 m. During breeding, it prefers autotrophic and shallow ponds with patches of open water, marshes, wet meadows, and oxbows of larger rivers. During the 1970s, the breeding density was about 5 pairs per km^2 at Anenske ponds (CH), 1–2.5 pairs per km^2 at ponds around Blatna (ST), and 0–30 pairs per km^2 at ponds around Sedlcany (PB). In the early 1980s, the overall spring density at about 150 ponds of varying size in s. Bohemia was 1.8 individual per km^2, dropping to 0.4 individuals per km^2 by the end of the decade. Practically any type of water body provides suitable habitat during migration. Wintering birds stay at ponds, lakes and gravel pits, until they freeze over, and later at the ice-free stretches on larger rivers. The number of wintering birds varies from year to year. Drainage of wetlands and habitat loss seem to be the major causes for the decline in the breeding population since the late 1960s and early 1970s.
Status: Resident. **Breeding season**: uncommon/local. **Winter**: uncommon. **Migration**: local/common. Critically endangered. Protected/not hunted all year round.
Population trends: The breeding population is between 140 and 200 pairs. It has decreased by more than 50% since the 1970s, when the breeding population was up to 740 pairs. Between 10 and 60 individuals usually winter.
Distribution: Regular breeding occurs in the following counties: JH, CB, ST, BV, PU, NJ, KI and OV. During migration, it is scattered nationwide. Wintering birds are regularly recorded at the Vltava (CB, AA), Labe (PU, ME), Morava (HO) and Dyje (BV) rivers.
Timing: Spring migration occurs from mid-March, mostly at the end of March until the end of April. Autumn migration occurs from August until mid-November. The majority of birds nest from mid-April until the end of May.

Red-crested Pochard *Netta rufina*

Zrzohlavka rudozoba Hrdzavka potapava Kolbenente

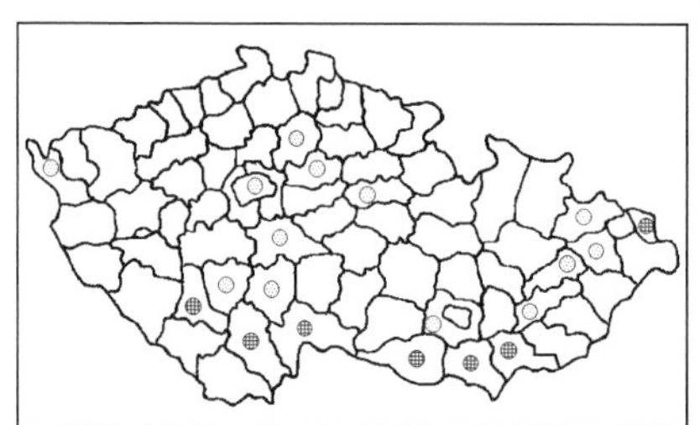

This is a regular but rather scarce breeder, and is mainly found in 2 areas in s. Bohemia and s. Moravia. Red-crested Pochard bred in Bohemia during the first half of the 19th century but disappeared over the following few decades. Recolonization started again about 90 years later, at the beginning of the 1950s, with a few nesting pairs at ponds in CB county. From here it expanded its range into other areas of s. Bohemia. The Lednicke ponds (BV) have been a traditional breeding site since the 19th century, and Red-crested Pochard spread into other pond areas in s. Moravia from here. This species prefers to breed at sites with relatively shallow, large ponds with islets, dense emergent vegetation and reedbeds. In the early 1980s, the overall breeding density at about 150 ponds of varying size in s. Bohemia was 0.3 individuals per km^2, rising to 0.8 indi-

Red-crested Pochard

viduals per km^2 at the end of the decade. During migration, solitary birds or small flocks may be found at any type of water body, including flooded meadows, but usually not rivers. Occasionally larger flocks of up to 200 birds can be seen, mostly in HO and BV counties.
Status: Migrant and summer visitor. Occasionally winters. **Breeding season**: uncommon/local. **Winter**: rare. **Migration**: local/common. Endangered. Protected/not hunted all year round.
Population trends: Breeding population is between 160 and 180 pairs, during 1973–1977 it was 120–170 pairs. Up to 5 individuals may be seen in winter.
Distribution: The breeding regularly occurs at Olesek pond (CB), Knizeci pond (CB), Vlhlavsky pond (CB), ponds around Hluboka nad Vltavou (CB) and Trebon (JH), ponds around Hodonin (HO), Lednicke ponds (BV), Pohorelicke ponds (CB) and Jaroslavicky pond (ZN). Occasional breeding, of usually 1 pair, may occur elsewhere in the lowlands; recently, for example, at ponds near Pardubice (PU), Vlkovicky pond near Lisov (CB), ponds near Karvina (KI), Zahlinicke ponds (KM), Stolarka pond (HO) and Pouzdransky pond (BV). Apart from the abovementioned sites, higher numbers of migrants or non-breeding birds during the summer months were recently observed at Zehunsky pond (NB), Vrazda pond (MB), Novy Vrbensky pond (CB), Dolni pond (CB), Rezabinec pond (PI), ponds near Strelske Hostice (ST), Tovacovske ponds (PR), Zahlinicke ponds (KM), Strachotinsky pond (BV) and Nove Mlyny (BV).
Timing: Spring migration occurs mostly in March and April, and continues until mid-May. Autumn migration starts in August and continues through to October. Breeding extends from the beginning of April to the end of May, with the peak at the end of April and the beginning of May.

Common Pochard *Aythya ferina*

Pochard   Polak velky   Chochlacka siva   Tafelente

Common Pochard was a rare and localized breeder in the Czech Republic in the middle of the 19th century. Since then, its breeding range has been expanding, and from the 1930s–1960s, it became a common nesting species, found mostly in the lowlands. Regular nesting was recorded up to 600 m in the Ceskomoravska vysocina highlands (HB, JI, PE, ZR), and to 700 m in the Sumava mountains (CK, PT, KT). Breeding habitats include large, shallow fishponds with abundant emergent vegetation, occasionally marshes with patches of open water, and small ponds. At ponds in some counties, Common Pochard is the dominant breeding duck. During the 1970s, breeding density at ponds around Sedlcany (PB) was 40–380 pairs per km^2, 220–560 pairs per km^2 at Velky Panensky pond (JH), 170 pairs per km^2 at Strpsky pond (ST)

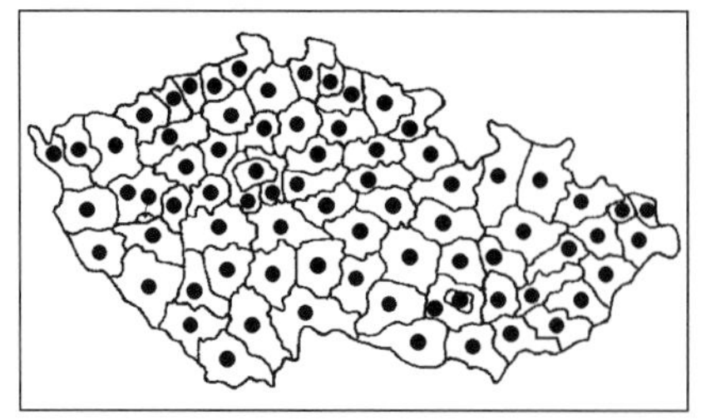

and, at Anenske ponds (CH), 19 pairs per km². At the beginning of the 1980s, breeding density was 28–62 pairs per km² at Stolarka pond (HO). In the early 1980s, the overall spring density at about 150 ponds of varying size in s. Bohemia was 48 individual per km², slumping to 20 individuals per km² at the end of the decade. After breeding and during migration, flocks of several hundred, and sometimes thousands, can be found at open water, especially in s. Moravia. Part of the breeding population is migratory, and the wintering population is joined by birds from ne. Europe (Hudec *et al.* 1994). The Vltava river in Praha (AA) seems to be a traditional wintering site with several hundred Common Pochards recorded every winter (Kren and Folk 1985,1990).

Status: Resident. **Breeding season**: common. **Winter**: local. **Migration**: common. Hunted during fixed season.

Population trends: The breeding population is estimated to be between 10,000 and 20,000 pairs. It has decreased by more than 20% since the beginning of the 1980s. During winter, 3,000–7,000 individuals may be seen.

Distribution: Nationwide. Breeding is rather uncommon in the following counties: AA, FM, VS, PR, BR, SU, ZL, UH, PV, BK, PT, LB, SE, TU, SO, RO and ME. Larger numbers of wintering birds have been recorded in the following counties: BV, PZ, AA, LN, LT, KO, PU, KI and PJ. Wintering birds are rare or do not occur in the following counties: FM, BR, OL, SU, TR, SY, TU, SE, DO and TC.

Timing: Spring migration starts in March, with the main arrival from mid-March to mid-April. Autumn migration occurs from mid-September until mid-October. Breeding extends from May to mid-June, occasionally later.

Ferruginous Duck *Aythya nyroca*

Ferruginous Pochard, White-eyed Pochard   Polak maly
Chochlacka bielooka   Moorente

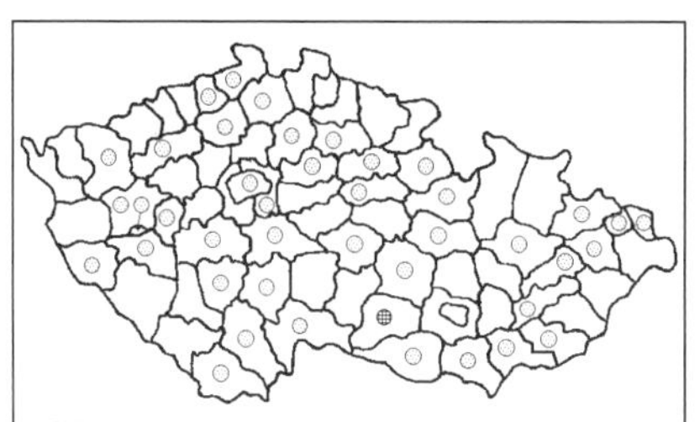

Ferruginous Duck was once a regular breeder, scattered across lowlands in the country. Over the past 40 years, it has become a rare and only occasional breeding species, and indeed may now no longer breed at all. Until the beginning of 1980s, irregular breeding occurred at ponds in the following counties: CL, PU, PI, PJ, DO, KV, JH, NB, ZR, TR, OV, KI, KM, HO and BV. Breeding habitats include shallow fishponds, lakes, and oxbows of various size with abundant emergent vegetation, mostly in lowlands, although breeding has been recorded up to about 500 m the Ceskomoravska vysocina highlands (HB, JI, PE, ZR). During migration, it occurs at any type of large water body. Wintering birds are found on ice-free stretches of the larger rivers across the country. A traditional wintering site is the Vltava river in Praha (AA). The factors leading to this species decline are unknown.

Status: Migrant and winter visitor. **Breeding season**: rare. **Winter**: uncommon. **Migration**: uncommon. Critically endangered. Protected/not hunted all year round.

Population trends: Between 1973 and 1977 the breeding population was between 10 and 30 pairs. From 1985 to 1989, only 1 pair was recorded breeding in s. Moravia. Recently, up to 3 pairs may breed irregularly. The number of wintering birds usually does not exceed 5 individuals.

Distribution: Year-round recent observations, usually of solitary or handfuls of birds, are from the Vltava river in Praha (AA), Tichy pond (PU), Budske ponds (MB), Mydlovarsky pond (CB), Blatec pond (CB), Volesek pond (CB), ponds around Borovany (CB), Chlebsky pond (BN), Velky Tisy pond (JH), Panensky pond (JH), Bartosovicke ponds (NJ), Tovacovske ponds (PR), Chomoutov gravel pit (OL), Opatsky pond (TR), Zahlinicke ponds (KM), Maly Budni pond (NJ), Nova Louka pond (NJ), Pouzdransky pond (BV), Mutenicke ponds (HO),

Stolarka pond (HO), and Lednicke ponds (BV).
Timing: Spring migration occurs from March to the beginning of April. Autumn migration occurs in October and November. Breeding extends from the end of April through to the end of May.

Tufted Duck *Aythya fuligula*

Polak chocholacka Chochlacka vrkocata Reiherente

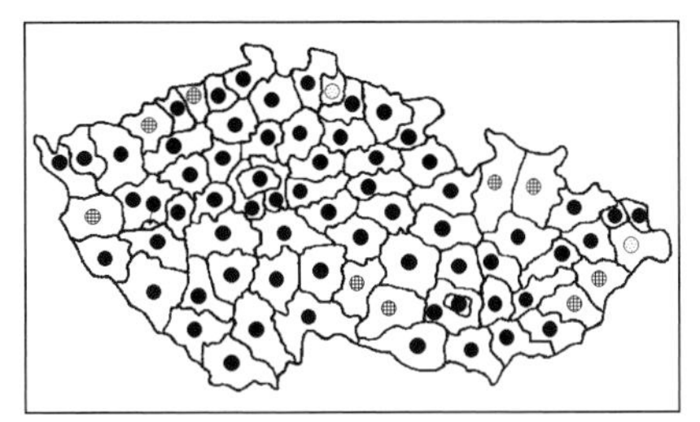

Although Tufted Duck is relatively new to the Czech avifauna, recorded for only about the last 80 years, it is still one of the most numerous breeding ducks. This species started to nest in the Czech Republic at ponds around Namest nad Oslavou (TR) in the mid-1910s. About 15 years later it was breeding in s. Bohemia, at the end of the 1950s at ponds in BV county, at the beginning of the 1960s at ponds around Pardubice (PU), and at the beginning of the 1970s at ponds around Cheb (CH). Between the mid-1970s and the end of the 1980s this species was still expanding its range into other areas of the country, but the total overall population was declining. The breeding population is distributed across the country, from lowland up to about 500 m in the Ceskomoravska vysocina highlands (HB, JI, PE, ZR) and TC county, 700 m in the Jizerske hory mountains (LB, JN), 760 m in the Krusne hory mountains (CV, KV, MO, TP), 830 m in CH county, and about 930 m in the Sumava mountains (CK, KT, PT). Breeding habitats include fishponds with abundant emergent vegetation and islets. During the 1970s, breeding density at ponds around Sedlcany (PB) was 40–430 pairs per km^2, at Velky Panensky pond (JH) 330–1,110 pairs per km^2, at Strpsky pond (ST) 250 pairs per km^2, and at Anenske ponds (CH) 50 pairs per km^2. At the beginning of the 1980s, it was 48–60 pairs per km^2 at Stolarka pond (HO). At the beginning of the 1980s, the overall breeding density at about 150 different-sized ponds in s. Bohemia was 131 individual per km^2, dropping to 39 individuals per km^2 at the end of the decade. The breeding population is migratory, and the majority of wintering birds are from ne. Europe (Hudec *et al.* 1994). Birds on passage occur at any type of water body, even small rivers. Wintering birds stay at industrial waters, and ice-free stretches of lowland rivers. Numerous flocks of Tufted Ducks winter on the Labe (HK, PU, NB, LT), Vltava (CB, AA), Ohre (LN), Morava (KM, UH, HO), Becva (PR), Odra (OV, KI) and Olse (KI) rivers (Folk and Kren 1987, Kren and Folk, 1985,1990).
Status: Resident. **Breeding season**: common. **Winter**: local. **Migration**: common. Hunted during fixed season.
Population trends: The breeding population is between 15,000 and 30,000, having declined by 20% since the beginning of the 1980s. Up to 5,000 individuals winter regularly.
Distribution: As a breeding bird it may be rather scarce in the following counties: UH, ZL, VS, FM, PR, SU, BR, TU, LB and ME. During migration it is found nationwide. Wintering birds occur rarely in the following counties: SU, BR, ZL, VS, FM, TR, SY, BK, RK, JI, HB, TU, SE, JN, LB, CL, CV, TC, DO, PT and RA.
Timing: The majority of birds arrive from mid-March to the end of April, and depart from the end of September to the end of October. Breeding extends from the beginning of May to the end of June, and occasionally later.

Greater Scaup *Aythya marila*

Scaup Polak kaholka Chochlacka morska Bergente

Greater Scaup is a regular but uncommon visitor to the Czech Republic. Records are normally of solitary birds or, occasionally, small flocks. Larger flocks have been recorded infrequently, for example at Plumlov dam (PV) in November 1995 (11 individuals), at Nove Mlyny (BV) in December 1994 (9 individuals), on the Vltava river in Praha (AA) in February 1992 (19 individuals), and in March 1986 (67 individuals). It occurs more often in the western half of

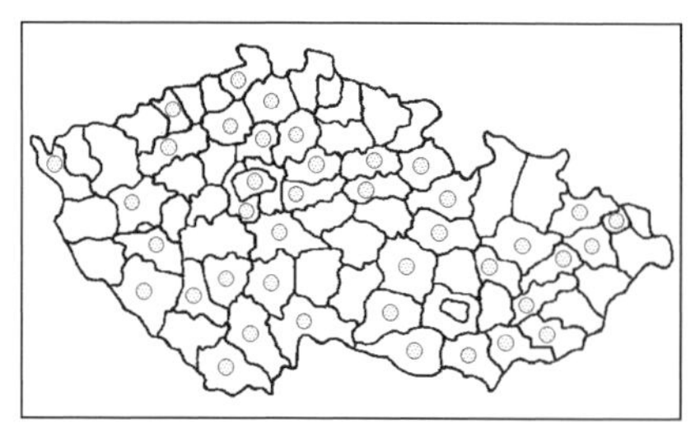

the country on the Vltava (CK, CB, PZ, AA, ME) and Labe (HK, PU, NB, LT, DC) rivers, and at ponds, dams and gravel pits. The only documented breeding occurred at the end of the 19th century in CB county.
Status: Migrant and winter visitor. **Breeding season:** rare. **Winter:** uncommon/local. **Migration:** uncommon/local. Protected/not hunted all year round.
Population trends: On passage, up to 20 birds, and roughly the same number of wintering individuals. No data available to estimate long-term trends.
Distribution: Scattered nationwide. Recent observations are from the Vltava river in Praha (AA), the Labe river near Podebrady (NB), the Ohre river in Cerncice (LN), Zehunsky pond (NB), Dremliny pond (ST), Chlebsky pond (BN), Plumlovska dam (PV), Velky Kosir pond (SY), Tovacovske ponds (PR), Sumvald pond (OL), Zahlinicke ponds (KM), Hulin gravel pit (KM), Jarohnevicky pond (HO), Stolarka pond (HO), the Morava river (HO), Vytazniky ponds (HO), Mutenicke ponds (HO) and Nove Mlyny (BV).
Timing: Recorded from September until May, with the highest numbers in November and December. There are also a few records from June and July.

Common Eider *Somateria mollissima*

Eider Kajka morska Kajka morska Eiderente

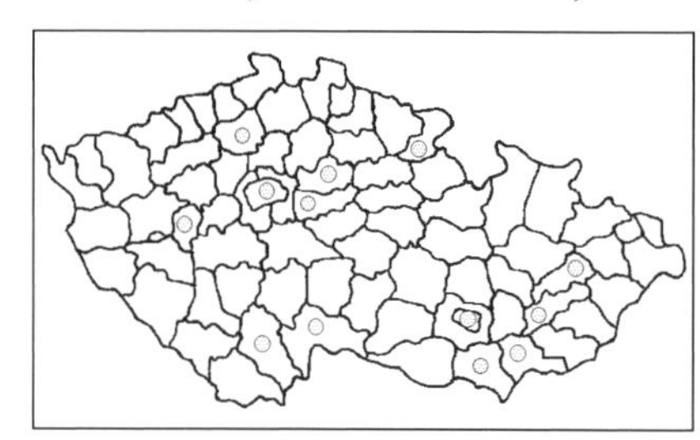

This species is an irregular visitor to the Czech Republic. Normally there are records of solitary birds scattered across the country at large ponds, gravel pits, dams, industrial waters, and rivers. Most of the birds recorded have been immatures or females.
Status: Migrant and winter visitor. **Breeding season:** rare. **Winter:** uncommon. **Migration:** uncommon. Protected/not hunted all year round.
Population trends: The number of individuals recorded on passage and in winter is usually fewer than 30. Over the past 20 years, the number of birds recorded has increased by 20–50%.
Distribution: May occur nationwide. Seems to be more common in the western part of the country. Recent observations are from the Vltava river in Praha (AA), the Labe river in Dobrin (LT), Donbas gravel pit (PR), Troubky gravel pit (PR), Tovacovske ponds (PR), Zahlinicke ponds (KM) and Nove Mlyny (BV).
Timing: Occurs from September until May, with the majority of records in September, November and December.

Long-tailed Duck *Clangula hyemalis*

Oldsquaw Hoholka ledni Ladovka dlhochvosta Eisente

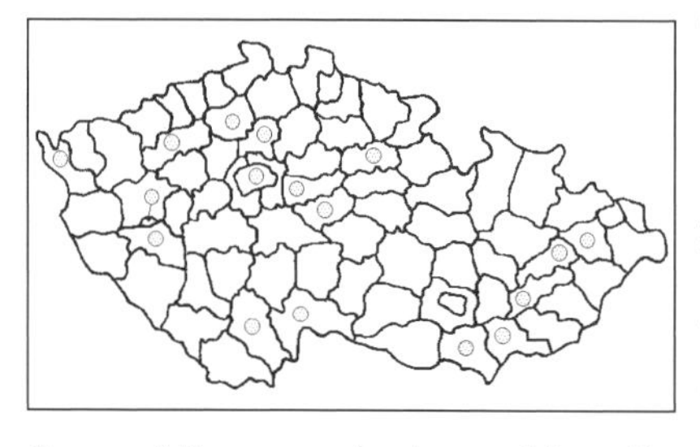

This species is a regular but rare visitor to the Czech Republic. Singles or small flocks have been recorded, with most of the observations from the western half of the country. Found at larger rivers, dams and gravel pits, but also occurs at ponds and industrial waters. One of the favoured wintering sites, with several Long-tailed Ducks recorded every year, is the Vltava river in Praha (AA). The majority of birds seen have been immatures or females, while males in full plumage occur only sporadically.
Status: Migrant and winter visitor. **Breeding season:** rare. **Winter:** uncommon. **Migration:**

uncommon. Protected/not hunted all year round.
Population trends: Up to 15 individuals have been recorded during migration and in winter. No data available to estimate long-term trends.
Distribution: Recent observations are from the Vltava river in Praha (AA), the Labe river (LT, ME), Ostruzensky pond (JC), Vavrinecky pond (KH), Tovacovske ponds (PR), Troubky gravel pit (PR), Hulin gravel pit (KM), Zahlinicke ponds (KM), Pisecne ponds (HO), Jarohnevicky pond (HO) and Nove Mlyny (BV).
Timing: From September until May, with the highest number of records from November and December.

Common Scoter *Melanitta nigra*

Black Scoter Turpan cerny Turpan cierny Trauerente

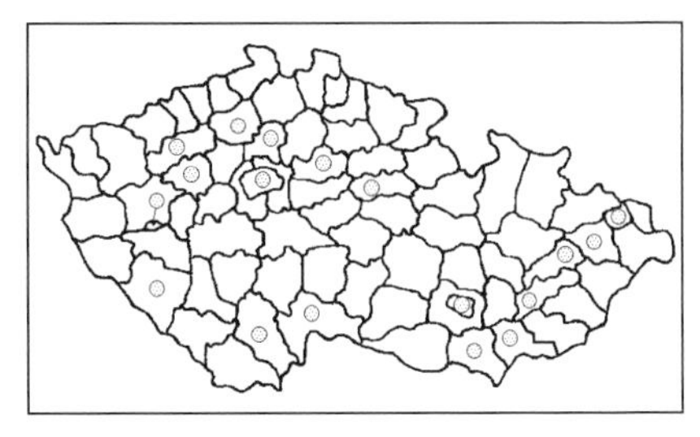

Common Scotter is one of the rarest ducks in the Czech Republic. Single birds on passage are normally seen at large ponds, dams and gravel pits. Wintering individuals stay on ice-free sections of larger rivers.
Status: Migrant and winter visitor. **Breeding season:** rare. **Winter:** uncommon. **Migration:** uncommon. Protected/not hunted all year round.
Population trends: Around 5 individuals have been recorded during migration and in winter. No data available to estimate long-term trends.
Distribution: Scattered nationwide. One or 2 birds were recently recorded at Velky pond near Jesenice (RA), the Vltava river in Praha (AA), the Ohre river near Cerncice (LN), the Labe river near Roudnice nad Labem (LT), Tovacovske ponds (PR), Brnenska dam (BM), Hodoninske ponds (HO), Lednicke ponds (BV) and Nove Mlyny (BV).
Timing: Occurs from September until January, and in April and May. The majority of birds have been seen in November.

Velvet Scoter *Melanitta fusca*

Turpan hnedy Turpan tmavy Samtente

This species occurs more commonly than Common Scoter in the Czech Republic. It has been seen regularly every winter for the last 10 years. It may be found across the country, being more frequently recorded in central Bohemia and s. Moravia than elsewhere. Usually found singly or in flocks of a few individuals, rarely more than a dozen birds. It prefers larger ponds, dams, industrial waters, and ice-free sections of larger rivers such as the Labe (ME, NB) and Morava (PR, KM, HO). The Vltava river in Praha (AA) seems to be a traditional wintering site with several individuals occurring annually.
Status: Migrant and winter visitor. **Breeding season:** rare. **Winter:** uncommon. **Migration:** uncommon. Protected/not hunted all year round.
Population trends: Up to 30 individuals may be found on passage and during winter. Over the past 15–20 years the population has increased by 20–50%.
Distribution: Recently observed at the Vltava river in Praha (AA), the Luznice river (TA), Naklo gravel pit (OL), Donbas gravel pit (PR), Tovacovske ponds (PR), Chropynske ponds (KM), Ostrozska Nova Ves gravel pit (UH), Vytazniky ponds (HO), Zbrodsky pond (HO) and Nove Mlyny (BV).
Timing: Recorded from September until April, with the majority of birds occurring in November and December.

Common Goldeneye *Bucephala clangula*

Goldeneye   Hohol severni   Hlaholka obycajna   Schnellente

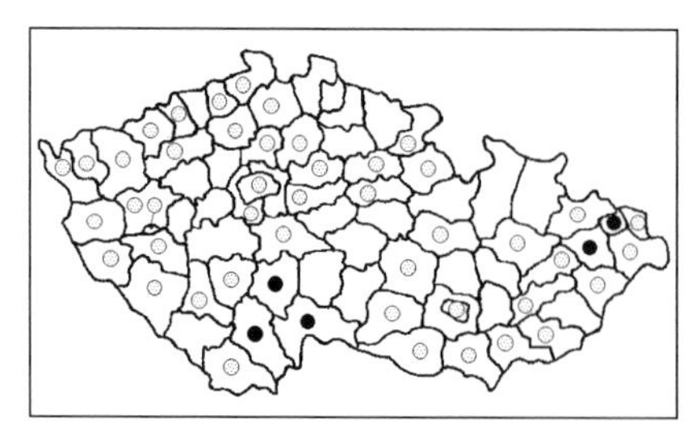

Common Goldeneye has been breeding in the Czech Republic since 1960. About 6 females nested for the first time at Praterske ponds near Trebon (JH). From here, the breeding population expanded to several other ponds around Trebon (JH), and Ceske Budejovice (CB) in 1975. About 15 years later, the breeding population had reached approximately 100 pairs (Janda 1991). Since 1974, regular breeding has started at ponds between Jesenik nad Odrou (NJ) and Ostrava (OV). Occasional nesting was also documented at other places accross the country. Breeding habitats include fishponds surrounded by deciduous woodland with old hollow trees. Nests are built in cavities in mature trees, and also in nest boxes. On passage and in winter, flocks of up to 50 individuals are fairly common, and occasionally flocks of 150–230 birds can be seen. Wintering birds frequent any type of water body, including larger rivers.

Status: Resident. **Breeding season**: uncommon/local. **Winter**: local/common. **Migration**: local/common. Critically endangered. Protected/not hunted all year round.

Population trends: At ponds around Trebon (JH), from 1973 to 1977, the number of breeding pairs was 70–80; it was about 100 pairs in 1980, and about 50 from 1987 to 1988. The breeding population at ponds between Jesenik nad Odrou (NJ) and Ostrava (OV) is now up to 20 pairs. The recent breeding population in the country is estimated to be 100 pairs. Since the 1980s, it has decreased by 20–50%. The wintering population is up to 1,000.

Distribution: Regular breeding is restricted to pond areas in JH, CB and NJ counties. During migration and winter it occurs nationwide. Large numbers of non-breeding birds were recently recorded at the Vltava river in Praha (AA), Zehunsky pond (NB), Donbas gravel pit (PR), Hulin gravel pit (KM), Jarohnevicky pond (HO), the Morava river (HO), Nove Mlyny (BV), and the Dyje river (BV).

Timing: Birds on passage and those wintering usually arrive in November, and depart in March through the beginning of April. The highest numbers of birds have been recorded during January, February and March. Breeding extends from the end of March until the end of April, rarely later.

Smew *Mergus albellus*

Morcak bily or Morcak maly   Potapac maly   Zwergsäger

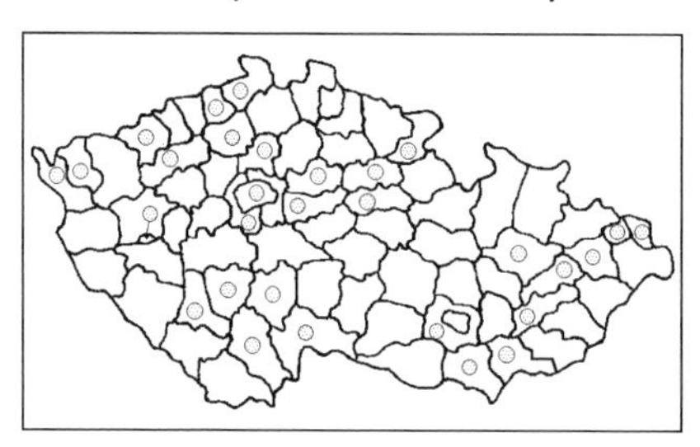

This species is a regular but uncommon visitor to the Czech Republic. The majority of birds are recorded mostly in n. Bohemia, s. Bohemia, e. Bohemia and s. Moravia. Usually there are a few birds together, rarely larger flocks of more than a dozen are found at ponds, lakes, reservoirs, industrial waters and larger rivers. The only breeding record in the Czech Republic was at about 800 m in CK county in 1984 (Hudec *et al.* 1994). A regular wintering site is the Vltava river in Praha (AA).

Status: Migrant and winter visitor. **Breeding season**: rare. **Winter**: local. **Migration**: local. Critically endangered (its breeding status). Protected.

Population trends: Up to 60–70 individuals can be recorded during migration, and in winter. No data available for estimation of long-term trends.

Distribution: Recent observations are from the Vltava river (AA, CB), the Labe river (LT, NB), the Luznice river (TA), Zehunsky pond (NB), Velky Tisy pond (JH), Bezdrev pond (CB), Divcicke ponds (CB), Vysatov pond (CB), Motovidlo pond (CB), Blatec pond (CB), ponds near Odry (NJ), the Odra river (OV), Olomouc (OL), Tovacovske ponds (PR), Zahlinicke ponds (KM), Kvasice gravel pit (KM), Pouzdransky pond (BV), Nove Mlyny (BV), the Svratka

river near Modrice (BO) and Vranovice (BV), the Morava river (HO), Nove Mlyny (BV), and the Dyje river (BV).
Timing: Occurs from November until April, with the maximum numbers in January and March.

Red-breasted Merganser *Mergus serrator*

Morcak prostredni   Potapac prostredny   Mittelsäger

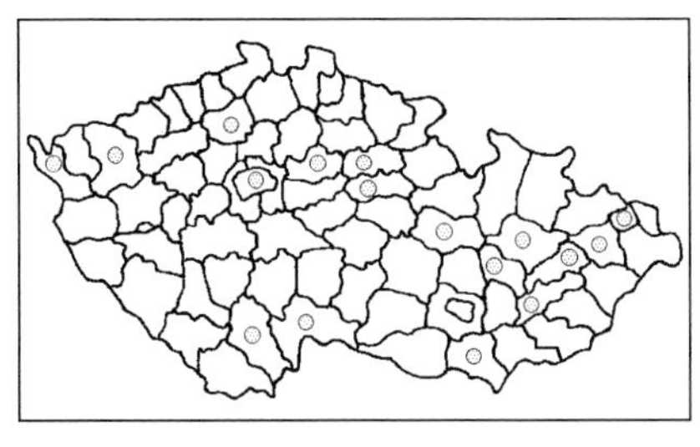

Even though Red-breasted Merganser is recorded annually in the Czech Republic, it is a rare visitor, and the number of birds seen is usually small. This species may occur nationwide at larger ponds, gravel pits, industrial waters, and larger rivers. However, it is recorded more frequently at open water in CH, BV, KM, PR, KI and OV counties, the Vltava river (CK, CB, AA), and the Labe river (PU, NB, ME, LT) than elsewhere. Usually solitary immature birds are recorded, rarely 2 individuals together.
Status: Migrant and winter visitor. **Breeding season:** rare. **Winter:** uncommon. **Migration:** uncommon. Protected.
Population trends: During migration up to 75 individuals, and fewer than a dozen birds during winter. No data available to estimate long-term changes.
Distribution: Recent observations are from the Vltava river in Praha (AA), Zehunsky pond (NB), Velky Tisy pond (JH), Bolesicky pond (CB), Velky Kosir pond (SY), Hvezda pond (SY), Bartosovicke ponds (NJ), Naklo gravel pit (OL), Tovacovske ponds (PR), Donbas gravel pit (PR), Plumlovska dam (PV), Zahlinicke ponds (KM), Hulin gravel pit (KM), Lednicke ponds (BV) and Nove Mlyny (BV).
Timing: Occurs from October until May, with the highest numbers of birds recorded in November, March and April.

Goosander *Mergus merganser*

Common Merganser   Morcak velky   Potapac velky   Gänsesäger

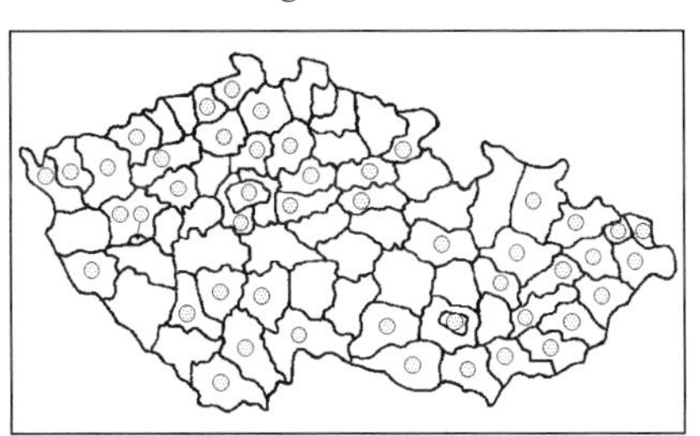

Goosander, which is a regular visitor to the Czech Republic, occurs nationwide, but larger numbers of birds are more frequently observed in n. Bohemia, central and e. Bohemia and Moravia than in other parts of the country. There are 3 breeding records from the country. Successful breeding was documented in MO county in 1977, and in PH county in 1989. Insufficient evidence was provided for reported breeding from s. Moravia in 1894. This species is found during migration and in winter more commonly at larger rivers, gravel pits and industrial waters than at ponds. It is usually found in flocks of up to 50–60 individuals, occasionally a solitary bird but also flocks of several hundred individuals. The following numbers of wintering birds were recorded from 1985–1987: in December, 228 individuals on rivers, and 391 individuals on other open water, in January, 1,273 and 694 individuals respectively, and in February, 1,355 and 954 individuals respectively (Folk and Kren 1987, Kren and Folk 1985).
Status: Migrant and winter visitor. **Breeding season:** rare. **Winter:** local. **Migration:** local. Critically endangered (its breeding status). Protected.
Population trends: Hundreds of individuals during migration, and up to 2,000 wintering birds. The number of wintering birds has increased by at least 20–50% in the past 20 years.
Distribution: Frequently occurs in the following counties: CH, KV, LN, LT, UL, PZ, AA, ME, HK, PU, BV, HO, PR, KM, OV and KI. Traditional wintering sites include the Vltava river in Praha (AA) and around Melnik (ME), the Ohre river (LT), Berounka river (BE), Zehunsky pond

(NB), the Labe river (HK, PU, NB, LT), Tovacovske ponds (PR), industrial waters around Karvina (KI) and Ostrava (OV), Zahlinicke ponds (KM), Hodoninske ponds (HO), the Morava river around Hodonin (HO), Lednicke ponds (BV), Nove Mlyny (BV), and the Dyje river (BV). **Timing:** Usually arrives at the beginning of October, and stays until the end of April, rarely May. The highest numbers have been recorded from January to March.

White-headed Duck *Oxyura leucocephala*

Kachnice belohlava Potapnica bielohlava Weiäkopf-Ruderente

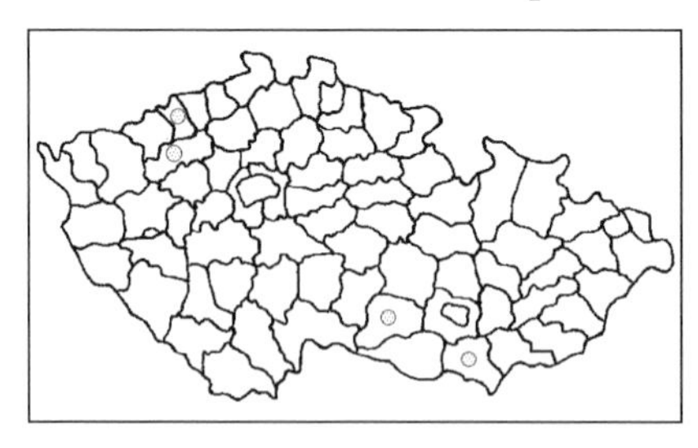

This is one of the country's rarest species of duck, occurring irregularly. Usually solitary birds have been seen at ponds, lakes, industrial waters, and occasionally rivers.
Status: Vagrant. **Breeding season:** rare. **Winter:** rare. **Migration:** rare. Protected.
Population trends: No data available.
Distribution: May occur nationwide. Since 1960 it has been recorded at Drinov lake (MO), Lenesicky pond (LN), Studenecky pond (TR), Lednicke ponds (BV), and Nove Mlyny (BV). The most recent observations are from BV county.
Timing: Recorded between the end of February and mid-October.

ACCIPITRIFORMES

Forty-five species in two families are known from the w. Palearctic. In the Czech Republic, the family **Accipitridae** is represented by 26 species, out of which 12 are regular, irregular or accidential breeders, 10 are regular migrants or vagrants, and 4 are accidentals. One species, a regular migrant, belongs to the family **Pandionidae**.

European Honey-buzzard *Pernis apivorus*

Honey Buzzard, Eurasian Honey Buzzard Vcelojed lesni Vcelojed obycajny Wespenbussard

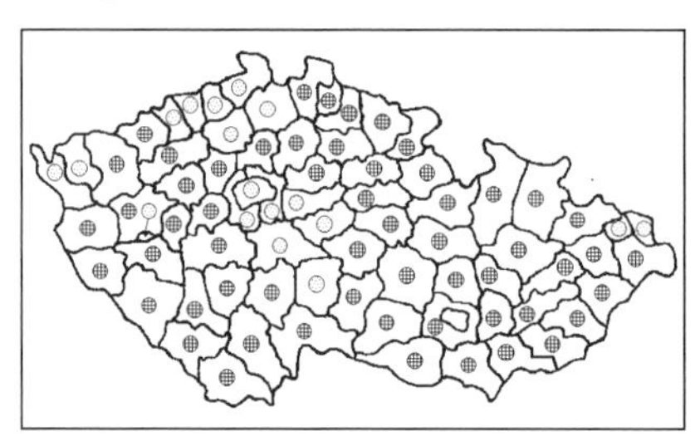

This is a regular breeding species with patchy distribution in the Czech Republic. Most of the breeding pairs are found from lowlands up to about 600 m. Breeding has also been recorded at 750 m in the Krusne hory mountains (CV, KV, MO, TP), 900 m in the Jeseniky mountains (BR, SU), and 1000 m in the Sumava mountains (CK, PT, KT). It is found in mature deciduous forest with clearings, surrounded by meadows, pastures and open land. It avoids mountains, large, dense and closed woodland, and flooded woodland. It occurs less commonly, but not rarely, in coniferous woods. Nests are built in fir, lime and spruce, 7.5–25 m above ground. In the mid-1980s, the breeding density was 0.02–0.03 pairs per km^2 aroud Trebon (JH) and, at the end of 1980s, 0.04 pairs per km^2 in e. Bohemia. The highest numbers seem to be in n. Moravia and s. Moravia, where about 200 and 170 pairs respectively nested in 1990. For example, in the Palava hills (BV) there were 5–8 breeding pairs. Human persecution, and possibly insufficient food, are major threats to this species.
Status: Summer visitor. **Breeding season:** local. **Winter:** does not occur. **Migration:** local. Vulnerable. Protected.
Population trends: The breeding population was estimated to be between 300 and 500 pairs from 1973–1977, about 640 pairs in 1990, and more recently between 600 and 850 pairs. Even though the population as a whole has increased, local falls in numbers have been reported from several counties.

Distribution: During migration it can be observed nationwide. Breeding pairs may be rather scarce in TR, TA, PI, PB, DO, TC, LB, JN, JI, ZL, VS, SU and OL counties.
Timing: Spring arrival occurs between the end of March and the end of April, mostly towards the middle and end of April. Autumn departure occurs from August, mainly in September, and rarely in October. Breeding starts at the end of April, but the main period extends from mid-May until the beginning of June.

Black Kite *Milvus migrans*

Lunak hnedy Haja tmava Schwarzmilan

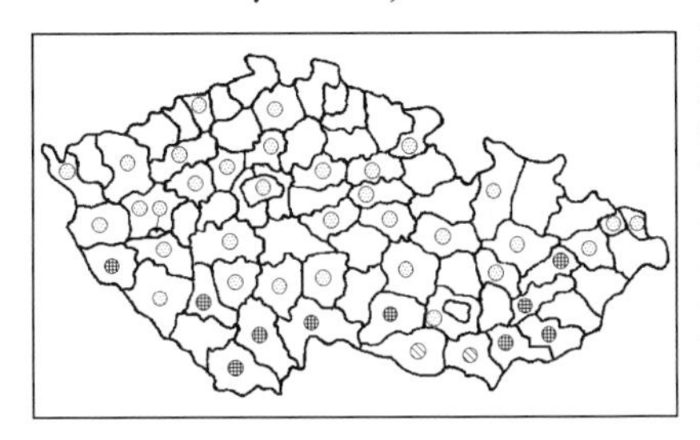

Regular breeding of this species is more or less restricted to a few lowland areas in s. Bohemia and s. Moravia. It occurs more commonly in s. Moravia than elsewhere in the country. Breeding habitats include mature, deciduous and mixed forest in the lowlands and highlands, which open into meadows and cultivated fields with ponds and other open water; but it is also found in riverine forest around larger rivers, ponds and lakes. Nests are built in deciduous trees, such as oaks and beeches, between 8 and 30 m above ground. This species reuses old nests of other larger birds as well. The breeding population in s. Moravia consisted of 8 pairs in 1983, 14 pairs in 1984, 21 pairs in 1987, 28 pairs in 1988, 29 pairs in 1989, and 35 pairs in 1990 (Danko *et al.* 1994). During migration, single birds, or rarely a small flock, can be seen in open country around larger rivers, ponds, lakes and gravel pits.
Status: Summer visitor. **Breeding season:** uncommon/local. **Winter:** rare. **Migration:** uncommon/local. Critically endangered. Protected.
Population trends: The breeding population is between 70 and 90 pairs; in 1994 there were only 30–50 pairs. An increase of at least 50% was recorded during the 20-year period starting in 1970, but since 1991, the total population has decreased by about 20%. The number of breeding pairs fluctuates annually.
Distribution: Breeding is confined mostly to the fishpond areas around Ceske Budejovice (CB), Jindrichuv Hradec (JH), Trebon (JH), and flooded woodland around the Morava (UH, HO) and Dyje rivers (BV, ZN). Occasional breeding attempts have been recorded elsewhere, for example at Zehunsky pond (NB), and in TC and CR counties. Regular non-breeding records come from areas around the Morava and Becva rivers (OL, KM, PR), Tovacovske ponds (PR) and Zahlinicke ponds (KM).
Timing: Spring migration occurs from the end of March to the end of April, with the majority of birds arriving at the beginning of April. Autumn migration starts in August and continues through September. Migrating birds may occasionally be observed in October. Breeding starts soon after arrival, and most eggs are laid during the second half of April, although egg-laying continues through mid-May.

Red Kite *Milvus milvus*

Lunak cerveny Haja cervena Rotmilan

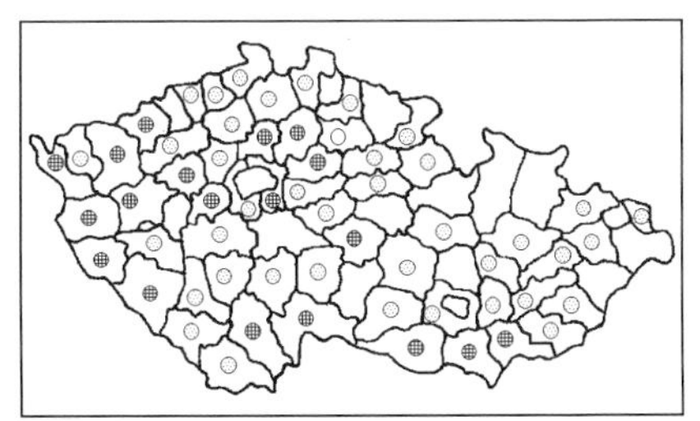

Red Kite was a regular breeder in CB and JH counties during the 19th century, but because of disturbance and persecution the species was almost extirpated. During the first 75 years of the 20th century, it was recorded infreqently on migration, and only occasional breeding attempts were documented in the Czech Republic. In 1976, breeding was recorded for the first time in riverine forest in s. Moravia, and in 1979 in Bohemia. Since the end of 1970s, it has been expanding its range in the country, and

during the mid-1980s breeding occurred in about 15 counties. Breeding habitat includes a mosaic of mature, not too dense, deciduous forest with clearings and meadows, cultivated fields and pastures in both lowlands and highlands. It is also found in flooded and riverine forest around larger rivers (typical in HO and BV counties). Nests are usually found close to the edge of woodland, normally placed in a beech, and 17–28 m above ground. Flocks of a few birds hovering above meadows or farmland can be seen during autumn migration. The best areas for seeing this species are lowlands in BV, HO and ZN counties.
Status: Summer visitor. **Breeding season**: uncommon. **Winter**: rare. **Migration**: uncommon/local. Critically endangered. Protected.
Population trends: The breeding population is estimated to be between 50 and 70 pairs. Since 1975, it has increased by at least 50%. Up to 5 individuals have been recorded in winter. In s. Moravia, there were 5 breeding pairs in 1985, 8 pairs in 1988, and 13–18 pairs in 1990 (Danko *et al.* 1994).
Distribution: Regular breeding is widespread (except in the abovementioned areas) including BE, RA, LN and CB counties, and riverine forest in s. Moravia around the Morava river (UH). It is recorded as an infrequent breeder or passage bird elsewhere.
Timing: Spring arrival occurs mostly in March and April. Autumn departure is from August to October. Breeding starts at the beginning of April and continues through to mid-May.

White-tailed Eagle *Haliaeetus albicilla*

Orel morsky Orliak morsky Seeadler

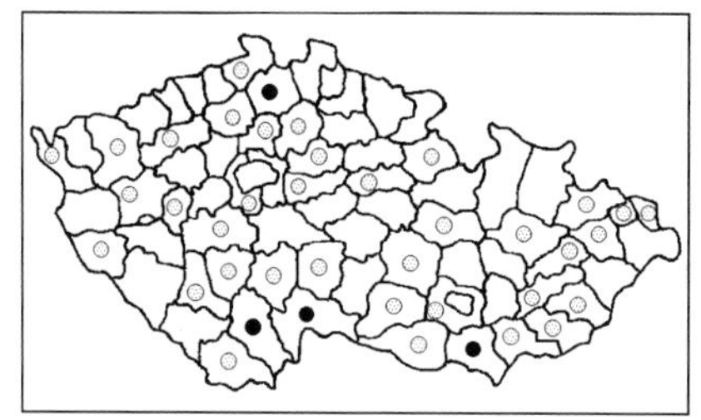

As a breeding species, White-tailed Eagle was extirpated from the Czech Republic in the 1880s in Bohemia, and the early 1920s in Moravia. From the 1920s to the early 1980s, birds on passage were observed more or less regularly across the country. Wintering individuals were recorded regularly in former traditional breeding areas such as fishponds around Trebon (JH), Lednicke ponds (BV), Pohorelicke ponds (BV), and the Dyje river (BV). At the end of the 1970s and beginning of the 1980s, young captive-bred birds were released at fishponds around Trebon, and they probably were founders of the re-established breeding population. The first, unsuccessful, breeding attempt was documented in 1984, followed by successful breeding in 1986. The first breeding record at ponds around Ceske Budejovice occurred in 1990. The first, unsuccessful, breeding attempt in s. Moravia was in 1984. Breeding habitats include mature flooded woodland and deciduous forest around fishponds and large rivers. Migrating birds are associated with large fishponds, gravel pits, reservoirs, and rivers in lowlands. Wintering birds probably include individuals from n. and ne. Europe.
Status: Resident. **Breeding season**: rare/uncommon. **Winter**: uncommon/local. **Migration**: uncommon/local. Critically endangered. Protected.
Population trends: Between 1984 and 1993, the breeding population was 7–10 pairs; since 1994, 10–15 pairs. Around 40–80 individuals winter annually, and this number is increasing. About 45–60 wintering individuals were recorded at Nove Mlyny (BV) in February 1997.
Distribution: Regular breeding occurs at fishponds around Trebon (JH), with 3–6 pairs, around Ceske Budejovice (CB), with 1–2 pairs, Brehynsky pond (CL), with 1 pair, and flooded woodland around the Dyje river (BV), with up to 3 pairs. Recent observations of wintering birds and birds on passage come from Zehunsky pond (NB), Bohdanecsky pond (PU), fishponds around Pisek (PI), Ceske Budejovice (CB), Jindrichuv Hradec (JH), Strakonice (ST), Tovacovske ponds (PR), Chomoutov gravel pit (OL), Zahlinicke ponds (KM), Mutenicke ponds (HO), Lednicke ponds (BV), Pohorelicke ponds (BV), and Nove Mlyny (BV); also around the Labe (PU), Morava (KM, HO), Becva (PR) and Dyje (BV) rivers.
Timing: Birds on passage occur mostly from mid-October, and numbers increase until December when the maximum is usually recorded. Wintering birds depart from February until March. Breeding usually starts in February, and the latest date for egg-laying is the beginning of March.

White-tailed Eagle

Griffon Vulture *Gyps fulvus*

Eurasian Griffon Vulture Sup belohlavy Sup bielohlavy Gänsegeier

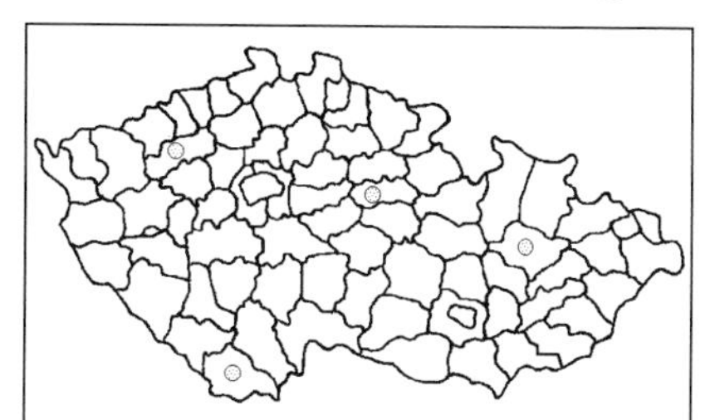

This species is a rare visitor to the Czech Republic, recorded for the last time in 1966. The lack of visiting birds during the past 30 years is probably due to the situation at European breeding grounds, where numbers of Griffon Vultures are decreasing (Hagemeijer and Blair 1997).

Status: Vagrant. **Breeding season:** rare. **Winter:** raren. **Migration:** rare. Protected.

Population trends: The following number is for the former Czechoslovakia: a total of 100 individuals recorded between 1800 and 1975. There is no data for estimating population trends.

Distribution: Since 1800, it has been observed in all 7 regions of the Czech Republic. The latest observations are from PU county from 1944, LN county from 1949, OL county from 1950, and CK county from 1966.

Timing: Recorded every month except February. Most observations are from May, June, September and October.

Monk Vulture *Aegypius monachus*

Black Vulture, Eurasian Black Vulture Sup hnedy Sup tmavohnedy
Mönchsgeier

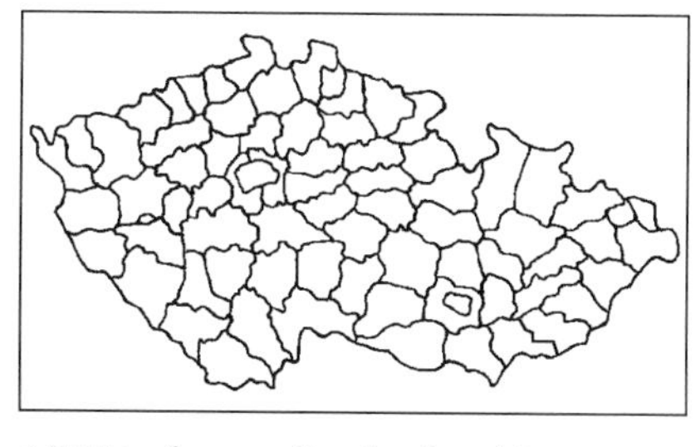

Monk Vulture occurs in the Czech Republic even more rarely than Griffon. Monk Vulture was more common at the end of the 19th century, numbers having decreased in the 20th century, mirroring a similar decline in Griffon (Hagemeijer and Blair 1997).

Status: Vagrant. **Breeding season:** rare. **Winter:** rare. **Migration:** rare. Protected.

Population trends: More than 60 individuals have been recorded at least 25 times between 1800 and 1975 in former Czechoslovakia.

Distribution: May occur nationwide. No current records.
Timing: Observed between May and August, with the majority of records in May.

Short-toed Eagle *Circaetus gallicus*

Snake Eagle   Orlik kratkoprsty   Hadiar kratkoprsty   Schlangenadler

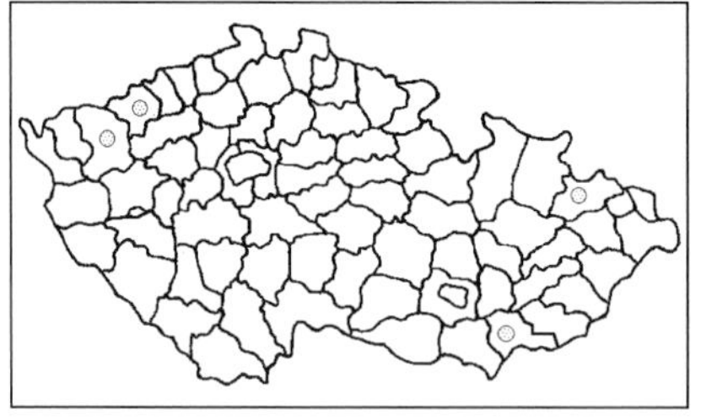

This species may have bred in the Czech Republic during the 19th century but there are no confirmed records (Hudec 1977). Regular breeding occurs in e. Slovakia, a part of former Czechoslovakia, where the breeding population is estimated to be between 20 and 30 pairs (Murin *et al.* 1994). The main prey of Short-toed Eagle is reptiles, thus this species depends on habitats with availability of such prey: open and dry pastures with extensive grazing, forest with clearings, and uncultivated land.
Status: Vagrant. **Breeding season**: rare. **Winter**: rare. **Migration**: uncommon. Protected.
Population trends: No data available.
Distribution: May occur nationwide. Most likely in the eastern and northeastern part of the country around the border with Slovakia. Recent observations of solitary birds are from Hradec nad Moravici (OP) and Milotice (HO).
Timing: From April until November, with the majority of observations in August, September and October.

Marsh Harrier *Circus aeruginosus*

Eurasian Marsh Harrier   Motak pochop   Kana mociarna   Rohrweihe

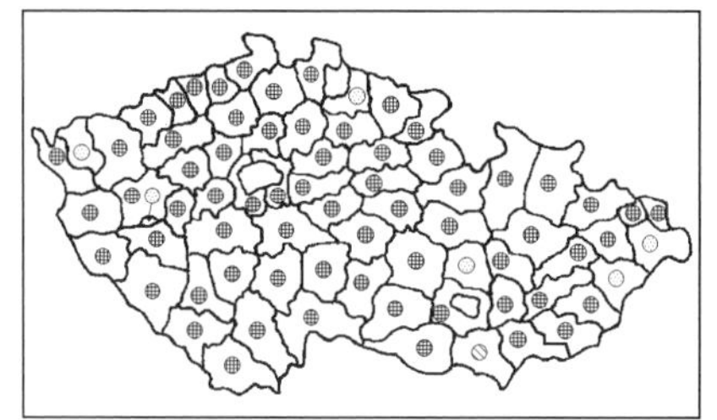

Breeding of Marsh Harriers in the Czech Republic was never recorded before 1940, although it was a regularly occurring species then. The most likely reason for non-breeding was intense hunting and other human persecution in the traditional fishpond areas of the country: s. Bohemia, e. Bohemia, s. Moravia, and n. Moravia. This species occurs in lowlands, up to about 450 m in s. Bohemia, 500 m in TR county, 600 m, and occasionally up to 700 m, in JI county, but also up to 750 m in the Sumava mountains (CK, PT, KT). Between the end of 1970s and 1980s, Marsh Harrier expanded its range virtually across the whole country, and occurred in previously unoccupied areas. Breeding habitats include fishponds and marshes with dense vegetation, preferably with reedbeds, a relatively stable water level, and usually surrounded by meadows and cultivated fields. This species generally does not like dry habitats for nesting, although nests have also been found on farmland (possibly a nest replacement) (Danko *et al.* 1994). Breeding density was 0.05 and 0.08 pairs per km^2 in NA county from 1978–1988 and 1990 respectively, and during the 1980s, 0.04–0.05 pairs per km^2 around Trebon (JH) and 0.04 pairs per km^2 in sw. Bohemia; it was 0.03 pairs per km^2 in HO county at the end of 1980s. Several pairs may nest at larger ponds or marshes. Migrants can be found in any type of open habitat with meadows or farmland, normally around open water, except rivers. Flocks of several dozen individuals have recently been reported during migration. Even though this is strictly a migrant, up to 5 wintering individuals have been recorded. The main threat to Marsh Harriers is habitat loss: drainage of marshes and their conversion into farmland, and the destruction of reedbeds around fishponds.
Status: Summer visitor. **Breeding season**: uncommon/local. **Winter**: rare. **Migration**: local/common. Vulnerable. Protected.
Population trends: The breeding population was less than 50 pairs until the early 1970s, between 250 and 450 pairs from 1973 to 1977. Since the 1970s, the population has increased

by at least 50%, and recently it is estimated to be between 900 and 1,200 pairs. About 200 pairs nest in s. Bohemia, and the same number in n. Bohemia.
Distribution: Breeding pairs may be rather rare in BR, SU, BK, PE, PT, LB and RA counties. Migrants are recorded nationwide.
Timing: This species arrives from the end of March, less commonly from mid-March, until the end of April, with a peak at the beginning of April. It departs from August until mid-October, with a peak in mid-September. Breeding occurs from mid-April until the end of May.

Hen Harrier *Circus cyaneus*

Marsh Hawk Motak pilich Kana siva Kornweihe

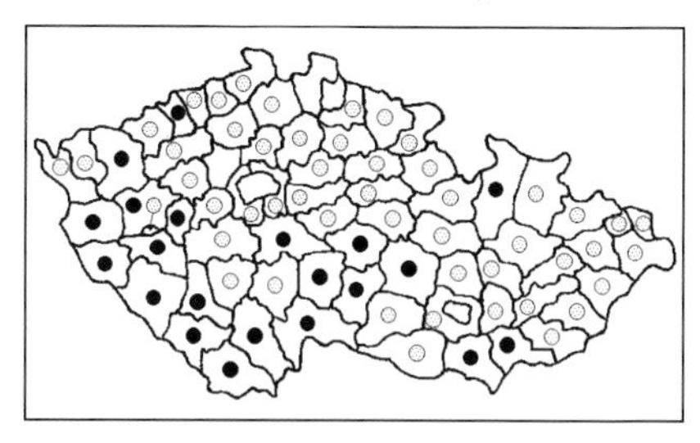

Breeding pairs of Hen Harrier are scattered across the country, being more common in the west than east. It is distributed from lowlands up to 750 m in w. Bohemia and the Ceskomoravska vysocina highlands (HB, JI, PE, ZR), up to 850 m in the Krusne hory mountains (CV, KV, MO, TP), and to 950 m in the Sumava mountains (CK, PT, KT). Breeding habitats include wet meadows, moorland, and marshes in open country; also large clearings with thickets and brush in woodland. It also breeds quite commonly in coniferous plantations, mostly in the Ceskomoravska vysocina highlands, where nests have been found in meadows, clearings, and thickets, usually close to forest edges. Wintering birds, which are probably individuals from n. and ne. Europe, occur mostly in open habitats and farmland in the lowlands. Small flocks of roosting birds are often found at the edges of marshes and ponds during winter months. During the early 1980s, the density of wintering birds was 0.8–1.5 individuals per km^2 in farmland in the foothills of the Bile Karpaty mountains (UH, HO, ZL) at about 480 m. Wild boar *Sus scrofa* may be one of the major threats to nesting pairs (Danko *et al.* 1994).
Status: Resident. **Breeding season:** uncommon. **Winter:** local. **Migration:** local. Endangered. Protected.
Population trends: The breeding population was 50–80 pairs between 1985 and 1989, but is now 50– 60 pairs. The wintering population may reach annually 700–1,500 birds.
Distribution: Regular breeding of most of the Czech population occurs in n. Bohemia (about 15 pairs), s. Bohemia (10 pairs), and w. Bohemia (10 pairs). Passage and wintering birds occur nationwide.
Timing: Birds on autumn passage occur during October, with increasing numbers in November. Wintering birds usually depart in March. Most clutches are laid at the end of April/beginning of May, rarely in mid-April.

Pallid Harrier *Circus macrourus*

Motak stepni Kana stepna Steppenweihe

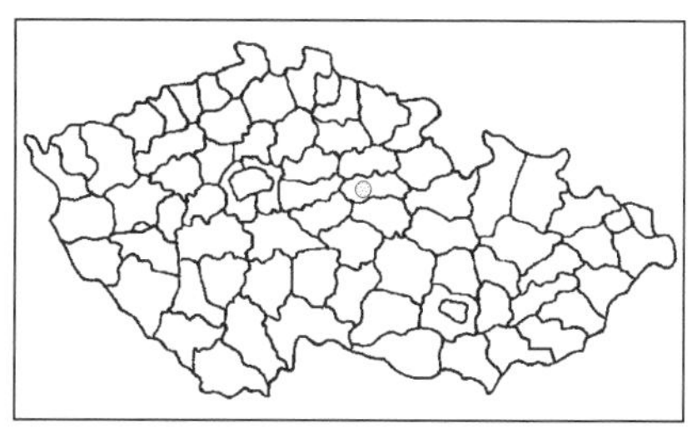

This is the rarest harrier in the Czech Republic. Individual birds, rarely flocks of a few birds, are scattered nationwide during migration. More birds are usually recorded during autumn rather than spring passage. Several autumn invasions have occurred during the 20th century, such as in 1923, 1930, 1933 and 1938 (Hudec and Cerny 1977). Pallid Harrier occurs in lowlands and highlands, where birds are usually associated with open and dry habitats such as pastures, meadows, cultivated fields, and occasionally around ponds. Juveniles form the bulk of records during autumn migration, although some of these could actually be misidentified Montagu's Harriers.
Status: Vagrant. **Breeding season:** rare. **Winter:** rare. **Migration:** uncommon. Protected.

Population trends: No data available.
Distribution: May occur nationwide. A recent record is from Rohovladova Bela (PU).
Timing: Spring passage occurs from the end of March until the beginning of May, autumn passage from the end of August until the end of September. Single birds are also recorded during summer months, and in December.

Montagu's Harrier *Circus pygargus*

Motak luzni Kana popolava Wiesenweihe

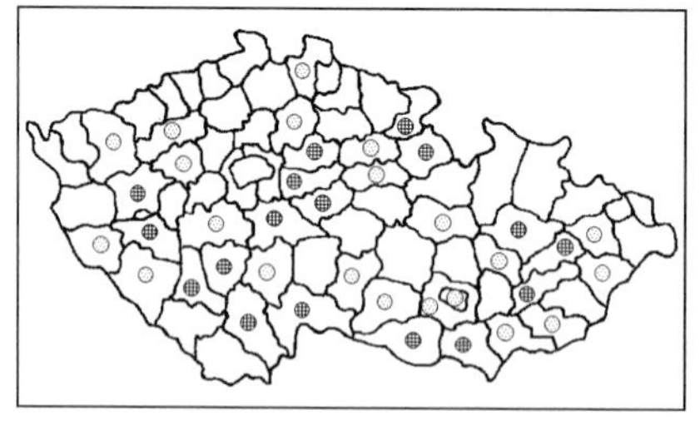

Breeding pairs of Montagu's Harriers usually occur in lowlands across the country. A fairly common local breeder in the 19th century, it became rarer during the first half of the 20th century. The decline of the breeding population is probably caused by habitat loss. Traditional breeding sites are found in the lowlands of s. Bohemia, and central Bohemia. The highest number of breeding pairs occurs in s. Bohemia, and around Unicov (OL), with up to 10 pairs at each site. This species has been extirpated from many traditional breeding sites in s. Moravia. Breeding habitats include wet meadows, marshes, grasses and thickets around larger rivers, and clearings in riverine woodland. Owing to the lack of suitable breeding habitats, the number of pairs nesting in cereals has been increasing during the past 20–25 years. Birds on passage occur in any type of open lowland habitat.
Status: Summer visitor. **Breeding season:** uncommon. **Winter:** does not occur. **Migration:** uncommon. Critically endangered. Protected.
Population trends: Between 1973 and 1977, there was regular breeding of 5–10 pairs, and during 1985–1989 about 20–30 pairs; after 1990, 20–40 pairs. There is some fluctuation in breeding numbers from year to year.
Distribution: There is more or less regular nesting in areas around Blatna (ST), Strakonice (ST), Tchorovice (ST), Jindrichuv Hradec (JH), Sedlcany (BN), Zehunsky pond (NB), Pardubice (PU), Msecke Zehrovice (RA), Dobris (PB), Ceske Budejovice (CB), Zabreh na Morave (SU), Unicov (OL), occasionally around Pohorelice (BV), and between Zahlinice (KM) and Tlumacov (ZL). Recent regular records of birds on passage, and possibly breeding, come from Milovice (MB), Rezabinec pond (PI), Vavrinecky pond (KH), Lodenicky pond (RA), Chvalovec pond near Radomysl (ST), Pasticky pond (ST), Lazany (ST), Jaderny pond (CB), Zliv (CB), Liderovice (JH), Lomnice nad Luznici (JH), Chorynske ponds (VS), Tovacovske ponds (PR), Zahlinicke ponds (KM), Krasonice (JI), Kojetin (PR), Hodoninske ponds (HO), Mistrin (HO), Vnorovy (HO), Blizkovice (ZN), between Valtice and Hlohovec (BV), Pouzdrany (BV), Drnholec (BV), around the Dyje river (BV), and several different sites in PR and KM counties.
Timing: This species arrives from mid-April, more often from the end of April, until mid-May. Birds on passage occur until the end of May. Departure starts in mid-July and continues through to the end of August. Migrating birds also occur in September. Breeding extends from the beginning of May to the end of June.

Northern Goshawk *Accipiter gentilis*

Goshawk Jestrab lesni Jastrab velky Habicht

Northern Goshawk is one of 4 relatively common raptor species in the Czech Republic. It occurs across the country, except in treeless areas and in dense forest, from lowlands up to 800 m in the Bile Karpaty (UH, HO, ZL) and Orlicke hory (RK) mountains, up to 900 m in the Krkonose mountains (SE, TU), to 1150 m in the Sumava mountains (CK, PT, KT), and to 1300 m in the Jeseniky mountains (BR, SU). As a breeder, Northern Goshawk prefers a mosaic habitat with mature coniferous, mixed and, less commonly, deciduous and riverine forest, ranging from small to large areas, and with openings to fields, pastures, meadows and clear-

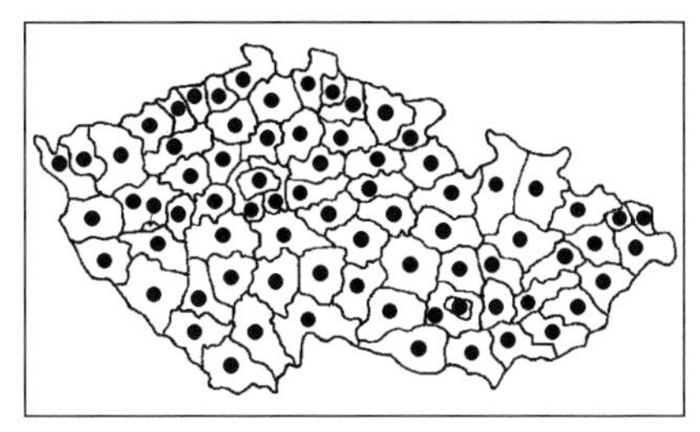

ings. In one study, out of 86 nests, 66 were placed in spruce, fir and pine, and 20 in deciduous trees, most commonly 15–20 m above ground. In the 1970s, breeding density was estimated to be 0.41 pairs per km^2 in woodland in w. Bohemia, 0.22 pairs per km^2 in s. Moravia, and 0.1 pairs per km^2 in e. Bohemia; at the end of the 1970s, it was 0.01–0.07 pairs per km^2 around Nachod (NA); during the 1980s, it was 0.08–0.1 pairs per km^2 around Trebon (JH), 0.03–0.07 pairs per km^2 in HO county, 0.1 pairs per km^2 in the Krkonose mountains, 0.03 pairs per km^2 in the Nizky Jesenik mountains (OL), 0.05–0.07 pairs per km^2 around Jindrichuv Hradec (JH), and 0.01 pairs per km^2 in central Bohemia. In winter, it may been seen more often in a farmland or open habitats farther from woodlands, and close to human settlements. At the beginning of the 1980s, winter density was 0.07–0.5 individuals per km^2 in mixed forest surrounded by farmland (UH) at about 220 m. The wintering population is probably augmented by birds from n. Europe. The breeding population is of the *gallinarium* race.

Status: Resident. **Breeding season**: common. **Winter**: common. **Migration**: common. Near-threatened. Hunted, with individual exceptions given by conservation authorities.

Population trends: The recent breeding population is between 2,000 and 2,370 pairs; it was 2,000–2,800 pairs between 1985 and 1989. It has fallen by about 20% in the past decade. The highest numbers are in n. Moravia, with about 460 pairs, s. Moravia with 410 pairs, and s. Bohemia and n. Bohemia with 400 pairs each. Local decreases have been reported from some areas, for example in s. Bohemia, and increases from areas such as s. Moravia. The number of wintering birds has been estimated to be between 2,500 and 5,000 individuals.

Distribution: Nationwide. Breeding pairs may be rather scarce in the following counties: ZN, FM, BM, UO, KT, LN, LT, PZ, AA and CR.

Timing: Breeding occurs from the end of March until the beginning of May, with the peak during the first half of April.

Eurasian Sparrowhawk *Accipiter nisus*

Sparrowhawk Krahujec obecny Jastrab krahulec Sperber

This is another relatively common species in most counties, although several decades ago it was generally considered as common, and its numbers were presumably higher. Eurasian Sparrowhawk occurs across the country, from lowlands up to 580 m in the Krkonose mountains (SE, TU), up to 700 m in the Bile Karpaty mountains (UH, HO, ZL), to 900 m in the Orlicke hory mountains (RK), and to 950 m in the Jeseniky mountains (BR, SU). Occasionally birds are seen at even higher altitudes, including during the breeding season. It prefers a landscape where mixed woods of varying size are patchily distributed amongst open habitats such as farmland and meadows, and is also found in younger coniferous plantations in larger areas of woodland. Breeding populations have become established in larger towns in parks and in other areas with mature trees, for example in Praha (AA) with 54–105 pairs during the period from 1977 to 1985, and 107 pairs in 1987, Brno (BM), Liberec (LB), and Ostrava (OV) with about 15 pairs in 1989. Nests in lowlands are found in relatively small clusters of deciduous trees around rivers, ditches and farmland. However, nests are usually placed in coniferous trees such as spruce, pine and fir, 5–10 m above ground. Breeding density in e. Bohemia was about 0.01–0.2 individuals per km^2 at the beginning of 1970s; 0.09–0.15 pairs per km^2 around Nachod (NA) at the end of the 1970s and, during the 1980s, 0.03–0.04 pairs per km^2 around Trebon (JH), 0.2 pairs per km^2 in the Krkonose mountains, 0.02 pairs per km^2 in the Nizky Jesenik mountains (OL), 0.05 pairs per km^2 around Jindrichuv Hradec (JH), and 0.3 pairs per km^2 in some parks in Praha (AA). In winter, this species occurs more commonly in open habitats, often close to human habitation

in villages, near arable farms, and quite often in towns. At the beginning of the 1980s, the density of wintering birds was about 0.2 individuals per km² in s. Bohemia, about 0.1 individuals per km² in w. Bohemia, and 0.16–0.28 individuals per km² in farmland at 170 m in UH county. Wintering birds may be joined by populations from n. Europe.
Status: Resident. **Breeding season:** common. **Winter:** common. **Migration:** common. Near-threatened. Protected/not hunted all year round.
Population trends: The breeding population is estimated to be between 3,200 and 3,900 pairs, although some authors give an upper limit of 4,500 pairs. The population seems to be stable, with little year-to-year fluctuation. The highest numbers are in e. Bohemia and n. Moravia with 1,200 and 1,100 breeding pairs respectively. The number of wintering birds is estimated to be between 4,000 and 8,000 individuals.
Distribution: Nationwide. Breeding pairs may be rather scarce in ZN, OP, TC, LN and LT counties.
Timing: Breeding starts at the end of April, with a peak during the first half of May, and continues until mid-June.

Common Buzzard *Buteo buteo*

Buzzard Kane lesni Mysiak horny Mäusebussard

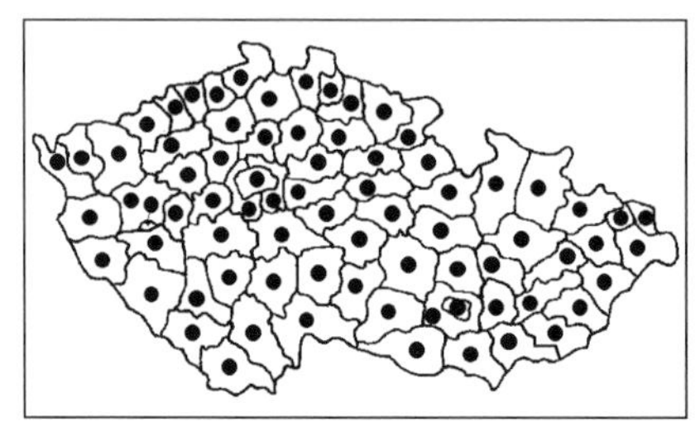

This is one of the most common raptors in the Czech Republic. Breeding pairs are distributed across the country from lowlands up to 650 m in the Bile Karpaty mountains (UH, HO, ZL), to 750 m in the Orlicke hory mountains (RK), to 800 m in the Sumava mountains (KT, PT, CK), to 900 m in the Krkonose mountains (SE, TU), and to about 1000 m in the Jizerske hory (LB, JN) and Beskydy (FM, VS) mountains. This species prefers a landscape with a range of forest types of varying size scattered in open habitats and surrounded by meadows, pastures and farmland. Breeding often occurs in woodland, hedgerows or a cluster of a few trees in cultivated fields. Breeding in solitary trees on farmland has also been recorded but is rather uncommon. Nests are placed in a variety of tree species, usually 15–20 m above ground. From 1973–1977 the average breeding density ranged from 0.11–0.17 pairs per km² across the country, depending on habitat type. During the 1980s, it was 0.2–0.3 pairs per km² in NA county, 0.2 pairs per km² in the Jeseniky mountains (BR, SU), 0.22 pairs per km² in the Nizky Jesenik mountains (OL), 0.26 pairs per km² around Hodonin (HO), 0.15–0.4 pairs per km² around Trebon (JH), 0.2–0.3 pairs per km² around Jindrichuv Hradec (JH), 1 pair per km² in a forest complex of about 30 km² near Trebon (JH), 0.26–0.33 pairs per km² in predominantly deciduous forest at about 580 m in the Bile Karpaty mountains, and 0.18–0.26 pairs per km² in mixed forest at 220 m in UH county. In winter, this species is recorded everywhere, but is most often associated with open habitats in the lowlands rather than at higher altitudes. It is often found sitting on poles along roads, or circling above alfalfa or cornfields. Birds on passage occur in flocks of up to 35–50 individuals, and often associate with Rough-legged Buzzards. The density of wintering birds varied from region to region during the 1980s: 0.7–0.9 individuals per km² in w. Bohemia, 0.5–1.9 individuals per km² in s. Moravia, 0.2–2.8 individuals per km² in s. Bohemia, and 1.7 individuals per km² in e. Bohemia; and it was 2.5–4.0 individuals per km² in farmland at 220 m in UH county. The breeding population belongs to the *buteo* race. Individuals of the *vulpinus* race have been recorded, mostly on passage during September and October, and February–April.
Status: Resident. **Breeding season:** common (*buteo*), rare (*vulpinus*). **Winter:** common (*buteo*), uncommon (*vulpinus*). **Migration:** common (*buteo*), local (*vulpinus*). Protected/not hunted all year round, with exceptions.
Population trends: The breeding population is between 9,500 and 13,000 pairs, and seems to be stable with no year-to-year fluctuations. The highest numbers occur in n. Moravia with about 3,000 pairs, s. Bohemia with 2,000 pairs, and e. Bohemia with 1,800 pairs. The wintering population is between 20,000 and 50,000 individuals, fluctuation depending on the

number of birds arriving from n. Europe.
Distribution: Nationwide.
Timing: Breeding occurs from the end of March until the end of May, peaking during the first half of April.

Long-legged Buzzard *Buteo rufinus*

Kane belochvosta Mysiak hrdzavy Adlerbussard

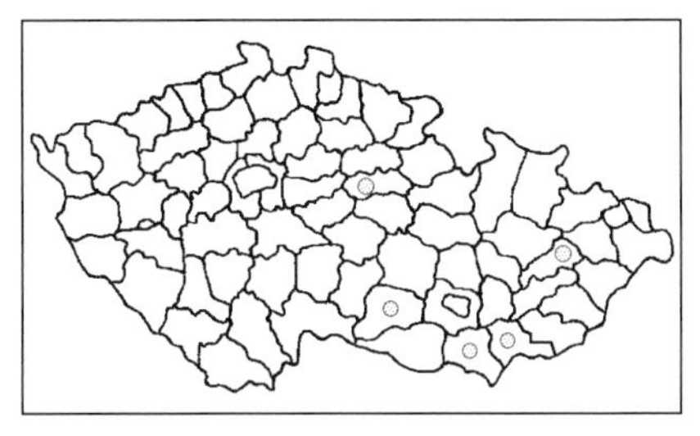

Long-legged Buzzard is a rare visitor, and does not occur annually. Birds recorded in the Czech Republic are most likely individuals from the closest breeding areas in Croatia and Hungary. The number of birds recorded during the last decade or so shows increasing occurrence compared with the years before 1980. This species prefers open and dry habitats with pastures, meadows and farmland. The most recent records are from lowland areas of the country.
Status: Vagrant. **Breeding season**: rare. **Winter**: rare. **Migration**: rare. Protected.
Population trends: No data available.
Distribution: May occur nationwide. Recent records come from Bukovka (PU), Mastnik (TR), Tovacov (PR), Cechy (PR), Hustopece nad Becvou (PR), Petrov (HO), Lednice (BV), and Brezi (BV).
Timing: Recorded from July until April. Recent dates are: 12 April, 10 July, 18 September, 3 October, and 24 December–27 March, 1997–1998.

Rough-legged Buzzard *Buteo lagopus*

Kane rousna Mysiak seversky Rauhfußbussard

Rough-legged Buzzard is an annual visitor to the Czech Republic. An invasion of a large number of birds is recorded in some years. Wintering birds are distributed across the country, with a preference for lowlands, where they are associated with a wide variety of open habitats.This species often stays close to farmland, particularly fields with alfalfa and corn. It is often seen in flocks together with Common Buzzards. It is not unusual to see flocks of up to 50 birds on passage. In the 1980s, the density of wintering birds was 0.02 individuals per km^2 in s. Bohemia, 0.36–0.86 individuals per km^2 in w. Bohemia, and 0.1-0.35 individuals per km^2 in farmland at about 220 m in UH county, but these numbers may vary from year to year. The ratio of wintering Common Buzzards and Rough-legged Buzzards varies between years and from county to county: it was 4–9 to 1 respectively in UH county during the 1980s. Reports of breeding in the Czech Republic have never been confirmed.
Status: Migrant and winter visitor. **Breeding season**: rare. **Winter**: local. **Migration**: local. Protected/not hunted all year round, with exceptions.
Population trends: The wintering population is estimated to be between 2,000 and 4,000 individuals.
Distribution: Nationwide, but year-to-year occurrence varies among counties. In some counties of n. Bohemia, s. Bohemia and Moravia it may not be recorded at all.
Timing: Occurs from September until May. The majority of birds arrive at the end of October and during November. Maximum numbers are recorded in January and February. It departs from the end of February through March. Individuals have also been recorded in June and August.

Lesser Spotted Eagle *Aquila pomarina*

Orel kriklavy Orol kriklavy Schreiadler

This is the only *Aquila* species more or less regularly nesting in the Czech Republic. A regular but not common breeder in several areas of the country in the 19th century, it has been almost extirpated in the past 100 years. From about the 1950s, occasional breeding attempts have been recorded, mostly in the Sumava mountains (CK, PT, KT), and there are more or less regular records from s. and w. Bohemia. Over the past 20 years, the breeding population in the Sumava mountains has been between 2 and 3 pairs, although recently breeding has not been documented. Breeding habitats include mature forest, of any type, in highlands and mountains or, less commonly, in lowlands, usually close to wet meadows, clearings, farmland and wide valleys. Nests are usually placed in oak and beech, rarely in conifers. During migration, this species can be seen in open habitats on farmland.

Status: Migrant and summer visitor. **Breeding season**: rare. **Winter**: rare. **Migration**: uncommon. Critically endangered. Protected/not hunted all year round.

Population trends: Breeding population was estimated to be up to 5 pairs between 1973 and 1977, and 3–6 pairs between 1985 and 1989; and since 1990, 2–4 pairs.

Distribution: Breeding is more or less restricted to the Sumava mountains with up to 3 pairs. Breeding may occur in the Krkonose (SE, TU) and Jeseniky (BR, SU) mountains, Oderske vrchy highlands (OL), flooded woodland around the Morava river (HO), and possibly the Bile Karpaty mountains (UH, HO, ZL). Migrating birds can be found nationwide. Recent records of breeding and passage birds come from Vrazda pond (MB), Dobesice (PI), Kourim (KO), Skocice (ST), Vitice (ST), Zenich pond (JH), Bystrovany (OL), Chorynske ponds (VS), ponds near Studenka (NJ), Lednice (BV), various locations in PR and KM counties, and the Bile Karpaty mountains.

Timing: Arrives from the end of April, usually in May, and departs in August. Recorded every month except December, January and February. Breeding usually starts in May, occasionally as early as the end of April or as late as the beginning of June.

Spotted Eagle *Aquila clanga*

Greater Spotted Eagle Orel volavy Orol hrubozoby Schelladler

Spotted Eagle is occasionally observed on passage in the Czech Republic. The only documented breeding in the country occurred in 1847 (Mrlik 1998). This author also provides detailed information on all records from the 20th century. During migration, it is normally recorded in lowland farmland.

Status: Vagrant. **Breeding season**: rare. **Winter**: rare. **Migration:** uncommon. Protected/not hunted all year round.

Population trends: No data available.

Distribution: May occur nationwide, but more likely in the east of the country. A recent record is from Olomouc (OL).

Timing: Spring migration occurs from mid-April until the end of May. Autumn migration starts in September and continues until November, with a peak in October. It has also been recorded in February, June, July and December.

Eastern Imperial Eagle *Aquila heliaca*

Imperial Eagle Orel kralovsky Orol kralovsky Kaiseradler

This is a rare visitor to the Czech Republic and a very recent breeder, most individuals probably come from nearby breeding sites in w. Slovakia. Some records from the Bile Karpaty mountains (UH, HO, ZL) may indicate possible breeding, but this has not been recorded yet. Eastern Imperial Eagle prefers large, mature and beech-dominated deciduous forest in highlands which open into farmland, meadows and other open habitats. Quite unexpected and successful breeding was recorded in Soutok (BV) riverine forest in 1998 and again in 1999.

Status: Vagrant and rare breeder. **Breeding season:** rare. **Winter:** uncommon. **Migration:** uncommon. Critically endangered. Protected/not hunted all year round.

Population trends: No data available.

Distribution: Most likely to be found in the eastern part of the country along the border with Slovakia, such as the Bile Karpaty and the Beskydy (VS, FM) mountains. It has recently been recorded 3 times in the Palava (BV) hills, once around Zahlinice (KM), Dolni pond (SY), Branna (SU), Lanzhot (BV), Nove Mlyny (BV) and Bzenec (HO).

Timing: Most records are from May, 2 from April, and singles from February, March, June, July, September and December.

Golden Eagle *Aquila chrysaetos*

Orel skalni Orol skalny Steinadler

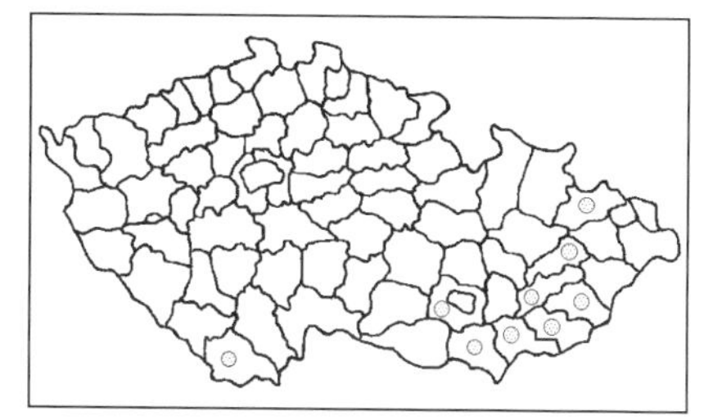

Until the end of the 19th century, Golden Eagle was a regular breeding species in the Beskydy (FM, VS) and Krkonose (SE, TU) mountains, and possibly in flooded wodland around Lanzhot (BV). During the first 60 years of the 20th century, a few breeding attempts were documented at various sites across the country but successful nesting was never recorded. On migration, this species occurs in open habitats in lowlands and highlands. Birds observed during autumn and early winter are usually immatures.

Status: Migrant. **Breeding season:** rare. **Winter:** uncommon. **Migration:** uncommon. Critically endangered. Protected/not hunted all year round.

Population trends: No data available.

Distribution: Birds on passage nationwide. Recent observations are from Horni Dvoriste (CK), Bulhary (BV), Klentnice (BV), Cejkovice (HO), Zeraviny (HO), Zahlinice (KM), and the Bile Karpaty mountains (UH, HO, ZL).

Timing: Occurs mostly from October until May.

Booted Eagle *Hieraaetus pennatus*

Orel nejmensi Orol maly Zwergadler

Booted Eagle is one of the rarest raptors recorded in the Czech Republic and is not seen annually. It is usually associated with deciduous and mixed forest in open habitats in lowlands and highlands. Most records are of single birds.

Status: Vagrant. **Breeding season:** rare. **Winter:** rare. **Migration:** uncommon. Critically endangered. Protected.

Population trends: No data available.

Distribution: Individual birds may be scattered across the country, but are most likely in the eastern part of the country and in the Sumava mountains (CK, PT, KT). Recent records are

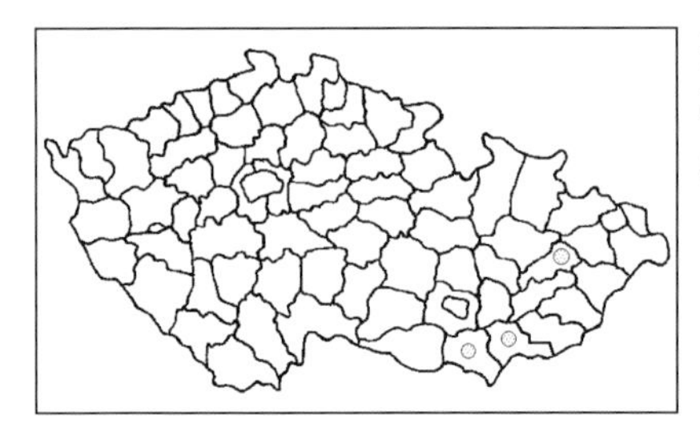

from Domazelice (PR), Pouzdrany (BV), and Mistrin (HO).
Timing: From May until October, with the peak in September when birds are on passage.

Osprey *Pandion haliaetus*

Orlovec ricni Krsiak rybar Fischadler

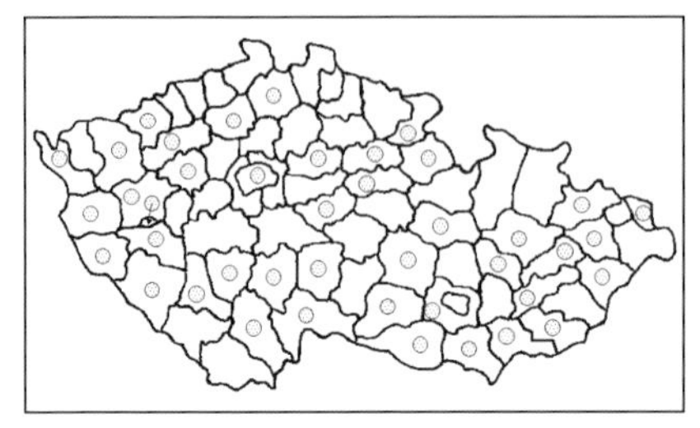

Osprey was a regular breeder in several counties of the Czech Republic until the end of the 19th century. The only breeding record in the 20th century was from the early 1920s in s. Bohemia. This species is a regular migrant with a few dozen individuals reported annually. Birds on passage occur across the country, but are most frequently found in the lowlands of s. Bohemia, e. Bohemia, s. Moravia and central Moravia. Several non-breeding birds may stay during summer. It is usually associated with larger fishponds, lakes, reservoirs, gravel pits and rivers, although birds have been seen on farmland far from water. Birds may stay for several days at the same place before moving on, particularly during autumn migration. Occasional wintering of a few birds has also been reported.
Status: Migrant. **Breeding season:** rare. **Winter:** rare. **Migration:** local. Protected/not hunted all year round.
Population trends: The number of birds on passage reported annually is as high as 15–20, and occasionally more.
Distribution: May occur nationwide. Recent regular observations of solitary birds, and rarely 2 to 4 individuals, are from Praha (AA), Zehunsky pond (NB), Brehynsky pond (CL), Riha pond (HK), Velky pond near Jesenice (RA), Cerveny pond (RA), ponds near Olsany (KT), Jivjanske ponds near Jivjany (TC), Metelsky pond (ST), Merklin (PJ), Rezabinec pond (PI), Velky Tisy pond (JH), Dacice (JH), Novy pond (SY), Opatovske ponds (SY), Chorynske ponds (VS), ponds in Novy Jicin (NJ) county, ponds near Karvina (KI), Chomoutov gravel pit (OL), Tovacovske ponds (PR), ponds near Hustopece nad Becvou (PR), Hulin gravel pit (KM), Zahlinicke ponds (KM), around the Morava river (KM, UH), Ostrozska Nova Ves gravel pit (UH), Hodoninske ponds (HO), Mutenicke ponds (HO), Rozkos dam (NA), Lednicke ponds (BV), and Nove Mlyny (BV).
Timing: First birds are usually recorded at the end of March. Peak migration is in April, with a few birds in May. There are also records of solitary birds from all the summer months. Autumn passage starts at the end of August and increases through September. Birds are recorded until the beginning of November. For both 1993 and 1994 combined, 4 birds were recorded in March, 11 in April, 2 in May, 3 in June, 2 in August, 11 in September, 3 in October, and 1 in November.

FALCONIFORMES

In the w. Palearctic includes 1 family with 13 species. In the Czech Republic, 9 species have been recorded: 5 are regular or irregular breeders, one is a vagrant, one is a winter visitor, and two are accidentals.

Lesser Kestrel *Falco naumanni*

Postolka jizni   Sokol bielopazuravy   Rötelfalke

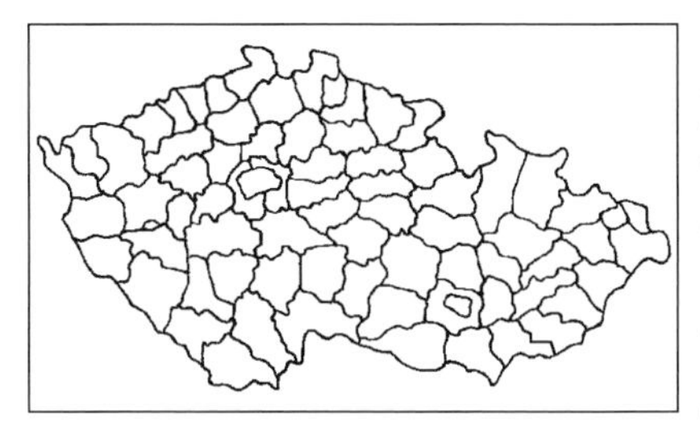

South Moravia was the only region in the Czech Republic where Lesser Kestrel occurred as a breeder. The breeding population of several dozen pairs at the end of the 19th century dwindled to only a few pairs during the 1910s. Breeding was last recorded in 1937 near Lednice (BV). Since then, this species has been observed irregularly in the Czech Republic, without any breeding attempts. There is not a record of a single bird for the 1985–1997 period. The closest breeding sites are in Croatia and Slovenia but the breeding population is small there.

Status: Vagrant. **Breeding season:** rare. **Winter:** rare. **Migration:** rare. Extinct in the wild. Protected/not hunted all year round.

Population trends: No data available.

Distribution: Most likely to be observed in s. Moravia but may occur nationwide.

Timing: From the beginning of April until the end of September.

Common Kestrel *Falco tinnunculus*

Kestrel, Eurasian Kestrel   Postolka obecna   Sokol mysiar   Turmfalke

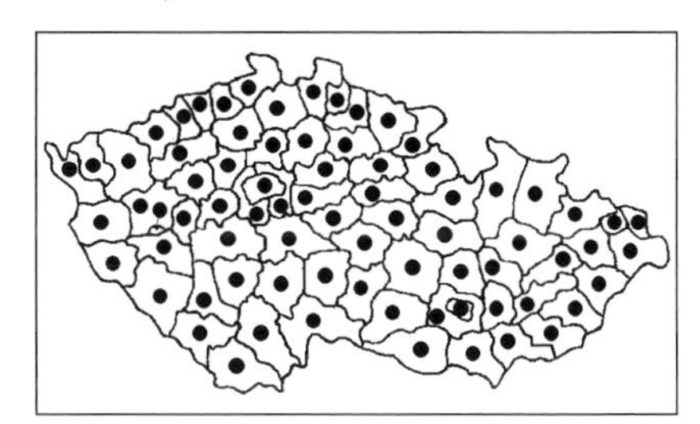

Common Kestrel is widely distributed in the Czech Republic from lowlands to the peaks of mountains. As a breeder, this species uses a wide range of habitats but usually avoids extensive, dense forest. It is most often found on farmland with scattered trees, woodland, windbreaks and hedgerows. As the likely result of the destruction of suitable breeding sites on farmland during the 1950s, birds started to move into urban habitats. Towns such as Praha (AA), Brno (BM), Plzen (PM), Ostrava (OV), Hradec Kralove (HK), Pardubice (PU), Ceske Budejovice (CB), Olomouc (OL) and many others have quite large breeding populations, with birds usually using towers and buildings for nest sites. Common Kestrels often breed in artificial nest boxes, which have been constructed for them in many counties around the country (for example HK, PU, PV, UH, ZL counties etc). During the 1970s, breeding density was 0.4 pairs per km^2 in e. Bohemia, 0.04–0.07 pairs per km^2 in n. Moravia, and 0.08 pairs per km^2 in farmland in s. Moravia; and during the 1980s, it was 0.06–0.09 pairs per km^2 around Trebon (JH), 0.02 pairs per km^2 in NA county, 0.03–0.07 in NJ county, 0.1 pairs per km^2 in the Nizky Jesenik mountains (OL), 0.07–0.1 pairs per km^2 in farmland in HK and PU counties, 0.35 pairs per km^2 in farmland at 170 m near Uherske Hradiste (UH), and 0.57 pairs per km^2 in highlands with pastures at 420 m in HO county. Some of the local breeding populations were supposedly supported by artificial nest boxes. Breeding density in various parts of Praha (AA) was 0.2–3.09 pairs per km^2 at the end of 1980s, with the total number of breeding pairs around 200. In Hradec Kralove (HK) it was 0.29 pairs per km^2, and in Pardubice (PU) 0.21–1.84 pairs per km^2 during the 1980s. During winter, Kestrels can usually be found in lowland farmland, preferring areas with alfalfa and cornfields. Winter density was 0.2 individuals per km^2 in central Bohemia, 0.2–0.5 individuals per km^2 in s. Moravia, and 0.9 individuals per km^2 in n. Moravia during the 1980s; and it was 0.8–1.1 individuals per km^2 in farmland at 180 m in UH county at the beginning of the

1980s. The breeding population is partially migratory, wintering birds joined by individuals from n. Europe.
Status: Resident. **Breeding season:** common. **Winter:** common. **Migration:** common. Protected/not hunted all year round.
Population trends: The breeding population was 9,000–13,000 pairs from 1985 to 1989. Some authors estimated it to be between 9,000 and 10,000 pairs at the beginning of the 1990s. The highest numbers are in s. Moravia with about 2,500 pairs, and s. Bohemia with 2,000 pairs. The lowest numbers are in central Bohemia and w. Bohemia with 500 and 350 pairs respectively. The number of wintering birds ranges from 15,000 to 30,000 individuals. The breeding population seems to be stable, with no significant year-to-year fluctuation.
Distribution: Nationwide.
Timing: The breeding population arrives from the end of February until the end of March, and departs mostly from the end of September through October. Breeding starts in April (earlier in towns) and continues to the end of June, with a peak at the beginning of May.

Red-footed Falcon *Falco vespertinus*

Postolka rudonoha Sokol cervenonohy Rotfußfalke

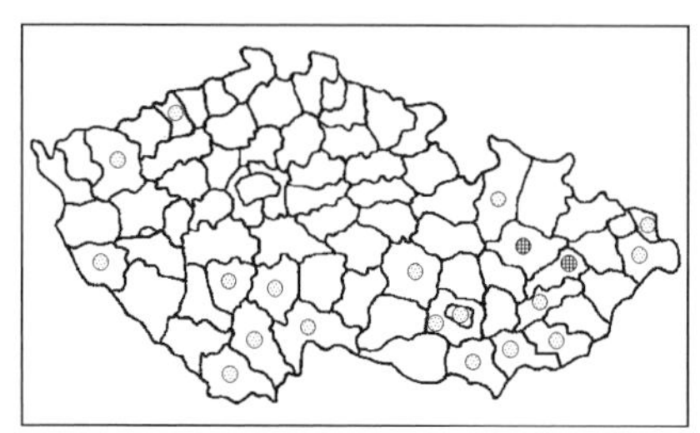

Although this is a colonially nesting species, only solitary breeding pairs have been recorded in the Czech Republic. Breeding does not occur annually, and so far has only been documented in lowlands and highlands in the eastern part of the country. This species prefers dry and open habitats with short vegetation and scattered trees, windbreaks and deciduous woodland. On migration it may also be found in open moist habitats, around ponds, rivers and meadows. Most of the recent records are from May and June.
Status: Vagrant/summer visitor. **Breeding season:** rare. **Winter:** does not occur. **Migration:** local. Critically endangered. Protected/not hunted all year round.
Population trends: No breeding records between 1975 and 1988. A pair with fledglings was observed near Unicov (OL) in 1989. Irregular breeding of up to 5 pairs may now occur, and up to a dozen birds may be seen on passage. No data available for evaluation of population trends.
Distribution: On migration nationwide. Irregular breeding recorded in OL and PR counties, and mostly seen in s. Moravia, occasionally elsewhere. Recent records of mainly solitary birds are from Janova Ves u Malont (CK), Pekna na Sumave (PT), Havran (MO), Rozmberk nad Vltavou (CK), Dobevsky pond (PI), Rezabinec pond (PI), Velky Tisy pond (JH), Zbudovska Blata (CB), Mydlovary (CB), Horni Dvoriste (CK), Horni Sucha (KI), Hlusovice (OL), Horni Mostenice (PR), Vlcnov (UH), Lednice (BV), and Mikulov (BV).
Timing: Spring migration starts in mid-April and continues through May until the beginning of June. Peak autumn migration is in August and September, and it occurs only occasionally after September.

Merlin *Falco columbarius*

Dremlik tundrovy Sokol kobec Merlin

Wintering Merlins usually occur in the lowlands and highlands of central Bohemia, e. Bohemia, s. Bohemia, s. Moravia and central Moravia. They are rarely found at higher altitudes. This species prefers open habitats with scattered trees, windbreaks, hedgerows and woodland, and is quite often associated with habitats around farms and villages. Usually only solitary birds or a few individuals together are recorded. Merlin has been seen several times during the breeding season in the Krkonose mountains (SE, TU), where nesting may possibly occur but has not been documented yet. Birds recorded in the Czech Republic belong to the *aesalon* race.

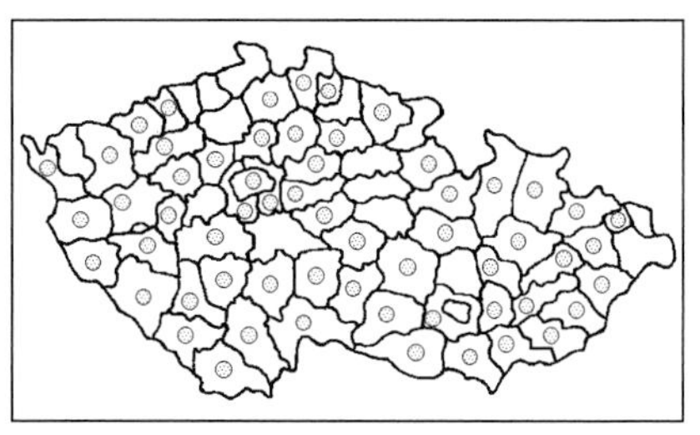

Status: Migrant and winter visitor. **Breeding season:** rare. **Winter:** local. **Migration:** local. Protected.
Population trends: The number of wintering birds is estimated to be between 90 and 150 individuals, and seems to be stable from year to year.
Distribution: Recent observations come from Mnichovo Hradiste (MB), Radostice (CB), Bosonohy (BM), Sluzebny pond (JH), Dolni Ujezd (SY), Veverske Kninice (BO), Olomouc (OL), Chomoutov (OL), Starnov (OL), Tovacov (PR), Dolni Ujezd (PR), Kurovice (KM), and Nove Mlyny (BV).
Timing: Occurs mainly from October until March, with maximum numbers in December, January and February.

Hobby *Falco subbuteo*

Eurasian Hobby Ostriz lesni Sokol lastoviciar Baumfalke

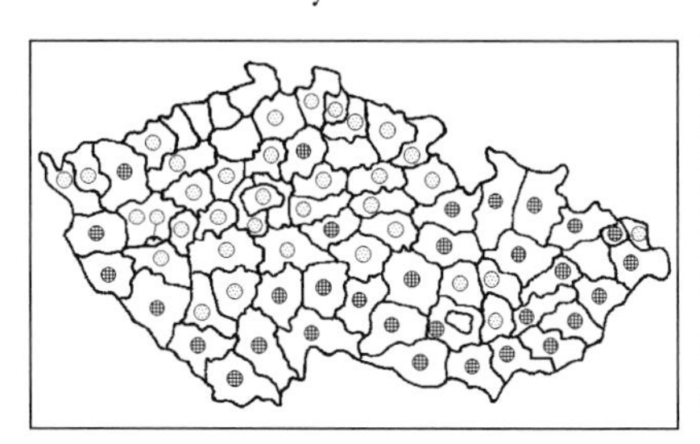

This is the second most common *Falco* species in the Czech Republic, even though the number of breeding pairs is much lower than that of Common Kestrel. The breeding population has been decreasing since the late 1960s, and Hobby has disappeared from many counties where it was once a regular breeder. This species is distributed from the lowlands up to about 650 m in the Jeseniky (BR, SU) and Bile Karpaty (HO, UH, ZL) mountains, up to 1050 m in the Krkonose mountains (SE, TU), and to about 1100 m in the Beskydy mountains (FM, VS). It is found most often in open country with pine plantations, pine-dominated mixed forest and, less commonly, purely deciduous forest of varying size. It often stays close to clearings and edges of forest, and also open water such as ponds. Hunting birds are regularly seen farther from woodland in farmland and around villages. In one study, 15 out of 17 nests were placed in conifers. During the 1980s, the breeding density was 0.008 pairs per km^2 in the Nizky Jesenik mountains (OL), 0.01 pairs per km^2 around Jindrichuv Hradec (JH), and 0.02–0.03 pairs per km^2 around Trebon (JH). On migration, Hobby is attracted to reedbeds around ponds where flocks of Barn Swallows and Sand Martins roost. Flocks of several birds can be seen together on passage.
Status: Migrant and summer visitor. **Breeding season:** uncommon. **Winter:** does not occur. **Migration:** local. Endangered. Protected.
Population trends: Between 1973 and 1977, the breeding population was up to 300 pairs, between 1985 and 1989 it was 150–230 pairs, and this is probably the population size today. Between 1973 and 1995 the population declined by approximately 20%. Although the population was then in decline compared with the 1970s, breeding in new, previously unoccupied areas was recorded in the mid-1980s.
Distribution: Migrating and non-breeding birds are found nationwide. Strongholds of the breeding population are in JH, CK, PT, ZR and FM counties.
Timing: Arrives usually from mid-April until mid-May, and departs from the end of August until the end of September. There are infrequent records from October. Breeding continues from the beginning of May until the end of June.

Saker Falcon *Falco cherrug*

Saker Raroh velky Sokol raroh Saker

Saker Falcon was an occasional breeder in the western part of the Czech Republic, where breeding was first documented at the beginning of the 1840s and continued until the 1940s. Since then, breeding has not been recorded there. The first breeding in Moravia occurred at the end of the 1920s in ZR county. Today, regular breeding is confined to about 5 counties in

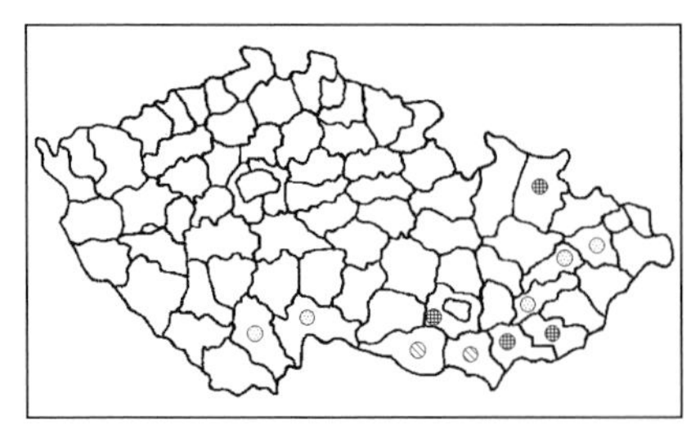

s. Moravia. At the end of the 1980s, breding was also recorded for the first time in BR county in n. Moravia. Breeding habitats include riverine forest in lowlands and highlands, farmland, meadows, and steppe-like habitat. This species usually uses old nests of other species for breeding, in beech, oak, cottonwood or alder. Young captive-bred birds have been reintroduced in both rural and urban habitats at various sites over the past 10–15 years in attempts to establish breeding populations. Stragglers may be seen elsewhere across the country, mostly in open areas in lowlands and highlands.

Status: Resident. **Breeding season:** rare/uncommon. **Winter:** uncommon/local. **Migration:** uncommon/local. Critically endangered. Protected.

Population trends: Between 1973 and 1977, the breeding population was 5–10 pairs, and 8–12 pairs from 1985 to 1989. At the beginning of the 1990s it was 10–15 pairs, and 9 pairs in 1994. Up to 8–12 pairs may breed annually. The wintering population is between 2 and 10 individuals.

Distribution: Breeding is more or less restricted to woodland around the Morava river, between Veseli nad Moravou (HO) and Hodonin (HO), and the Dyje river (ZN, BV). Recent observations, of usually solitary birds, come from Blatec pond (CB), Zbudovsky pond (CB), Velky Tisy pond (JH), Tovacov (PR), Domazelice (PR), Drevohostice (PR), Zahlinice (KM), Modrice (BO), Ostrozska Nova Ves (UH), Veseli nad Moravou (HO), Drnholec (BV), Ladna (BV), Pouzdrany (BV), Breclav (BV), and the Palava highlands (BV).

Timing: Breeding usually starts at the end of March and continues to the beginning of May.

Peregrine Falcon *Falco peregrinus*

Peregrine Sokol stehovavy Sokol stahovavy Wanderfalke

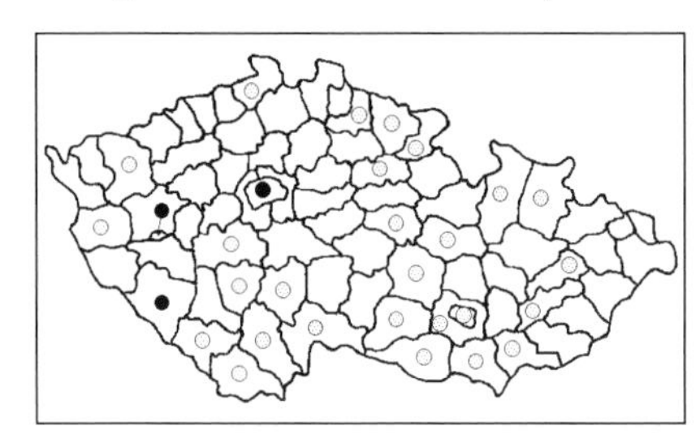

Once a regular breeder in several counties of w. Bohemia, s. Bohemia, central Bohemia, and Moravia, Peregrine Falcon has become one of the rarest nesting raptors in the Czech Republic. From about the mid-1960s, occasional breeding was recorded at various places across the country, but between the mid-1970s and mid-1980s there ware no breeding records at all. During the second half of the 1980s, breeding occurred in the Sumava mountains (CK, PT, KT), and also in Praha (AA) in 1995, 1996 and 1997. Breeding birds are found in large areas of woodland, usually in mountains where rocks and cliffs are available, but nesting has also been recorded in riverine forest in lowlands, and at a church tower in Praha (AA). On migration or after breeding, it may occur elsewhere across the country. Mrlik (1992) evaluated the suitability of some of the traditional breeding sites for Peregrine Falcon with the view to a reintroduction programme. The criteria he used focus on potential human disturbance and the availability of prey. Out of 19 sites, 8 may still provide adequate conditions for breeding Peregrines. The number of Peregrine Falcons recorded in the country increases during migration. Although there are recent records from the winter months, and winter records are also provided by Hudec *et al.* (1977), Peregrine is not listed as a wintering species by Bejcek *et al.* (1995). The breeding race has been recognized as *peregrinus*. Several specimens collected from December to February belong to the *calidus* race which breeds in Eurasian tundra.

Status: Migrant and summer visitor. **Breeding season:** rare (*peregrinus* and *calidus*). **Winter:** uncommon (*peregrinus*), rare (*calidus*). **Migration:** uncommon (*peregrinus*), rare (*calidus*). Critically endangered. Protected.

Population trends: Between 1985 and 1990 up to 3 breeding pairs, since 1990 up to 5 breeding pairs: a significant decrease in the breeding population compared with numbers before 1950.

Distribution: Breeding may occur in the Sumava, and Jeseniky (BR, SU) mountains (probably 2 pairs), and the Krkonose mountains (SE, TU). Recent records, of usually solitary birds, are from Putkov (PT), Mlada Vozice (TA), Plana nad Luznici (TA), Padrtske ponds (PB), Zehunsky pond (NB), Ceske Budejovice (CB), Horni Petrovicky pond (BN), Dasensky pond (CB), Hluboka nad Vltavou (CB), Novosedly (CB), Volesek pond (CB), Dehtare (CB), Velky Tisy pond (JH), Rezabinec pond (PI), Brloh (CK), Rozkos dam (NA), Litomysl (SY), Zhejral pond (TR), Dluhonice (PR), Tovacov (PR), Brno (BM), Chrlice (BO), Bzenec-Privoz (HO), Mistrin (HO), Zahlinice (KM), and Nove Mlyny (BV).
Timing: All year round with most records from September, October and January–March.

GALLIFORMES

In the w. Palearctic there are 4 families with 28 species. Seven species in 2 families have been recorded in the Czech Republic. Three resident breeding species belong to the family **Tetraonidae**; 4 regular breeding species, one of which is a summer visitor, belong to the family **Phasianidae**.

Hazel Grouse *Bonasa bonasia*

Hazellhen Jerabek lesni Jariabok horny Haselhuhn

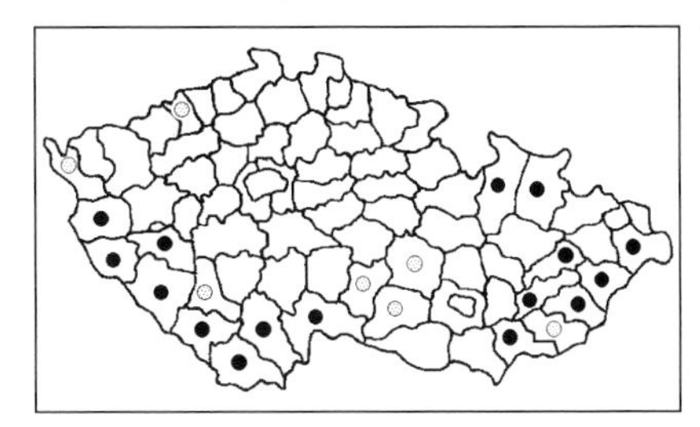

This species was a fairly common breeder in some parts of the Czech Republic until the 1920s, when the population started to decline. Hazel Grouse occurs in highlands and mountains between 500 m and 1200 m, but as a breeder it has also been recorded at altitudes of 200 m. The strongholds of the breeding population are in the Sumava (CK, PT, KT) and Novohradske hory (CK, CB) mountains in Bohemia, and the Beskydy mountains (VS, FM) in Moravia. This species inhabits large mature woodland of any type, preferably with growths of pine, spruce or larch and with a dense brush undergrowth. Nests are usually placed at the base of trees or rocks. During the 1980s, breeding density was 0.4–0.6 pairs per km^2 in the Beskydy mountains (FM, VS). Two races have been recognized in the Czech Republic (Hudec *et al.* 1977): race *styriacus* occurs in the highlands and mountains of e. Moravia, such as in the Bile Karpaty (HO, UH, ZL) and Beskydy mountains, and in the Javorniky (ZL, VS), Vsetinske (VS) and Hostynske (ZL) vrchy hills; race *rupestris* occurs in the rest of the country.
Status: Resident. **Breeding season:** uncommon/local. **Winter:** local. **Migration:** local. Vulnerable. Protected/not hunted all year round.
Population trends: The current breeding population is between 800 and 1,600 pairs; from 1973 to 1977 it was 500–800 pairs. The number of wintering birds is estimated to be between 500 and 900 individuals.
Distribution: The main breeding areas are the central Sumava mountains, with about 700 individuals, the Novohradske hory mountains, the Jeseniky mountains (BR, SU), with 50-65 pairs, and the Beskydy mountains, with about 100–200 pairs. A smaller population occurs in the Javorniky, Vsetinske and Hostynske vrchy hills, and in the Bile Karpaty mountains. Small flocks or individual birds can be scattered in suitable habitat elsewhere around the country. Recent records of varying numbers come from Krchleby-Horni Kamenice (DO), Flaje in Krusne hory (MO), Skocice (ST), Jeleni-Plechy (PT), Rajcherov (JH), Velesin (CK), Petrovy kameny (BR), and Javornik nad Velickou (HO). From the beginning of the 1990s, there have been numerous records from areas where the species was absent in the 1980s.
Timing: All year round. Breeding usually starts in mid-April and continues until the end of May, peaking at the end of April and beginning of May.

Hazel Grouse

Black Grouse *Tetrao tetrix*

Tetrivek obecny Tetrov obycajny Birkhuhn

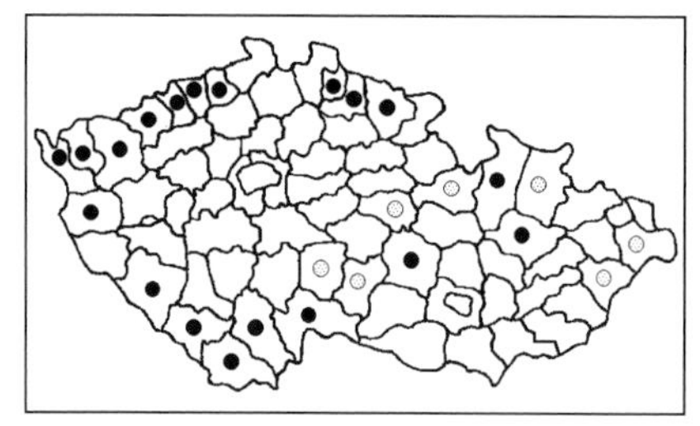

The highest numbers of this species in the Czech Republic were recorded at the beginning of the 20th century. Since the mid-1930s, the population has been declining steadily, and Black Grouse has been extirpated from some traditional breeding sites. This trend has been documented at a lek in the Sumava mountains (CK, PT, KT): about 70 males were displaying in 1966, around 30 in 1968, 16 in 1973, 7 in 1977, and only 3 in 1985 (Hanzak 1987). During mid-April in 1991, a total of between 150 and 200 males were found at all leks in the Sumava mountains. On the other hand, interesting evidence on population trends was provided by Stastny *et al.* (1996): at the same time as population declines in the traditional breeding areas, numbers at clearings in acid-rain-damaged spruce forest in the Krusne hory mountains (CV, KV, MO, TP) were increasing, and the density at one study site in 1994 was 1 male per km^2. Black Grouse is distributed in highlands from about 250 m up to the dwarf-pine zone in mountains. Typical habitats include any type of forest with clearings, undergrowth vegetation, and surrounded by pastures, wet meadows and peatbogs. Leks, which are usually used for several consecutive years, are located in clearings, birch-dominated areas of forest, and at woodland edges. The exact causes of the population decline are unclear. However, the most likely reasons include habitat destruction, including drainage of wetland, commercial exploitation of peatbogs, and disturbance at the leks.

Status: Resident. **Breeding season:** uncommon/local. **Winter:** local. **Migration:** local. Endangered. Hunted, with individual exceptions given by conservation authorities.

Population trends: From 1973 to 1977, the number of males was between 2,500 and 4,500 individuals, more recently 1,100–2,200 have been recorded. The population has decreased by 20–50% over the past 20 years. Winter numbers are between 1,000 and 2,000 individuals.

Distribution: The strongholds of this species are Doupovske hory mountains (KV), with about 400 males, the Sumava mountains, the Krusne hory mountains, the Jizerske hory mountains (LB, JN), the Krkonose mountains (SE, TU), with about 100 individuals, and the Jeseniky mountains (BR, SU) with 25–45 males. Individual birds can be scattered in other non-breeding areas with suitable habitat, particularly during autumn and winter.

Timing: All year round. Males usually display from mid-March, but later at higher altitudes. Displaying at leks may last, with decreasing intensity, until the end of June. Breeding occurs in May and June.

Capercaillie *Tetrao urogallus*

Western Capercaillie Tetrev hlusec Hluchan obycajny Auerhuhn

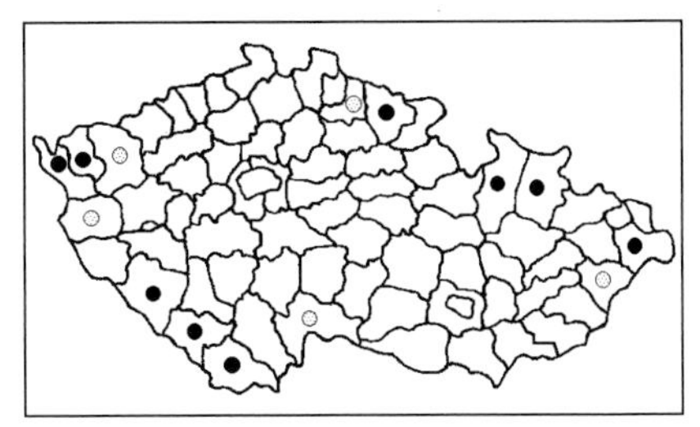

Capercaillie is the rarest galliforme occurring in the Czech Republic. Since the 1940s, the breeding population has been declining dramatically, as may be shown by 2 examples: 111 individuals were recorded in the Krkonose mountains in 1964 (SE, TU), 8 in 1971, and 3 in 1972. Between 1967 and 1976, the overall population in the country decreased from 1,229 males to about 550. Distribution of the majority of the population is restricted to mountains in s. Bohemia, e. Bohemia, and n. Moravia, where it occurs between 750 m and 1300 m. It is found in mature coniferous or mixed woodland with a shrub undergrowth, and areas with access to peatbogs or marshes. It generally avoids deciduous forest. Many factors can probably be linked to the decline of this species: destruction of mature woodland and forest, antipathetic forestry management, commercial exploitation of peatbogs, and hunting are certainly the most critical.

Status: Resident. **Breeding season**: uncommon. **Winter**: uncommon. **Migration**: uncommon. Critically endangered. Protected/not hunted all year round.

Population trends: Between 1973 and 1977, about 530–700 males were recorded; recently 100–150. The population has decreased by more than 50% over the past 20 years. In winter about 110–140 individuals are usually recorded.

Distribution: Regularly occurs in the Sumava mountains (CK, PT, KT), with about 55 males, the Krkonose mountains, with up to 20 males recorded historically, the Beskydy mountains (VS, FM), with 5–10 males, and the Jeseniky mountains (BR, SU) with 3–7 males. Small groups may be scattered in the Novohradske hory mountains (CK, CB), the Cesky les mountains (DO, TC), the Krusne hory mountains (CV, KV, MO, TP), the Jizerske hory mountains (LB, JN), and the Ceskomoravska vysocina highlands (HB, JI, PE, ZR).

Timing: All year round. Males start to display in March and continue through May (at higher altitudes). The egg-laying period extends from the beginning of April until mid-May.

Grey Partridge *Perdix perdix*

Partridge Koroptev polni Jarabica polna Rebhuhn

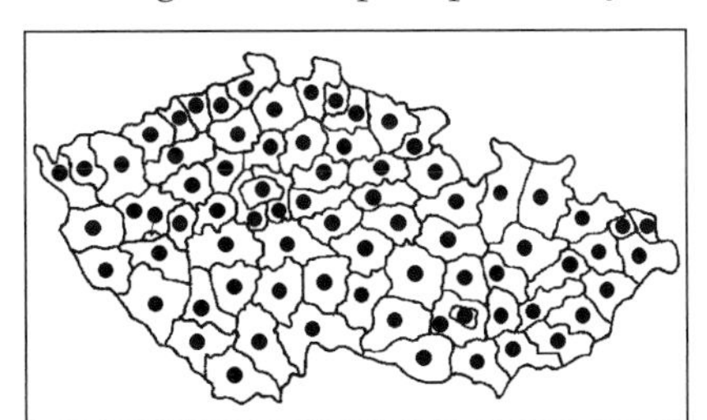

This is one species whose population has declined dramatically in the Czech Republic over the past 55–60 years, most likely as a result of agricultural intensification. At the beginning of the 20th century, it was such an abundant species that about 1,250,000 individuals were shot annually, and about 1,500,000 individuals each year between 1930 and 1940. Grey Partridge is distributed across the country, with a preference for lowland areas. It has been recorded up to 500 m in the Bile Karpaty mountains (HO, UH, ZL), and from 650–800 m in the Sumava (CK, PT, KT), Novohradske hory (CK, CB), Cesky les (DO, TC), Krusne hory (CV, KV, MO, TP), Orlicke hory (RK), Krkonose (SE, TU), Jeseniky (BR, SU) and Beskydy (VS, FM) mountains. It is found in open country with grassy patches, pastures, hedgerows, banks and ditches between cultivated fields. Nests are often placed in cereal crops, alfalfa and other cultivated plants. Grey Partridge can also be seen around villages and farms, as well as at grassy areas around the edges of large towns. In the early 1970s, the breeding density was 1.0–2.7 pairs per km^2 around Trebon (JH), and from 1978–1980 2.1–3.2 pairs per km^2 in meadows and in farmland around Veseli nad Moravou (HO).

Status: Resident. **Breeding season**: local/common. **Winter**: common. **Migration**: common. Near-threatened. Hunted, with individual exceptions given by conservation authorities.

Population trends: The breeding population was about 770,000 individuals in the mid-1960s.

Since the mid-1980s it has crashed to between 18,000 and 36,000 individuals. Winter numbers range from 7,000–15,000 individuals.
Distribution: Nationwide, except at higher altitudes in mountains. Breeding pairs may be rather scarce in LB, DC, BK, ZL and SU counties.
Timing: All year round. Breeding occurs between the end of March and the beginning of June, with the peak from mid-April until the beginning of May.

Common Quail *Coturnix coturnix*

Quail Krepelka polni Prepelica polna Wachtel

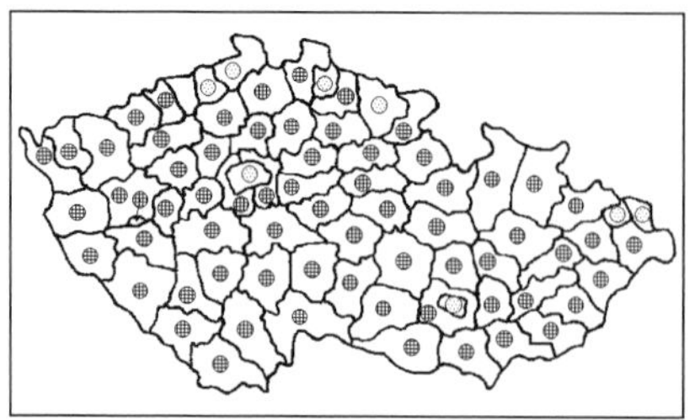

This is the only species of galliforme which does not occur in the Czech Republic all year round. Once a common breeder, this species has become rare and is scattered across the country. At the end of the 19th century and during the first decade of the 20th century up to 15,000 birds were shot annually. Since then, the population has been decreasing steadily. The main cause of Common Quail's decline is considered to be agricultural intensification (Tucker and Heath 1994). However, in the Czech Republic, the population was declining 25–30 years before the changes in agricultural practices occurred. It is distributed throughout lowlands and highlands, up to about 750 m in the mountains, occasionally at higher altitudes such as 1100 m in the Beskydy mountains (FM, VS). This species is found in open habitats such as grassland and farmland, where it feeds amongst cereal crops, vetches, clover and alfalfa. Reports from the past 10 years indicate that its numbers might be increasing, at least locally, and particularly in the highlands and montane foothills. Breeding density around Trebon (JH) was 0.5 individuals per km^2 in the period from 1973 to 1978. At the beginning of the 1980s, 0.9–1.4 calling males per km^2 were recorded in meadows and cultivated fields around Veseli nad Moravou (HO) at 180 m, 0.7–0.9 calling males per km^2 in the foothills of the Bile Karpaty mountains (HO, UH, ZL) at about 450 m. At the end of the 1980s, there were 0.37–0.75 calling males per km^2 around Jindrichuv Hradec (JH), 0.07 males per km^2 in the foothills of the Krkonose mountains (SE, TU), and 2.5 males per km^2 around Holysov (DO). The numbers of breeding Common Quails may fluctuate significantly from year to year.
Status: Migrant and summer visitor. **Breeding season:** uncommon/local. **Winter:** does not occur. **Migration:** local. Least concern. Protected.
Population trends: The breeding population is estimated to be between 3,000 and 6,000 pairs, and numbers have been increasing since 1989.
Distribution: Scattered nationwide. Breeding pairs may be rather scarce in SE, TU, LN, LT, PB, ZN, BK, ZL, FM and OP counties.
Timing: Arrives from the end of April until to the end of May, and departs from August to September. It is rare at the beginning of October. Breeding occurs from mid-May until the beginning of August, peaking in June.

Reeve's Pheasant *Syrmaticus reevesi*

Bazant kralovsky Bazant kralovsky Königsfasan

Reeve's Pheasant is a game species introduced to the Czech Republic during the 19th and first half of the 20th centuries. Most of the birds are bred in pheasantries, and released in surrounding areas. It is distributed in riverine forest in central and n. Moravia.
Status: Resident. **Breeding season:** uncommon/local. **Winter:** uncommon/local. **Migration:** uncommon/local. Hunted in fixed season.
Population trends: The population is between 200 and 400 individuals. However, the numbers may fluctuate from year to year, depending on game management. No data available for an estimate of population trends.
Distribution: This species is restricted to PR and KM counties where it occurs in riverine for-

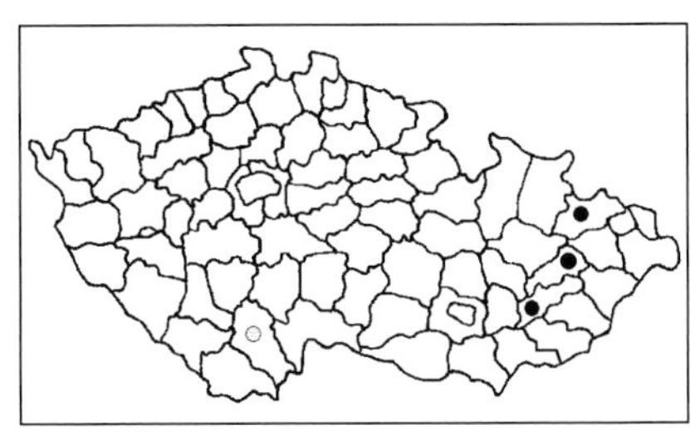

est around the Morava river, and in OP county where it is restricted to the area around the village of Silherovice; and in meadows, fields and forest around Hluboka (CB) at the end of the 1990s.
Timing: All year round.

Common Pheasant *Phasianus colchicus*

Pheasant, Ring-necked Pheasant Bazant obecny Bazant obycajny Fasan

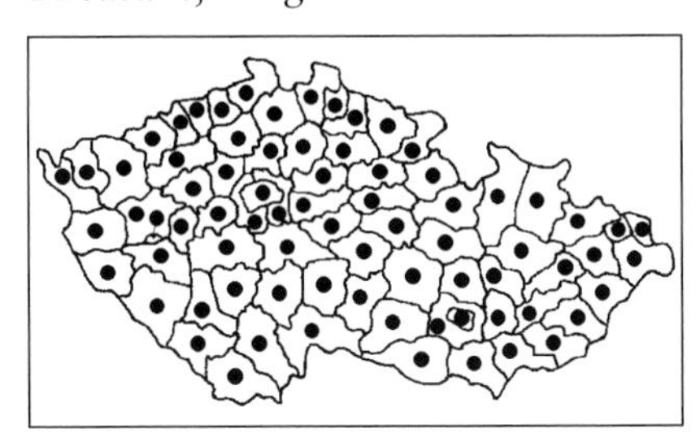

Common Pheasant was introduced to Bohemia probably more than 1,000 years ago and was already being bred in captivity in the 11th century (Hudec *et al.* 1977). Until the 20th century, Common Pheasant was predominantly kept in pheasantries, from where it has dispersed slowly into the wild. The population increased rapidly between 1950 and 1980. The highest numbers in the country were recorded at the beginning of the 1970s. At the beginning of the 1980s, the population suddenly decreased, probably as a result of changes in agricultural practice (Stastny *et al.* 1987). However, this is still the most common galliforme in the Czech Republic. It occurs mostly in lowlands and highlands, but up to 600 or 700 m in most mountain areas, and occasionally at higher altitudes (1200 m). It is found in farmland, where hedgerows, windbreaks, woodland, small stands of trees, and brush are scattered among cultivated fields and meadows. It is also found around rivers and in reedbeds surrounding ponds. It generally avoids farmland with no scrub or trees, and large complexes of dense forest. Thousands of Common Pheasants are released into the wild from pheasanteries annually. The majority of the population belongs to the *colchicus* race. However, other races have been realeased as well.
Status: Resident. **Breeding season:** common. **Winter:** common. **Migration:** common. Least concern. Hunted in fixed season.
Population trends: The population is estimated to be between 300,000 and 600,000 individuals. It has decreased by more than 50% in the past 25 years.
Distribution: Nationwide.
Timing: All year round. Breeding extends from the beginning of April, but more commonly from mid-April, until the beginning of June, rarely later.

GRUIFORMES

Includes 4 families with 26 species recorded in w. Palearctic. Twelve species of 3 families have been recorded in the Czech Republic. Six out of 8 species of the family **Rallidae** are regular or irregular breeders, and 2 species are accidentals. One regular breeder belongs to the family **Gruidae**. One species in the family **Otididae** is an irregular breeder, one a vagrant, and one an accidental.

Water Rail *Rallus aquaticus*

Chrastal vodni Chriastel vodny Wasserralle

Although this species occurs across the country, the majority of the breeding population is restricted to fishpond areas in s. Bohemia, e. Bohemia and s. Moravia. It is distributed mainly in the lowlands, but up to 610 m in the Ceskomoravska vysocina highlands (HB, JI, PE,

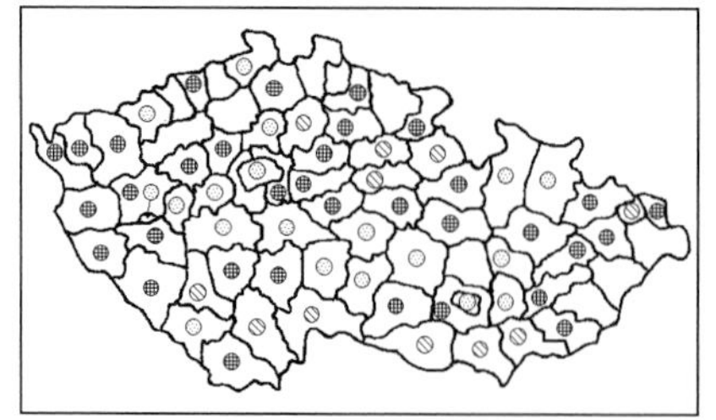

ZR), and to about 730 m in the Sumava mountains (CK, PT, KT). Breeding birds are associated with marshes, swamps and ponds, where surrounding vegetation is quite dense but there are patches of exposed mud; also ditches and occasionally oxbows of rivers overgrown by reedmace, sedges and reeds. Nests are usually placed in sedges. The number of nesting pairs may vary significantly from year to year, even at the same site. However, the general trend has been a steadily declining population over the past few decades. During the 1970s, the breeding density was 40–110 pairs per km^2 at ponds around Sedlcany (BN), 6 pairs per km^2 at Kobylske jezero (BV), 90 pairs per km^2 at Nesyt pond (BV), 220 pairs per km^2 at Velky Panensky pond (JH), and 130–150 pairs per km^2 at Opatovicky pond (JH). During the 1980s it was 10–60 pairs per km^2 at various ponds in s. Bohemia, 80 and 250 pairs per km^2 respectively at 2 ponds around Vodnany (ST). At the end of the 1980s, 18–25 nests per km^2 were found in reedbeds around Nesyt pond (BV). The overall density at about 150 ponds of varying size in s. Bohemia at the beginning of the 1980s was 1.4 individuals per km^2 and, in the mid-1980s, 0.5 individuals per km^2, and 1.1 individuals per km^2 in 1991. Horal (1996) used playback to investigate the number of breeding pairs in s. Moravia. Even though densities were not provided, his results revealed the following: 5 pairs were found at Novy pond near Mikulov (BV), 4 individuals at Breclav-Pastvisko (BV), 6 pairs at a pond near Miroslav (ZN), 6 pairs at Branisovicke ponds (ZN), 2 pairs at Jaroslavicky pond (ZN), and 2–3 individuals at ponds near Popuvky (BO). The majority of the population is migratory, but several dozen birds may overwinter. Wintering birds, as well as birds on migration, can be found around brooks and rivers. The most likely cause of Water Rail's disappearance is the destruction of breeding habitat.

Status: Resident. **Breeding season:** uncommon/local. **Winter:** uncommon. **Migration:** common. Endangered. Protected.

Population trends: The breeding population is estimated to be between 400 and 800 pairs, and over the past 25 years it has declined by 20–50%. About 20–50 individuals winter annually.

Distribution: Some of the counties with higher numbers of breeding pairs may include CL, MB, JC, PU, HK, PI, JH and BV.

Timing: Spring migration starts in mid-March, with the peak at the beginning of April, and continues through the beginning of May. Autumn migration extends from August until the end of October.

Spotted Crake *Porzana porzana*

Chrastal kropenaty Chriastel bodkovany Tüpfelsumpfhuhn

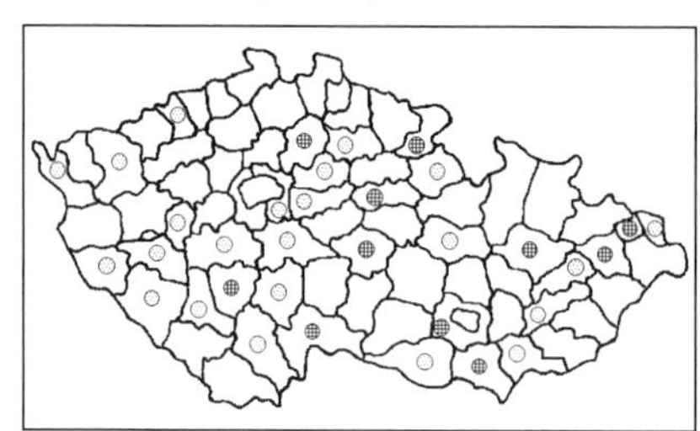

The breeding population of Spotted Crake is scattered across the country, with the majority of breeding pairs at ponds in s. Bohemia and n. Moravia. This species occurs mostly in lowlands, but as a breeder has been found at up to 750 m in the Kasperske hory mountains (KT). Favoured breeding habitats include shallow marshes and edges of ponds, but birds may also nest close to rivers and ditches, and at drier places farther from water. During migration it is often found at drained ponds, but always requires dense vegetation cover. Some of the places where regular breeding occurs include ponds around Trebon (JH), with up to 7 pairs, Rezabinec pond (PI), with up to 3 pairs, Zehunsky pond (NB), with up 3 pairs, ponds near Opatov (SY), with 1–2 pairs, Lednicke ponds (BV), with up to 2 pairs, Pohorelicke ponds (BV), with up to 3 pairs, and ponds between Jesenik nad Odrou (NJ) and Ostrava (OV), with 10–20 pairs. At the beginning of the 1980s, the overall density at about 150 ponds of varying size in s. Bohemia was 0.04 individuals per km^2, and 0.04 individuals per km^2 in the mid-1980s, with no records at

all in 1991. The population is threatened by habitat destruction.
Status: Migrant and summer visitor. **Breeding season:** uncommon. **Winter:** rare. **Migration:** local. Critically endangered. Protected.
Population trends: Between 20 and 40 pairs breed annually. The population has decreased by about 20–50% since 1973.
Distribution: Recent observations come from Smikov pond (BN), Kanov pond (JH), Velky Tisy pond (JH), Vysatov pond (CB), Vrbenske ponds (CB), Kaclezsky pond (JH), Rod pond (JH), Zehunsky pond (NB), Kardas pond (JH), Strpsky pond (ST), Letinsky pond (JH), Jordan pond near Vodnany (ST), Tichy pond (PA), Brezovec pond (CB), Zahlinicke ponds (KM), Kosarske meadows near Lanzhot (BV), and Lednice-Pastvisko (BV).
Timing: Spring migration starts at the end of March and the beginning of April, and continues through the beginning of May. Autumn migration occurs from July until the beginning of October. Breeding extends from the end of April to the beginning of July, with the peak during the first half of May. Occasionally, a few individuals may winter. It has been recorded in all months except January.

Little Crake *Porzana parva*

Chrastal maly Chriastel maly Kleines Sumpfhuhn

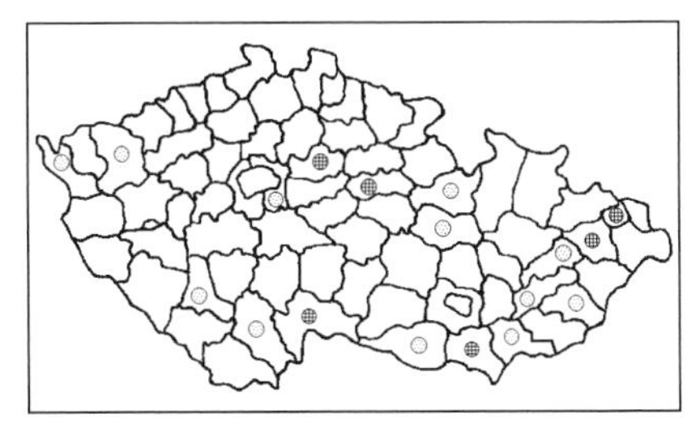

Little Crake is a regular but rare breeder in the Czech Republic. Although this species was reported breeding in the 19th century, breeding was never documented. The first documented report of a breeding is of several pairs at ponds near Sakvice (BV) in 1946. During the following 20 years, when the bird was expanding its range, breeding Little Crake was found at ponds around Pardubice (PU), Ceske Budejovice (CB), Trebon (JH), Velichov (KV), Zahlinice (KM), Hodonin (HO), and ponds in BV county. From the beginning of the 1970s, the population declined and many breeding areas became unoccupied. This trend continued until the end of the 1980s; but since the beginning of the 1990s the number of breeding records has been increasing. This species normally occurs in lowlands, but from 450–500 m in s. Bohemia, and has also been recorded at 730 m in the Sumava mountains (CK, PT, KT). It occupies shallow marshes, edges of larger fishponds with stretches of open water, and oxbows of rivers. The presence of dense littoral vegetation and a steady water level is necessary for this species. Probable breeding sites may include Velky Tisy pond (JH), with 1 pair, Zehunsky pond (NB), with 1–2 pairs, Lednicke ponds (BV), with 1–2 pairs, and ponds between Jesenik nad Odrou (NJ) and Ostrava (OV), with 2–5 pairs. The major threat to this species is habitat destruction.
Status: Migrant and summer visitor. **Breeding season:** uncommon. **Winter:** does not occur. **Migration:** uncommon. Critically endangered. Protected.
Population trends: The breeding population between 1970 and the early 1990s was up to 10 pairs, and during that period there was an overall decline of 20–50% compared to numbers before 1970. Between 15 and 30 pairs bred in 1994 and the population was increasing at that time.
Distribution: Recent observations are from Novy pond near Strpy (ST), Zbudovsky pond (CB), Brezovec pond near Nakri (CB), Zadni Zablatsky pond (CB), Strpsky pond (CB), Velky Tisy pond (JH), Zehunsky pond (NB), Matka pond (PU), Rutnik pond near Slatina (UO), Vidlak pond (SY), Novy pond (SY), Zahlinicke ponds (KM), Bartosovicke ponds (NJ), Tovacovske ponds (PR), Horni Belotin pond near Hranice nad Moravou (PR), Tecovice (ZL), Lednicke ponds (BV), Vrbovec pond (ZN), Kosarske meadows near Lanzhot (BV), Novy pond near Mikulov (BV), and Lednice-Pastvisko (BV).
Timing: Arrives from mid-March until mid-May, with the peak in April, and departs in August and October. Breeding occurs between the beginning of May and the end of June, with the majority of nests found in the second half of May.

Corn Crake *Crex crex*

Corncrake Chrastal polni Chrapkac polny Wachtelkönig

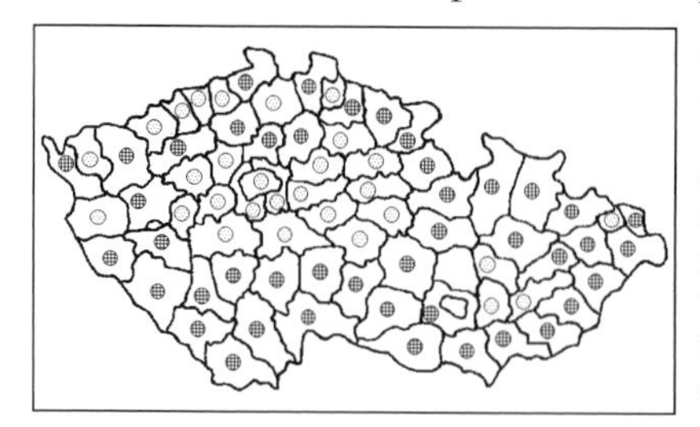

After several decades of decline, the breeding population of Corn Crake is increasing again in the Czech Republic. During the first half of the 20th century it was a common species in many counties, especially in lowlands with an abundance of flood meadows. The main cause of its sharp decline, particularly in lowlands, between 1950 and 1960 was thought to be the drainage of wet meadows and agricultural intensification. Although distributed from lowlands up to the mountains, it is now usually found above 400 m. It occurs up to 620 m in the Bile Karpaty mountains (UH, HO, ZL), from 750–800 m in the Vsetinske vrchy hills (VS), the Ceskomoravska vysocina highlands (HB, JI, PE, ZR), and the Novohradske hory (CK, CB) and Beskydy (FM, VS) mountains, up to 1000 m and occasionally higher in the Krkonose mountains (SE, TU), and up to 1200 m in the Sumava mountains (CK, PT, KT). These mountains and highlands, except the Ceskomoravska vysocina highlands, are also strongholds of the breeding population. Breeding birds are associated with meadows, and man-made habitats such as alfalfa fields and cornfields along brooks and rivers, and moorland fringes. The nest is built on the ground in patches of grass or herbs. At the end of the 1960s and beginning of the 1970s the breeding density was 0.5 individuals per km^2 in the Vsetinske vrchy (VS) hills, 0.2 individuals per km^2 in the foothills of the Novohradske hory mountains (CK, CB), and 2.7 individuals per km^2 at meadows around Trebon (JH). At the end of the 1980s, it was 1.5–2 calling males per km^2 in meadows and pastures in OL county. It was 2–5 calling males per km^2 in the Bile Karpaty mountains at about 570 m in May and June 1998. The following numbers of calling males were recorded in some areas in 1995: Beskydy mountains (97 males), Jeseniky mountains (BR, SU) (93 males), the Novohradske hory mountains (37 males), the Sumava mountains (97 males), and the Orlicke hory mountains (RK) (30 males). In 1997, 114 calling males were recorded around Laskroun (UO), and 70 males around Luhacovice (ZL). Pykal *et al.* (1998) stated that this species is recolonizing areas where it occurred before the decline began in the 1950s.

Status: Migrant and summer visitor. **Breeding season:** uncommon/local. **Winter:** does not occur. **Migration:** uncommon. Vulnerable. Protected.

Population trends: From 1970 until the early 1990s, the breeding population was 200–400 pairs. Between 1960 and 1990, the population decreased by about 50% compared to numbers before 1960. It has increased since 1990: 483 calling males were recorded in 1995, 681 males in 1996, and 1,118 males in 1997 (Pykal *et al.* 1998).

Distribution: Nationwide. Counties with higher densities include CK, PT, HB, NJ, VS, ZL, RK, SU and UO.

Timing: It arrives from mid-April but mostly during the first half of May, and departs from the beginning of September until mid-October. Breeding starts in mid-May and continues until mid-July, with the majority of nests found at the end of May and the beginning of June.

Moorhen *Gallinula chloropus*

Common Moorhen Slipka zelenonoha Sliepocka vodna Teichhuhn

Moorhen occurs nationwide from lowlands up to about 600 m in the Ceskomoravska vysocina highlands (HB, JI, PE, ZR), the Krkonose mountains (SE, TU), and up to 730 m in the Sumava mountains (CK, PT, KT); as a breeder, it is rarely found above this altitude. This species is found in a wide variety of aquatic habitats, although it prefers ponds with littoral vegetation and surrounding marshes. However, as a breeding species, it is generally found at any lake, gravel pit, lagoon or dam with shallow water and peripheral vegetation. It is often found in vegetation around ditches, oxbows, canals, though rarely around slow-flowing rivers. Nests are built either on islets or, more commonly, in emergent vegetation and reedbeds. At the beginning of the 1970s the breeding density was 20–50 pairs per km^2 in

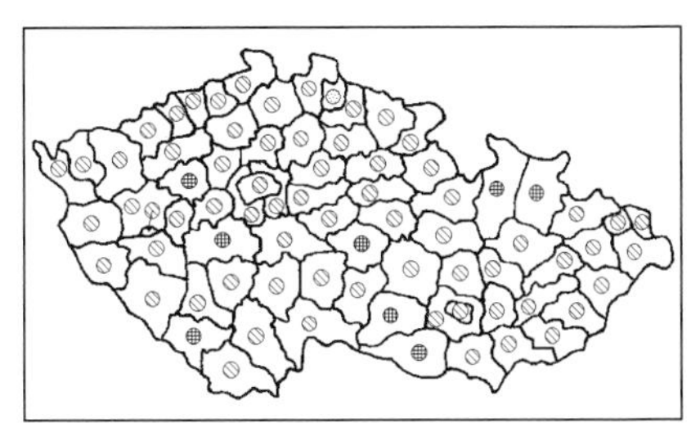

reedbeds around Lednicke ponds (BV); in the mid-1970s, 80 pairs per km^2 at ponds around Sedlcany (BN); and at the end of the 1970s, 1 pair per km^2 at Anenske ponds (CH), 70 pairs per km^2 in reedbeds around Dvoriste pond (JH), and 440 pairs per km^2 at Velky Panensky pond (JH). At the beginning of the 1980s, it was 40 pairs per km^2 around ditches and canals in HO county at about 180 m, and 35–47 pairs per km^2 around ditches and canals in UH county at the same elevation. At the beginning of the 1980s, the overall density at about 150 ponds of varying size in s. Bohemia was 2 individuals per km^2, dropping to 1.3 individuals per km^2 in the mid-1980s, and to 0.9 individuals per km^2 in 1991. At Dremliny pond (ST) it was 130 pairs per km^2 at the beginning of 1990s. In late summer, and during autumn migration, flocks of dozens and, less commonly, several hundred birds can be seen. The majority of the population is migratory but hundreds of individuals can be found in winter. These birds usually stay at large sluggish rivers; for example a regular wintering site is the Vltava river in Praha (AA). The reasons for its decline during the past 20–25 years are unknown.
Status: Resident. **Breeding season:** local/common. **Winter:** local. **Migration:** common. Near-threatened. Protected.
Population trends: The breeding population is estimated to be between 5,000 and 10,000 pairs, a decline of 20–50% since the 1970s. Up to 1,500 individuals winter regularly.
Distribution: It breeds nationwide, although it is rather scarce in PT, KT, UL, LT, LB, SE, TU, SU, BR, ZL, VS, FM and BK counties. The wintering range is concentrated in central Bohemia, s. Moravia, KM, PR and OL counties in central Moravia, and open water between Jesenik nad Odrou (NJ) and Ostrava (OV).
Timing: Birds arrive from mid-March until mid-April. Autumn migration extends from mid-August until the end of October. Breeding occurs from mid-April until the end of June, with the peak in May.

Common Coot *Fulica atra*

Coot, Eurasian Coot   Lyska cerna   Lyska cierna   Bläßhuhn

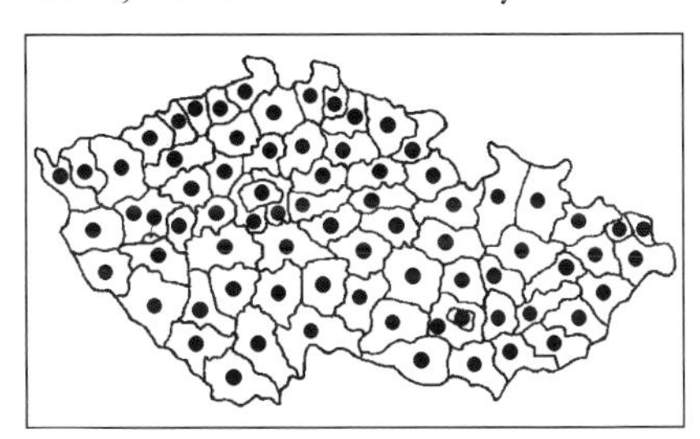

This is the most common species of gruiforme in the Czech Republic, found predominantly in lowlands. Breeding regularly occurs up to about 600 m in the Ceskomoravska vysocina highlands (HB, JI, PE, ZR), and Krkonose mountains (SE, TU), and up to 730 m in the Sumava mountains (CK, PT, KT). Breeding habitats include relatively shallow ponds of varying size, marshes and lagoons. It also breeds around oxbows, canals and ditches. Nests are usually built in growths of reedmace and reedbeds, but also on floating vegetation in open water. It occasionally nests at places with very little vegetation. At the beginning of the 1970s, the breeding density was 70 pairs per km^2 in reedbeds around Nesyt ponds (BV) and 1,070 pairs per km^2 at Lednicke ponds (BV), excluding Nesyt pond, 380 pairs per km^2 at ponds around Sedlcany (BN) in the mid-1970s, and 230 pairs per km^2 at Opatovicky pond (JH), 450 pairs per km^2 in reedbeds around Dvoriste pond (JH), and 51 pairs per km^2 at Anenske ponds (CH) at the end of the 1970s; at the beginning of the 1980s, it was 105–128 pairs per km^2 around ditches and canals in HO county at 180 m. At the beginning of the 1980s the overall density at about 150 ponds of varying size in s. Bohemia was 67 individuals per km^2, dropping to 33 individuals per km^2 in the mid-1980s. Breeding population trends were studied by Tichy (1993) at Lenesicky pond (LN). His findings concur with the general pattern for the Czech breeding population: declining numbers from 1981 to 1985, a levelling of numbers in 1986 and 1987, followed by a sharp increase in 1988. Since 1989 the population has declined again. After the breeding season, flocks of hundreds, and occasionally thousands, of Common Coots, often mixed with other waterfowl, are

found at large areas of open water such as dams, gravel pits and ponds. The breeding population is partially migratory. During migration, and particularly in winter, birds stay at the larger rivers such as the Vltava (CB, AA, ME), Labe (HK, PU, NB, ME, LT, DE), Ohre (LN), Morava (OL, KM, UH, HO), Dyje (BV) and Odra (KI, OV, NJ).
Status: Resident. **Breeding season:** common. **Winter:** common. **Migration:** common. Least concern. Hunted in fixed season.
Population trends: The breeding population is between 30,000 and 60,000 pairs, a decrease of 20–50% from the mid-1970s. Between 18,000 and 36,000 individuals regularly winter.
Distribution: Nationwide. Rather scarce breeder in SU, VS, FM, BR and ZL counties.
Timing: Spring migration extends from the end of February until mid-April, with the peak in the second half of March. Autumn migration occurs from the end of August and beginning of September until the beginning of November.

Common Crane *Grus grus*

Crane Jerab popelavy Zeriav popolavy Kranich

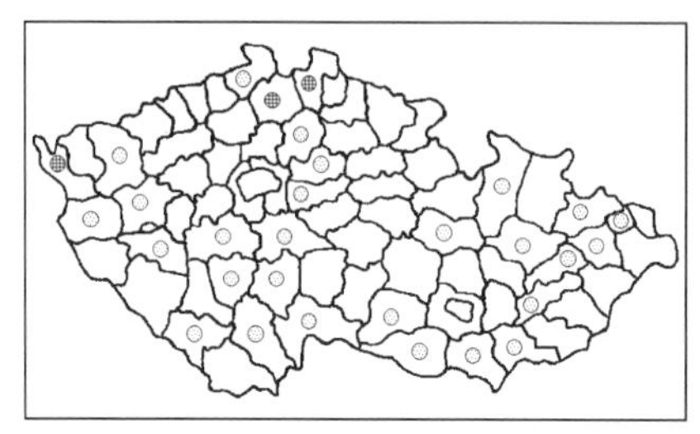

Breeding Common Cranes were not recorded in the 20th century in the Czech Republic until 1989 when 2 nests were found at 2 sites in CL county. The following year, 3 pairs bred in the same county (Kurka 1991). In 1992, breeding was also documented in CH county. Since then, Common Crane has been nesting annually. Breeding in the Czech Republic is linked most probably to the increasing numbers of Common Cranes in Germany and Poland. Breeding habitats include extensive marshes and large ponds with reedbeds. On passage, it may be scattered nationwide as indicated by recent records. Birds are usually associated with meadows, farmland, and drained fishponds.
Status: Migrant and summer visitor. **Breeding season:** rare/uncommon. **Winter:** rare/uncommon. **Migration:** uncommon. Critically endangered. Protected.
Population trends: Irregular breeding of 1–5 pairs probably occurred between 1981 and 1988. From 1990 until 1994, 3–10 pairs bred. Recently the breeding population is between 4 and 6 pairs.
Distribution: Breeding distribution is restricted to CL county, although it probably breeds in a few other counties as well. Recent observations of solitary birds or small flocks of up to 25 birds come from Rezabinec pond (PI) in February, Velky Tousny (JH) pond in May, Kanov pond (JH) in May, Olesnice (CB), Velky Tisy pond (JH) in October, Milhostov near Frantiskovy Lazne (CH) in April and May, Horni Podluzi (DC) in March, Doksy (CL) in April, Novozamecky pond (CL) in May, Dubice (CL) in March, Novorecke mocaly marsh (JH) in April, Postrelna (CL) in May, Proudnicky pond (KO) in May, Novy pond (SY) in March, Hermanicky pond (CL) in May and June, Bystrice pod Hostynem (KM) in October, Strizovice (KM) in May, Tovacov (PR) in November, Chropyne (KM) in April, Kojetin (PR) in September, Sumvald (OL) in September, Hulin gravel pit (KM) in April, Bohuslavice (SU) in April, Sedlec u Mikulova (BV) in April, ponds around Namest nad Oslavou (TR) in October, Nova Ves u Pohorelic (BV) in November, Dubnansky pond (HO) in April, Zelnavske tune (PT) in November, and Nove Mlyny (BV) in September. A flock of 350 birds was recorded at Musik pond near Sedlcany (BN) in April 1998.
Timing: It arrives at the breeding grounds during March, and is on spring passage until May. Birds on autumn passage occur mostly from September until October, but are also recorded in November.

Little Bustard *Tetrax tetrax*

Drop maly Drop maly Zwergtrappe

This species was occasionally recorded during spring and autumn migration until the 1920s, from which point it became a rare visitor to the Czech Republic. A report of breeding from s.

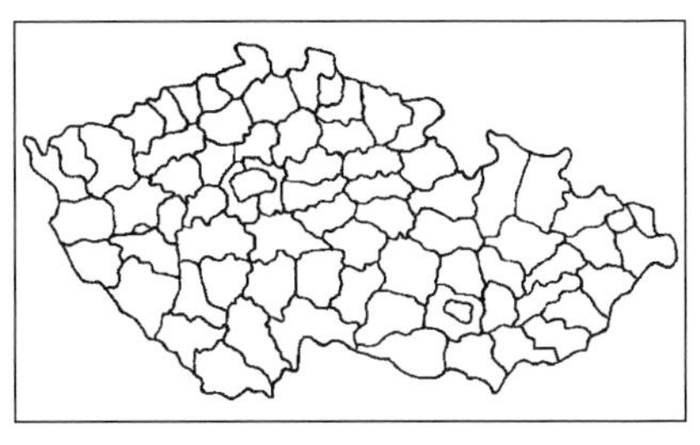

Moravia at the end of the 19th century is unreliable. Little Bustard has been recorded more often in the east of the county (22 times) than the west (18 times) since 1800. Up to 6 birds have been seen together. There are no records since 1985.
Status: Vagrant. **Breeding season**: rare. **Winter**: rare. **Migration**: rare. Protected.
Population trends: No data available.
Distribution: Individual birds may be scattered nationwide.
Timing: Recorded from March until the end of April, and from July until December.

Great Bustard *Otis tarda*

Drop velky Drop velky Großtrappe

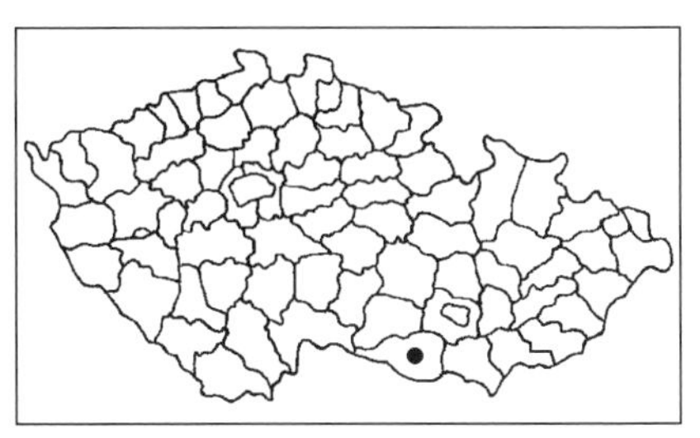

This species was recorded breeding for the first time in the Czech Republic at the beginning of the 20th century, and has generally been restricted to a few areas at about 120–220 m in ZN and BV counties. Occasional breeding has also been recorded outside these areas. The breeding population has probably never exceeded 100 individuals. Over the past 20 years, the population has declined steadily. It is likely that Great Bustard has been extirpated as a breeding species from the Czech Republic. It is found in open areas in farmland with meadows, pastures, clover, alfalfa and cereal fields. Pesticides, unsympathetic planting and harvesting, land management, agricultural intensification through irrigation schemes, and nest destruction due to agricultural management, are the main causes of the decline in Great Bustard numbers. In 1985 there were 24 individuals, in 1987 20–25 individuals; and from 1991–1993 only 6 individuals
Status: Resident. **Breeding season**: uncommon. **Winter**: uncommon. **Migration**: uncommon. Critically endangered. Protected/not hunted all year round.
Population trends: The population was about 28 individuals in 1964, 35 between 1973 and 1977, 37 in 1982, and 26 the following year. In 1994 it was down to only 2–5 individuals.
Distribution: The recent range is restricted to the area between Hodonice-Prace-Lechovice-Dyjakovice-Bozice and Hradek villages, east from Znojmo (ZN). In 1920, breeding occurred

Great Bustard

near Veseli nad Moravou (HO). Birds during the breeding season were observed near Hustenovice (UH) and Opava (OP) in the 1920s. There are about 25 non-breeding records from various sites in Bohemia, and the same number from other areas of Moravia from the 20th century. A recent record of a displaying male is from Borotice (ZN).
Timing: All year round. Males start to display at the end of March, and continue until the end of June. Breeding occurs between the end of April and the end of July.

CHARADRIIFORMES

In the w. Palearctic includes 13 families with 158 species. In the Czech Republic, 84 species from 10 families have been recorded. The family **Haemotopodidae** includes one vagrant. Family **Recurvirostridae** includes two summer visitors which breed irregularly. One irregular breeder belongs to the family **Burhinidae.** Three species from the family **Glareolidae** occur in the Czech Republic as accidentals. Family **Charadriidae** includes 3 regular or irregular breeders, 4 regular migrants or vagrants, and 3 accidentals. Thirty-four species belong to the family **Scolopacidae:** 7 are regular breeders, 19 are regular migrants or vagrants, and 8 are accidentals. Family **Stercorariidae** includes 4 vagrants to the Czech Republic. Four species in the family **Laridae** are regular or irregular breeders, 5 are migrants or vagrants, and 7 have been recorded as accidentals. Nine species belong to the family **Sternidae:** 3 are regular or irregular breeders, 5 are migrants or vagrants, and 1 is an accidental. Four species of the family **Alcidae** have occurred as accidentals.

Oystercatcher *Haematopus ostralegus*

Eurasian Oystercatcher Ustricnik velky Lasturniciar strakaty Austernfischer

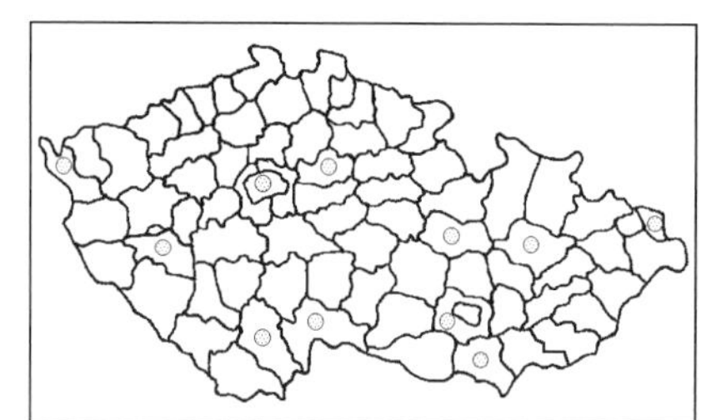

There are over 50 records of Oystercatchers from the Czech Republic since the beginning of the 19th century. Most of the records were individual birds, rarely 2 or more together. An exceptional occurrence was a flock of 10 birds recorded at Nove Mlyny (BV) in August 1994. This species may occur at any type of open water, including rivers. However, Oystercatchers prefer muddy edges of ponds or dams. Birds occurring in the Czech Republic belong to the nominate *ostralegus* race. One specimen from sw. Moravia was identified as race *longipes*.
Status: Vagrant. **Breeding season:** rare (both races). **Winter:** uncommon (*ostralegus*), rare (*longipes*). **Migration:** uncommon (*ostralegus*), rare (*longipes*). Protected.
Population trends: No data available.
Distribution: Scattered nationwide. Recent observations are from the Vltava river (AA), Volesek pond (CB), Zehunsky pond (NB), Brilicky pond (JH), Velky Kosir pond (SY), Terlicka dam (KI), Chomoutov gravel pit (OL), Tesany (BO), and Nove Mlyny (BV).
Timing: Records come from all months, except November and December. Most of the records are from March, April, September and October.

Black-winged Stilt *Himantopus himantopus*

Pisila caponoha Sisila bocianovita Stelzenläufer

Black-winged Stilt was reported as a breeding species in s. and e. Bohemia during the 19th century, but reliable evidence was missing. The first documented breeding occurred in 1958, when 3 nests were found near Zlutice (SO), Svitavy (SY) and at Lednicke ponds (BV). Seven years later, nesting was reported from Horni Pocaply (ME). The next, most recent record is from Mydlovary (CB) in 1997. A few cases of probable breeding have been reported from several sites around the country since then. This species is usually not recorded annually in the Czech Republic. It usually occurs at partly or completely drained ponds or shallow man-made areas of open water.

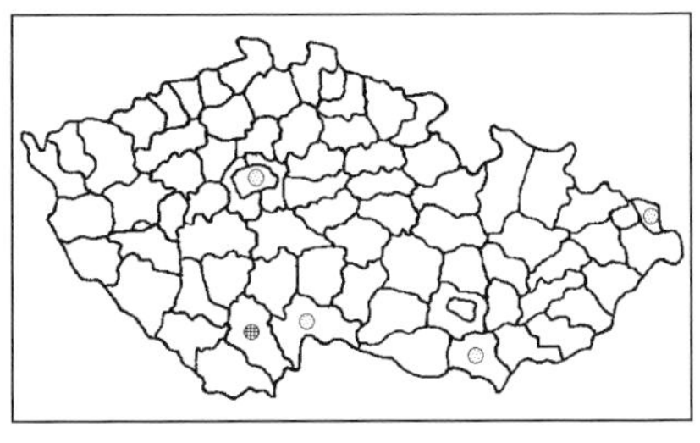

Status: Vagrant. **Breeding season:** rare. **Winter:** does not occur. **Migration:** uncommon. Conservation-dependent. Protected.
Population trends: No data available.
Distribution: May occur nationwide. Recent records of non-breeding birds are from Novy pond in Praha-Milicov (AA), Maly Machovec pond (CB), Farsky and Ostojkovicky ponds (JH), and several from Brezovec pond (CB).
Timing: From March until September, with the majority of observations in May and August.

Avocet *Recurvirostra avosetta*

Pied Avocet Tenkozobec opacny Sabliarka modronoha Säbelschnäbler

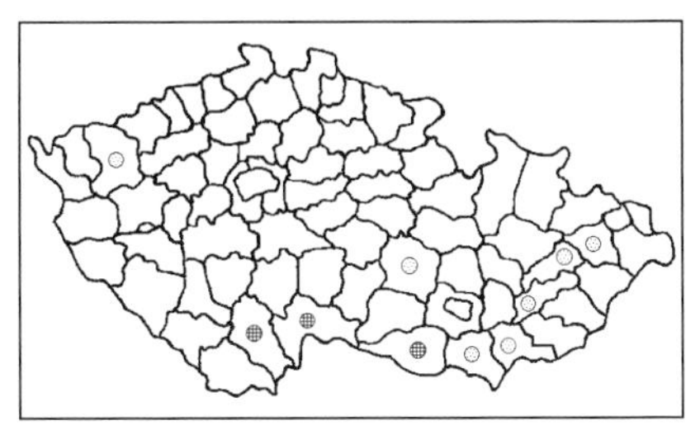

This species was considered to be a rare visitor and breeder in the Czech Republic until 1990. Since 1990, the number of breeding attempts has been increasing. It was first recorded in the Czech Republic at Bezdrev pond (CB) in 1943, and in the following years of 1946 and 1947 at Dehtar pond (CB). Nine pairs nested at Lednicke ponds (BV) in 1948, with a regular 1–6 pairs until 1958. In s. Moravia (including Lednicke ponds (BV)) 1–9 pairs nested until 1961. Since 1990, breeding pairs have been reported from s. Bohemia: 6 pairs from ponds around Ceske Budejovice (CB), and 4 pairs from Hlasenec pond (CB) in 1991, 2 pairs from Koclirov pond (JH) in 1993, and 1 pair from Vlhavsky pond (CB) in 1995. Two nests were found at Olesnik pond (CB), and 1 nest at Maly Strachovicky pond (CB) in 1998. The annual number of breeding pairs in s. Bohemia may range from 5 to 7. In s. Moravia, successful breeding of 1 pair was observed at Jaroslavicky pond (ZN) in 1995. Nests are built at the muddy edges of semi-drained or drained ponds with a cover of low vegetation. Non-breeding birds are seen in the same habitats.
Status: Summer visitor. **Breeding season:** uncommon. **Winter:** does not occur. **Migration:** uncommon. Conservation-dependent. Protected.
Population trends: Between 1943 and 1961 there was irregular breeding of up to 10 pairs. Since 1990, up to 8 pairs have bred.
Distribution: Breeding and non-breeding birds occur mostly in fishpond areas of s. Bohemia and s. Moravia; non-breeding birds occasionally elsewhere. Recent frequent records of 2–10 individuals come from Vysatov pond (CB), Volesek pond (CB), Brezovec pond (CB), Bezdrev pond (CB), Blatec pond (CB), Zbudovsky pond (CB), Dasensky pond (CB), Dehtar pond (CB), Nuzov pond (CB), Mydlovarsky pond (CB), and Nove Mlyny (BV). Other records are from Zahlinicke ponds (KM), Tovacovske ponds (PR), Lednicke ponds (BV), Jaroslavicky pond (ZN), and ponds near Studenka (NJ).
Timing: It occurs from the end of March, but more often from the first 10 days of April until the end of October. Breeding pairs are found between the end of April and the end of May.

Stone-curlew *Burhinus oedicnemus*

Stone Curlew Dytik uhorni Leziak obycajny Triel

This species was a regular breeder, with dozens of nesting pairs, particularly in central Bohemia and s. Moravia, during the first half of the 20th century. Stone-curlews have been declining steadily since the early 1960s, and breeding is only sporadic these days. Between the mid-1970s and the end of the 1980s, this species was extirpated from all the traditional nesting areas, except for a small area around Znojmo (ZN). Reports of breeding and non-breeding birds became scarce after 1990. Found in open country with poor soil, pastures, sand dunes covered with sparse vegetation, and also vineyards and clearings in scattered stands of

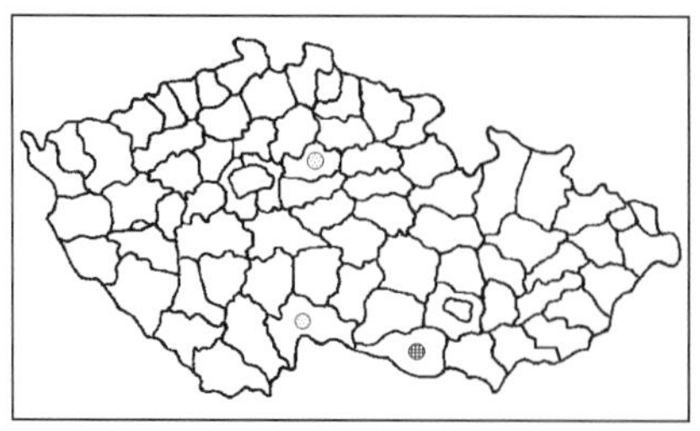

pines in farmland. The latest nesting records are from near Konice (ZN) in 1988 and Bozice (ZN) in 1991. The decline of the Stone-curlew population in the Czech Republic is most likely linked to habitat loss and agricultural intensification.
Status: Migrant and summer visitor. **Breeding season**: rare. **Winter**: does not occur. **Migration**: uncommon. Critically endangered. Protected.
Population trends: Between 1973 and 1977 the breeding population was estimated to be between 10 and 20 pairs. Between 1985 and 1989 it was 1–5 pairs, and the population is probably still in this region today.
Distribution: Traditional breeding sites included NB, MB, ME and LT counties in Bohemia, and BO, BV, HO and ZN counties in Moravia. Recent observation of non-breeders are from Branna (JH) and Mlada (NB).
Timing: Spring migration occurs from late March until May. Autumn migration occurs from the end of August until the beginning of November, with the peak in October. Breeding extends from late April to the end of June, with the peak during early May.

Little Ringed Plover *Charadrius dubius*

Little Plover   Kulik ricni   Kulik riecny   Flußregenpfeifer

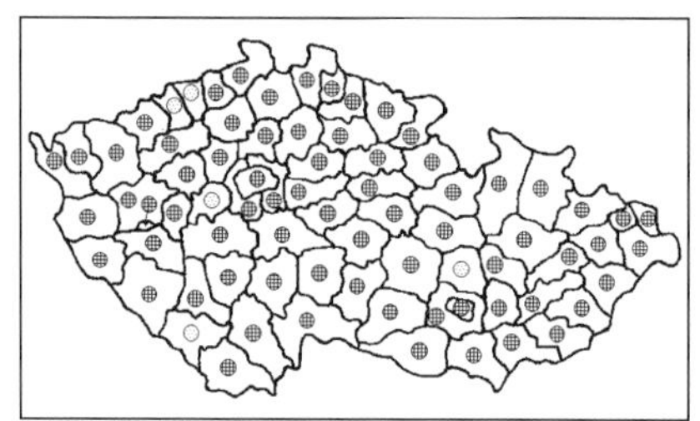

This is the most common plover in the Czech Republic, distributed widely across the country. It is recorded from lowlands, which it prefers, up to about 650 m in the Ceskomoravska vysocina highlands (HB, JI, PE, ZR), to 730 m in the Sumava mountains (CK, PT, KT), and occasionally at higher altitudes such as 850 m in the Jizerske hory mountains (JN, LB). Breeding habitats include banks of rivers, ponds, gravel pits, reservoirs and lakes with sand or gravel for nesting. It is occasionally found farther from water in drier habitats with short vegetation. Breeding density may fluctuate from year to year at the same sites. At the beginning of the 1980s at 120 ponds around Trebon (JH) it was 52 individuals per km^2, and 5 individuals per km^2 in the mid-1980s. The average density at about 150 ponds in s. Bohemia at the beginning of the 1980s was 1.9 individuals per km^2, 0.7 individuals per km^2 in the mid-1980s, and 2.5 individuals per km^2 in 1991. In suitable habitats, breeding density might be quite high when several pairs may nest close to each other; it was 100 pairs per km^2 at Ponedrazkovsky pond (JH) in 1979. Between the mid-1970s and the end of the 1980s, Little Ringed Plover expanded its range into new areas across the country. During migration it occurs around rivers, at semi-drained or drained fishponds, and at temporary pools in farmland. On passage it may be found in flocks of up to 25 individuals, occasionally more.
Status: Migrant and summer visitor. **Breeding season**: uncommon/local. **Winter**: rare. **Migration**: local. Least concern. Protected.
Population trends: Between 1985 and 1989 the population was 700–1,400 pairs, and these numbers are probably the same today. The population has been more or less stable over the past 20 years.
Distribution: Nationwide. Locally common. The number of breeding pairs may be rather scarce in CK, TC, CH, LB, PB, SE, TU, VY, SU, BR, OP and PE counties.
Timing: It arrives from mid-March with the peaks at the end of March and the beginning of April, and migration continues until the end of April. It departs from the beginning of August to mid-October, occasionally at the end of October. Breeding occurs between mid-April and the end of June, with the peak during early May.

Great Ringed Plover *Charadrius hiaticula*

Ringed Plover, Kulik pisecny Kulik piesocny Sandregenpfeifer

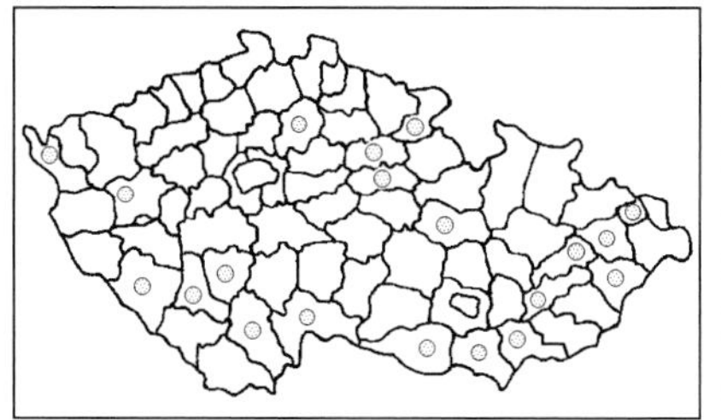

Great Ringed Plover is a regular migrant and is recorded annually in the Czech Republic. There is only 1 breeding record from the country: a pair nested at a pond near Blatna (ST) in 1952. Possible and probable breeding has been reported from various sites across the country since then, but nesting has never been confirmed. As a migrant, this species usually occurs in lowlands at semi-drained or drained fishponds, banks of gravel pits and, rarely, around larger rivers. It is usually found in small flocks of up to 15–20 birds, rarely up to 100, and only occasionally are solitary birds recorded. The majority of birds belong to the *hiaticula* race, although 2 individuals of the *tundrae* race were collected in the 1950s.
Status: Migrant. **Breeding season**: rare (both races). **Winter**: rare (both races). **Migration**: uncommon (*hiaticula*), rare (*tundrae*). Protected.
Population trends: No data available.
Distribution: Scattered nationwide. Recent observations of usually small flocks on migration come from Dehtar pond (CB), Stary Haklovsky pond (CB), Opatovicky pond (JH), Koclirov pond (JH), Kaclezsky pond (JH), Rezabinec pond (PI), Rojicky pond (ST), Budske ponds (MB), Velky Kosir pond (SY), Hvezda pond (SY), Riha pond (HK), Rozkos dam (NA), Tovacovske ponds (PR), Zahlinicke ponds (KM), Hermansky pond (OV), Chorynsky pond (VS), Bzenec-Privoz (HO), Lednicke ponds (BV), and Nove Mlyny (BV).
Timing: On spring passage it is found from mid-March until the end of May. Autumn passage is from August to the end of October, rarely the beginning of November, and peaking in September.

Kentish Plover *Charadrius alexandrinus*

Kulik morsky Kulik morsky Seeregenpfeifer

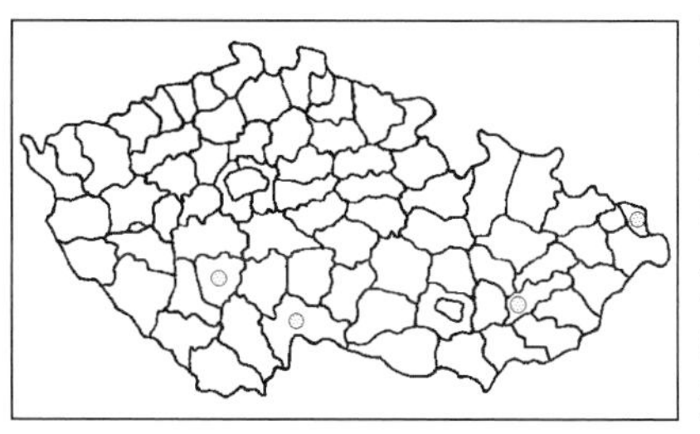

Kentish Plover is a rare visitor to the Czech Republic, and is not observed annually. The closest breeding sites are in e. Austria (Neusiedler See). Birds recorded in the Czech Republic have been found at fishponds in TR, ST, OV, KM, KI, BV, NJ, JH and PI counties but may occur elsewhere across the country.
Status: Vagrant. **Breeding season**: rare. **Winter**: does not occur. **Migration**: uncommon. Protected.
Population trends: No data available.
Distribution: Recent observations of 1–5 individuals are from Talinsky pond (PI), Koclirov pond (JH), Zahlinicke ponds (KM), and ponds around Karvina (KI).
Timing: Recorded in March, April, July, August and September.

Dotterel *Charadrius morinellus*

Eurasian Dotterel Kulik hnedy Kulik vrchovsky Mornell-Regenpfeifer

Dotterel was a regular breeding species in the Krkonose mountains (SE, TU) until the beginning of the 20th century, the last breeding record being from 1903. Since then, there have been 2 successful breeding attempts: in the Krkonose mountains in 1946, and in the Jeseniky mountains (BR, SU) in 1985. There are a few records of non-breeding birds from 1977–1990, and 1993. On migration, this species occurs in small flocks of up to 10 individuals on dry and stony alpine meadows, as well as in cultivated fields in farmland.
Status: Migrant. **Breeding season**: rare. **Winter**: does not occur. **Migration**: uncommon.

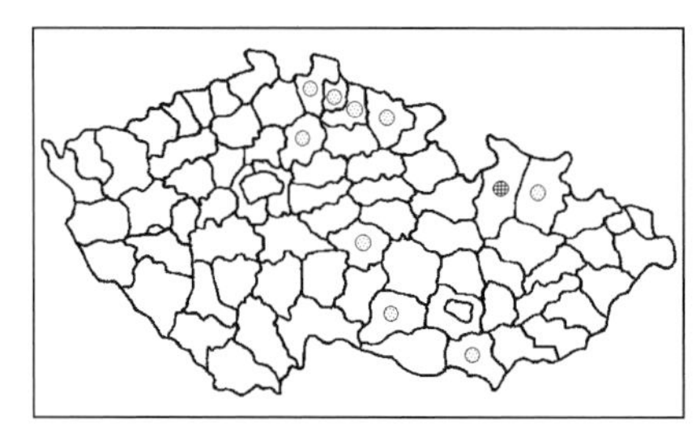

Critically endangered. Protected.
Population trends: There was a sharp decline at the end of the 19th century leading almost to extirpation from the Czech Republic.
Distribution: As a migrant it is mostly restricted to the Krkonose mountains (SE, TU), the Jizerske hory mountains (LB, JN), and the Jeseniky mountains (BR, SU) but has also been recorded in lowlands and highlands in MB, BV, TR and HB counties. The most recent regular records of migrating birds came from the Krkonose mountains.
Timing: The majority of records of birds on passage are from May, August and September, with a few from October and November.

European Golden Plover *Pluvialis apricaria*

Golden Plover, Eurasian Golden Plover Kulik zlaty Kulik zlaty Goldenregenpfeifer

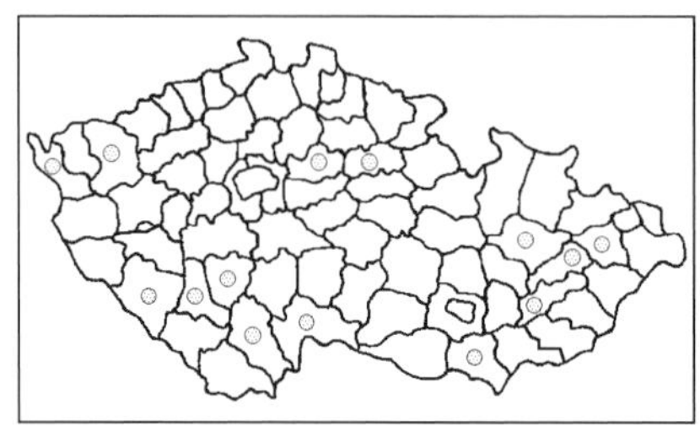

European Golden Plover occurs regularly on spring and autumn passage in flocks of up to 150 birds, although smaller flocks of up to 30 individuals are more common. It is most frequently reported from fishpond areas in CB, PI and JH counties in s. Bohemia, and PR and KM counties in central Moravia, particularly from Tovacovske ponds (PR). It may occur in other lowland areas as well. This species is usually found at drained fishponds, and in surrounding meadows, but also on agricultural land, often in flocks with other species such as Northern Lapwing. Exceptional observations come from farmland near Unicov (OL), from 30 March–1 April 1998. A flock of 277 individuals and a flock of another 150 individuals were observed the first day; a flock of 354 individuals with 150 Northern Lapwings the following day; and 640 individuals the last day (Suchy 1998). Flocks of 10–54 individuals were seen near Dolni Ujezd (SY) in mid-March 1998.
Status: Migrant. **Breeding season**: rare. **Winter**: rare. **Migration**: uncommon. Protected.
Population trends: No data available.
Distribution: Recent, and usually frequent, records of small flocks of birds on passage come from Zehunsky pond (NB), Katovice (ST), meadows around Klokocin (PI), meadows around Skaly (PI), Miletice near Protivin (PI), Rozmberk pond (JH), Dehtar pond (CB), meadows around Jindrichuv Hradec (JH), Vysatov pond (CB), Dynin (CB), Chrastany (KM), Zahlinicke ponds (KM), Henclov (PR), Lysky (PR), Bartosovicke ponds (NJ), and Tovacovske ponds (PR).
Timing: Spring passage is from mid-March until the end of May, rarely later. Autumn passage is from September until the end of November. There are records from all months except February.

Grey Plover *Pluvialis squatarola*

Kulik bledy Kulik bledy Kiebitzregenpfeifer

Grey Plover is more common on autumn than spring passage in the Czech Republic. Usually individual birds or small flocks of up to 15 birds can be found in the same habitat as European Golden Plover. This species usually occurs in the major fishpond areas in CB, JH, ST and PI counties in s. Bohemia, PU county in e. Bohemia, BV and KM counties in s. Moravia, and PR and OV counties in n. Moravia, but occasionally may be recorded elsewhere across the country.
Status: Migrant. **Breeding season**: rare. **Winter**: does not occur. **Migration**: local. Protected.
Population trends: No data available.
Distribution: Recent records of individual birds and flocks of up to 14 come from Riha pond

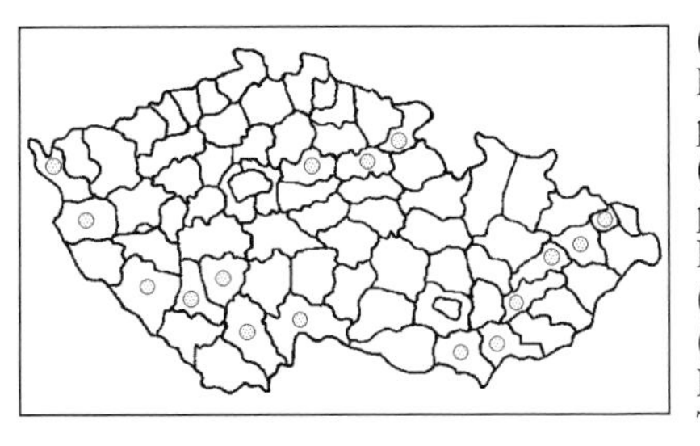

(HK), Zehunsky pond (NB), Rezabinec pond (PI), Dehtar pond (CB), Bezdrev pond (CB), Volesek pond (CB), Zbudovsky pond (CB), Blatec pond (CB), Horni pond near Novosedly (CB), Rojicky pond (ST), Radov pond (ST), Podkostelni pond near Putim (PI), Velky Tisy pond (JH), Koclirov pond (JH), Tovacovske ponds (PR), Zahlinicke ponds (KM), Luzicke ponds (HO), Lednicke ponds (BV), Pohorelicke ponds (BV), and Nove Mlyny (BV).
Timing: Spring migration is in April and May; autumn migration from September until November.

Northern Lapwing *Vanellus vanellus*

Lapwing Cejka chocholata Cibik chochlaty Kiebitz

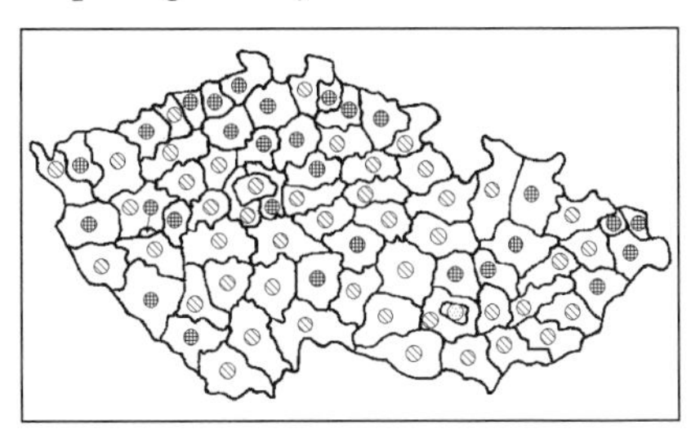

Northern Lapwing is a typical bird of open habitats in lowlands, and is usually less common in the highlands of the Czech Republic. Occasional breeding has been recorded up to 750 m in the Orlicke hory mountains (RK), up to 800 m in the Krkonose mountains (SE, TU), to 840 m in the Krusne hory mountains (CV, KV, MO, TP), and to about 1000 m in the Sumava mountains (CK, KT, PT). As a breeder, this species prefers wet meadows, marshes, edges of ponds with sparse vegetation, and pastures. Probably owing to the drainage of meadows and other habitat loss, it will also nest in cultivated fields farther from water. Breeding density varies from place to place, depending on the suitability of the breeding habitats. During the 1970s, breeding density was 1 pair per km^2 in the foothills of the Krkonose mountains (SE, TU), 3–10 individuals per km^2 at wet meadows around Trebon, and 40 pairs per km^2 in a field near Branna (JH). It was 5–8 pairs per km^2 in meadows around Veseli nad Moravou (HO) at about 180 m at the end of the 1970s and beginning of the 1980s; 2–13 pairs per km^2 in farmland (CB), and 4–16 pairs per km^2 in farmland around Pisek (PI) during the 1980s; at the beginning of 1990s, it was 4 pairs per km^2 around Ceske Budejovice (CB) and Trebon (JH). The average density recorded during the first half of 1990s in open country in w., s. and central Bohemia was 1.1 pairs per km^2. The decline of the breeding population can be illustrated by an example from breeding sites around Ostrozska Nova Ves (UH). At the end of the 1970s and beginning of the 1980s, the breeding density was 17–25 pairs per km^2 at wet meadows, patches of gravel, and in farmland. In the mid-1980s, after drainage of meadows, and no other changes in the habitat, it was 7–10 pairs per km^2; and at the end of the 1980s, it was 2–4 pairs per km^2. After breeding and during migration, this species frequents semi-drained and drained fishponds, and temporary pools in farmland. Flocks of several hundred or thousand birds, especially during peak migration, can be seen. Birds found in winter are usually late autumn migrants from December or early spring migrants from February.
Status: Migrant and summer visitor. **Breeding season**: local. **Winter**: uncommon. **Migration**: common. Least concern. Protected.
Population trends: The breeding population is between 20,000 and 40,000 pairs. It has declined over the past 20 years by 20–50%. In winter there are up to 1,600 individuals.
Distribution: Nationwide. May be a rather scarce breeder in SU, BR, LB and PB counties.
Timing: Recorded every month except January. Migration occurs from the beginning of February until the beginning of April, with a peak during the first half of March. Autumn migration is from September until mid-November. Breeding extends from mid-March until the beginning of June, with the peak at the beginning of April.

Red Knot *Calidris canutus*

Knot Jespak rezavy Pobreznik hrdzavy Knutt

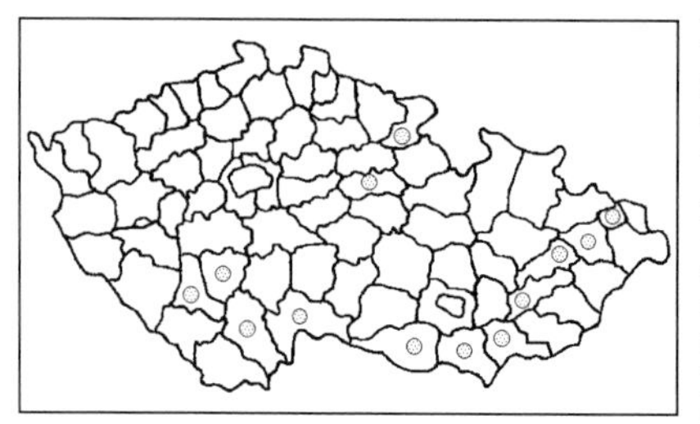

Red Knot is considered a rare migrant by Hudec *et al.* (1977). The number of records since 1990 indicates increasing passage. Up to 10, rarely more, birds are recorded annually (individual, or in small flocks). Flocks of 7, 4 and 3 birds were observed in July and August of 1993 at Zahlinicke ponds (KM). Migrating birds are found on semi-drained or drained fishponds, mostly in the lowlands of s. Bohemia, s. Moravia and n. Moravia.

Status: Migrant. **Breeding season**: rare. **Winter:** does not occur. **Migration**: uncommon. Protected.
Population trends: No data available.
Distribution: May occur nationwide in fishpond areas. Recent records are from Rezabinec pond (PI), Dehtar pond (CB), Zbudovsky pond (CB), Kojetinske ponds (PR), Hermansky pond (OV), Zahlinicke ponds (KM), Bzenec-Privoz (HO), Stary pond (BV), Lednicke ponds (BV), and Nove Mlyny (BV).
Timing: Recorded in April, May, July, August, September and October.

Sanderling *Calidris alba*

Jespak pisecny Pobreznik belavy Sanderling

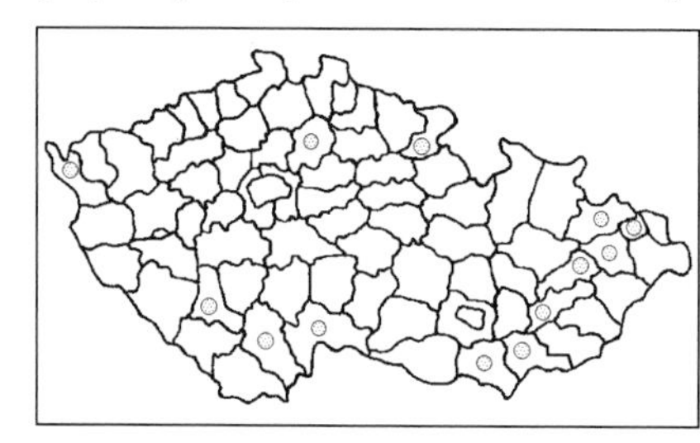

This is a rather scarce migrant in the Czech Republic, occurring in the major fishpond areas in CB and JH counties in s. Bohemia, BV, HO and KM counties in s. Moravia, and PR and OV counties in n. Moravia. The 2 sites with the highest occurrence of Sanderlings are Zahlinicke ponds (KM) and Tovacovske ponds (PR). Reports of singles or a couple of birds are made annually, with the total number up to 10 individuals. As with other shorebirds on passage, Sanderlings are usually found on semi-drained or drained fishponds.

Status: Migrant. **Breeding season**: rare. **Winter:** does not occur. **Migration**: uncommon. Protected.
Population trends: No data available.
Distribution: Recently recorded from Budske ponds (MB), Dehtar pond (CB), Bezdrev pond (CB), Dombas gravel pit (PR), Hermansky pond (OV), Zahlinicke ponds (KM), Bzenec-Privoz (HO), Mutenicke ponds (HO), Pisecne ponds (HO), Komarovsky pond (HO), and Nove Mlyny (BV).
Timing: Recorded in April (rare), May, June, August, September, October and November (rare). The largest number of records are from September.

Little Stint *Calidris minuta*

Jespak maly Pobreznik maly Zwergstrandläufer

Little Stint is one of the more common *Calidris* migrants occurring annually in the Czech Republic. Migrating birds frequent semi-drained or drained fishponds, mostly in CB and JH counties in s. Bohemia, BV, HO and KM counties in s. Moravia, and PR and OV counties in n. Moravia, but may be found elsewhere around the country. Flocks of 28–40 birds on autumn passage are regularly reported from Zahlinicke ponds (KM), and smaller flocks from Tovacovske ponds (PR). During spring migration it is also observed on flooded meadows and in farmland. More birds are recorded in autumn than spring.
Status: Migrant. **Breeding season**: rare. **Winter**: does not occur. **Migration**: local. Protected.

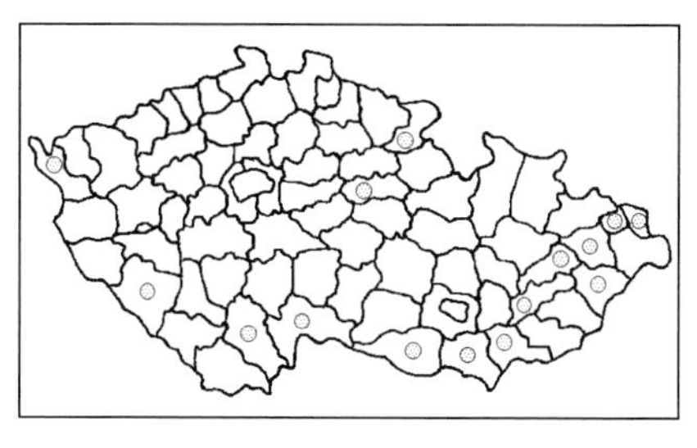

Population trends: No data available.
Distribution: May occur nationwide. Recent observations come from Jesenice dam (CH), Vlhavsky pond (CB), Dehtar pond (CB), Blatec pond (CB), Zbudovsky pond (CB), Svojetin (RA), Dvoriste pond (JH), Koclirov pond (JH), Horni pond near Novosedly (CB), Tovacovske ponds (PR), Hermansky pond (OV), Chorynske ponds (VS), Kojetin (PR), Zahlinicke ponds (KM), Lednicke ponds (BV), Mutenicke ponds (HO), Jaroslavicky pond (ZN), and Nove Mlyny (BV).
Timing: Spring migration is during the second half of April and in May. Autumn migration starts during the second half of August and continues until the first half of October.

Temminck's Stint *Calidris temminckii*

Jespak sedy Pobreznik sivy Temminckstrandläufer

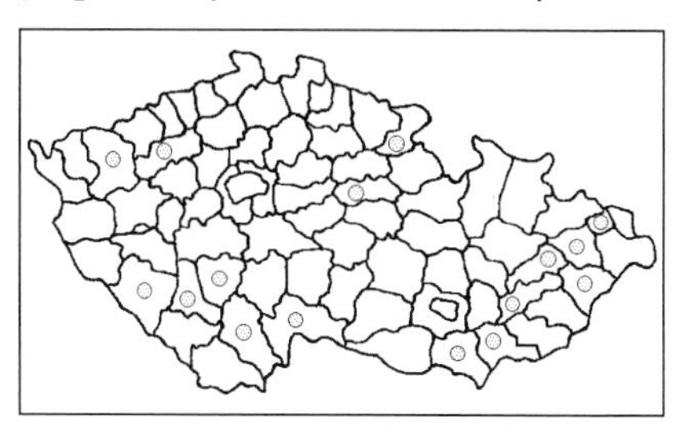

Temminck's Stint is a regular migrant in the Czech Republic. It may occur nationwide, but most records are from the larger fishpond areas in CB, JH and PI counties in s. Bohemia, BV and KM counties in s. Moravia, and PR and OV counties in n. Moravia. This species is seen in smaller flocks of about 4–7 individuals, occasionally up to 20 birds during autumn migration. It is often found in mixed flocks with other *Calidris* species, and is almost always associated with drained or semi-drained fishponds.
Status: Migrant. **Breeding season**: rare. **Winter**: does not occur. **Migration**: local. Protected.
Population trends: No data available.
Distribution: May occur nationwide. Recent reports are from Lenesicky pond (LN), Dolejsi pond (ST), Bezdrev pond (CB), Kardas pond (JH), Opatovicky pond (JH), Koclirov pond (JH), Novy pond near Dvorce (JH), Horni pond near Novosedly (CB), Podkostelni pond near Putim (PI), Hermansky pond (OV), Kojetinsky pond (PR), Tovacovske ponds (PR), Chorynske ponds (VS), Zahlinicke ponds (KM), Mutenicke ponds (HO), Lednicke ponds (BV), and Nove Mlyny (BV).
Timing: Found on spring passage from mid-April until the end of May. Autumn migration extends from mid-July until the beginning of October, with the peak from mid-August until the middle of September.

Curlew Sandpiper *Calidris ferruginea*

Jespak krivozoby Pobreznik krivozoby Sichelstrandlaufer

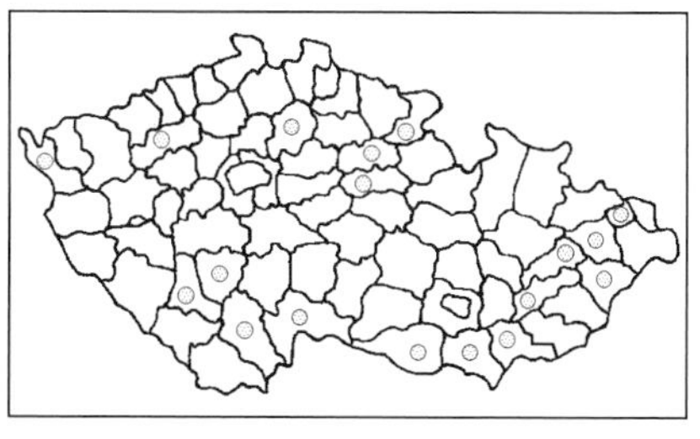

Migrating Curlew Sandpipers are more common in autumn than spring in the Czech Republic. It may occur nationwide, but most of the records are from fishpond areas in ST, CB, JH and PI counties in s. Bohemia, BV, HO and KM counties in s. Moravia, and PR, OV and VS counties in n. Moravia. Ponds around Ceske Budejovice (CB) and Zahlinicke ponds (KM) are sites where this species is observed annually in larger numbers. Curlew Sandpiper shows a preference for drained or semi-drained ponds with muddy margins. It is usually found in flocks of up to 10, occasionally up to 60 individuals, rarely more. Individuals recorded in July are often found in breeding plumage.
Status: Migrant. **Breeding season**: rare. **Winter**: does not occur. **Migration**: local/common. Protected.

Population trends: No data available.
Distribution: May occur nationwide. Recent records are from Riha pond (HK), Tresicky pond (HK), Budske ponds (MB), Talinsky pond (PI), a pond near Leskovice (ST), Stary Trebonsky pond (JH), meadows near Zbudov (CB), Horni pond near Novosedly (CB), Dehtar pond (CB), Bezdrev pond (CB), Koclirov pond (JH), Nadeje pond (JH), Kojetinske ponds (PR), Chorynske ponds (VS), industrial waters near Tovacov (PR), Tovacovske ponds (PR), Zahlinicke ponds (KM), Vytazniky ponds (HO), Jarohnevicky pond (HO), Mutenicke ponds (HO), Hodoninske ponds (HO), Jaroslavicky pond (ZN), Pohorelicke ponds (BV), Lednicke ponds (BV), and Nove Mlyny (BV).
Timing: Spring migration is from mid-April until the end of May. Autumn migration occurs between mid-July and the end of September, with the majority of birds recorded during the first half of September.

Dunlin *Calidris alpina*

Jespak obecny Pobreznik obycajny Alpenstrandläufer

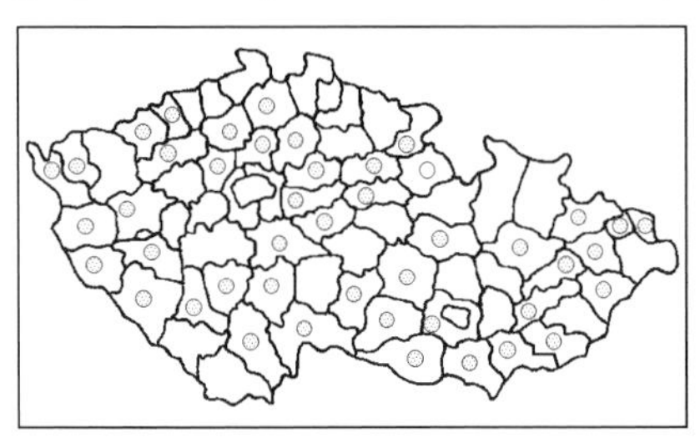

Dunlin is the most common *Calidris* species recorded in the Czech Republic. It is found in larger numbers, and at more places across the country, than any other species of the same genus. It is usually found in lowlands, occasionally in highlands, where it frequents drained or semi-drained ponds, and less frequently on shores of man-made areas of water. During spring migration it is also found in flooded meadows and farmland. It occurs in flocks of variable size, often with other species, and solitary birds are seen less commonly. For example, flocks of up to 35 individuals were observed at Hermansky pond (OV) in August, 30 at Zahlinicke ponds (KM) in October, 50 at Tovacovske ponds (PR) in October, 90 at Dehtar pond (CB) in October, and 30 at Nove Mlyny (BV) in May. Late migrants are known from December, when a flock of 15 birds was recorded at Novovesky pond (BV) on 10 December 1982, and 150 birds at Vavrinecky pond (KH) on 2 December 1984. Birds occurring in the Czech Republic belong to the *alpina* and *schinzii* races.
Status: Migrant. **Breeding season**: rare. **Winter**: does not occur. **Migration**: local/common. Protected.
Population trends: No data available.
Distribution: Nationwide. Regularly found at the same sites as other abovementioned *Calidris* species, but may be seen more often in other areas as well.
Timing: Spring migration occurs between the end of March and the end of May; autumn migration from mid-August until mid-November, with the peak between mid-September and mid-October. A few non-breeding birds may oversummer.

Broad-billed Sandpiper *Limicola falcinellus*

Jespacek ploskozoby Breharik ploskozoby Sumpfläufer

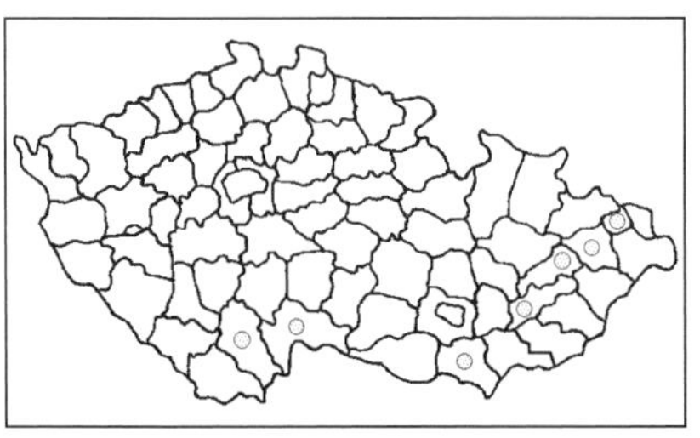

Broad-billed Sandpiper is a rare migrant, which is not observed annually in the Czech Republic. This species normally occurs on ponds in KM and PR counties in central Moravia, OV county in n. Moravia, and CB county in s. Bohemia, but occasionally is recorded elsewhere at fishpond areas. Most records are of solitary birds, rarely flocks of up to 6 individuals. Birds are associated with semi-drained or drained ponds.
Status: Migrant. **Breeding season**: rare. **Winter**: does not occur. **Migration**: uncommon. Protected.
Population trends: No data available.

Distribution: May occur nationwide. However, the majority of observations are from central Moravia. It was recently recorded at Nadeje pond (CB), Kojetinske ponds (PR), Hermansky pond (OV), Tovacovske ponds (PR), and Zahlinicke ponds (KM).
Timing: Records are from April, May, July, August, September (most records) and October.

Ruff *Philomachus pugnax*

Jespak bojovny Bojovnik bahenny Kampfläufer

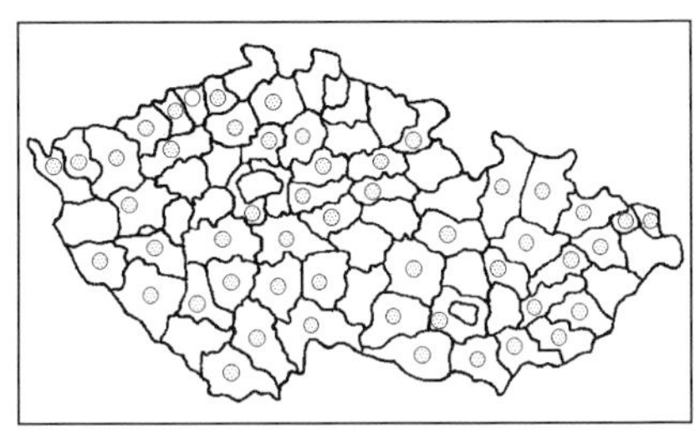

This species is a more common spring than autumn migrant in the Czech Republic. Ruff occurs mostly in lowlands, at marshes, fishponds, flooded meadows and temporary pools in farmland. Ponds in counties such as KM in central Moravia, OV in n. Moravia, and CB and JH in s. Bohemia seem to be particularly attractive to migrating Ruffs, and larger numbers of them are recorded there annually. For example, at Zahlinicke ponds (KM), flocks of up to 100 individuals have been recorded regularly in March, up to 30 in April, up to 60 in August, and up to 80 in September. At Tovacovske ponds (PR), flocks of up to 40 have occurred in April; at Hermansky pond (OV), flocks of up to 100 have been seen in July and August, and up to 25 in October; near Sumvald (OL), up to 64 have been recorded in April; at Lednice-Pastvisko (BV) up to 35 in March; and at Pohorelicke ponds (BV) up to 45 have visited in April. An unusual record of late migrants comes from Vavrinecky pond (KH), where 50 individuals were seen on 2 December 1984. It is often seen in flocks with other shorebirds. Males on spring passage are often displaying, and may stay at the same place for a couple of weeks. There are summer records of individual birds from June and July, but breeding has never been documented in the country.
Status: Migrant. **Breeding season:** rare. **Winter:** rare. **Migration:** local/common. Protected.
Population trends: No data available.
Distribution: Nationwide. Recent regular records are from Sluzebny pond (JH), Koclirov pond (JH), Starnov (OL), Velky Bor pond (TR), Vrkoc pond (BV), Chomoutov gravel pit (OL), Tovacovske ponds (PR), Zahlinicke ponds (KM), Lednice-Pastvisko (BV), Pohorelicke ponds (BV), Miroslav (ZN), ponds near Karvina (KI), Hermansky pond (OV), meadows near Kouty (OP), and Sumvald (OL).
Timing: Spring migration occurs from mid-March (occasionally earlier) until mid-May; autumn migration from mid-July until the end of October.

Jack Snipe *Lymnocryptes minimus*

Slucka mala Mociarnicka ticha Zwergschnepfe

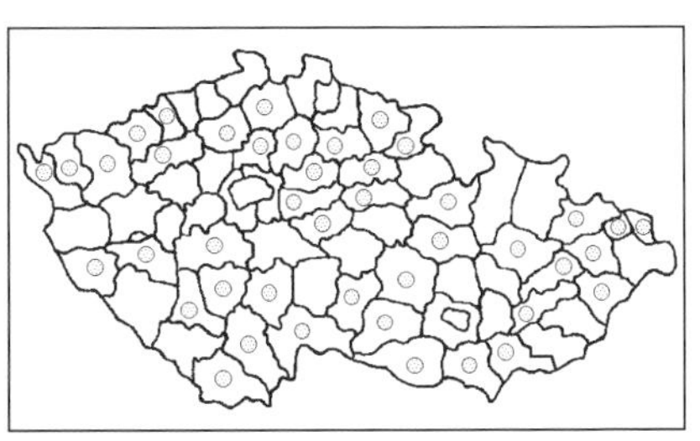

This is a regular but rather scarce migrant, observed more commonly in spring than autumn. It occurs from lowlands up to highlands, occasionaly at higher altitudes, at marshes and ponds of any size, and in flooded meadows. Solitary birds are most common, but sometimes small flocks of up to 10 may occur. It may be seen in mixed flocks with other waders. Rare wintering of a few birds has also been recorded.
Status: Migrant. **Breeding season:** rare. **Winter:** rare. **Migration:** local. Protected.
Population trends: No data available.
Distribution: Nationwide. It was recently recorded at Jordanek pond in Praha (AA), Vysatov pond (CB), Cejkovicky pond (CB), Nakri (CB), meadows near Klokocin (PI), Kaclezsky pond (JH), Motovidlo pond (CB), meadows around Putim (PI), Horusice (TA), Velky Kosir pond (SY), Zehunsky pond (NB), Hvezda pond (SY), Zahlinicke ponds (KM), Prusy (PR), and Lednice-Pastvisko (BV).

Timing: Spring migration occurs from mid-March until the end of April; autumn migration between August and mid-November.

Common Snipe *Gallinago gallinago*

Snipe Bekasina otavni Mociarnica mekotava Bekassine

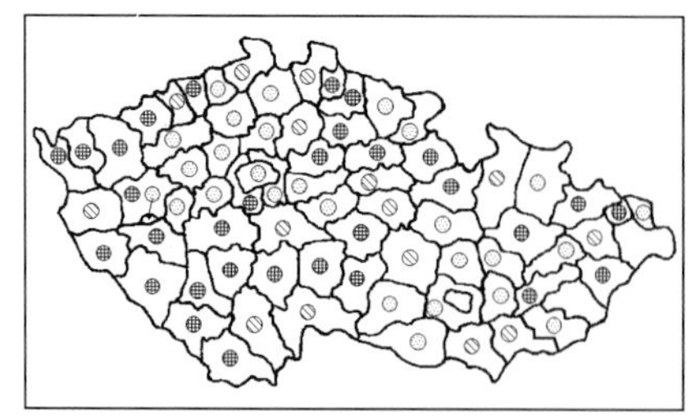

Common Snipe is a rather uncommon breeding wader in the Czech Republic, although its numbers have declined severely since the 1960s. It is distributed from lowlands up to highlands, where it occurs more commonly these days. Breeding has been recorded up to about 650 m in the Ceskomoravska vysocina highlands (HB, JI, PE, ZR), up to 750 m in the Jeseniky (BR, SU) and Orlicke hory (RK) mountains, up to 840 m in the Krusne hory mountains (CV, KV, MO, TP), and to 1100 m in the Sumava mountains (CK, PT, KT). Breeding habitats include flooded meadows, marshes, peatbogs, and marshy edges of lakes and ponds. In 1980, breeding density was 6 pairs per km^2 aroud Zliv (CB) and 4 pairs per km^2 at peatbogs in the Jizerske hory mountains (LB, JN) at the end of the 1980s. At the beginning of the 1980s, the average density at about 150 ponds in s. Bohemia was 1.1 individuals per km^2, 0.2 individuals per km^2 in the mid-1980s, and 0.5 individuals in 1991. Breeding density was 27 individuals per km^2 at wet meadows around Trebon (JH) in 1972, but the following year, after the meadows had been drained, this had fallen to only 5 individuals per km^2. This case illustrates the most likely cause of Common Snipe's decline in the country. During the past 20–25 years it has become a rare breeder or disappeared from many counties where it was once fairly common. A few birds are regularly reported during the winter months.

Status: Resident. **Breeding season:** uncommon. **Winter:** uncommon. **Migration:** local/common. Vulnerable. Protected/not hunted all year round.

Population trends: The breeding population was between 1,200 and 2,400 pairs from 1985 to 1989. In 1994, the population was estimated to be between 500 and 1,000 pairs, a decrease of 20–50% from the mid-1970s to the end of the 1980s, and the numbers of breeding birds are still falling. The wintering population ranges from 30 to 70 individuals.

Distribution: Scattered nationwide. Flocks of 16–56 birds were recently seen on migration at Hermansky pond (OV), Novy Ptacovsky pond (TR), Zahlinicke ponds (KM), and Jarohnevicky pond (HO). Flocks of up to 450 individuals were recorded in September and October in 1997 in Grygov (OL) and Bzenec-Privoz (HO).

Timing: Spring migration usually starts during the second half of March and continues until mid-April; autumn migration occurs between mid-July and the end of October. Breeding extends from the beginning of April, occasionally from the end of March, until the end of June, peaking in the second half of April.

Great Snipe *Gallinago media*

Bekasina vetsi Mociarnica ticha Doppelschnepfe

Great Snipe is a regular, but quite rare, migrant in the Czech Republic. It has been reported only occasionally during the past decade. Birds may occur across the country, from lowlands up to the highlands. However, more reports come from wetland and fishpond areas in the lowlands. Birds are usually associated with a variety of habitats such as flooded meadows, marshes, muddy edges of ponds and lakes and drained ponds, but may also be found in drier areas.

Status: Migrant. **Breeding season:** rare. **Winter:** rare. **Migration:** uncommon. Protected.

Population trends: No data available.
Distribution: Birds are scattered nationwide. Recent records are from Tovacovske ponds (PR), Olomouc (OL), and Lednicke ponds (BV).
Timing: Spring migration starts during the second half of March and continues until mid-May; autumn migration occurs between the second half of August and mid-October. This species has also been recorded in February, June and July.

Woodcock *Scolopax rusticola*

Eurasian Woodcock Sluka lesni Sluka horna Waldschnepfe

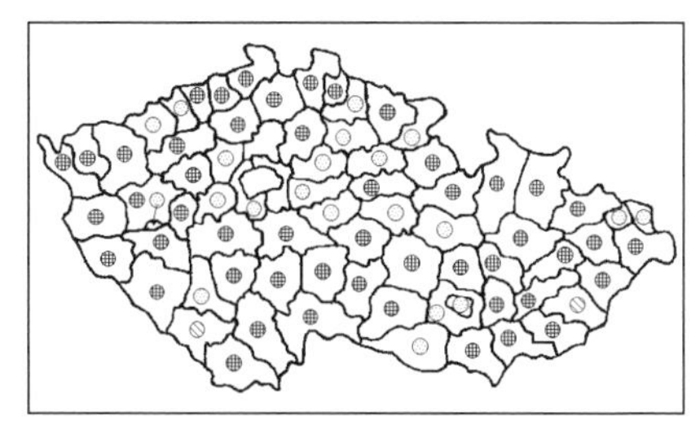

Woodcock is generally an uncommon breeder distributed widely across the country, although in a few areas, for example the Sumava mountains (CK, PT, KT) and its foothils, it remains fairly common. As a breeder, it usually occurs in highlands and mountains up to about 1100 m, but on migration it is also found in lowland areas. Breeding habitat is normally moist deciduous or mixed forest with an abundant scrub undergrowth. It usually avoids coniferous plantations, but nests have been found in pine forest. There are no confirmed breeding records from a number of counties, however, this may be due to the difficulty of locating nests. During migration, birds can be seen at woodland edges, in clearings, and often farther afield. During the mid-1960s and the beginning of the 1970s, about 250 birds were shot annually.
Status: Migrant and summer visitor. **Breeding season**: uncommon/local. **Winter**: uncommon. **Migration**: common. Conservation-dependent. Hunted, with individual exceptions given by conservation authorities.
Population trends: From 1985 to 1989, the breeding population was between 1,500 and 3,000 pairs, and these numbers have probably not changed during the 1990s. The population has remained stable, at least during the past 10–15 years.
Distribution: During migration it is found nationwide. It may be a rather scarce breeder in UH, ZL, KM, VY, PV, UO, JI, RK, NA, BN, CL, TP, LT, TC and PI counties.
Timing: Spring migration starts at the end of February and continues until the beginning of April with the peak during the second half of March. Autumn migration occurs between the end of August and the beginning of November. Occasionally, birds are found at the beginning of December. The breeding season extends from mid-March to the beginning of July, but most nests are found at the end of March and beginning of April.

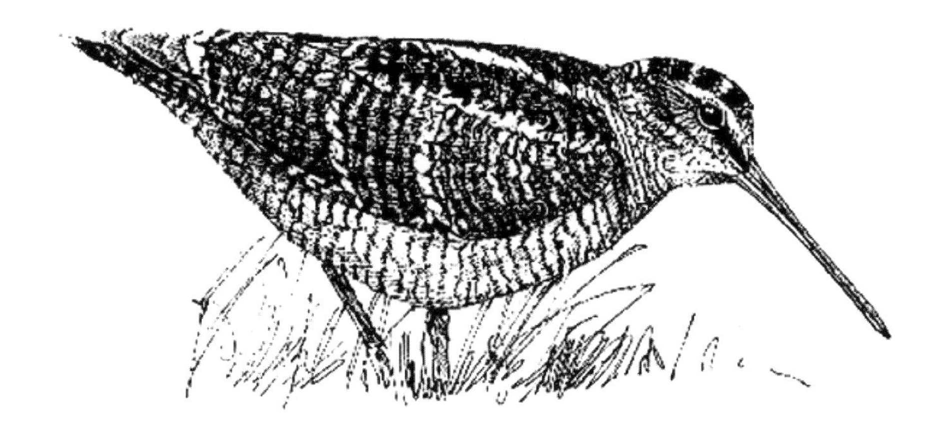

Woodcock

Black-tailed Godwit *Limosa limosa*

Brehous cernoocasy Brehar obycajny Uferschnepfe

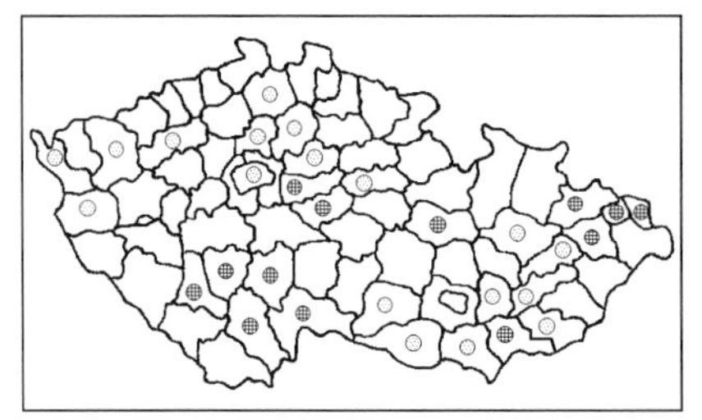

During most of the 19th century, Black-tailed Godwit was a rare, non-breeding species in the Czech Republic. The first breeding attempts were recorded in the mid-1890s in s. Bohemia, and from then on the breeding population increased and spread across the country. At the end of the 1920s, it was breeding around Pardubice, and in the mid-1940s in s. Moravia. However, at the end of the 1960s, the breeding population started to decline, and during the following decade it decreased by one half (Hajek 1980). Black-tailed Godwit has become a scarce breeder in the Czech Republic during the past 15–20 years. The majority of the breeding population occurs in a few lowland areas in s. Bohemia and n. Moravia, but nesting has also been recorded up to 450 m. This species is typical of flooded meadows and marshes with low growth, marshy edges of ponds and lakes or, less commonly, drained fishponds with short vegetation. From 1972–1973, breeding density was 28 individuals per km^2 in wet meadows around Trebon (JH), and 21.6 pairs per km^2 around Zliv (CB) in 1980. In the mid-1980s, 33–40 pairs occurred in 2 fishpond areas in s. Bohemia; at the end of the 1980s it was only 10–15 pairs, and 21 pairs from 1990–1992. The sharp decline in the population was apparently caused by loss of nesting habitat. During migration it is usually found at drained fishponds, muddy shores of ponds, and flooded meadows on spring passage. Migrants may occur nationwide, usually in lowland areas.

Status: Migrant and summer visitor. **Breeding season:** uncommon. **Winter:** does not occur. **Migration:** local. Critically endangered. Protected.

Population trends: From 1973–77 the breeding population was estimated to be between 250 and 500 pairs, and between 1985 and 1989 from 30 to 60 pairs. The same numbers are valid for the 1990s.

Distribution: Recent records of up to 15 individuals, during migration as well as in the summer months, come from a pond near Seberov (AA), Zehunsky pond (NB), Budske ponds (MB), Vrazda pond (MB), ponds near Strelske Hostice (ST), Mnichovske ponds (ST), Rabsky pond (ST), Zly pond (ST), Kanov pond (JH), Velky Tisy pond (JH), Novy pond (SY), Velky Bor pond (TR), meadows near Kouty (OP), Hermansky pond (OV), Chomoutov (OL), Tovacovske ponds (PR), Zahlinicke ponds (KM), Pisecne ponds (HO), and Lednicke ponds (BV).

Timing: It arrives from the end of March until the end of April, and departs mainly from early July to mid-August; it is occasionally observed later. Breeding extends from the beginning of April to the beginning of June, peaking during the second half of April.

Bar-tailed Godwit *Limosa lapponica*

Brehous rudy Brehar hrdzavy Pfuhlschnepfe

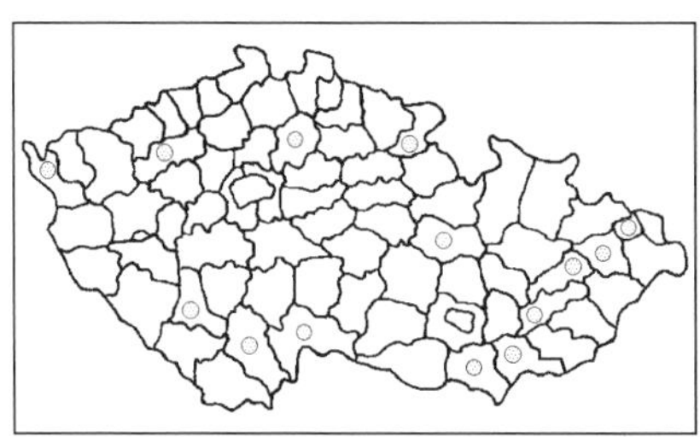

Bar-tailed Godwit is a rather scarce migrant in the Czech Republic, and is not observed annually. Birds on passage are usually found near muddy ponds, marshes or flooded meadows near ponds. Most birds recorded are singles or small flocks of a few individuals and are found in fishpond areas in the lowlands.

Status: Migrant. **Breeding season:** rare. **Winter:** does not occur. **Migration:** uncommon. Protected.

Population trends: No data available.

Distribution: May occur nationwide. It was recently recorded at a man-made water area near Mnichovo Hradiste (MB), Dehtar pond (CB), Blatec pond (CB), Divcicke ponds (CB), Horusicky pond (JH), Male Jezero pond near Klinovice (ST), Dolni pond (SY), Tovacovske ponds (PR), Lednicke ponds (BV), and Nove Mlyny (BV).

Timing: Found on spring passage in April and May; autumn passage is from July until October, peaking in September.

Whimbrel *Numenius phaeopus*

Koliha mala Hvizdak maly Regenbrachvogel

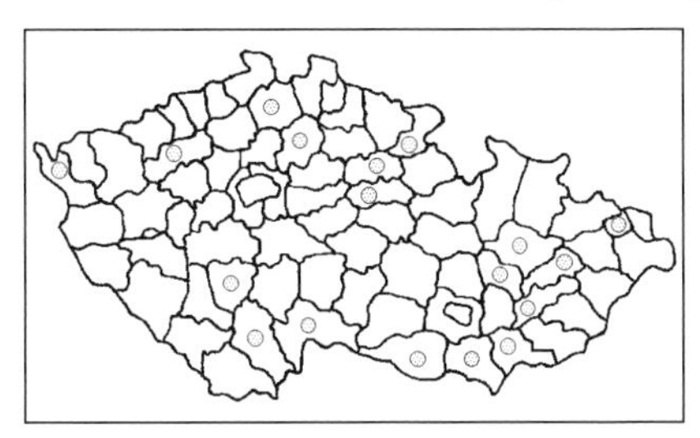

Whimbrel occurs as an occasional migrant in the Czech Republic. It is more common in spring than autumn. Mainly single birds are observed, usually at semi-drained fishponds and their environs in the lowlands, less commonly in highland areas.
Status: Migrant. **Breeding season**: rare. **Winter**: does not occur. **Migration**: uncommon. Protected.
Population trends: No data available.
Distribution: May occur nationwide. It was recently recorded at Olesnik pond near Nakri (CB), Vysatov pond (CB), Koclirov pond (JH), Horni Vytopa pond (JH), Stary pond (JH), Razicky pond (PI), Budske ponds (MB), Rezabinec pond (PI), Hermansky pond (OV), Lednicke ponds (BV), Branisov (CB), Tovacov (PR), Straznice (HO) and Nove Mlyny (BV). A flock of 4 individuals was seen near Grygov (OL) in August 1997.
Timing: Found on spring migration, between March and the end of April, ocasionally in May. Autumn migration extends from August to mid-September. There are very few records from June or July.

Eurasian Curlew *Numenius arquata*

Curlew, Western Curlew Koliha velka Hvizdak velky Großer Brachvogel

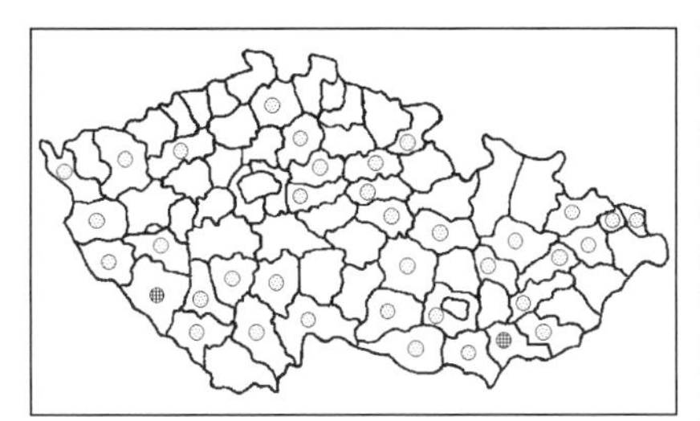

Even though Eurasian Curlew occurs regularly in the Czech Republic, it is a rare species. Breeding was first documented in Bohemia in DO county in 1942, and in Moravia in HO county in 1954. Eurasian Curlew expanded its breeding range until changes in agriculture practice, starting in the 1960s, restricted its expansion in the country. During the early 1970s, it expanded its local breeding range in s. and w. Bohemia. However, during the past 20 years, the total population has decreased significantly, and Curlews have disappeared from some of their traditional breeding sites. For example, at meadows around the Morava river, between Uhersky Ostroh (UH) and Hodonin (HO), 20, 16, 11, and 9 pairs respectively nested between 1974 and 1977. In the years between 1985 and 1989 it was 8, 5, 3, 2 and 3 pairs respectively (Gahura in Stastny *et al.* 1996). As a breeder, it is distributed through lowlands, and up to about 450 m in the highlands. Breeding habitats include open wet meadows, with short vegetation, and pastures, but nesting has also been observed in arable fields (not usually successful owing to destruction of nests). On migration, it can be seen at drained ponds, at the muddy shores of ponds, as well as in farmland. Migrating birds occur nationwide, mostly in the lowlands. The population decline is most likely due to habitat loss and fragmentation, and agricultural intensification.
Status: Migrant and summer visitor. **Breeding season**: uncommon. **Winter**: rare. **Migration**: local. Critically endangered. Protected.
Population trends: Between 1973 and 1977, the breeding population was between 25 and 50 pairs; between 1985 and 1989 it was 5–15 pairs. The numbers have probably not changed much during the 1990s. Up to 20 individuals may be recorded during the winter period.
Distribution: More or less regular breeding may occur in about 3–4 counties. Individual birds, and flocks of up to 50 on passage, have recently been observed at Riha pond (HK), Zehunsky pond (NB), Nakri (CB), Dehtar pond (CB), Zvikov (CB), Olsany (PV), ponds near Polanka nad Odrou (NJ), Koclirov pond (JH), Brezovec pond (CB), Bezdrev pond (CB), Dubovec pond

(TR), Chomoutov (OL), Hermansky pond (OV), Tovacovske ponds (PR), Zahlinicke ponds (KM), Tesany (BO), Jarohnevicky pond (HO), Strachotin (BV), Lednicke ponds (BV), and Nove Mlyny (BV).
Timing: Arrives from March until early April, with the peak during the second half of March. Departure occurs from the end of July until November, with the peak in September and October. There are records of individual birds from winter months. Breeding extends from the end of March until the end of May.

Spotted Redshank *Tringa erythropus*

Vodous tmavy Kaluziak tmavy Dunkelwasserläufer

Spotted Redshank is a fairly common migrant, found mostly in the major fishpond areas of CB, JH, ST, MB, PU, PR, OV, KM and BV counties. A small number of birds may occur elsewhere. Spotted Redshank is usually seen at drained or semi-drained fishponds, muddy shores of ponds, shores of artificial water bodies, and occasionally at banks of larger rivers. It often associates with other shorebirds. Flocks of 20–50 regularly occur during migration, particularly at Zahlinicke ponds (KM), Tovacovske ponds (PR), and Hermansky pond (OV). A single bird wintered in HO county in 1997–1998.
Status: Migrant. **Breeding season:** rare. **Winter:** rare. **Migration:** local/common. Protected.
Population trends: No data available.
Distribution: May occur nationwide. Recent records of individual birds and flocks of up to 100 come from Praha-Hostavice (AA), Zehunsky pond (NB), Budske ponds (MB), Zbudovsky pond (CB), Volesek pond (CB), Dehtar pond (CB), Vlhavsky pond (CB), Kardas pond (JH), Sluzebny pond (JH), Hermansky pond (OV), Sumvald (OL), Chomoutov (OL), Tovacovske ponds (PR), Chorynske ponds (VS), Slavkov (VY), Zahlinicke ponds (KM), Lednicke ponds (BV), Sakvicky pond (BV), and Nove Mlyny (BV).
Timing: Spring migration starts at the end of March, with the peak from mid-April until mid-May. Autumn migration occurs between mid-July and the end of October. Peak autumn migration is from mid-September until the end of October. Birds are occasionally seen in November and at the beginning of December.

Common Redshank *Tringa totanus*

Redshank Vodous rudonohy Kaluziak cervenonohy Rotschenkel

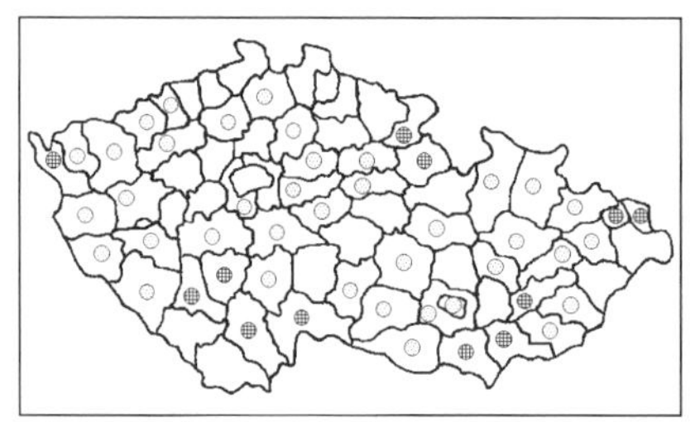

Common Redshank is another shorebird whose population in the Czech Republic has crashed over the last 25–30 years as a result of agricultural intensification and habitat loss due to drainage of wetland sites. Once a fairly common breeder in all major fishpond areas in s. Bohemia, w. Bohemia, e. Bohemia, s. Moravia, and n. Moravia, this species has become a scarce nesting bird. More or less regular nesting occurs in a few areas across the country these days. As a breeder, Common Redshank prefers lowlands, but has been recorded up to 550 m in the Ceskomoravska vysocina highlands (HB, JI, PE, ZR). It is found in flooded meadows, marshes, wet pastures, at the marshy edges of ponds and, less commonly, at drained ponds with sparse vegetation. At the beginning of the 1980s, breeding density at meadows near Ostrozska Nova Ves (UH) was 23 pairs per km^2, but after the meadows were drained most of the Common Redshanks disappeared and only 2 pairs were nesting in that area 4 years later. At the end of the 1980s, only migrant birds were recorded there. During migration it occurs at semi-drained or drained ponds with muddy shores, flooded meadows, temporary pools in farmland, as well as at the edges of industrial

waters. The major threat to this species is habitat destruction.
Status: Migrant and summer visitor. **Breeding season:** uncommon. **Winter:** does not occur. **Migration:** local/common. Critically endangered. Protected.
Population trends: Before 1970, the breeding population was between 150 and 300 pairs; during the 1970s it was 80–150 pairs; and from 1985 to 1989 it was only 40–60 pairs, and the population is probably still in this region today.
Distribution: On migration it may be seen in suitable habitat across the county. Regular breeding occurs in JH, CB, PI, ST, BV, HO and KI counties. Recent observations of up to 30 birds on passage as well as breeding come from Lenesicky pond (LN), Milavy pond (ST), Dehtar pond (CB), Oblanov pond (CB), Basta pond (CB), Novy pond near Dvorce (JH), Velky Tisy pond (JH), Sluzebny pond (JH), Budske ponds (MB), Zviroticky pond near Sedlcany (BN), Novy pond (SY), Maly Bor pond (TR), meadows near Kouty (OP), Dehylov (OP), Hermansky pond (OV), Hulin (KM), industrial complexes near Tovacov (PR), Tovacovske ponds (PR), Drevohostice (PR), Zahlinicke ponds (KM), meadows between Ostrozska Nova Ves and Uhersky Ostroh (UH), Pohorelicke ponds (BV), and Nove Mlyny (BV).
Timing: Arrives from mid-March until mid-April, occasionally the end of April, and departs from the beginning of July to mid-September. Individual birds may occasionally be found later. Breeding extends from the beginning of April to the beginning of June, peaking during the first half of April.

Marsh Sandpiper *Tringa stagnatilis*

Vodous stihly Kaluziak stihly Teichwasserläufer

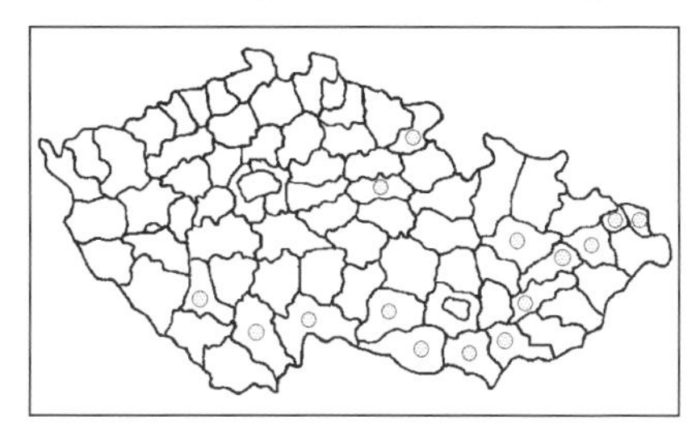

Marsh Sandpiper is an occasional visitor to the Czech Republic and is not recorded annually. The species is normally recorded in central and s. Moravia. However, recent records also come from the west of the country. Solitary migrant birds or, rarely, flocks of a few individuals, occur more often during spring than autumn. It is usually found along muddy shores and at semi-drained fishponds.
Status: Vagrant. **Breeding season:** rare. **Winter:** does not occur. **Migration:** uncommon. Protected.
Population trends: No data available.
Distribution: Mostly found in BV and TR counties in s. Moravia, KM and PR counties in central Moravia, and KI, OL and OV counties in n. Moravia. Recent records of 1–3 individuals come from Koclirov pond (JH), Sluzebny pond (JH), Dehtar pond (CB), Stary Ptacovsky pond (TR), Sumvald (OL), Hermansky pond (OV), ponds near Karvina (KI), Tovacovske ponds (PR), Zahlinicke ponds (KM), Nove Mlyny (BV), and a pond near Strachotin (BV).
Timing: Observed mostly in April and May; other records are from June, July, August and September.

Greenshank *Tringa nebularia*

Common Greenshank Vodous sedy Kaluziak sivy Grünschenkel

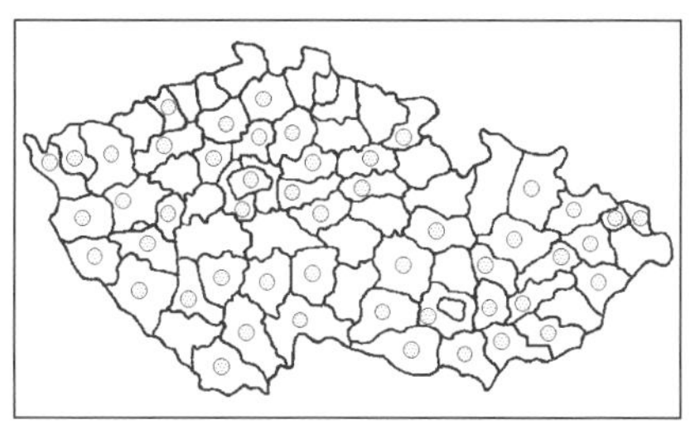

This is a regular migrant, recorded across the country from lowlands up to about 500 m in the Ceskomoravska vysocina highlands (HB, JI, PE, ZR). Flocks of varying size are regularly seen at Zahlinicke ponds (KM) and Tovacovske ponds (PR) in central Moravia. It is usually found at drained or semi-drained ponds of any size, along muddy shores of ponds, shores of gravel pits, temporary pools in farmland, riverbanks, and also brooks. During spring migration mostly solitary birds or small flocks are often seen on flooded meadows; but during autumn passage there are larger flocks

of Greenshanks, often mixed with other shorebirds.
Status: Migrant. **Breeding season**: rare. **Winter**: does not occur. **Migration**: local/common. Protected.
Population trends: No data available.
Distribution: May occur nationwide. Recent records of single birds and flocks of up to 36 individuals on spring or autumn passage come from Lenesicky pond (LN), Cervenak pond (LN), Piskovy pond (TC), Chodsky pond (TC), Pradlo pond (TC), Zehunsky pond (NB), Velka Cerna pond (JH), Velky Tisy pond (JH), Spitalsky pond near Klenov (JH), Novy pond near Pluhuv Zdar (JH), Blatec pond (CB), Novy pond (SY), Velky Bor pond (TR), Salak pond near Trebic (TR), Dehylov (OP), Grygov and Bolelouc (OL), Sumvald (OL), Hermansky pond (OV), ponds in Karvina (KI), near Prerov (PR), Tovacovske ponds (PR), Chorynske ponds (VS), ponds in Slavkov (VY), Zahlinicke ponds (KM), Jarohnevicky pond (HO), Lednicke ponds (BV), and the river Dyje near Stara Breclav (BV).
Timing: Spring migration occurs between mid-April and mid-May. Autumn migration starts during the second half of July and continues until the end of October, rarely into November. Peak autumn migration is in August. Individual birds have been recorded in late May and June, and in early July.

Green Sandpiper *Tringa ochropus*

Vodous kropenaty   Kaluziak perlavy   Waldwasserläufer

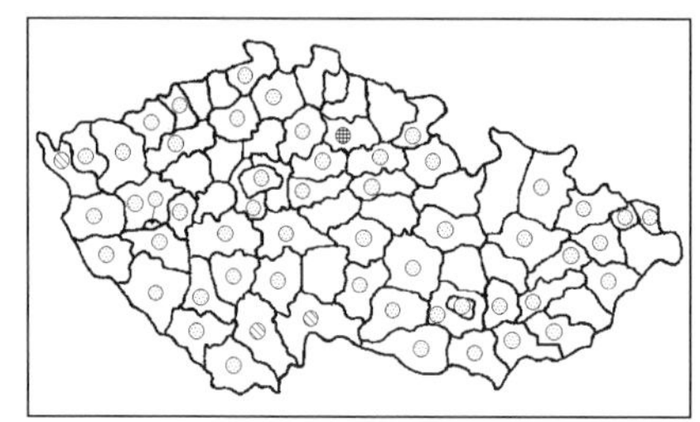

Although Green Sandpiper is a permanent resident in the Czech Republic, it occurs in large numbers only during migration. As a breeder, Green Sandpiper is relatively new to the country. The nesting of 2 pairs was first documented at Bohdanecsky pond (PU) in 1935. The next record was of 1 pair at Dlouhopolsky pond (NB) in 1938, and 1 pair near Planice (KT) in 1942. The next documented nesting occurred near Hradec Kralove (HK) in 1981. During the 1980s, intermittant breeding was recorded at different sites across the country, from lowlands up to 800 m. However, birds were recorded up to 900 m in the Sumava mountains (CK, PT, KT) during the breeding season, and to 1400 m in the Krkonose mountains (SE, TU). Breeding habitats include a range of wetland, including woody areas around ponds, canals, rivers, ditches, edges of ponds, and peatbogs. At the beginning of the 1980s, average density at about 150 ponds in s. Bohemia was 0.2 individuals per km^2, and 0.5 individuals per km^2 in 1991; it was 0.02 pairs per km^2 around Trebon (JH) in 1992. On migration, this species occurs more commonly at marshes in close proximity to forest, in the vicinity of rivers and brooks, and along the shores of man-made areas of open water. The same habitats are used by wintering birds.
Status: Resident. **Breeding season**: uncommon. **Winter**: local. **Migration**: local. Critically endangered. Protected.
Population trends: Breeding was not recorded between 1973 and 1977. From 1981, the breeding population fluctuated between 5 and 15 pairs, but was increasing. In 1994, it was estimated to be between 15 and 30 pairs. The wintering population is between 40 and 100 individuals.
Distribution: On migration found nationwide. Regular breeding occurs around Trebon (JH) at Purkrabsky pond, Novy pond, Zofinka pond, Novy Hospodar pond, which hosts at least 5–10 pairs, and around the Nova reka river (JH). More or less regular breeding has been recorded in HK, JC, CB and PR counties. Wintering birds are mostly recorded in s. and e. Bohemia, central and s. Moravia, and at ponds in OV and KI counties. Regular records of individual birds, flocks of up to 17 birds on passage and in winter, and up to 20 birds during the breeding season, come from Praha (AA), Dobromerice gravel pit (LN), Budske ponds (MB), Bohdanecsky pond (PU), Svital pond near Kardasova Recice (JH), Podsedek pond (JH), Stary Hospodar pond (JH), the river Vltava near Hluboka nad Vltavou (CB), Razicky pond (PI), Novy Vdovec pond (JH), Novy Hospodar pond (JH), Grygov, Bolelouc and Chomoutov (OL), meadows near Kouty (OP), industrial complexes in Drevohostice (PR), Tovacovske

ponds (PR), Prerov (PR), Lysecky pond (PR), Zastudanci (PR), Prusy (PR), Maly and Velky Bor ponds (TR), Bystrice pod Hostynem (KM), Zahlinicke ponds (KM), Vytazniky ponds (HO), Pisecne ponds (HO), Kyjovka brook (HO), Lednicke ponds (BV), Vrkoc pond (BV), Nove Mlyny (BV), and the river Dyje near Ladna (BV).
Timing: Spring migration occurs between the end of March and the beginning of May; autumn migration from mid-July to mid-September. Breeding starts at the end of April and continues through May.

Wood Sandpiper *Tringa glareola*

Vodous bahenni Kaluziak mociarny Bruchwasserläufer

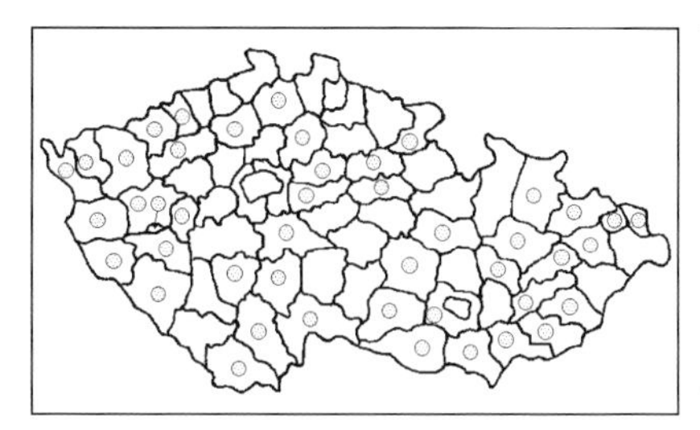

There are a few reports of breeding Wood Sandpiper in the Czech Republic from the 1920s and 1930s but they lack credibility. This species is a regular migrant, occurring across the country with the highest numbers in the east. It is mainly recorded in the lowlands, but up to about 480 m in the Ceskomoravska vysocina highlands (HB, JI, PE, ZR). Most reports of flocks of 20–75 individuals come from Zahlinicke ponds (KM), and other areas of open water in PR county. Wood Sandpiper is usually seen in small flocks of up to 30 individuals on passage, and is more common in autumn than spring. Breeding in the country has not been recorded yet, although birds have been seen in June, and at the beginning of July in PR and OV counties.
Status: Migrant. **Breeding season**: rare. **Winter**: rare. **Migration**: local/common. Protected.
Population trends: No data available.
Distribution: May occur nationwide. Recent reports of solitary birds and small flocks, as well as up to 190 individuals, come from meadows near Kouty (OP), Karvina (KI), Kojetin (PR), Hermansky pond (OV), Sumvald (OL), Chomoutov (OL), Prerov (PR), Drevohostice (PR), Prusy (PR), Tovacovske ponds (PR), Velky Bor pond (TR), Novy Studenecky pond near Namest nad Oslavou (TR), Pohorelicke ponds (BV), Zahlinicke ponds (KM), and Lednicke ponds (BV).
Timing: Spring migration starts at the end of April and continues through May. Individual birds have occasionally been seen in March and the first half of April. Autumn migration extends from mid-July to the beginning of September. Individual birds have also been recorded in October and November.

Common Sandpiper *Actitis hypoleucos*

Pisik obecny Kaluziacik maly Flußuferlaufer

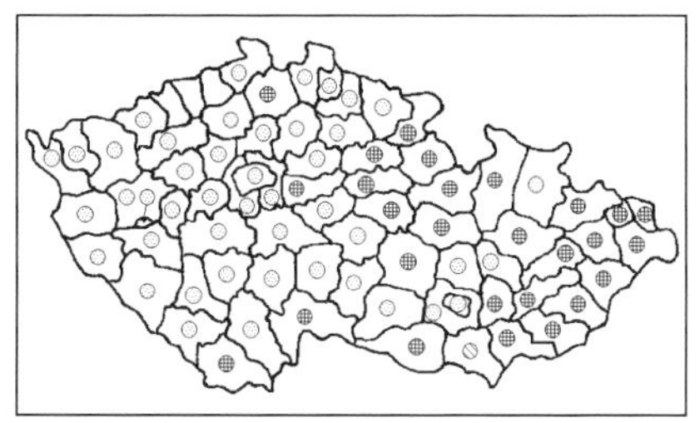

Common Sandpiper is distributed across the country, from lowlands, in which it is most likely to be found, up to 700–750 m. Locally, higher numbers of breeding pairs can still be found in Moravia, in valleys along the major rivers. Breeding habitats include banks of rivers, streams with gravel, sand and sparse vegetation overgrown with willow or poplar thickets and, less commonly, edges of gravel pits or dams. It does not seem to be particularly attracted to fishponds and other open water with muddy margins. Nests are placed on the ground, usually in short grass or other vegetation. During the 1980s, the breeding density was 0.7–1.0 pairs per km along the Becva river (VS), and 1.3–1.5 pairs per km along the Morava river (OL). At the beginning of the 1980s, the average breeding density at about 150 ponds in s. Bohemia was 0.18 individuals per km^2, 0.04 individuals per km^2 in the mid-1980s, and 0.13 individuals per km^2 in 1991. Along an 18-km stretch of the Morava river between Veseli nad Moravou (HO) and Rohatec (HO), 80–120

pairs bred between 1945 and 1980, and 20–30 pairs during the 1980s (Pellantova and Martisko 1993). Wintering birds have been reported regularly, but the number does not usually exceed more than 10 individuals. The main threat to this species seems to be habitat destruction and water pollution.
Status: Migrant and summer visitor. **Breeding season**: uncommon/local. **Winter**: rare. **Migration**: local/common. Endangered. Protected.
Population trends: The breeding population was 400–800 pairs between 1985 and 1989, and these numbers have remained the same during the 1990s. The population has been more or less stable over the past decade, but long-term changes over the past 50 years indicate an overall decline.
Distribution: Nationwide. Higher numbers of breeding pairs occur in the following counties: NA, RK, OL, UH, HO, VS, NJ, OV and KI.
Timing: Arrives from mid-March until the end of April. The peak of migration is during the first half of April. It departs from mid-July until the end of September, with the peak in August and the beginning of September. Breeding occurs from the beginning of April, with the highest numbers at the end of April and beginning of May, until mid-June.

Turnstone *Arenaria interpres*

Ruddy Turnstone   Kamenacek pestry   Kamenar strakaty   Steinwälzer

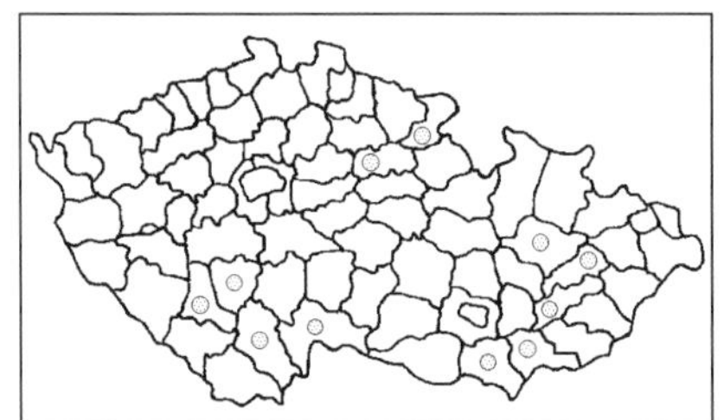

Turnstone is a rather scarce migrant, and is not observed annually in the Czech Republic. It may occur across the country, more commonly as an autumn than spring migrant. On passage, this species is found at muddy shores of ponds and lakes, and gravel pits.
Status: Migrant. **Breeding season**: rare. **Winter**: does not occur. **Migration**: uncommon. Protected.
Population trends: No data available.
Distribution: Recent observations, usually of solitary birds, come from Rezabinec pond (PI), Volesek pond (CB), Tresicky pond (HK), Chomoutov gravel pit (OL), Tovacovske ponds (PR), Zahlinicke ponds (KM), and Nove Mlyny (BV).
Timing: Recorded every month between May and October, with the majority of observations in September.

Red-necked Phalarope *Phalaropus lobatus*

Lyskonoh uzkozoby   Lyskonoh uzkozoby   Odinshühnchen

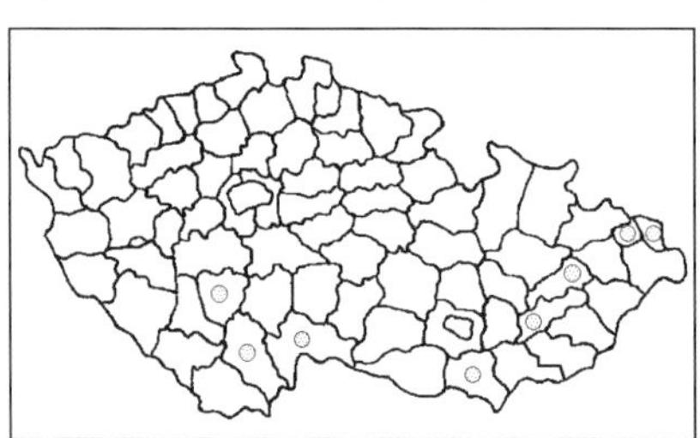

Red-necked Phalarope occurs annually in the Czech Republic, but in small numbers. There are records of solitary birds, and occasionally of small flocks. This species is more common on autumn than spring passage. Birds are most likely to be found at ponds, gravel pits, and occasionally at large, slow-moving rivers.
Status: Migrant. **Breeding season**: rare. **Winter**: rare. **Migration**: uncommon. Protected.
Population trends: No data available.
Distribution: May occur nationwide. Recent records of solitary birds come from Koclirov pond (JH), Obecni pond near Kardasova Recice (JH), Nesyt pond (BV), and Hermansky pond (OV). Up to 4 individuals were recently recorded at Rezabinec pond (PI).
Timing: Observations are from May, June, July, August and September (the majority of records), October and November.

Grey Phalarope *Phalaropus fulicarius*

Red Phalarope Lyskonoh ploskozoby Lyskonoh ploskozoby Thorshühnchen

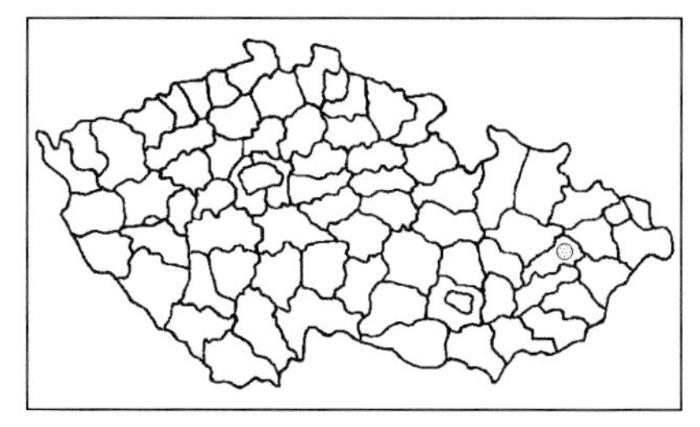

Grey Phalarope is rarer in the Czech Republic than Red-necked Phalarope. There are only 3 records from the last 20 years, the latest from Tovacovske ponds (PR) in 1987. Previously, sightings were scattered across the country. Found at shallow ponds, temporary pools, and muddy, drained fishponds.
Status: Vagrant. **Breeding season**: rare. **Winter**: rare. **Migration**: rare. Protected.
Population trends: No data available.
Distribution: May occur nationwide.
Timing: Records are from June, July, August, October, November and December.

Pomarine Skua *Stercorarius pomarinus*

Pomarine Jaeger Chaluha pomoranska Pomornik stredny Spatelraubmöwe

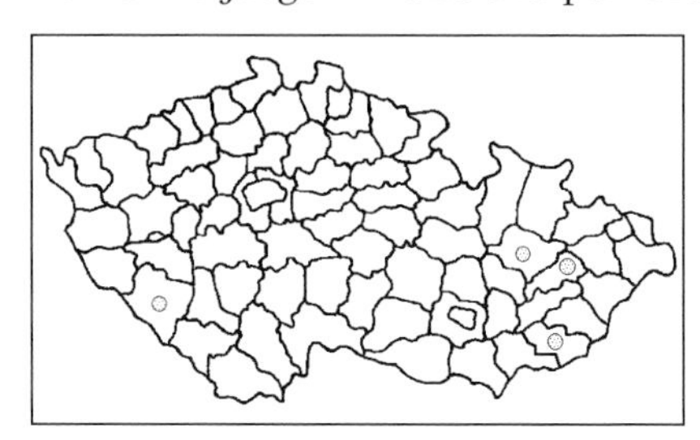

Pomarine Skua is irregularly observed in the Czech Republic. Usually solitary birds are seen, rarely flocks of up to 4, and found at larger fishponds, dams, gravel pits and rivers.
Status: Vagrant. **Breeding season**: rare. **Winter**: uncommon. **Migration**: uncommon. Protected.
Population trends: No data available.
Distribution: May occur nationwide. There are recent records of 1 individual at Tovacovske ponds (PR) and 1 at Ostrozska Nova Ves gravel pit (UH).
Timing: Records are from every month, with the highest numbers in September and October.

Arctic Skua *Stercorarius parasiticus*

Parasitic Jaeger Chaluha prizivna Pomornik prizivny Schmarotzerraubmöwe

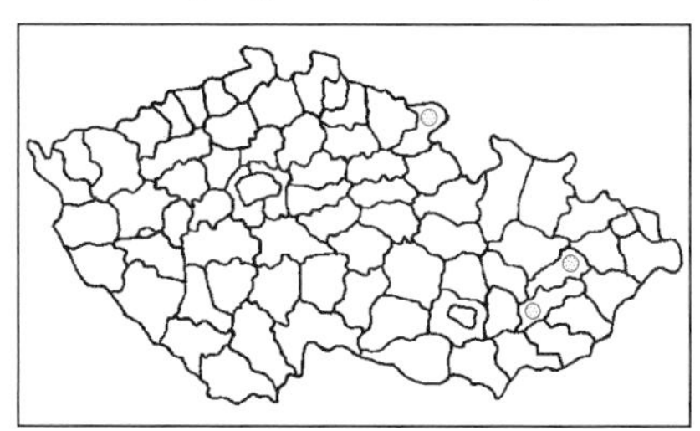

Arctic Skua occurs less commonly in the Czech Republic than Pomarine. Usually solitary birds, occasionally up to 3, are found at large areas of open water such as dams, gravel pits, lakes and ponds.
Status: Vagrant. **Breeding season**: rare. **Winter**: uncommon. **Migration**: uncommon. Protected.
Population trends: No data available.
Distribution: May occur nationwide. Recent records of solitary birds come from Rozkos dam (NA), Dombas gravel pit (PR), and Zahlinicke ponds (KM).
Timing: Recorded from June until December, with the majority of observations in September.

Long-tailed Skua *Stercorarius longicaudus*

Long-tailed Jaeger Chaluha mala Pomornik maly Falkenraubmöwe

Long-tailed Skua is irregularly seen in the Czech Republic, mostly in the west of the country, where solitary birds are usually recorded. Occasionally during invasion years, several individuals are recorded. It occurs at larger areas of open water of all types.
Status: Vagrant. **Breeding season**: rare. **Winter**: does not occur. **Migration**: uncommon. Protected.
Population trends: No data available.
Distribution: May occur nationwide. Most recently it was recorded near Radnice (RO).

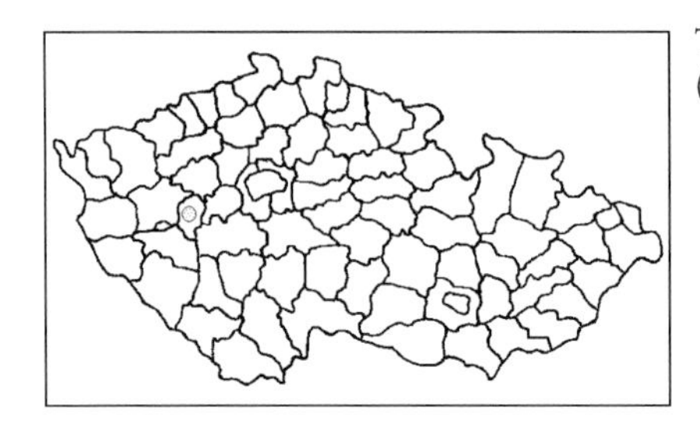

Timing: Records are from July, August, September (the majority of sightings) and October.

Great Skua *Catharacta skua*

Chaluha velka Pomornik velky Skua

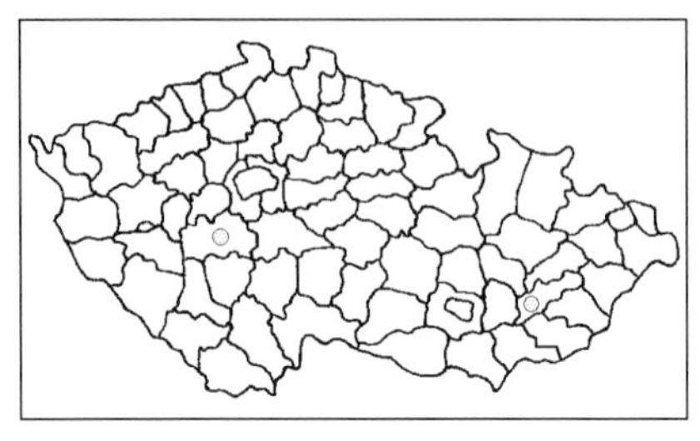

This is the rarest skua in the Czech Republic. Observations are more or less evenly distributed between the west and east of the country. Great Skuas occur at large areas of open water.
Status: Vagrant. **Breeding season**: rare. **Winter**: rare. **Migration**: uncommon. Protected.
Population trends: No data available.
Distribution: May occur nationwide. A recent record of 1 bird is from Zahlinicke ponds (KM), and an exhausted bird was captured near Xaverov (PB) in September 1988.
Timing: Most records are from September and October, the others from December and January.

Mediterranean Gull *Larus melanocephalus*

Racek cernohlavy Cajka ciernohlava Schwarzkopfmöwe

This is a relatively new breeding species in the Czech Republic. Breeding was first documented at Lednicke ponds (BV) in 1967 and, 2 years later, breeding probably occurred in KI county. Regular breeding is restricted to Nove Mlyny (BV), where Mediterranean Gulls have been breeding in low numbers (1–7 pairs) since 1983. Occasional breeding, usually of 1 pair, may occur elsewhere, as was recently documented at Rezabinec pond (PI), Rozkos dam (NA), Domin pond (JH), and in n. Moravia. Breeding habitats in the Czech Republic include large, man-made water bodies with islets and sparse vegetation (Nove Mlyny), reservoirs and ponds. Stragglers have been reported from other parts of the country as well, usually from fishpond areas.
Status: Summer visitor. **Breeding season**: uncommon. **Winter**: rare. **Migration**: uncommon. Critically endangered. Protected.
Population trends: Between 1985 and 1989, 1–5 pairs bred. During the 1990s, up to 10 pairs bred. There were 7 nesting pairs at Nove Mlyny in 1997.
Distribution: There is regular breeding at Nove Mlyny (BV), and occasional breeding in 5 other counties. Recent records of 1–2 birds come from Praha (AA), Rezabinec pond (PI), Zehunsky pond (NB), Koclirov pond (JH), Dolni pond (SY), Soprec pond (PU), Chomoutov gravel pit (OL), Tovacovske ponds (PR), Zahlinicke ponds (KM), and Sumvald (OL).
Timing: Arrives from mid-March until the end of April. Departs in October and November. Breeding occurs between the end of April and the end of May.

Little Gull *Larus minutus*

Racek maly Cajka mala Zwergmöwe

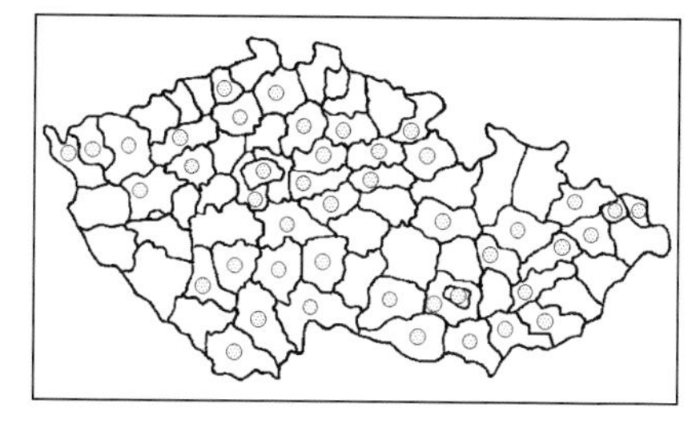

This is a fairly common migrant in the Czech Republic, occurring in higher numbers in spring than autumn. Flocks of several dozens birds can be seen regularly, but flocks of hundreds of birds are much less frequent. Migrating Little Gulls occur across the country, but higher concentrations are known from sites such as Nove Mlyny (BV), Zahlinicke ponds (KM), Tovacovske ponds (PR), and ponds around Trebon (JH) and Ceske Budejovice (CB). Although Little Gull pairs have been seen in suitable habitat during summer months, breeding in the Czech Republic has not been confirmed. Birds on passage favour ponds of varying size rather than rivers.

Status: Migrant and occasional winter visitor. **Breeding season:** rare. **Winter:** uncommon. **Migration:** uncommon. Protected.

Population trends: No data available. The number of birds reported annually seems to be more or less stable.

Distribution: Nationwide. Recent records of solitary birds, but more commonly flocks of up to 100, come from the Vltava river in Praha (AA), Soprec pond (PU), Zrcadlo and Mlynec ponds (JC), Zehunsky pond (NB), Zabakor pond (MB), Vavrinecke ponds (KH), Vitkovsky pond (ST), Milavy pond (ST), Litovicky pond near Hostivice (PZ), Volesek pond (CB), Vysatov pond (CB), Blatec pond (CB), Rezabinec pond (PI), Velky Tisy pond (JH), Koclirov pond (JH), Opatovicky pond near Trebon (JH), Svet pond near Trebon (JH), Tobolky pond near Branna (JH), Novy pond, and Hvezda pond (SY), Chomoutov gravel pit (OL), Sumvald (OL), Hermansky pond (OV), Tovacovske ponds (PR), Veversky Bityska (BO), Kvasice gravel pit (KM), Zahlinicke ponds (KM), Chropynsky pond (KM), Dvorsky pond (HO), Pisecne ponds (HO), Stary pond (BV), Lednicke ponds (BV), and Nove Mlyny (BV).

Timing: Spring migration occurs from mid-April until the end of May, with the peak in the first half of May. Autumn migration extends from mid-August to the beginning of October. Solitary birds have been seen until mid-December. Records of wintering birds, from the end of December–February, are rare.

Black-headed Gull *Larus ridibundus*

Racek chechtavy Cajka smajiva Lachmöwe

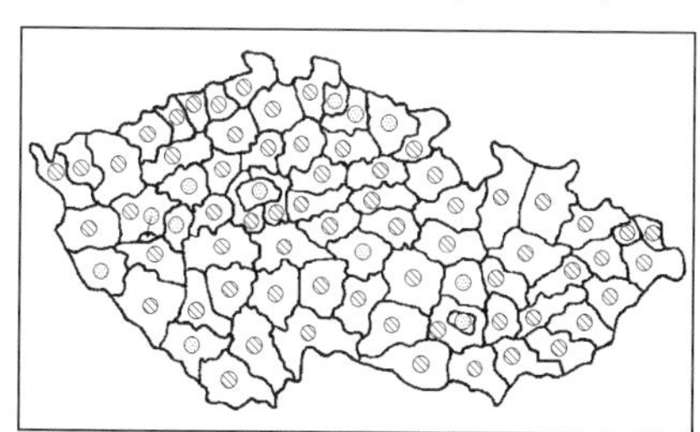

Black-headed Gull is the most common *Larus* species in the Czech Republic, occurring all year round. Breeding colonies are normally located in fishpond areas and wide river valleys in lowlands, but breeding is also known from about 550 m in the Ceskomoravska vysocina highlands (HB, JI, PE, ZR), at 720 m in the Sumava mountains (CK, PT, KT), and at 730 m in the Doupovske hory mountains (KV). Breeding habitats include fishponds, lakes and reservoirs with reedbeds, marshy edges of ponds, and marshes. The size of breeding colonies ranges from several dozen up to several hundred pairs. Until about 1980, there were colonies with thousands of pairs, for example at Chropynsky pond (KM), Zahlinicke ponds (KM), Tovacovske ponds (PR), Horusicky pond (JH), Velky Tisy pond (JH), Rezabinec pond (PI), and Novozamecky pond (CL). The largest ever breeding colonies in the Czech Republic were at the Nove Mlyny reservoirs (BV) during their construction: between 1979 and 1988 the size of colonies was between 10,000 and 30,000 pairs. During the 1970s and 1980s, the number of breeding pairs across the country decreased. For example, at ponds around Ceska Lipa (CL) it was about 15,000 pairs in the mid-1970s, and 15 years later about 2,000 pairs; at Novozamecky pond (CL) 10,000 pairs before 1980, 2,000 pairs in 1980, and 1 pair in 1992; at Rezabinec pond (PI) it was 10,000 pairs before 1985 and 3,000 pairs in 1988; at a gravel pit in Ostrozska Nova Ves (UH) it was 2,000–2,600 pairs at the beginning of the 1980s, about 200 pairs 10 years later, with none in 1997 and 1998. At the beginning of the 1980s, the average breeding density at about 150 ponds in s. Bohemia was 360 individuals per km^2, 184 individuals per km^2 in the mid-1980s, and 194 individuals per km^2 in 1991. During migration and in winter birds occur elsewhere at most types of open water, including rivers, industrial complexes and dumps. High numbers of non-breeding Black-Headed Gulls are seen at rivers in towns across the country. Flocks of thousands of birds can be seen in spring at freshly ploughed fields and, in autumn, at drained and semi-drained fishponds. Although this species is a permanent resident, part of the population is migratory. One of the most important factors causing the decline in the breeding population seems to be the intake of toxins in prey and from rubbish dumps (causing botulism). The former results in a decrease in the number of eggs and poor hatching results (Kloubec and Svecova in Stastny *et al.* 1996).

Status: Resident. **Breeding season**: local. **Winter**: common. **Migration**: common. Least concern. Protected/not hunted all year round, with exceptions.

Population trends: Between 1973 and 1977 the breeding population was between 200,000 and 350,000 pairs; from 1985–1989 it was 80,000–150,000 pairs, and these numbers still obtain in the 1990s, although the breeding population seems to be decreasing. The wintering population was estimated to be between 80,000 and 140,000 individuals. These numbers have fallen recently.

Distribution: Nationwide. As a breeder it is rather scarce in SU, BR, UH, ZL, VS, FM, PV, VY, LB, PE, NA and CR counties.

Timing: Spring migration starts at the end of February and continues through March, with the highest numbers in mid-March. Autumn migration extends from the end of July to mid-November, but is not so extensive as in the spring. Breeding occurs from the beginning of April until early June, peaking at the end of April and beginning of May.

Common Gull *Larus canus*

Mew Gull Racek bourni Cajka siva Sturmmöwe

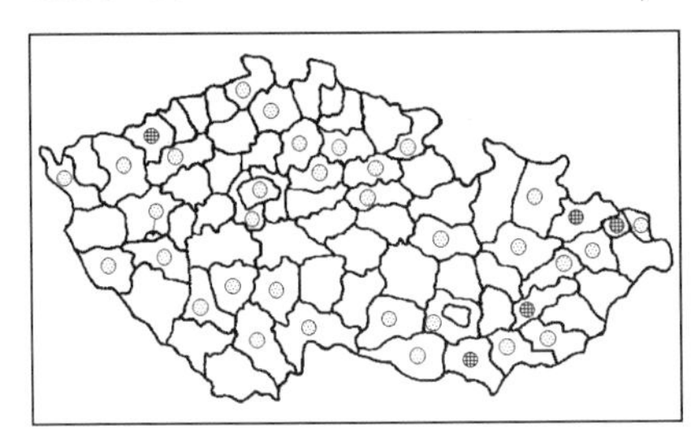

Over the past 20 years, Common Gull has become a fairly common migrant and wintering species in the Czech Republic. Until the mid-1970s, it was usually found in flocks of up to 10 birds, rarely more. Flocks of dozens and even hundreds of birds on passage and in winter are fairly common these days. Recent winter reports include 4,000 birds in Bohumin (OV), up to 1,600 birds at Tovacovske ponds (PR), hundreds at Nove Mlyny (BV) and Troubky gravel pit (PR). Major wintering areas are CB, JH, PI and ST counties in s. Bohemia, BV county in s. Moravia, and PR, OV and KI counties in n. Moravia, where Common Gulls are often found in flocks with Black-headed Gulls. Breeding of a single pair in the country was recorded at Nove Mlyny (BV) in 1986. Since then, regular breeding of 3–7 pairs, mostly in the east of the country, has been recorded annually. More or less regular breeding from the end of the 1980s was also recorded at gravel pits in Dolni Benesov (OP) and Hlucin (OP), Zahlinicke ponds (KM), and industrial complexes near Tusimice (CV). Birds on migration and non-breeders occur all year round, frequenting larger fishponds, gravel pits, dams, industrial complexes and larger rivers. The majority of birds belong to the *canus* race, although some of the wintering birds may belong to the *heinei* race: a bird caught in n. Moravia was of this race.

Status: Resident. **Breeding season**: uncommon (*canus*), rare (*heinei*). **Winter**: uncommon/local (*canus*), rare (*heinei*). **Migration**: uncommon/local (*canus*), rare (*heinei*). Critically endangered. Protected.

Population trends: Three to 10 pairs have bred yearly since 1986. There is a regular wintering population of up to 5,000 individuals, occasionally more, such as the 7,000 individuals in the winter of 1995/96.

Distribution: Migrating and non-breeding birds in summer occur nationwide. Recent records

of flocks, ranging from a few individuals up to 500 birds, all year round, are from the Vltava river in Praha (AA), Vinarsky pond (CV), Velky pond (DC), Horusicky pond (TA), Rozkos dam (NA), Zrcadlo and Mlynec ponds (JC), Mnichovo Hradiste (MB), Vlhavsky pond (CB), Volesek pond (CB), Rezabinec pond (PI), Podkostelni pond near Putim (PI), Koclirov pond (JH), Novy pond near Pluhuv Zdar (JH), Velky Tisy pond (JH), Kanov pond (JH), Velky Ustavni pond near Vodnany (ST), Okrouhlicky pond (ST), Postovni pond near Dehylov (OP), Benesov (OP), Karvina (KI), Fojtuv pond (NJ), Lysecky pond (PR), Sumvald pond (OL), Tovacovske ponds (PR), Prerov (PR), Hulin gravel pit (KM), Zahlinicke ponds (KM), Lednicke ponds (BV), Nove Mlyny (BV), and the Dyje river near Stara Breclav (BV).
Timing: All year round, with the highest numbers between November and the end of March. Breeding extends from the end of May to the beginning of July.

Lesser Black-backed Gull *Larus fuscus*

Racek zlutonohy Cajka tmava Heringsmöwe

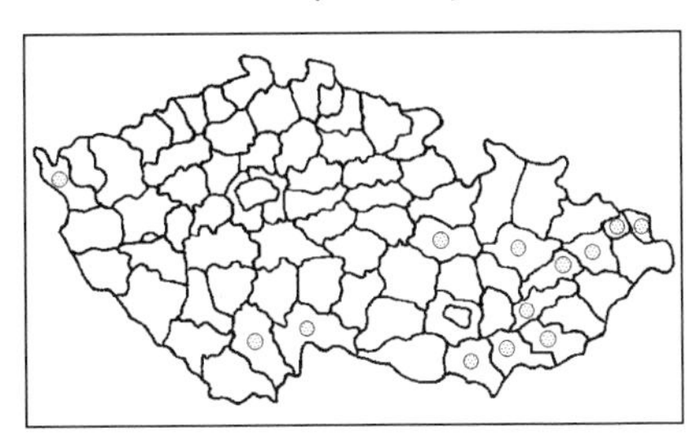

This species occurs annually, but the number of birds varies from year to year, and usually does not exceed 10 individuals a year. Lesser Black-backed Gulls are regularly observed at fishponds in JH county in s. Bohemia, and also from central Moravia (PR, OL), where most of the recent records come from Tovacovske ponds (PR). This species is found at larger fishponds, industrial complexes, gravel pits, and larger rivers. Solitary birds are most common, with flocks of a few birds quite rare. Some of the individuals reported in juvenile plumage may have been misidentified birds.
Status: Migrant and occasional winter visitor. **Breeding season:** rare. **Winter:** uncommon. **Migration:** uncommon. Protected.
Population trends: No data available. Up to 10 birds may be recorded a year.
Distribution: May occur nationwide. Recent records of solitary birds and, less frequently, of flocks of up to 4, come from Nadeje pond (JH), Koclirov pond (JH), Velky Kosir pond (SY), Hvezda pond (SY), Chomoutov gravel pit (OL), Karvina (KI), Hermansky pond (OV), Tovacovske ponds (PR), Sumvald pond (OL), Chropynsky pond (KM), Prerov (PR), Zahlinicke ponds (KM), Pisecne ponds (HO), Jarohnevicky pond (HO) and Ostrozska nova ves (UH).
Timing: Recorded every month, although most of the records are from April–May and October–November.

Herring Gull *Larus argentatus*

Racek stribrity Cajka striebrista Silbermöwe

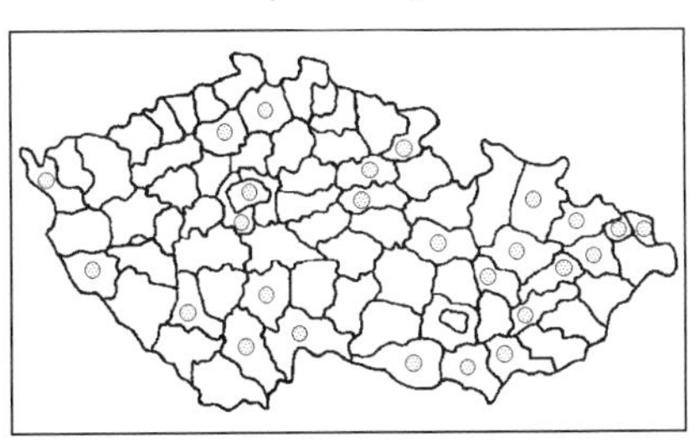

Herring Gull occurs regularly, but less commonly than Common Gull, in the Czech Republic. Birds on passage have usually been recorded in lowlands across the country. This species is often recorded in large numbers, on migration, for example at Doubrava (KI), with 1,050 individuals in September, and 1,010 individuals in October, the river Vltava in Praha (AA), Koclirov pond (JH), Rozmberk pond (JH), Nove Mlyny (BV), Tovacovske ponds (PR), and Zahlinicke ponds (KM) with dozens of birds. Wintering birds occur most commonly in CB and JH counties in s. Bohemia, AA and PZ counties in central Bohemia, BV and KM counties in s. Moravia, and PR, OV and KI counties in n. Moravia. Herring Gull exploits a variety of habitats, from larger rivers, lakes, fishponds, and gravel pits to industrial waters and rubbish dumps. It is often seen in mixed flocks with other gull species. Most of the birds occurring in the Czech Republic

belong to the *argentatus* race, possibly a few are of the *heuglini* race.
Status: Migrant and winter visitor. **Breeding season**: rare. **Winter**: local. **Migration**: local. Critically endangered. Protected.
Population trends: The number of birds recorded on passage and in winter has increased by 20–50% over the past 20 years. In winter, up to 200 individuals, occasionally more, may occur.
Distribution: On migration Herring Gulls may occur nationwide. Recently, solitary birds, but more commonly flocks as large as 40, have been recorded at the Vltava river in Praha (AA), Riha pond (HK), Bohdanecsky pond (PU), Rozkos dam (NA), Municky pond (CB),Volesek pond (CB), Zarsky pond (CB), Rozmberk pond (JH), Potesil pond (JH), Koclirov pond (JH), Velky Tisy pond (JH), Horusicky pond (TA), Velke jezero pond near Klinovice (ST), Novy pond near Opatov (SY), Dolni pond (SY), Otice (OP), Hlucin (OP), Krnov (BR), Hermansky pond (OV), Sumvald (OL), Troubky (PR), Dombas gravel pit (PR), Tovacovske ponds (PR), Hradecky pond (PR), ponds near Jistebnik nad Odrou (NJ), Zahlinicke ponds (KM), Luzicke ponds (HO), Mutenicke ponds (HO), Vytopa pond (HO), Lednicke ponds (BV), and Nove Mlyny (BV).
Timing: Recorded every month. Numbers are highest from August until the beginning of November.

Yellow-legged Gull *Larus cachinnans*

Racek belohlavy   Cajka bielohlava   Weißkopfmöwe

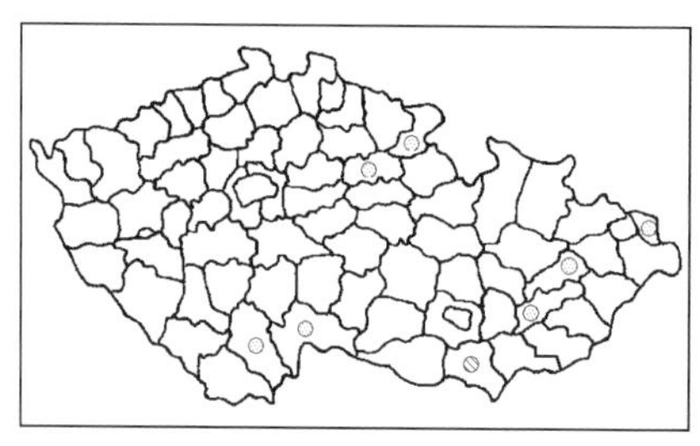

Until recently, Yellow-legged Gull was treated as a race of the Herring Gull *L. a. cachinnans*. Hence, most of the data valid for the previous species may be applied to Yellow-legged Gull. So far, most records of Yellow-legged Gull come from the east of the country. A single pair bred at Nove Mlyny reservoir (BV) in 1990 and 1996, and mating behavior of 2 pairs was observed in 1997. The following year, 2 pairs again nested at Nove Mlyny reservoir (BV), and the first breeding for Bohemia was recorded at Stare Jezero pond (JH).
Status: Local resident. **Breeding season**: rare. **Winter**: uncommon. **Migration**: uncommon. Critically endangered. Protected.
Population trends: The number of birds recorded on passage may reach 50.
Distribution: Recent regular records of up to 10 individuals come from Koclirov pond (JH), Stary Haklovsky pond (CB), Zehunsky pond (NB), Karvina (KI), Tovacovske ponds (PR), Zahlinicke ponds (KM), Lednicke ponds (BV), and Nove Mlyny (BV).
Timing: Recorded all year round, mainly from February–April and July–November.

Great Black-backed Gull *Larus marinus*

Racek morsky   Cajka morska   Mantelmöwe

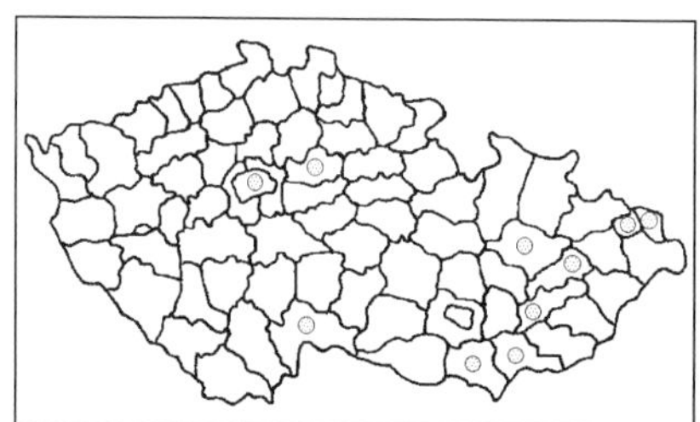

Great Black-backed Gull is a rather scarce species, and is not recorded annually in the Czech Republic. The majority of records were of individual birds, and were at large rivers and ponds.
Status: Migrant and winter visitor. **Breeding season**: rare. **Winter**: uncommon. **Migration**: uncommon. Protected.
Population trends: No data available.
Distribution: May occur nationwide. Recent records, of 1 individual at each site, come from the river Vltava in Praha (AA) during March, Zehunsky pond (NB), Rozmberk pond (JH) in April, Zahlinicke ponds (KM) in April, Hulin gravel pit in October, Tovacovske ponds (PR)

in November, Donbas gravel pit (PR) in December, and Pisecne ponds (HO) in May.
Timing: Recorded from March–May, and August–December, but mainly September–November.

Kittiwake *Rissa tridactyla*

Black-legged Kittiwake Racek triprsty Cajka trojprsta Dreizehenmöwe

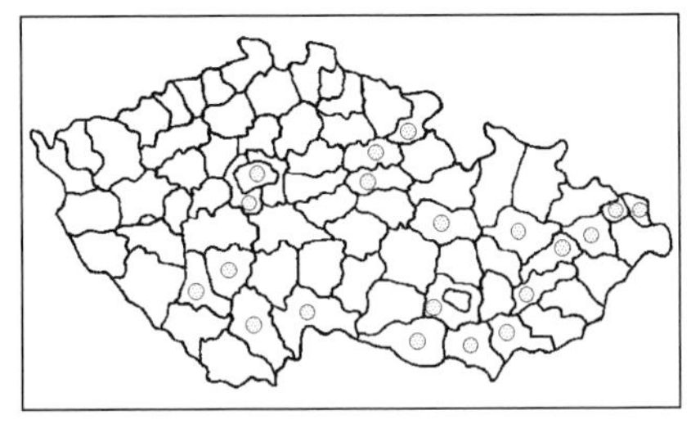

Kittiwakes are observed regularly in the Czech Republic, but in small numbers. Although this species may be seen across the country, most of the recent records are from the east, for example in HO, KM, PR and OL counties. This species is usually found at larger rivers, ponds, and gravel pits. Most records are of immatures.
Status: Migrant. **Breeding season:** rare. **Winter:** uncommon. **Migration:** uncommon. Protected.
Population trends: Up to 20–30 individuals may occur annually on passage; and up to 15 birds winter. No data available to estimate population trends.
Distribution: May occur nationwide. Recent records of 1–3 birds come from Rozmberk pond (JH), Velky Kosir pond near Litomysl (SY), Polanka nad Odrou (NJ), Karvina (KI), Sumvald pond (OL), Chomoutov gravel pit (OL), Dombas gravel pit (PR), Tovacovske ponds (PR), Prerov (PR), Zahlinicke ponds (KM), Vytazniky pond (HO), Dubnansky pond (HO), and Nove Mlyny (BV).
Timing: It occurs mostly from January until April, and from October until November. There are fewer records from July, September and December.

Gull-billed Tern *Sterna nilotica*

Rybak cernozoby Rybar kratkozoby Lachseeschwalbe

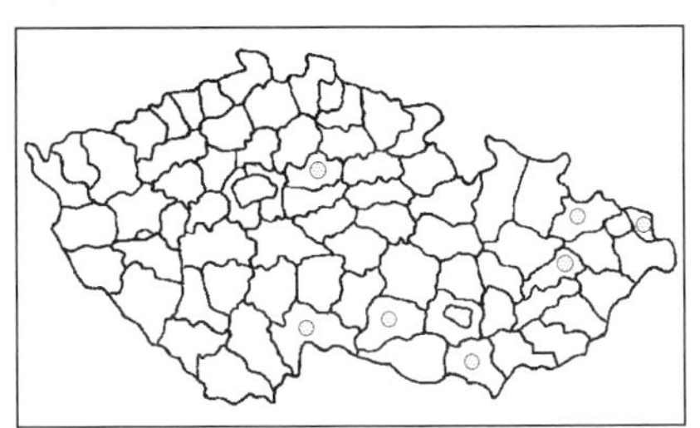

Gull-billed Tern is an irregular visitor to the Czech Republic, occurring mostly in the east of the country. All records are of single birds, usually found at fishponds. A report of possible breeding was reported by Chytil and Machacek (1991). Three or 4 adult birds were seen at Nove Mlyny (BV) between 19 June and 27 June 1991. The birds were seen displaying, but nesting was not recorded.
Status: Vagrant. **Breeding season:** rare. **Winter:** rare. **Migration:** uncommon. Protected.
Population trends: No data available. Between 1980 and 1990, there were 3 records of 6 individuals, more than in any previous decade.
Distribution: Recently up to 8 individuals have been seen at Zehunsky pond (NB) in May and August, and 2 individuals near Karvina (KI) in August.
Timing: Recorded in May, June, July, August and November.

Caspian Tern *Sterna caspia*

Rybak velkozoby Rybar velkozoby Raubseeschwalbe

Caspian Tern is a relatively new species to the Czech Republic. It was seen for the first time in KH county in 1942. Since 1949, Caspian Terns have been recorded annually (Hudec *et al.* 1977). It occurs in fishpond areas in lowlands across the country, most commonly in s. Bohemia, e. Bohemia, and Moravia. This species prefers shallow ponds and lakes, or semi-drained ponds. Recent regular and frequent records of solitary birds or, less frequently, small flocks, come from KM and BV counties in s. Moravia, and PR county in n. Moravia.

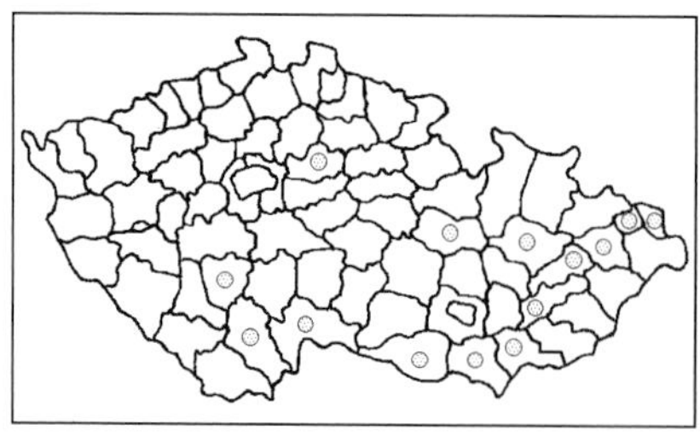

Although there are records of birds from summer months, breeding has not been confirmed in the Czech Republic.
Status: Migrant. **Breeding season:** rare. **Winter:** does not occur. **Migration:** uncommon. Protected.
Population trends: No data available.
Distribution: May occur nationwide. Recently, 1–5 individuals were recorded at Zehunsky pond (NB), Rezabinec pond (PI), Dehtar pond (CB), Koclirov pond (JH), Stary Vdovec pond (JH), Domin pond (JH), Hvezda pond (SY), Terlicka dam (KI), Sumvald (OL), Tovacovske ponds (PR), Zahlinicke ponds (KM), Jaroslavicky pond (ZN), Lanzhot (BV), and Nove Mlyny (BV).
Timing: Spring migration occurs between mid-April and the end of May, peaking at the end of April and beginning of May. Autumn migration extends from mid-August to the end of October, peaking at the end of August and beginning of September. It is then rare until the beginning of November.

Caspian Tern

Common Tern *Sterna hirundo*

Rybak obecny   Rybak obycajny   Flußseeschwalbe

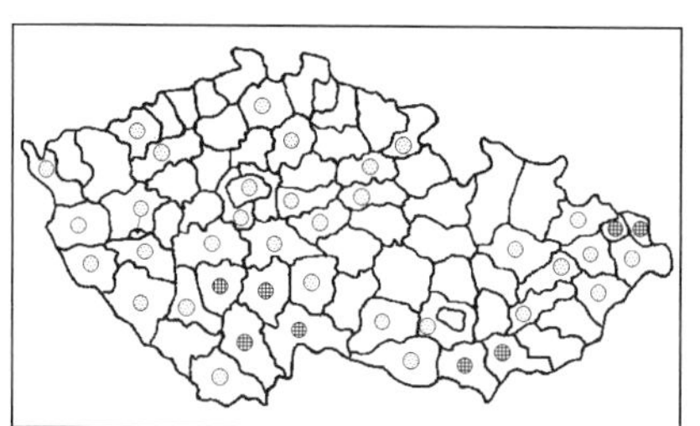

This is the most common tern in the Czech Republic, distributed across the country, usually in lowlands, and from 400–450 m in the highlands. Although breeding pairs occur in various areas in the country, the major regular breeding sites are located in the lowlands of s. Bohemia, s. Moravia, and n. Moravia. Breeding birds are found at larger shallow ponds, marshes, flooded areas, reservoirs, and rivers with small islets with pebbles and sand and covered by sparse vegetation. Nesting has also been recorded on the banks of industrial waterways. At the beginning of the 1980s, the average breeding density at about 150 ponds in s. Bohemia was 2.6 individuals per km^2, 2.4 individuals per km^2 in the mid-1980s, and 1 individual per km^2 in 1991. Sites with regular breeding include ponds around Trebon (JH), with 100–220 pairs, Dehtar pond (CB), with up to 25

pairs, Rezabinec pond (PI), with up to 40 pairs, industrial waterways near Hodonin (HO), with up to 25 pairs, Pohorelicke ponds (BV), with up to 10 pairs, and Nove Mlyny (BV), with up to 200 pairs.
Status: Migrant and summer visitor. **Breeding season:** uncommon/local. **Winter:** does not occur. **Migration:** local. Endangered. Protected.
Population trends: From 1973 to 1977 the breeding population was 100–300 pairs, and from 1985–1989 it was 250–300 pairs. Since then, it has increased by about 50%, with 300–500 pairs now breeding annually.
Distribution: On migration nationwide. Recent records of up to 25 individuals outside the traditional breeding sites include the Vltava river in Praha (AA), Naklo gravel pit (OL), Chomoutov gravel pit (OL), Tovacovske ponds (PR), Hulin gravel pit (KM), Zahlinicke ponds (KM), Dvorsky pond (HO), and Dyjakovice (ZN).
Timing: Spring migration starts in April, with the peak in the second half of the month, and continues until the middle of May. Autumn migration extends from the end of July to the beginning of September. Birds are rare during October, and occasional at the beginning of November. Breeding occurs between the end of April and the beginning of July, with the peak in the second half of May.

Arctic Tern *Sterna paradisaea*

Rybak dlouhoocasy Rybar dlhochvosty Küstenseeschwalbe

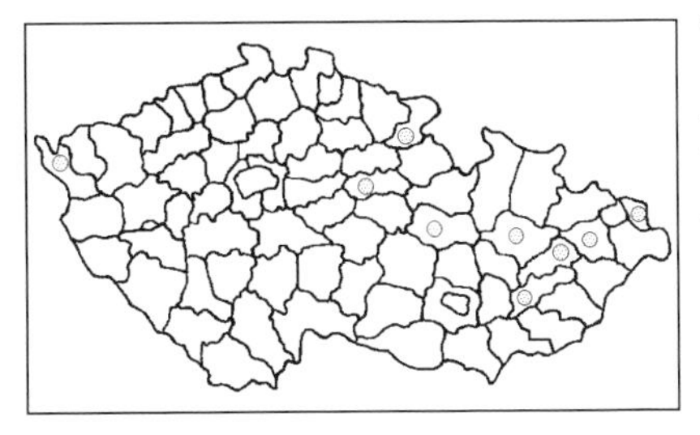

There is 1 reliable record of Arctic Tern fom the 19th century, and 4 records before 1992. Nine additional records since 1992 indicate that this species is becoming more common. Most of the records are from central Moravia. Arctic Tern is usually found at ponds and gravel pits in the lowlands.
Status: Vagrant. **Breeding season:** rare. **Winter:** does not occur. **Migration:** rare. Protected.
Population trends: Increasing in numbers since the beginning of the 1990s.
Distribution: May occur nationwide, but is more likely in the east of the country. Recent records of single birds come from Rozkos dam (NA), Sumvald (OL), and Zahlinicke ponds (KM).
Timing: Recorded from April until August, with the majority of sightings in April and May.

Little Tern *Sterna albifrons*

Rybak maly Rybar maly Zwergseeschwalbe

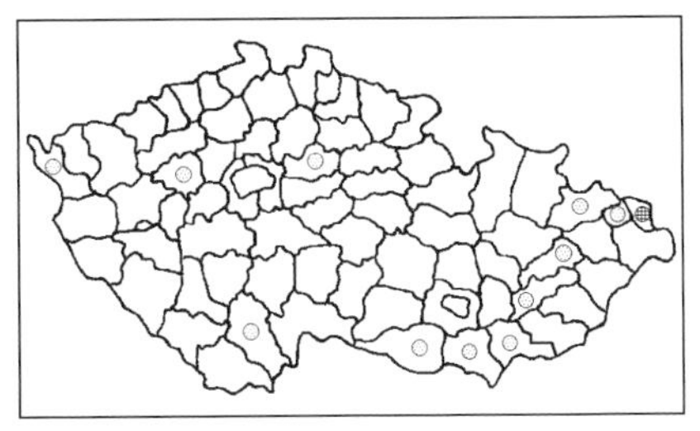

Over the past 20 years, Little Tern has occurred irregularly in the Czech Republic, usually as a solitary bird at dams, ponds, and around larger rivers in lowlands. Breeding was confirmed in the Czech Republic for the first time in KI county in July 1995, and again in the same county in 1998.
Status: Vagrant. **Breeding season:** rare. **Winter:** does not occur. **Migration:** rare. Protected.
Population trends: No data available.
Distribution: May occur nationwide. Recent records of single birds come from Velky pond near Jesenice (RA), Zehunsky pond (NB), Blatec pond (CB), Terlicka dam (KI), Tovacovske ponds (PR), Zahlinicke ponds (KM), and Nove Mlyny (BV).
Timing: Recorded from April until September.

Whiskered Tern *Chlidonias hybridus*

Rybak bahenni Corik bahenny Weißbart-Seeschwalbe

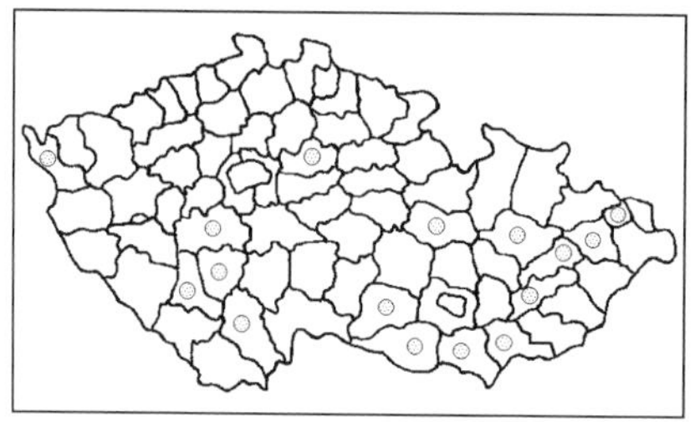

Whiskered Tern occurs only in small numbers, and irregularly in the Czech Republic. Breeding was recorded once in the second half of the 19th century in s. Bohemia, and once in s. Moravia in 1959. Solitary birds or flocks of 2–6 individuals are usually more frequent during spring than autumn migration. This species favours shallow lakes and ponds which have abundant floating vegetation, and, less commonly, marshes. Most recent records are from Zehunsky pond (NB).

Status: Vagrant. **Breeding season:** rare. **Winter:** does not occur. **Migration:** uncommon. Protected.

Population trends: No data available.

Distribution: Scattered in lowlands across the country. Recent May and June records of up to 14 birds come from Zehunsky pond (NB), Markovec pond (ST), Novy Vrbensky pond (CB), Rezabinec pond (PI), Novy pond near Lhotka (PB), Hvezda pond (SY), Sumvald pond (OL), Bartosovicke ponds (NJ), Luzicke ponds (HO), Jaroslavicky pond (ZN), ponds around Namest nad Oslavou (TR), and Tovacovske ponds (PR).

Timing: Recorded in May, June, July, August and October.

Black Tern *Chlidonias niger*

Rybak cerny Corik cierny Trauerseeschwalbe

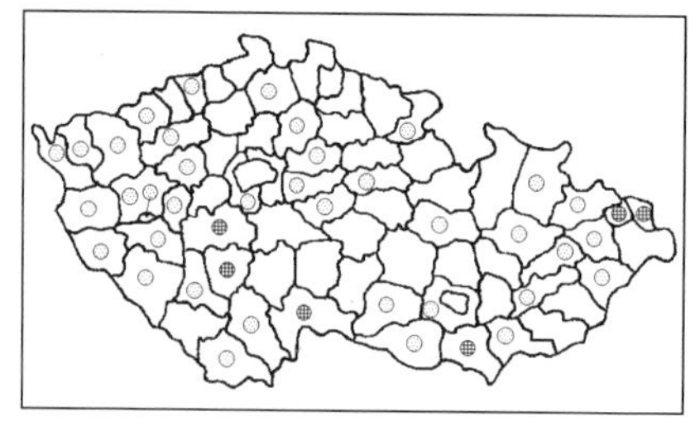

Black Tern is a fairly common migrant, occurring across the country, but a rare breeder, restricted to a few areas in the lowlands, and up to 400–450 m in highlands (JH). Regular breeding in small colonies occurs at ponds around Trebon (JH) in s. Bohemia, with up to 20 pairs, at Nove Mlyny (BV), with up to 5 pairs, and at industrial complexes around Ostrava. During the 1970s, this species disappeared from many traditional breeding areas in s. Bohemia, and the population started to decrease. Breeding habitats include marshes, edges of ponds, and occasionally oxbows of large rivers, but always with abundant floating vegetation. Nests are built in short emergent vegetation, usually at the water's edge. On migration, it can be seen at ponds, gravel pits, less commonly around the larger rivers. The main threat to this species seems to be habitat loss caused by drainage of marshes, and by destruction of littoral vegetation at ponds.

Status: Migrant and summer visitor. **Breeding season:** uncommon. **Winter:** does not occur. **Migration:** local. Critically endangered. Protected.

Population trends: The breeding population between 1973 and 1977 was 80–120 pairs, and from 1985–1989 it was 20–50 pairs. The latter numbers also hold for the 1990s. The number of nesting pairs may vary from year to year.

Distribution: Found on migration nationwide. Regular breeding is restricted to JH, BV and OV counties. Occasional breeding may occur in other counties across the country, as in KI, PI and PB. Recent records of passage birds, in flocks of 5–35 and occasionally up to 100, come from Lenesicky pond (LN), Silnicni pond near Bor u Tachova (TC), Velky pond (RA), Vavrinecke ponds (KH), Zehunsky pond (NB), Rozkos dam (NA), Soprec pond (PU), ponds near Opatov (SY), Novovesky pond (DO), Milavy pond (ST), ponds near Strelske Hostice (ST), Lipno dam near Borkova (CK), the river Vltava near Nova Pec (CK), Rezabinec pond (PI), Siroky and Chlum ponds near Ceske Budejovice (CB), Kardas pond (JH), Novy pond near Branna (JH), Opatovicky pond (JH), Ruda, Tobolky, Hurky, Svet, and Zenich ponds (JH), Bedny pond near Studenka (NJ), ponds near Polanka nad Odrou (BR), Chorynske ponds (VS), Chomoutov gravel pit (OL), Sumvald pond (OL), Hermansky pond (OV), Tovacovske

ponds (PR), Opatsky pond (TR), Velky Bor pond (TR), Kvasice gravel pit (KM), Zahlinicke ponds (KM), Mutenicke ponds (HO), Dvorsky pond (HO), Zbrodsky pond (HO), Lednicke ponds (BV), and Nove Mlyny (BV).
Timing: Spring migration starts in April, and continues until the end of May. Migration peaks during the second half of May. Autumn migration occurs between the end of July and the beginning of October, peaking at the end of August. Breeding starts in mid-May, with increasing number of nesting pairs at the end of May and the beginning of June, and continues until the beginning of July.

White-winged Black Tern *Chlidonias leucopterus*

White-winged Tern   Rybak belokridly   Corik bielokridly   Weißflugel-Seeschwalbe

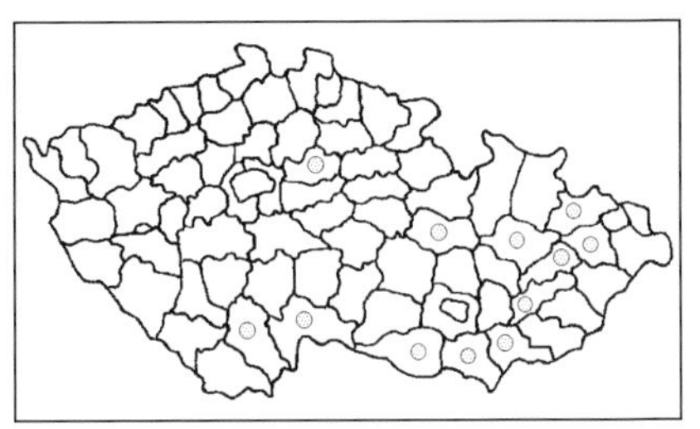

This species occurs annually in varying numbers (normally 10–20 individuals), and mostly in the east of the Czech Republic. White-winged Black Tern is more common on spring than autumn passage. Birds are usually seen at ponds, lakes and, less commonly, around larger slow-flowing rivers in lowlands. Breeding has never been confirmed in the country. Reports of breeding from the end of the 19th century are dubious. Most recent records, particularly of birds on spring passage, are from ponds near Opatov (SY).
Status: Migrant. **Breeding season:** rare. **Winter:** does not occur. **Migration:** uncommon. Protected.
Population trends: No data available.
Distribution: May occur nationwide, but is mostly found in Moravia. Recent records of individuals and flocks of up to 50 birds come from Zehunsky pond (NB), Siroky and Kamenny Ujezd ponds (CB), Blatec pond (CB), Koclirov pond (JH), Hvezda pond (SY), Novy pond (SY), Dolni Benesov (OP), Tovacovske ponds (PR), Chomoutov gravel pit (OL), Zahlinicke ponds (KM) (280 in 1997), Stolarka pond (HO), Luzicke ponds (HO), Jaroslavicky pond (ZN), and Nove Mlyny (BV).
Timing: Spring migration occurs between the end of April and beginning of June, peaking during the second half of May. Autumn migration begins at the end of June, and is over by the end of September.

PTEROCLIDIFORMES

Includes a sole family with 7 species in the w. Palearctic. One species from the family **Pteroclididae** has been recorded as a vagrant in the Czech Republic.

Pallas's Sandgrouse *Syrrhaptes paradoxus*

Stepokur kirgizsky   Labkan stepny   Steppenhuhn

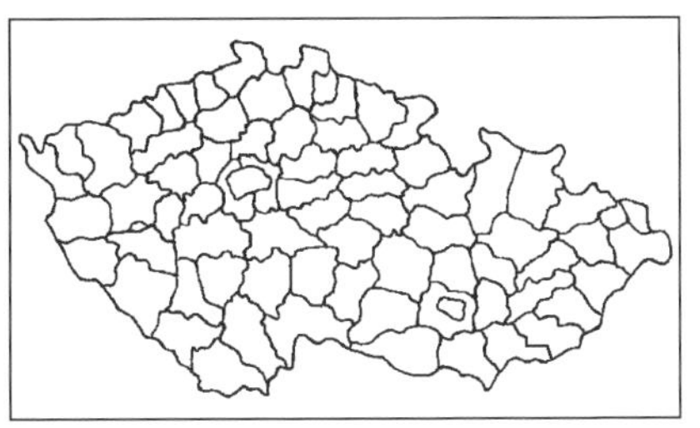

Pallas' Sandgrouse occurred in the Czech Republic during periodic invasions in the second half of the 19th and first decade of the 20th centuries. During the invasions in 1863, 1864, 1880, 1888, 1891 and 1908 varying numbers were recorded. Apart from these invasions, when larger numbers of birds were seen, records of solitary birds come from other years as well. The last record for the country is from November 1934, when a dead bird was found in n. Moravia (Hudec *et al.* 1977). Birds were found in open habitats in farmland, and usually occurred in flocks, rarely alone.
Status: Vagrant. **Breeding season:** rare. **Winter:** rare. **Migration:** rare. Protected.

Population trends: Has not been recorded since 1934.
Distribution: May occur nationwide.
Timing: Most available records are from May, followed by April, June, October, November, December and January.

Pallas's Sandgrouse

COLUMBIFORMES

Fifteen species from the family **Columbidae** occur in the w. Palearctic. Five species occur in the Czech Republic and are regular breeders, either as residents or summer visitors.

Rock Dove *Columba livia domestica*

Rock Pigeon, Feral Pigeon   Holub domaci   Holub domovy   Felsentaube

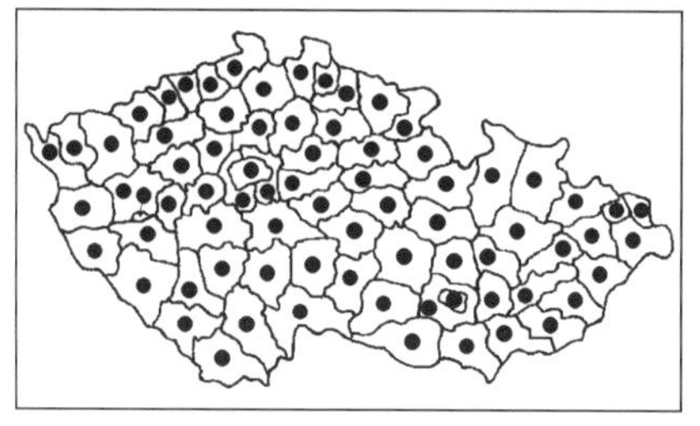

All Rock Doves observed in the Czech Republic have their origin in domestic stocks. The wild form, *Columba livia*, has probably never been recorded in the Czech Republic (Hudec *et al.* 1977). This species is usually found in human settlements, and occurs mostly in towns across the country. However, breeding in rural habitats, under bridges, away from human settlement, and on rocks has also been documented in BV, LT, MB and JC counties. This species usually nests in colonies of varying size. It occurs in most larger cities. The breeding population in Praha (AA) was between 95,000 and 145,000 in the mid-1980s.
Status: Resident. **Breeding season**: local/common. **Winter**: common. **Migration**: common.
Population trends: The population is estimated to be between 800,000 and 1,600,000 pairs.
Distribution: Nationwide.
Timing: All year round. Breeding in towns occurs almost throughout the year, except during moulting and in winter.

Stock Dove *Columba oenas*

Stock Pigeon   Holub doupnak   Holub pluzik   Hohltaube

Although Stock Dove is the rarest species of Columbiforme occurring in the Czech Republic, it is a fairly common local breeder in some counties. The breeding range extends from lowlands up to 800–850 m in the Jeseniky (BR, SU) and Rychlebske hory (SU) mountains, up to 900 m in the Krusne hory mountains (CV, KV, MO, TP), to 970 m in the Orlicke hory moun-

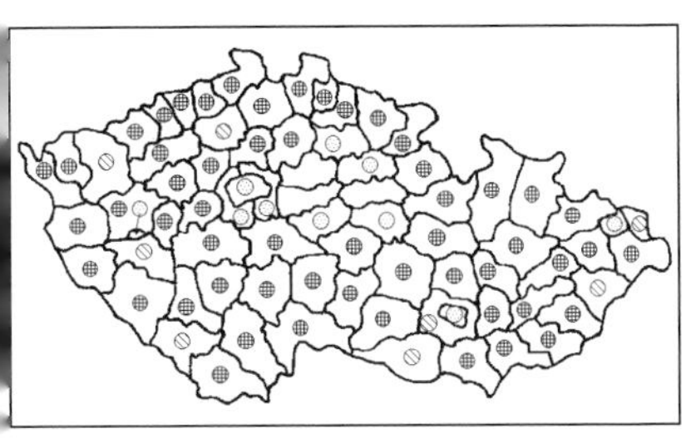

tains (RK), to 1000 m in the Krkonose mountains (SE, TU), and to about 1200 m in the Sumava (CK, PT, KT) and Beskydy (FM, VS) mountains. This species is more common in lowlands and highlands than in mountains. Breeding habitats include mature mixed and deciduous, but not too dense, forest, especially with an abundance of oak and beech. It may also nest in larger parks, avenues and orchards with hollow trees. Nest holes are usually located in oaks and beeches, often those previously used by Black Woodpeckers, and mainly 3–7 m above ground. During the 1980s, breeding density was 19 pairs per km^2 in a mountain village at about 730 m in VS county, 5 pairs per km^2 in the Beskydy mountains, 26 pairs per km^2 in a 100 year-old beech forest in the Jizerske hory mountains (LB, JN) and Cesky raj (MB) rocks, and 60 pairs per km^2 in mixed forest in the Krusne hory and Sumava mountains. It was 38 pairs per km^2 in the Novohradske hory mountains (CB, CK), and 3 pairs per km^2 in a park around the castle in Blatna (ST) at the beginning of the 1990s. During migration, flocks of varying size occur in farmland. Even though it is a migatory species, several dozen birds may be found in winter, particularly around human habitation in villages and on farms.

Status: Migrant and summer visitor. **Breeding season:** local. **Winter:** rare. **Migration:** local. Vulnerable. Protected/not hunted all year round.

Population trends: The breeding population is between 3,000 and 6,000 pairs. Locally, in some parts of the country, the population has been increasing but has otherwise remained more or less stable over the past 10 years. The wintering population can be up to 60 individuals.

Distribution: Found on passage nationwide. Regular breeding of larger numbers may occur in PT, PJ, RA, SU, VS, ZL and UH counties.

Timing: Spring migration starts at the end of February and continues to the beginning of April, peaking during the first half of March. Autumn migration occurs in September and October, with the peak at the beginning of October. Breeding extends from the end of March to the end of June, rarely later. Breeding peaks between mid-April and mid-May.

Wood Pigeon *Columba palumbus*

Woodpigeon, Common Woodpigeon   Holub hrivnac   Holub hrivnak   Ringeltaube

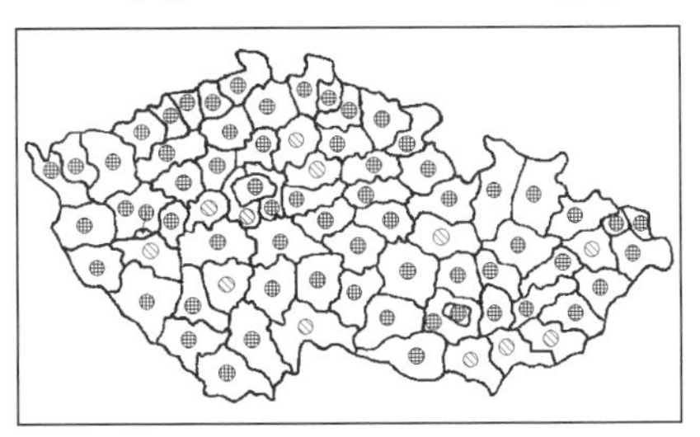

Wood Pigeon is a common species in the Czech Republic. Its range extends from lowlands up to about 900 m in the Orlicke hory mountains (RK), to 1100 m in the Krkonose mountains (SE, TU), and to about 1200 m in the Jeseniky (BR, SU), Krusne hory (CV, KV, MO, TP) and Beskydy (FM, VS) mountains. Breeding density decreases at higher altitudes in the mountains. This species exploits a wide range of habitats, such as woods of any type, copses or groups of trees in extensive areas of farmland, windbreaks, hedgerows, and riverine growths. It can also be found in parks, larger orchards and cemeteries, although this is a quite recent phenomenon. Nests are usually built in a spruce, pine, oak or willow, 2–12 m above ground. During the 1970s, breeding density was 11–30 pairs per km^2 in mixed woods and 42 individuals per km^2 in pine forests in TA county. During the 1970s, it was 15 pairs per km^2 in spruce-pine forest near Trebon (JH), 18 individuals per km^2 in the same habitat in the Cesky les mountains (DO, TC), 9 individuals per km^2 in riverine forest in OL county, 370 and 70 pairs per km^2 in hedgerows around Trebon (JH) and Strakonice (ST) respectively, 10–14 pairs per km^2 in avenues along a river at 180 m in farmland in UH county, 16–21 pairs per km^2 in mixed mature woods at about 260 m in UH county, and 2 pairs per km^2 in fir-beech forest in the Beskydy mountains. In forests damaged by acid-rain in the Krkonose mountains it was 1–5 pairs per km^2, in the Krusne hory mountains 7 pairs per km^2, and 13 pairs per km^2 in the Jizerske hory mountains (LB, JN) during the

1980s and early 1990s. It was 7 pairs per km² at about 1180 m in the Beskydy mountains, 19 pairs per km² in the Novohradske hory mountains (CB, CK), and 35 pairs per km² in the park around Blatna castle (ST) at the beginning of the 1990s. On passage and after breeding, flocks of varying size commonly occur in farmland. Wintering individuals, either solitary birds or small flocks, often visit human habitations and may be seen with Feral Pigeons. The numbers of wintering Wood Pigeons have been increasing over the past 10–15 years.
Status: Migrant and summer visitor. **Breeding season**: common. **Winter**: uncommon/local. **Migration**: common. Hunted during fixed season.
Population trends: The breeding population is between 120,000 and 240,000 pairs, and the numbers have been stable over the past 20 years. In winter up to 150 individuals may occur.
Distribution: Nationwide.
Timing: Arrives from mid-February until mid-April, numbers peaking in March. Departs mostly from the end of September until mid-October. Breeding occurs between the end of March and the beginning of July, with the peak from mid-April to the beginning of May.

Collared Dove *Streptopelia decaocto*

Eurasian Collared Dove   Hrdlicka zahradni   Hrdlicka zahradna   Türkentaube

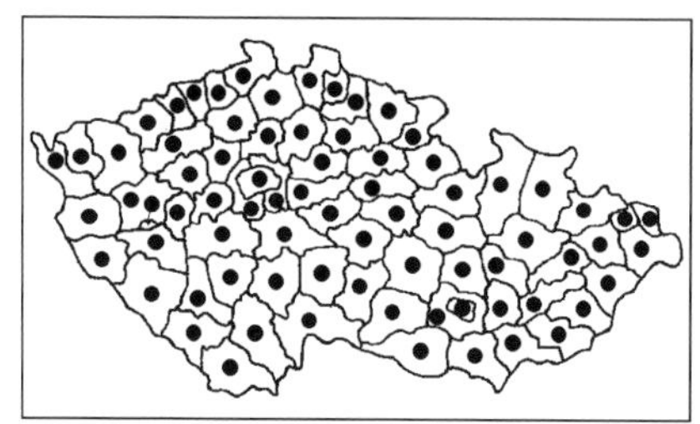

Sixty years ago, Collared Dove was an unknown species in the Czech Republic. However, its invasion and exploitation of man-made habitats has been quick, and Collared Dove has become an abundant species, occurring countrywide. At the beginning of the 1940s, this species was recorded in s. Moravian towns such as Brno (BM), Hodonin (HO) and Kyjov (HO). Most of the 14 s. Moravian counties were inhabited by 1945. In 1947, it was observed in PU, HK, RK and CR counties in e. Bohemia, and AA and KH counties in central Bohemia. A year later, LN and CV counties in n. Bohemia, and OV county in n. Moravia became nesting areas. In the following years it became a breeder in s. Bohemia and w. Bohemia. In 1955, its range was established nationwide. However, expansion at higher altitudes has been slower: in the Krkonose mountains (TU, SE) it started to nest at 750 m in 1972 (Stastny *et al.* 1987). Collared Dove is more common in lowlands than in highlands and mountains. Breeding was recorded at 580 m in the Jeseniky mountains (BR, SU), at 700 m in the Cesky les (DO, TC) and Orlicke hory (RK) mountains, and at 730 m in the Sumava mountains (CK, PT, KT). This species is typically found in human settlements. It frequents towns, villages, orchards, parks, cemeteries, farms and surrounding habitats. Nests are normally built in a spruce, pine, pear or poplar, as well as on buildings, electric poles and other artificial constructions, usually between 2 and 10 m above ground. From 1977 to 1978 breeding density was 10–90, but locally up to 500 pairs per km², in Praha (AA); average breeding density in Brno (BM) was 131 individuals per km² at the beginning of the 1970s, and 970–1,090 pairs per km² in a park in Cesky Brod (KO) in the mid-1970s. It was 60–65 pairs per km² in a park in Ostrava (OV), 32–129 pairs per km² in various habitats in Tachov (TC), 370–410 pairs per km², and 290–530 pairs per km² around 2 farms in UH county during the 1980s. In the mid-1980s, winter density was 750–806 individuals per km² around a farm at 180 m in UH county. At roosting sites, often close to farms or other feeding places, flocks of hundreds and sometimes thousands can occur.
Status: Resident. **Breeding season**: common. **Winter**: common. **Migration**: common. Hunted during fixed season.
Population trends: The breeding population is between 200,000 and 400,000 pairs. Over the past 20 years, it has decreased by 20–50%. The wintering population is between 250,000 and 400,000 individuals.
Distribution: Nationwide.
Timing: All year round. Breeding has been recorded from January until November, particularly at places with a favorable microclimate, and it may even nest in late autumn or early spring. However, breeding peaks between early April and mid-May.

Turtle Dove *Streptopelia turtur*

European Turtle Dove   Hrdlicka divoka   Hrdlicka polna   Turteltaube

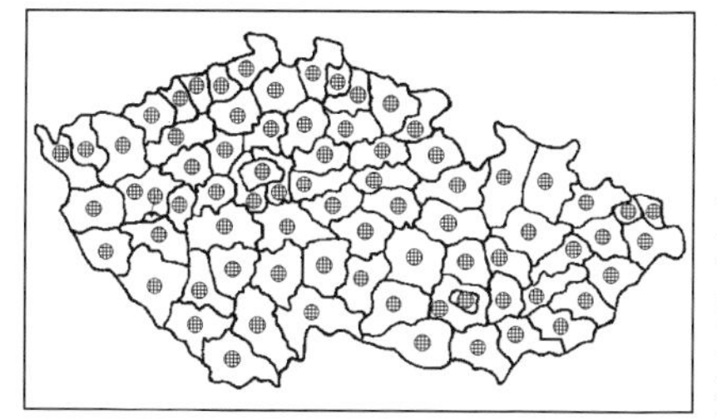

Turtle Dove is a fairly common breeder across the country. It occurs from lowlands up to about 750 m in the Orlicke hory mountains (RK), to 800 m in the Sumava (CK, PT, KT) and Jeseniky (BR, SU) mountains, to 850 m in the Krusne hory mountains (CV, KV, MO, TP), and to 1000 m in the Krkonose mountains (SE, TU). It is more abundant in lowlands than at higher altitudes. This species frequents farmland with a mosaic of mixed woodland, hedgerows, windbreaks, growths along rivers and around ponds, orchards and parks. It is also found at the edges of deciduous forest. It usually avoids large dense forest. Nests are normally built in a blackthorn, spruce, European elder, rose or hawthorn, usually between 1 and 4 m above ground. During the 1970s, breeding density was 11–13 and 50 pairs per km^2 respectively in riverine forest in KM and PR counties, 10 pairs per km^2 in small areas of deciduous forest in the Cesky les mountains (DO, TC), 10–11 pairs per km^2 in spruce forest near Milevsko (TA), 24 individuals per km^2 in pine forest in TC county, and 5–24 pairs per km^2 in mixed forest around Praha (AA). During the 1980s, it was 1–20 and 100 pairs per km^2 respectively in hedgerows in farmland in TC and ST counties, 20 pairs per km^2 in an avenue of oak in ST county, 18 individuals per km^2 in riverine forest in OL county, 12 pairs per km^2 in oak forest in MO county, 2 and 15 pairs per km^2 respectively in pine forest in TC and TA counties, 12–25 pairs per km^2 in mature riverine woodland with dense undergrowth at 180 m in UH county, and 18–22 pairs per km^2 in hedgerows in farmland at the same elevation in UH county. Flocks of Turtle Doves can be seen feeding in fields after harvest and during autumn migration. Loss of suitable breeding habitats and use of herbicides are probably the main threats, and hunting in its wintering grounds a secondary threat to this species (Tucker and Heath 1994).

Status: Migrant and summer visitor. **Breeding season**: common. **Winter**: does not occur. **Migration**: common. Protected/not hunted all year round.

Population trends: The breeding population is between 60,000 and 120,000. It has decreased by 20–50% over the past 20 years.

Distribution: Nationwide.

Timing: Spring migration occurs from the end of March until the beginning of May, peaking during the second half of April. Autumn migration is between mid-August and the beginning of October, with the peak during the second half of September. Breeding extends from the beginning of May to the end of July, occasionally later. Breeding peaks during the second half of May.

Turtle Dove

CUCULIFORMES

Includes a sole family with 8 representatives occurring in the w. Palearctic. One species from the family **Cuculidae** is a common summer visitor to the Czech Republic.

Common Cuckoo *Cuculus canorus*

Cuckoo, European Cuckoo   Kukacka obecna   Kukacka obycajna   Kuckuck

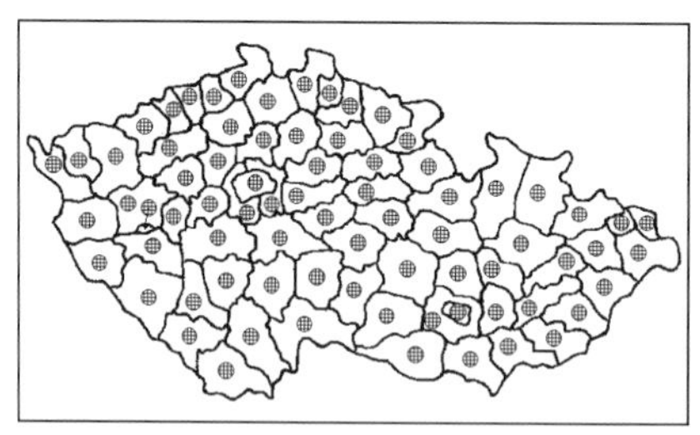

Common Cuckoo is a widespread species in the Czech Republic. It is distributed from lowlands up to 1150 m in the Beskydy mountains (FM, VS), to 1200 m in the Sumava mountains (CK, PT, KT), and to 1400 m in the Krkonose mountains (SE, TU), but is usually found in lowlands and highlands. It exploits the wide range of habitats where potential host species nest: open habitats with thickets, woodlands, hedgerows, windbreaks, avenues, brush around rivers, scrubby wasteland, parks, and reedbeds around ponds, and is also found in mixed and deciduous forest, less often in alpine meadows, dense coniferous plantations and orchards. The main host species are Robin, Common Redstart, White Wagtail, Red-backed Shrike, Wood Warbler, Garden Warbler and Reed Warbler. Among the other 27 frequently exploited hosts are, for example, Yellowhammer, Blackcap, Lesser Whitethroat, Common Whitethroat, Great Reed Warbler and Willow Warbler (Hudec *et al.* 1983). Common Cuckoo's density varies significantly among habitats and from county to county. During the 1970s, it was 14–55 individuals per km^2 in growths along ponds, and 5 individuals per km^2 at meadows with sparse areas of bush around Trebon (JH). In 1980, it was 8 individuals per km^2 in windbreaks and hedgerows in BV and TC counties, 4 individuals per km^2 in parkland around a castle (LN), and 5–11 calling males per km^2 in windbreaks and hedgerows in farmland at 180 m in UH county. Higher densities of Cuckoos can often be seen around ponds.

Status: Migrant and summer visitor. **Breeding season**: common. **Winter**: does not occur. **Migration**: common. Protected.

Population trends: The breeding population is between 52,000 and 105,000 individuals, and has been stable over the past 20 years.

Distribution: Nationwide.

Timing: Arrives from the beginning of April to early May. Migration peaks during the second half of April. Males arrive first, and are followed by females. It departs from the beginning of August to the end of September, with the majority of birds leaving at the end of August and beginning of September. The egg-laying period starts from the end of April, but is mainly between mid-May and mid-June, with sporadic clutches until the beginning of July.

Common Cuckoo

STRIGIFORMES

Includes 2 families with 17 species in the w. Palearctic. Twelve species have been recorded in the Czech Republic. There is one regular breeder from the family **Tytonidae.** The family **Strigidae** is represented by 8 regular breeders, 1 irregular breeder which is a summer visitor, and 2 vagrants.

Barn Owl *Tyto alba*

Sova palena Plamienka driemava Scheiereule

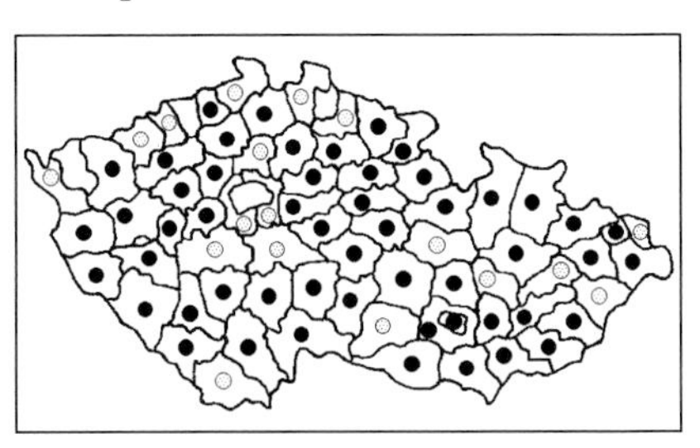

This is one owl whose numbers have declined severely in the Czech Republic over the past 30 years or so. Barn Owl prefers lowlands and highlands up to about 400 m in the Ceskomoravska vysocina highlands (HB, JI, PE, ZR), up to 520 m in the foothills of the Cesky les mountains (DO, TC), to 600 m in the Krusne hory mountains (CV, KV, MO, TP), to 700 m in the Orlicke hory (RK) and Jeseniky (BR, SU) mountains, to 800 m in the Sumava (CK, PT, KT) and Krkonose (SE, TU) mountains, and to 860 m in the Jizerske hory mountains (LB, JN). This species is found in farmland and near human habitations, and depends on the nesting opportunities offered by farm buildings, haylofts and church towers. It occasionally nests in the cavities of trees and rock crevices. Nests are most commonly placed in church towers and haylofts. Nest sites are usually occupied for several years. It feeds in grassy patches around ditches, hedgerows, pastures, meadows, and at the edges of forest in farmland. In the mid-1980s, breeding density was 0.03–0.04 pairs per km^2 around Trebon (JH), and 0.03–0.06 pairs per km^2 around Nachod (NA). Breeding density based on the number of active nests in church towers was 0.01 pairs per km^2 in OL county at the beginning of the 1990s. Several factors may be involved in Barn Owls' population decline: loss of breeding sites due to replacement of old farm buildings, loss of foraging habitats, and use of organochloride pesticides. A number of studies show that after severe winters with heavy snow the breeding population decreases. The Czech Republic's breeding population belongs to the *guttata* race.

Status: Resident. **Breeding season**: uncommon. **Winter**: local. **Migration**: local. Endangered. Protected.

Population trends: The breeding population is between 400 and 700 pairs, although Danko *et al.* (1994) estimated it to be only 300–350 pairs at the beginning of the 1990s. A decline of 20–50% was recorded between the mid-1970s and 1995. The highest numbers are in n. Moravia, with about 100 pairs, and e. Bohemia, with 60 pairs. The lowest numbers are in central Bohemia, with 15 pairs. The wintering population is between 900 and 1,800 individuals.

Distribution: Barn Owl is scattered across the country. In winter, Barn Owls usually move from altitudes of 700–800 m to the lowlands.

Timing: All year round. Breeding extends from mid-March to the end of August. When there are 2 broods, nestlings are recorded after August.

Eurasian Scops Owl *Otus scops*

Scops Owl Vyrecek maly Vyrik obycajny Zwergohreule

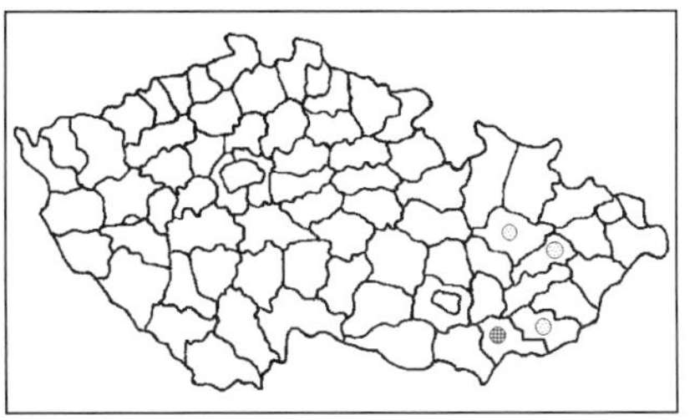

The Czech Republic lies at the northern edge of Eurasian Scops Owl's distribution, and it is an irregular visitor. The closest regular breeding sites are in Slovakia (Murin *et al.* 1994), and Hungary (Gorman 1996). Most of the records are of individuals, rarely 2 birds. The most recent breeding probably occurred near Moravsky Krumlov (ZN) in 1973 (Klejdus 1980), and there was probable breeding near Kyjov (HO) in 1985 (Stastny *et al.* 1996).

Successful nesting was recorded at about 530 m in Suchovske Mlyny (HO) in June 1998: a pair nested in an old orchard at the edge of a village. Found in open country with a mosaic of hornbeam- and oak-dominated forest, pastures, old orchards, vineyards, and the edges of villages in lowlands and highlands.
Status: Vagrant. **Breeding season:** rare. **Winter:** does not occur. **Migration:** rare. Critically endangered. Protected/not hunted all year round.
Population trends: No data available.
Distribution: May occur more frequently in the east of the country. A calling male was recorded near Prerov (PR) in May 1998.
Timing: Recorded between the end of March and mid-September.

Eagle Owl *Bubo bubo*

Eurasian Eagle Owl Vyr velky Vyr skalny Uhu

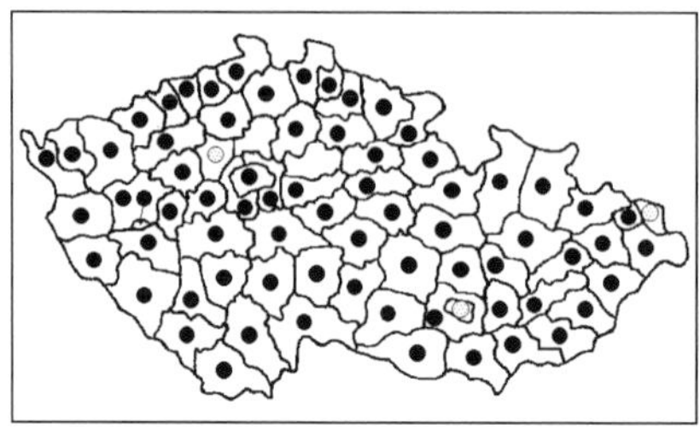

At the beginning of the 20th century, Eagle Owl was almost extirpated as a breeding bird from the Czech Republic due to persecution, and the breeding population was as low as 20 pairs. After changes in the law were made in 1929, the numbers have increased. Between 1940 and 1945, the breeding population was about 75 pairs, and in 1949 about 200 pairs. Although this species occurs across the country, it is more common in highlands and mountains. As a breeder, it occurs infrequently in the lowlands of central Bohemia, e. Bohemia, and s. Moravia. It was recorded up to about 800 m in the Krusne hory mountains (CV, KV, MO, TP), to 1000 m in the Sumava mountains (CK, PT, KT), and to 1150 m in the Jeseniky mountains (BR, SU). It breeds in any type of mature forest with rocks, and rocky hills adjacent to open areas, occasionally close to human habitation. In 1 study, out of 158 nests, 83 were placed in cliffs, and 50 in rocky hills. The remaining 25 nests were placed under dead trees, in old hawks' nests and in the ruins of castles. During the first half of 1980s, breeding density was 0.015, 0.012 and 0.013 pairs per km^2 respectively in PI, KT and ST counties; at the end of the 1980s, it was 0.018 pairs per km^2 in the Jeseniky mountains, 0.016 pairs per km^2 in RK county, 0.04–0.05 pairs per km^2 around Krivoklat (RA), 0.045 pairs per km^2 in the area between Bruntal (BR) and Rymarov (BR), 0.084 pairs per km^2 in the Cesky raj rocks (MB), and 0.013 pairs per km^2 inthe Ceskomoravska vysocina highlands (HB, JI, PE, ZR). In some areas with an abundance of prey, the distance among nests was 700–1000 m (Stastny *et al.* 1996). Persecution, disturbance at nests, road kills, and collision with power lines are the major threats to this species.
Status: Resident. **Breeding season:** uncommon/local. **Winter:** local. **Migration:** local. Conservation-dependent. Hunted, with individual exceptions given by conservation authorities.
Population trends: Between 1973 and 1977 it was 400–600 breeding pairs. Since then, it has increased roughly by 50%, and is now 600–950 pairs. At the beginning of the 1990s, about 150 pairs were found in each of the following regions: s. Bohemia, w. Bohemia, and n. Bohemia; and the lowest number, about 55 pairs, was recorded in s. Moravia. The wintering population is between 1,000 and 2,000 individuals.
Distribution: Non-breeding individuals may occur nationwide.
Timing: All year round. Breeding, depending on weather conditions, may start in mid-February and continues until mid-April. Breeding peaks in March.

Snowy Owl *Nyctea scandiaca*

Sovice snezni Belana tundrova Schnee-Eule

Snowy Owl is an irregular winter visitor to the Czech Republic. Ones, rarely 2 or 3 birds together, may be observed across the country, usually in both lowlands and highlands. It is found in open country with farmland, pastures and meadows. Quite often it may be found sitting on poles close to roads.

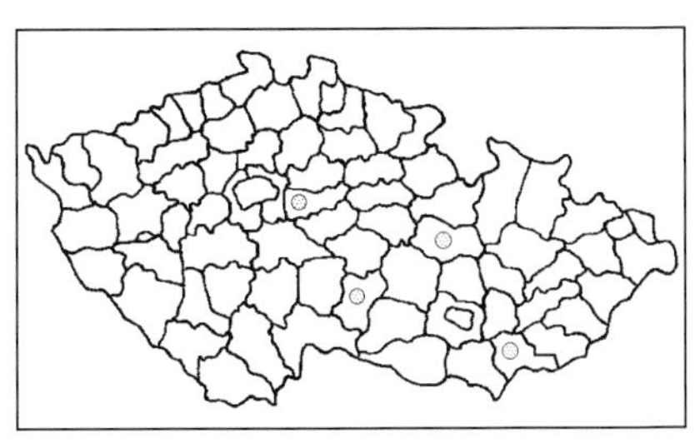

Status: Vagrant. **Breeding season:** rare. **Winter:** rare. **Migration:** rare. Protected/not hunted all year round.
Population trends: No data available. The number of wintering birds may reach 5 individuals.
Distribution: May occur nationwide.
Timing: Found between the end of October and the end of March, with the majority of records from January and February.

Hawk Owl *Surnia ulula*

Northern Hawk Owl   Sovice krahujova   Krahula horna   Sperbereule

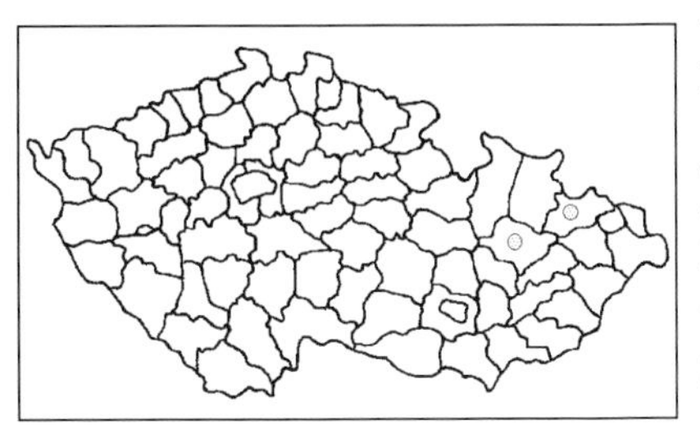

This species occurs irregularly in the Czech Republic, with up to 10 individuals per decade (Hudec *et al.* 1983). Probable breeding was reported from the Nizky Jeseniky mountains (OL), where 4–5 individuals were regularly observed in suitable habitats between 1960 and 1962. However, no sufficient evidence of breeding exists. This species prefers mature coniferous or mixed woodland as well as a variety of open habitats.
Status: Vagrant. **Breeding season:** rare. **Winter:** uncommon. **Migration:** uncommon. Protected/not hunted all year round.
Population trends: Data, which have been available since the 1820s, show that the number of individuals recorded per decade has fluctuated from 1 to 10 individuals. The highest numbers of birds per decade occurred at the end of the 19th century.
Distribution: May occur nationwide. Recent records come from Velky Polom (OP).
Timing: Recorded between October and April, with the highest numbers in November, December and March.

Pygmy Owl *Glaucidium passerinum*

Eurasian Pygmy Owl   Kulisek nejmensi   Kuvicok vrabci   Sperlingskauz

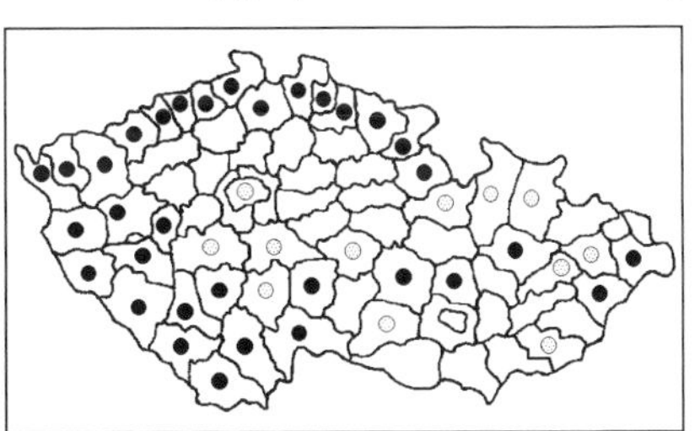

Pygmy Owl is locally a fairly common breeder in the Czech Republic. In some parts of the Sumava mountains (CK, PT, KT), it may be the commonest owl. Until the mid-1970s, it was mostly restricted to mountains in s. Bohemia, w. Bohemia and n. Bohemia. Since then, the breeding population has increased, and Pygmy Owl has extended its breeding range to other parts of the country, including the easternmost mountains (Pavelcik pers. comm.). This species occurs regularly from about 350 m up to 1000 m in the Novohradske hory (CK, CB), and Krusne hory (CV, KV, MO, TP) mountains, and to about 1200 m in the Sumava and Beskydy (FM, VS) mountains. Breeding habitat is large mature coniferous, mixed or conifer-dominated forest. Nest holes are usually placed in spruce, pine or beech, between 4 and 8 m above ground. During the 1980s, breeding density was 0.2 pairs per km^2 in the Beskydy mountains, 0.8 pairs per km^2 in TC county, 0.25–5 pairs per km^2 around Trebon (JH), 0.5–0.7 pairs per km^2 around Vodnany (ST), and 0.2–0.5 pairs per km^2 in the central Sumava mountains. Breeding density increases with altitude. Areas with high breeding numbers include the Sumava mountains, with 210–280 pairs, and the area around Trebon, with up to 60 pairs. Threats to the local populations of Pygmy Owl are the lack of suitable nest holes and, at places with higher densities of Eagle Owl, predation by this species.

Status: Resident. **Breeding season:** uncommon/local. **Winter:** local. **Migration:** local. Vulnerable. Protected/not hunted all year round.
Population trends: The breeding population is between 900 and 1,300 pairs, and has increased by 20–50% over the past 20 years. The wintering population ranges from 500 to 1,000 individuals.
Distribution: Regular breeding is restricted to about 25 counties in Bohemia and fewer than 5 counties in Moravia. Because of the recent expansion of its range, occasional breeding may occur elsewhere in suitable habitats. Birds from mountains move to lower altitudes in winter.
Timing: All year round. The egg-laying period extends from the end of April to the end of May.

Pygmy Owl

Little Owl *Athene noctua*

Sycek obecny Kuvik obycajny Steinkauz

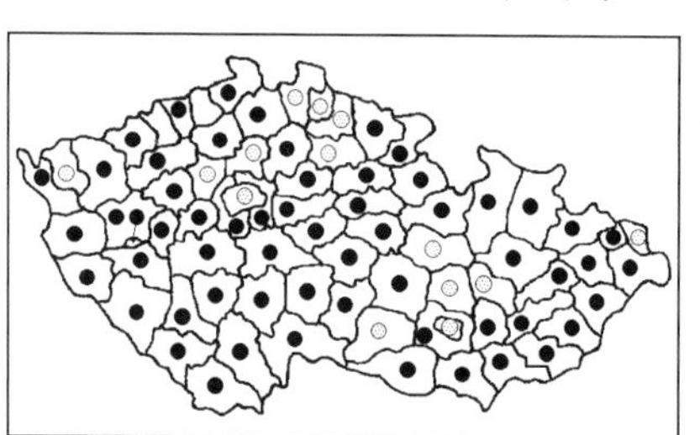

The population of Little Owl has been declining steadily for the past 30–35 years in the Czech Republic, probably as a result of the intensification of farming and use of pesticides, and the removal of mature hollow trees and haylofts on farms. A relatively common breeder until the end of the 1950s, this species became extirpated locally, and in other counties occurs infrequently. It is distributed in lowlands and highlands, and has been recorded up to about 500 m in the Ceskomoravska vysocina highlands (HB, JI, PE, ZR), to about 570 m in the Krusne hory (CV, KV, MO, TP) and Jeseniky (BR, SU) mountains, occasionally up to 900 m in the Sumava mountains (CK, PT, KT), and to 1000 m in the Krkonose mountains (SE, TU).This species prefers open habitats in farmland with a mosaic of mature orchards, clusters of hollow trees, windbreaks, hedgerows, avenues of trees and meadows. It also occurs at the edges of villages, around farms and in cemeteries. Breeding has also been recorded occasionally in larger towns. Nests are usually placed in cavities in willows, limes and beeches, less commonly in crevices in buildings, usually between 0.5 and 4 m above ground. At the end of the 1980s, breeding density was 0.03–0.04 pairs per km^2 around Trebon (JH). During the first half of the 1990s, it was 0.02 pairs per km^2 in CH and TC counties, 0.01 pairs per km^2 in RK county, 0.06 pairs per km^2 in PJ county, 0.02 pairs per km^2 in JH county, 0.05 pairs per km^2 in CR county, 0.01–0.02 pairs per km^2 in HK and BV counties, and 0.03–0.04 (locally 0.07) pairs per km^2 in HO county. The average breeding den-

sity from 16 study areas across the country was 0.03 pairs per km^2 (Schröpfer 1996). In 1998, the average breeding density from 20 study areas (including those previously studied) was 0.01 pairs per km^2, and Little Owls were not found in 13 of these areas (Schröpfer 1999).
Status: Resident. **Breeding season**: uncommon. **Winter**: local. **Migration**: local. Endangered. Protected/not hunted all year round.
Population trends: The breeding population was 700–1,100 pairs from 1985–1989. It decreased by 20–50% between the mid-1970s and the end of the 1980s. The number of breeding pairs estimated by Schröpfer (in Stastny *et al.* 1996) for 1994 was 1,000–2,000. The highest numbers occur in s. Bohemia with about 300 pairs, and n. Bohemia with 100 pairs. At the end of the 1980s, the lowest numbers were recorded in central Bohemia with 20 pairs, and s. Moravia with 30 pairs. The wintering population is between 1,000 and 2,000 individuals.
Distribution: Breeding pairs are scattered nationwide.
Timing: All year round. Breeding extends from the beginning of April to mid-May, peaking during the second half of April.

Tawny Owl *Strix aluco*

Pustik obecny   Sova obycajna   Waldkauz

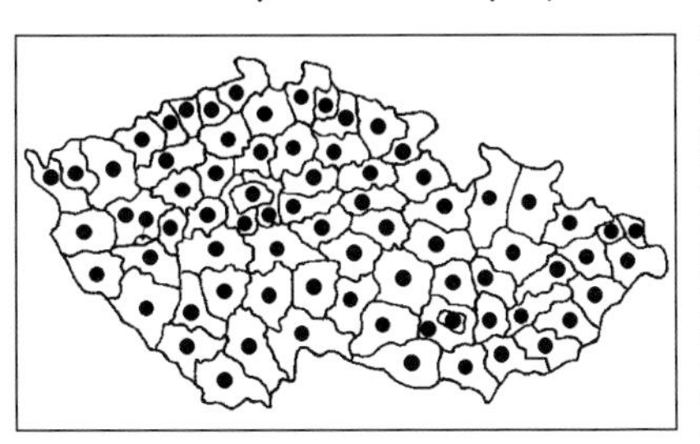

This is the most common owl in the Czech Republic, and is distributed across the country, although it may be absent from some counties, and less abundant at higher altitudes. It is distributed from lowlands up to about 800 m in mountains, but has been recorded at 900 m in the Krusne hory (CV, KV, MO, TP), Krkonose (SE, TU) and Beskydy (VS, FM) mountains, up to 1050 m in the Orlicke hory (RK) and Jeseniky (BR, SU) mountains, and to 1200 m in the Sumava mountains (CK, PT, KT). It breeds in any type of mature deciduous or mixed woodland, larger parks in towns, parkland, cemeteries, and avenues with hollow trees. It is less common in coniferous plantations. Nests are usually placed in cavities in mature trees at forest edges and in clearings, occasionally in crevices in buildings in rural habitats, and some local populations breed in nest boxes provided in large numbers in windbreaks and hedgerows, particularly in HK, PU, ZL, KM and UH counties. At the end of the 1970s, breeding density was 2 pairs per km^2 in a fir-beech-dominated forest at about 900 m in the Beskydy mountains, and 0.25 pairs per km^2 in the Krkonose mountains (SE, TU). During the 1980s it was 0.92–1.0 pairs per km^2 in farmland with windbreaks, mature riverine woodland with oxbows at 180 m in UH county, 0.08–0.1 pairs per km^2 around Trebon (JH), although locally (in growths of mature hollow trees around ponds and along the Nova reka river) the density was 0.7–1.4 pairs per km^2, 0.37–0.93 pairs in various habitats around Tyniste nad Orlici (RK), 0.16 pairs per km^2 in e. Bohemia, 0.07–0.15 pairs per km^2 in the Ceskomoravska vysocina highlands (HB, JI, PE, ZR), and 0.39–0.44 pairs per km^2 in ZL county. The population in ZL county was supported by artificial nest boxes. Wintering birds usually move from mountains to lower altitudes.
Status: Resident. **Breeding season**: common. **Winter**: common. **Migration**: common. Protected/not hunted all year round.
Population trends: The breeding population was between 6,000 and 9,000 pairs between 1985 and 1989, and was stable between the mid-1970s and the end of the 1980s. At the beginning of the 1990s, the population was esimated to be between 5,000 and 7,000 individuals (Danko *et al.* 1994). The highest numbers were recorded in n. Moravia, with about 2,000 pairs, and e. Bohemia, with 1,200 pairs. The lowest number of pairs occur in n. Bohemia, with 200 pairs, and central Bohemia and w. Bohemia, with 300 pairs in each region. The wintering population ranges from 5,000 to 10,000 individuals.
Distribution: Nationwide.
Timing: All year round. Breeding starts in mid-February and continues to the beginning of May. Breeding peaks in March.

Ural Owl *Strix uralensis*

Pustik belavy Sova dlhochvosta Habichtskauz

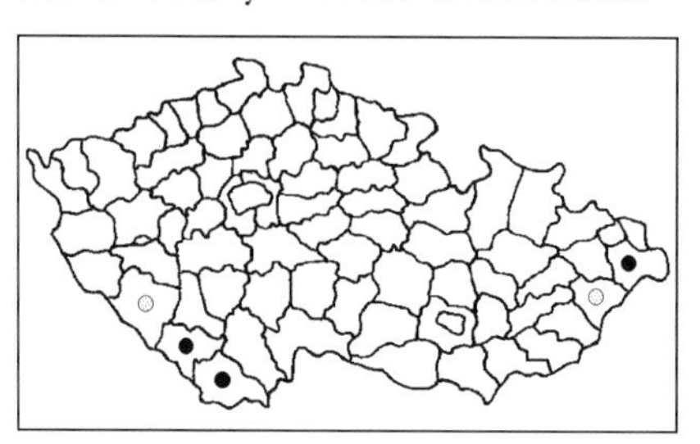

Ural Owl is a rare species in the Czech Republic, occurring in the Beskydy (FM, VS) and Sumava (CK, PT, KT) mountains. Breeding is usually restricted to the Beskydy mountains, where it was recorded for the first time in 1983 (Kondelka 1984). Until the 1920s, Ural Owl was an occasional breeder in the Sumava mountains; nowadays, usually solitary birds are seen, but 1 pair did breed in 1998 and 1999. It is found in mature, mixed and deciduous, beech-dominated forest with clearings or neighbouring meadows and pastures, usually at altitudes of 650–900 m. This species has high site-fidelity, and pairs occupy the same territories for several years. When breeding, Ural Owl often uses old hawk nests. The breeding population belongs to the *macroura* race.

Status: Resident. **Breeding season**: rare/uncommon. **Winter**: uncommon. **Migration**: uncommon. Critically endangered. Protected/not hunted all year round.

Population trends: The recent population is estimated to be between 3 and 10 pairs in the Beskydy mountains, and 2–3 pairs in the Sumava mountains.

Distribution: Recorded in VS, FM, CK and PT counties, but occasionally solitary birds may be found in other counties adjacent to the Beskydy and Sumava mountains.

Timing: All year round. Breeding runs from the beginning of March until mid-April, or from mid-February if small rodents are plentiful.

Long-eared Owl *Asio otus*

Kalous usaty Mysiarka usata Waldohreule

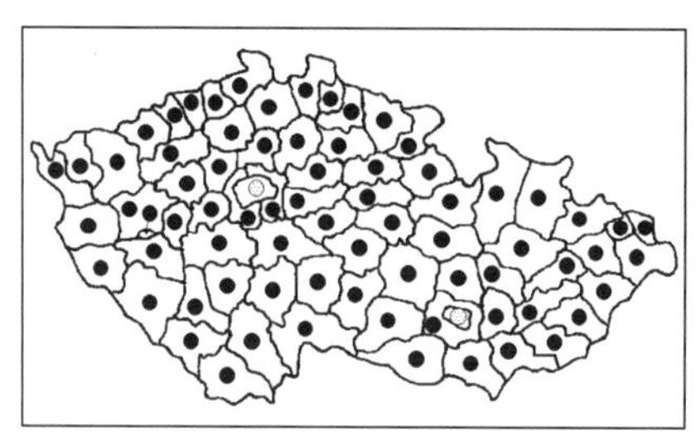

This is a fairly common owl, distributed widely across the country in lowlands and highlands. It has been recorded up to about 650 m in the Orlicke hory (RK) and Jeseniky (BR, SU) mountains, from 800–900 m in the Krusne hory (CV, KV, MO, TP) and Jizerske hory (LB, JN) mountains, to 1070 m in the Sumava mountains (CK, PT, KT), and from 1100–1270 m in the Krkonose (SE, TU) and Beskydy (FM, VS) mountains. Long-eared Owl occurs in woodland surounded by farmland, in windbreaks, hedgerows, larger parks, avenues of old trees, and in mature wooded habitats around open water. In the mountains, it is found in coniferous thickets as well as any type of mature forest. The close proximity of meadows, pastures and fields, for hunting, is important. This species uses the old nests of other larger birds, quite often those of Magpies, for breeding, usually between 2 and 10 m above ground. It occasionally breeds in nest boxes. The breeding population is partially migratory and, between September and March, the overwintering birds are joined by individuals mainly from n. and ne. Europe. At the beginning of the 1970s, breeding density was 3.6 individuals per km^2 in abandoned orchards around Chomutov (CV); and during the 1980s, it was 60 pairs per km^2 in avenues of oak around Strakonice (ST), 2 pairs per km^2 in parkland around a castle in LN county, and 0.08–0.1 pairs per km^2 around Trebon (JH). From mid-autumn and through winter, Long-eared Owls stay in flocks of about 15–35 individuals, and occur in old cemeteries, parks with conifers, and in woodlands on farmland.

Status: Resident. **Breeding season**: local. **Winter**: common. **Migration**: common. Protected/not hunted all year round.

Population trends: The breeding population is between 4,000 and 7,000 pairs and seems to be stable without long-term fluctuations. The highest number of breeding pairs is about 1,100 in n. Moravia, and 1,000 pairs in s. Bohemia. The lowest numbers, about 200 pairs, occur in w. Bohemia and n. Bohemia. The number of wintering birds ranges from 5,000 to 25,000 individuals, depending on the number of birds arriving from n. and ne. Europe.

Distribution: Nationwide.
Timing: All year round. Breeding extends from the beginning of March to the end of May, peaking between mid-March and the beginning of April.

Short-eared Owl *Asio flammeus*

Kalous pustovka Mysiarka mociarna Sumpfohreule

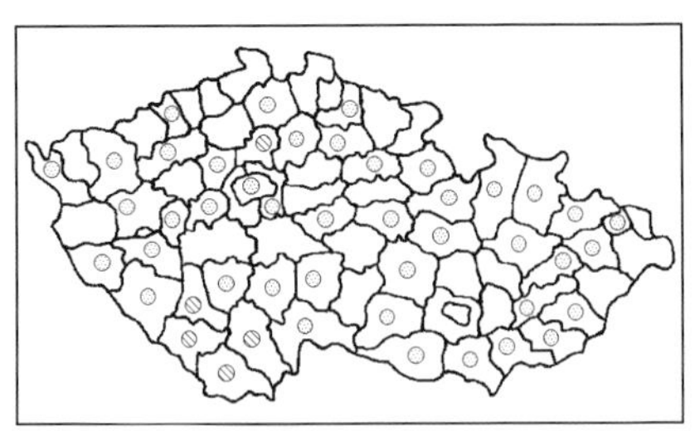

Short-eared Owls occur in the Czech Republic, mostly in winter, with numbers usually varying from year to year. Breeding is rare and does not occur every year, although larger numbers breed during invasion years, such as 1978, when at least 23 pairs nested in CB, JH and ST counties in s. Bohemia. Breeding usually does not occur at the same site in successive years. Migrating, as well as breeding birds are scattered nationwide, mainly in lowlands, less commonly in highlands. It is found in a variety of open habitats such as wet meadows, marshes, pastures, areas adjacent to ponds, and fields with groups of shrubs and trees. Nests are placed on the ground, in short grass and in stubble. Small flocks as well as up to 50 birds can be seen. Between 250 and 300 individuals were recorded around Nove Mlyny (BV) between October 1997 and February 1998 (Pavelcik, pers. comm.).
Status: Migrant and winter visitor. **Breeding season:** uncommon. **Winter:** common. **Migration:** common. Critically endangered. Protected/not hunted all year round.
Population trends: The wintering population is between 200 and 1,000 individuals. Up to 5 pairs breed.
Distribution: Breeding has been recorded in CB, JH, ST, UL, PH, PV, PR, BO, HO and UH counties during the past 20 years, but it may occur across the country. The most recent breeding record is from near Mydlovary (CB). Recent records, of up to 15 birds, and from all year round, come from Mnichovo Hradiste (MB), Riha pond (HK), Kozohludky (TA), Strelske Hostice (ST), Putim (PI), Velice (CB), Ruda near Veseli nad Luznici (JH), Nedvezi (OL), Hlusovice (OL), Rokytnice (PR), Tovacovske ponds (PR), Besov (MO), Chrastany (KM), Biskupice (ZL), Vlcnov (UH), Lednicke ponds (BV), Lednice-Pastvisko (BV), and Pasohlavky (BV).
Timing: Wintering birds regularly occur between September and March. Breeding has been recorded from mid-March until the beginning of May. There are 2 breeding records from November, birds probably taking advantage of high numbers of small rodents.

Tengmalm's Owl *Aegolius funereus*

Syc rousny Potik kapcavy Rauhfußkauz

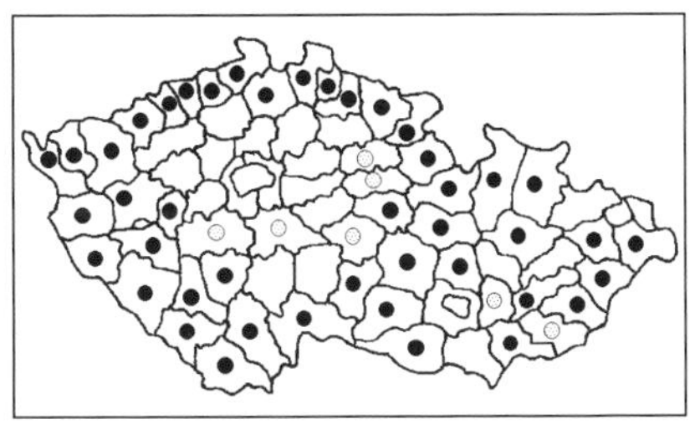

Tengmalm's Owl is a regular breeder, occurring mainly in mountains along the border of the Czech Republic. However, since the beginning of the 1980s it has been expanding its range. It is distributed from about 400 m, and occasionally at lower altitudes, up to 850–900 m in the Orlicke hory (RK) and Krusne hory (CV, KV, MO, TP) mountains, from about 1100–1150 m in the Jizerske hory (LB, JN) and Beskydy (FM, VS) mountains, to 1200 m in the Krkonose mountains (SE, TU), and to 1300 m in the Sumava mountains (CK, PT, KT). Its relative density increases at higher altitudes and it seems to be most abundant between 700 and 1000 m. It breeds in mature coniferous and, less commonly, beech-dominated deciduous forest at higher altitudes, and at lower altitudes, such as 500–600 m, in coniferous plantations. Nests, often old holes made by Black Woodpeckers, are placed in holes in beech, spruce and pine, usually 4–12 m above ground. During the 1980s and 1990s, breeding density was 0.3 pairs per km^2 around Vimperk (PT) and Volary (PT), there were 0.2–0.1 calling males per km^2 around Vodnany (ST), Pisek (PI) and Trebon (JH),

0.5 pairs per km^2 in RO county, and 0.2–0.8 pairs per km^2 at about 1000 m in the Beskydy mountains (FM, VS). Larger numbers breed in the Krkonose mountains, with about 30 pairs, the Sumava mountains, with 210–250 pairs, the area around Trebon, with 30–55 pairs, and in the Beskydy mountains, with at least 20–35 pairs. This species is found all year round at the same sites because of its fidelity to breeding areas and little post-breeding movement of adults.
Status: Resident. **Breeding season**: uncommon/local. **Winter**: local. **Migration**: local. Vulnerable. Protected/not hunted all year round.
Population trends: The breeding population is between 550 and 800 pairs; in s. Bohemia there are about 400 pairs. The wintering population ranges from 500 to 1,000 individuals, and has increased by 20–50% over the last 20 years.
Distribution: Regular breeding occurs in almost 50 counties. It is a rather scarce breeder in OL, RK, CR and JC counties. It may occasionally be recorded in suitable habitat elsewhere.
Timing: All year round. Breeding starts in mid-March and continues until the end of May.

CAPRIMULGIFORMES

Includes a sole family with 6 species in the w. Palearctic. One species from the family **Caprimulgidae** is a regular breeder in the Czech Republic.

European Nightjar *Caprimulgus europaeus*

Nightjar, Eurasian Nightjar Lelek lesni Lelek obycajny Ziegenmelker

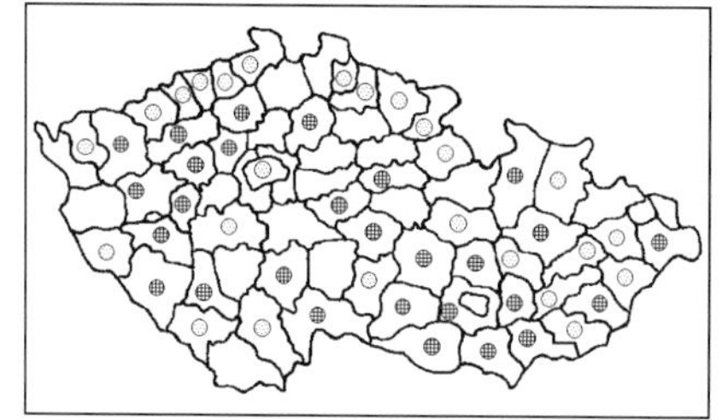

European Nightjar is a regular but rather scarce breeder with patchy distribution in the Czech Republic. There are about 10 counties where it occurs more frequently than elsewhere. It is distributed from lowlands, where it is more common, up to about 900 m in the Sumava (CK, PT, KT), Krkonose (SE, TU) and Jeseniky (BR, SU) mountains. It is found at edges and in clearings of deciduous and pine-dominated coniferous forest, in peat-bogs and in ravines with scattered brush. Nests are built on sparsely vegetated ground in clearings and at woodland edges, usually in pine or spruce, less commonly in mixed and deciduous forest. At the end of the 1980s, breeding density was 10 pairs per km^2 in young pine forest in TA county. Sites with higher number of breeding pairs are found around Trebon (JH), with up to 50 pairs, the area between Majdalena (JH) and Stara Hlina villages (JH), with about 10 pairs, and in the Doupovske hory mountains (KV), with 10–15 pairs. The number of counties with breeding European Nightjars decreased between the mid-1970s and the end of the 1980s. The causes for the

European Nightjar

decline of this species are not entirely clear, but are most likely to be degradation of habitat and the use of pesticides. The breeding population belongs to the *europaeus* race.
Status: Migrant and summer visitor. **Breeding season**: uncommon/local. **Winter**: does not occur. **Migration**: local. Endangered. Protected.
Population trends: The breeding population is estimated to be between 600 and 1,200 pairs. It has decreased by 20–50% over the last 20 years.
Distribution: Regular breeding occurs in MB, RA, RO, KV, PS, PJ, ST, TA, JH, CR, PV, BV and HO counties.
Timing: Spring migration starts in mid-April, with the peak at the end of this month and the beginning of May, and continues until the end of May. Autumn migration occurs from the end of August until the beginning of October. Breeding extends from mid-May to the beginning of July, peaking in June.

APODIFORMES

Includes 11 species from one family in the w. Palearctic. In the Czech Republic, one regular breeder and one accidental belong to the family **Apodidae**.

Common Swift *Apus apus*

Swift Rorys obecny Dazdovnik obycajny Mauersegler

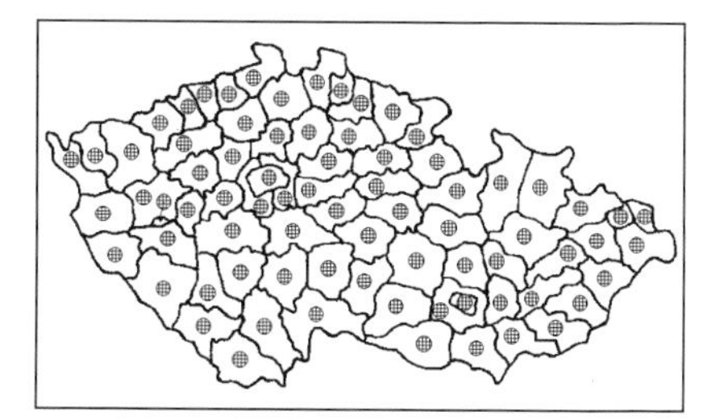

Common Swift is widely distributed, and is found most often near human habitation. Their breeding range extends from lowlands up to between 750 and 800 m in most mountain areas in the country. Foraging birds can be seen at the ridge line in the mountains. The majority of the population occurs in urban habitats, where nesting sites include buildings, churches and towers; also ruins of castles in rural areas. Nest boxes are often used by breeding birds in mountains. Occasional nesting occurs in cavities in ancient oaks along the Nova reka river (JH), in rocks in the Palava hills (BV), and in nests of House Martins in the Jeseniky mountains (BR, SU) (Stastny *et al.* 1987). During the 1970s, breeding density was 13–160 individuals per km^2 in Brno (BM); 23–25 pairs per km^2 in various parts of Bor u Tachova (TC) during the first half of the 1980s; and 32 pairs per km^2 in Tachov (TC) at the beginning of the 1990s.

Common Swifts

Status: Migrant and summer visitor. **Breeding season:** common. **Winter:** does not occur. **Migration:** common. Protected.
Population trends: The number of breeding pairs is estimated to be between 60,000 and 120,000. The breeding population has been stable over the past 20 years.
Distribution: Nationwide.
Timing: Arrives from mid-April until the end of May, with the majority arriving during the first half of May. Departs from the end of July until the end of September, with the peak during the first half of August. Breeding occurs during May and June, peaking in the second half of May.

CORACIIFORMES

Includes 13 species in 4 families in the w. Palearctic. In the Czech Republic, one regular breeder belongs to the family **Alcedinidae**, one regular breeder to the family **Meropidae**, one vagrant to the family **Coraciidae**, and a regular breeder to the family **Upupidae**.

Common Kingfisher *Alcedo athis*

Kingfisher Lednacek ricni Rybarik obycajny Eisvogel

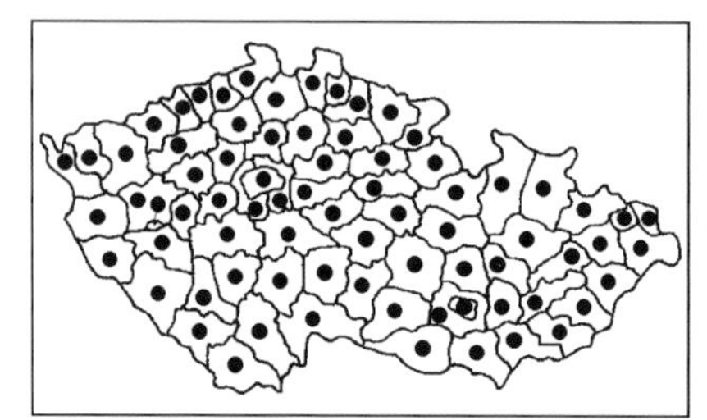

Common Kingfisher is a regular but rare breeder in the Czech Republic. Its range extends across the country, from lowlands up to about 480 m in the Krkonose mountains (SE, TU), to 500 m in the Jeseniky mountains (BR, SU), to 650 m in the Orlicke hory mountains (RK), and to 800 m in the Sumava mountains (CK, PT, KT). It occurs more commonly in highlands than lowlands, because there are better nesting opportunities, but is rare in mountains. It is found more frequently around rivers, brooks and streams with unpolluted water, and less commonly around ponds, gravel pits and lakes. It requires sand or clay soil banks for nest holes, and plentiful perches for fishing. At the beginning of the 1970s, breeding density was about 1 individual per km^2 in e. Bohemia ; it was 2–3 pairs at a 300-m stretch of the Becva river (PR), 5 pairs at a 5-km stretch of the Becva river (VS), 0.1–0.4 pairs per km along the Morava river (OL), and 1–2 pairs at a 3-km stretch of the Olsava river (UH) during the 1980s. Areas with the highest numbers of

Common Kingfisher

breeding pairs include Trebon (JH), with 10–25 pairs, the Beskydy mountains (VS, FM), with 5–20, and the Bile Karpaty mountains (HO, UH, ZL), with up to 10 pairs. Part of the population, particularly young birds, is migratory, and winters in Mediterranean areas (Hudec *et al.* 1983). Long- and short-term fluctuations occur in this species, and the number of breeding pairs may vary from year to year. Distribution during the breeding and non-breeding season is more or less the same but, during harsh winters, Common Kingfishers move to ice-free rivers in the lowlands. Common Kingfisher is threatened by habitat loss due to canalization of rivers, and water pollution. After severe winters, local populations may become extinct, and recolonization may take several years. The breeding population belongs to the *ispida* race.
Status: Resident. **Breeding season**: uncommon/local. **Winter**: common. **Migration**: common. Vulnerable. Protected.
Population trends: The breeding population is estimated to be between 300 and 700 pairs, and the number of wintering birds from 400 to 800 individuals. The population has been declining steadily over the past decades.
Distribution: Scattered across the country. Occurs less commonly in the following counties: KT, DO, SO, LN, KL, RA, TP, LT, SY, VY and ZN.
Timing: All year round. Breeding extends from the beginning of April to mid-July. Breeding peaks during the second half of April, and again in June if there is a second brood.

European Bee-eater *Merops apiaster*

Bee-eater Vlha pestra Vcelarik zlaty Bienenfresser

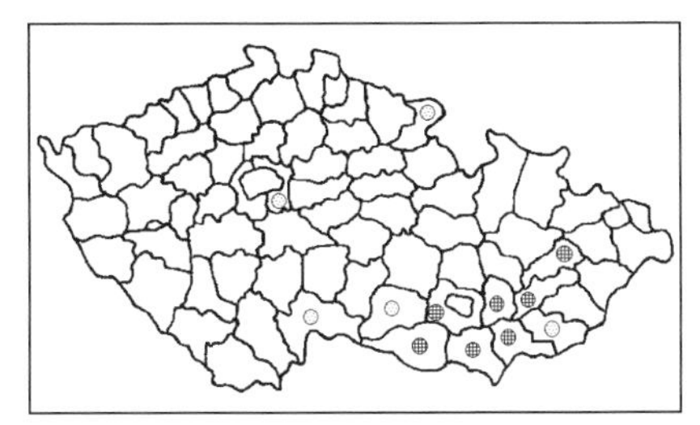

Although there were reports of European Bee-eaters nesting in the 19th century, none of these was sufficiently supported by reliable data. Breeding was first documented in Bohemia in CL county (in n. Bohemia) in 1952, and was followed by nesting near Lysa nad Labem (NB) in 1968. Pairs have possibly bred in this part of the country several times since the end of the 1960s. Breeding first occurred in Moravia near Lednice (BV) in 1954. Even though the number of breeding pairs has increased, and rapid expansion occurred, particularly in s. Moravia, over a 5–7 year period, European Bee-eater is still a local and rare breeder in the Czech Republic. The usual number of breeding pairs at one site is from 2 to 7, less commonly 10–13, occasionally more, for example a colony of 35 pairs in 1996 (Viktora 1997). This species frequents dry and warm lowland areas. It is found in open country with pastures, meadows, scattered trees or brush and sand or clay banks. European Bee-eaters often nest in banks close to rivers, and in sandpits. After breeding, flocks of varying size can be seen in reedbeds around ponds. Flocks recorded in the mid-1990s ranged from 13–78 individuals. The most likely threats to this species are loss of breeding sites, depletion of food resources due to pesticides, and disturbance at breeding sites.
Status: Summer visitor **Breeding season**: uncommon. **Winter**: does not occur. **Migration**: uncommon. Critically endangered. Protected.
Population trends: Between the mid-1970s and the end of 1980, the breeding population fluctuated between 3 and 10 pairs. In 1990, it was 8–10 pairs, in 1991, 4–5 pairs (cold and rainy weather in May and at the beginning of June), in 1992, 10–12 pairs, in 1993, 20–23 pairs, and in 1994, 28–31 pairs. Breeding of 87 pairs at 19 sites, and 107 pairs at 29 sites was recorded in 1995 and 1996 respectively (Viktora 1997); in 1997, it was 45–48 pairs at 18 sites (Simecek 1998).
Distribution: Breeding is now more or less restricted to HO, BO, ZN, KM, VY and BV counties. It is usually found around Karlin, Cejc, Mutenice, Hovorany (all HO county), Zidlochovice (BV), Melcany (BO), and Pouzdrany, Valtice and Kobyli (all BV county). A few pairs, occasionally more, may unexpectedly occur and nest in other counties as well. Recent records of up to 11 non-breeding individuals come from Stara Hlina (JH), and Jaromer (NA).
Timing: This species arrives during the second half of May, occasionally earlier, and departs in August and September. Breeding extends from the end of May to the end of July.

European Roller *Coracias garrulus*

Roller Mandelik hajni Krakla belasa Blauracke

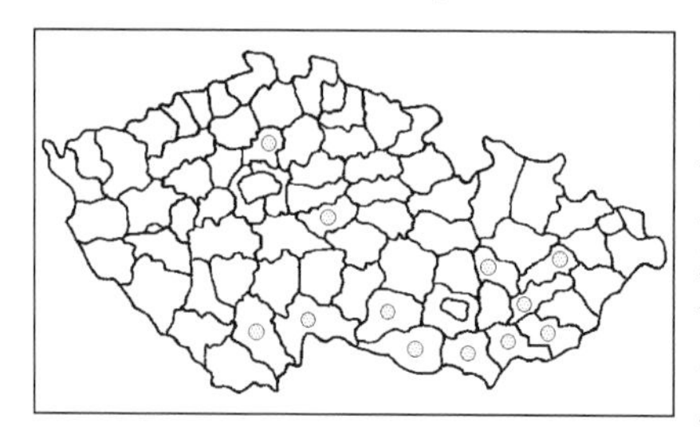

Once a common breeding species in the Czech Republic, European Roller has probably not bred since the beginning of the 1990s. Colonies and solitary breeding pairs were known from many counties across the country during the 19th century. The population started to decline at the beginning of the 20th century, and the process continued until the 1960s, when European Roller became rare. This can be illustrated by an example from a site in NB county in central Bohemia: in the mid-1920s, the breeding population was 30 pairs, at the beginning of the 1940s it was 15 pairs, and in the mid-1960s, there was no further breeding (Hudec *et al.* 1983). In the mid-1970s, breeding was still recorded at several sites in central and e. Bohemia, and s. Moravia. Ten years later, breeding was recorded at 2 sites, in BV and HO counties only. European Roller usually occurs in lowlands, and up to 300–400 m in highlands; occasionally, during the breeding season, up to 800 m in the Krkonose mountains (SE, TU), and to 1000 m in pastures in the Sumava mountains (CK, PT, KT). It frequents open country with meadows and pastures with scattered solitary mature trees, woodland, hedgerows, windbreaks or large orchards. It occurs less commonly in large woodlands. Nest holes are frequently placed in an oak, pine or elm, and breeding has also occurred in nest boxes. The loss of pastures, intensification of agriculture, and habitat degradation are probably the main factors in its disappearance, although the exact causes are probably more complex.

Status: Summer visitor/vagrant. **Breeding season:** rare. **Winter:** does not occur. **Migration:** uncommon. Critically endangered. Protected.

Population trends: Between the mid-1970s and 1989 up to 3 breeding pairs were recorded. Between 1990 and 1995 there were no breeding records.

Distribution: Recent records of solitary birds or 1 pair come from Zehusice (KH), Prerov (PR), Vracov (HO), and Breclav (BV).

Timing: Arrives from the second half of April until mid-May. Departs from the beginning of August until the end of September. Breeding occurs from mid-May until the end of June.

Hoopoe *Upupa epops*

Eurasian Hoopoe Dudek chocholaty Dudok obycajny Wiedehopf

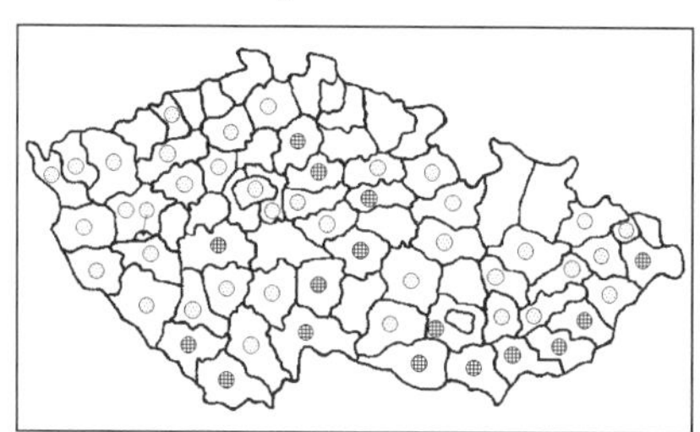

As with European Roller, Hoopoe was once a widespread breeder in the Czech Republic, but disappeared from most of its original range during the first 60 years of the 20th century. Until the 1950s, Hoopoe bred regularly in s. Moravia, and the lowlands of s., e., and central Bohemia. However, between the 1950s and mid-1970s it was extirpated from most of its remaining breeding sites, and this decline has continued. Despite the decreasing numbers, there are still a few places where relatively high number of pairs can be seen: among these are the Palava hills (BV), Milovicky les forest (BV), and around Mistrin (HO). Hoopoe prefers warmer areas in lowlands and highlands, but as a breeder has been recorded up to 700 m in the Krkonose mountains (SE, TU), and to 830 m in the Jeseniky mountains (BR, SU). During migration, it has been seen at even higher altitudes in mountains. This species is found in open habitats, where pastures and meadows alternate with woodland, hedgerows, avenues, and clumps of trees. It can also be found in mature deciduous trees around ponds, and in deciduous forest with clearings, but it avoids dense forest. Nests are usually made in hollow trees such as willow, oak, apple, and cottonwood, usually 0.5–3 m above ground, less commonly they are found in holes and cavities in ruins, buildings and on the ground. Breeding density in suitable habitats was 0.15 pairs per km^2 (1983),

0.11 pairs per km^2 (1984), 0.03 pairs per km^2 (1987), 0.02 pairs per km^2 (1988) and 0.01 pairs per km^2 (1989) in an area of 133 km^2 in HO county. Breeding density of 0.07–0.15 pairs per km^2 was reported from Milovicky les, an area of 18 km^2, in 1995. The population decline has most likely been caused by habitat degradation and loss of food supplies and natural breeding sites.
Status: Migrant and summer visitor. **Breeding season**: uncommon. **Winter**: does not occur. **Migration**: local. Endangered. Protected.
Population trends: The breeding population is between 60 and 120 pairs; it has decreased by 20–50% between the mid-1970s and mid-1990s.
Distribution: Regular breeding occurs in about 15 counties. Recent records of singles, or 2 birds, usually on passage, come from Veseli nad Luznici (TA), Pisek (PI), Usti nad Orlici (UO), Jabkenice (MB), Novosedly (RA), Sedlcanky (PH), Visnova (JH), Merklin (PJ), Horni Porici (ST), Opatov (TR), Postrekov (DO), Cervena Lhota (JH), around Trebon (JH), Sobeslav (TA), Rojice (ST), Zvikov (CB), Praha (AA), Dacice (JH), Klasterec (PT), Chomoutov (OL), Lastany (OL), Uncovice (OL), Steborice (OP), Drevohostice (PR), Kojetin (PR), Sobechleby (PR), Tovacov (PR), Prusy (PR), Domazelice (PR), Horni Mostenice (PR), Ujezdec (PR), Zernava (PR), Zasova (VS), Hulin (KM), Zahlinice (KM), Chvalcov (KM), Bedihost (PV), Bzenec (HO), Bunov (ZL), Podoli (UH), Bozice (ZN), Slavkov (VY), Ricky (VY), Bulhary (BV), and Lednice (BV).
Timing: It arrives from the end of March until the beginning of May. Migration peaks during early April. It departs from the beginning of August to the end of September (mostly at the end of August). Breeding extends from the end of April to the end of June, peaking at the beginning of May.

PICIFORMES

Thirteen species in one family have been recorded in the w. Palearctic. Out of the 10 species from the family **Picidae** occurring in the Czech Republic, 1 is a summer visitor and 9 are residents. All are regular breeders.

Wryneck *Jynx torquilla*

Eurasian Wryneck   Krutihlav obecny   Krutohlav obycajny   Wendehals

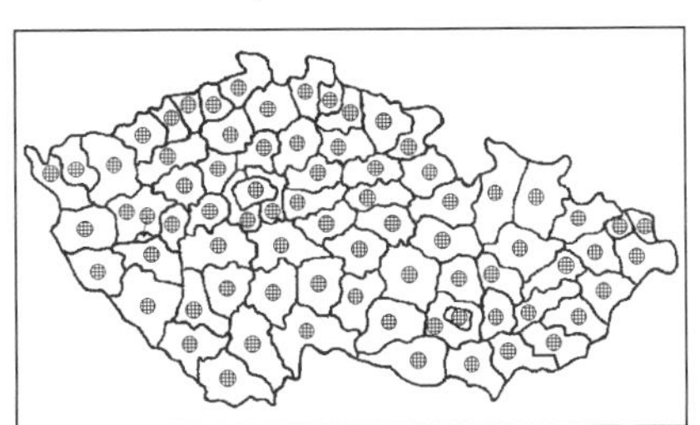

Wryneck is distributed widely, although it is rather uncommon in some areas. The population has decreased, and it has almost disappeared from many counties where it was a common breeder 35–40 years ago. Wryneck occurs more frequently in lowlands and highlands up to about 400 m than at higher altitudes. It has been recorded up to 500 m in the Jeseniky mountains (BR, SU), to 700 m in the Cesky les mountains (DO, TC), to 750 m in the Krkonose mountains (SE, TU), to 870 m in the Krusne hory mountains (CV, KV, MO, TP), to 950 m in the Beskydy mountains (VS, FM), and to 1000 m in the Sumava mountains (CK, PT, KT). It is usually found at the edges of and clearings in deciduous and mixed forest, while dense forest and coniferous plantations are avoided. It also occurs in open habitats with orchards, parks, cemeteries, avenues, hedgerows, and in mature trees along rivers. It favours warm areas surrounded by grassland, with abundant ants. It frequently nests in cavities in apple, willow, pear, and oak trees, 1–3 m above ground. During the 1970s, breeding density was 4 individuals per km^2 in the Ceske Stredohori highlands (LN, LT), 10 pairs per km^2 in riverine forest near Prerov (PR), and 0.4 individuals per km^2 in the parks and gardens of Brno (BM); and during the 1980s, it was 2–3 pairs per km^2 in farmland with old or abandoned orchards in the Bile Karpaty mountains at about 410 m in UH county, 1.5–2.5 pairs per km^2 in gardens and orchards in a village at 180 m in UH county; and 17 pairs per km^2 in CR county at the beginning of the 1990s. The major factor in its decline is probably the reduced food supply caused by agricultural intensification and excessive use of pesticides.

Status: Migrant and summer visitor. **Breeding season:** local/common. **Winter:** does not occur. **Migration:** common. Vulnerable. Protected.
Population trends: The breeding population is estimated to be between 2,500 and 5,000 pairs, and it has declined by 20–50% over the past 20 years.
Distribution: Nationwide, with densities varying from county to county.
Timing: Spring migration occurs from mid-March until the beginning of May, peaking during the first half of April. Autumn migration starts during the second half of August and continues through to the end of September. Breeding extends from the end of April to the beginning of July, peaking in the second half of May.

Grey-headed Woodpecker *Picus canus*

Zluna seda Zlna siva Grauspecht

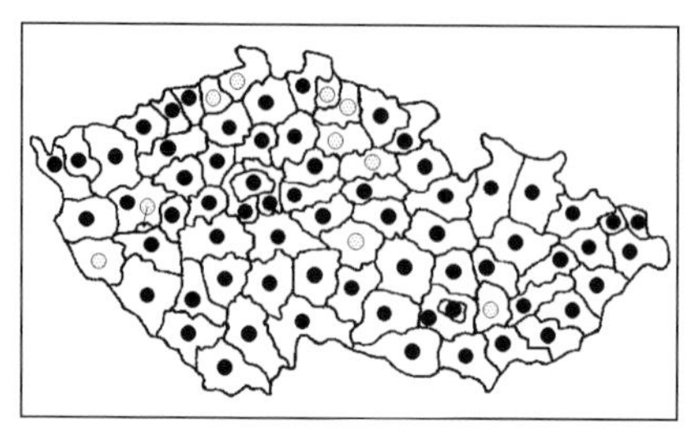

Grey-headed Woodpecker is a regular but rather uncommon breeder in some counties of the Czech Republic. It is distributed from lowlands, where it is more common, up to the mountains. Breeding was recorded up to 900 m in the Rychlebske hory mountains (SU), to 930 m in the Jeseniky mountains (BR, SU), to 1000 m in the Beskydy mountains (VS, FM), and to 1200 m in the Sumava mountains (CK, PT, KT). It breeds in not too dense, dry deciduous and mixed woodland, but in mountains will also use coniferous forest, always with stands of mature trees. It is also found in larger parks, and in growths of mature trees around open water. During winter, it is more common around human habitations such as gardens and parks with mature deciduous trees. Nests are frequently placed in cavities in a beech, lime or oak, 1–8 m above ground, occasionally higher. Areas with relatively high numbers of breeding pairs include the Krkonose mountains (SE, TU), with 20–25 pairs, the Sumava mountains, with dozens of pairs, the area around Trebon (JH), with about 50 pairs, the Beskydy mountains, with 50–80 pairs, the Jeseniky mountains, with up to 10 pairs, and the area between Jesenik nad Odrou (NJ) and Ostrava (OV), with 10–20 pairs. During the 1970s, breeding density was 2 pairs per km^2 in fir-beech forest in the Beskydy mountains and 10 pairs per km^2 in mature spruce forest near Milevsko (TA). During the 1980s, it was 2 individuals per km^2 in riverine forest in OL county, 2 pairs per km^2 in the Novohradske hory mountains (CK, CB), and 1.5–2.5 pairs per km^2 in abandoned orchards in the foothils of the Bile Karpaty mountains (UH, HO, ZL) at about 540 m in UH county. Winter density was 0.1–0.15 individuals per km^2 in hedgerows and riverine woodland at 180 m in UH county during the 1980s. The main threat to this species is habitat degradation and loss through clearance of old trees.
Status: Resident. **Breeding season:** local/common. **Winter:** common. **Migration:** common. Least concern. Protected.
Population trends: The population is somewhere between 3,000 and 6,000 pairs, and has been stable for the past 20 years.
Distribution: Nationwide. It may occur less frequently in OP, BR, VY, TR, SY, PE, HB, DO, TC, RA, KL, UL, DC, CL, LB, JN, JC and HK counties.
Timing: All year round. Breeding extends from the beginning of April to the end of May, peaking at the beginning of May.

Green Woodpecker *Picus viridis*

European Green Woodpecker, Eurasian Geen Woodpecker Zluna zelena
Zlna zelena Grünspecht

Green Woodpecker is more common and widespread in the Czech Republic than Grey-headed Woodpecker. It is found across the country, from lowlands up to lower altitudes than Grey-headed Woodpecker in the mountains. Breeding has been recorded up to 650 m in the Orlicke hory mountains (RK), to 730 m in the Cesky les mountains (DO, TC), to 800 m in the Beskydy

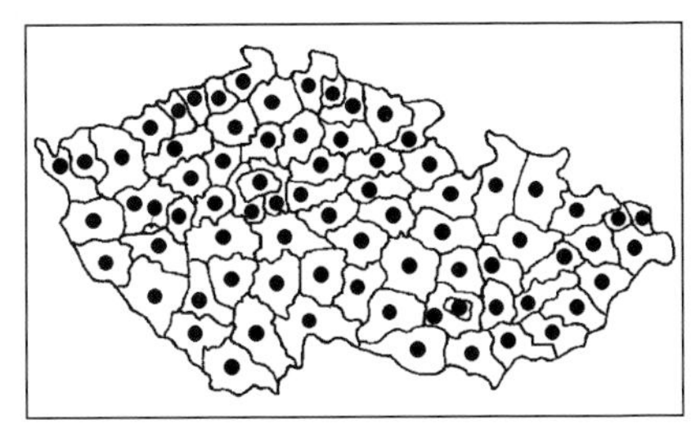

mountains (VS, FM), and 850–900 m in the Jeseniky mountains (BR, SU). It is more common in lowlands and highlands than in mountains. It is usually found in semi-open habitats, with scattered woodland, groups of trees, avenues, hedgerows, orchards and parks. In mountains, it occurs mostly in willow- or alder-dominated growths around streams and clearings, and it avoids dense forest. It always needs mature deciduous trees for nesting. Nests are normally found in cavities in willow, spruce, oak or poplar, between 2 and 7 m above ground. During the 1970s, breeding density in the Ceske Stredohori highlands (UL, LT) was 6 individuals per km^2 in beech-dominated forest, 8 individuals per km^2 in oak-dominated forest, 4–8 individuals per km^2 in forest fringes around the Ohre river (LN), 0.2 individuals per km^2 in Brno (BM), and 0–28 individuals per km^2 in 2 town parks in VS and ZL counties. During the 1980s, it was 3 individuals per km^2 in oak-dominated riverine forest in OL county, 5 pairs per km^2 in sw. Bohemia, 1–1.5 pairs per km^2 in farmland with hedgerows, woodland and mature growths along a river at 180 m, in UH county, 3–17 pairs per km^2 in parks in several towns in w. Bohemia, and 4 pairs per km^2 in a park in Ostrava (OV). During the same period (1980s), winter density was 0.5–1 individuals per km^2 in hedgerows and growths along a river, at 180 m, in UH county. In winter, it occurs more commonly around human settlements than during the breeding season. Loss of feeding habitats and intensive clearance of hollow trees are the most likely major threats to this species.

Status: Resident. **Breeding season**: local/common. **Winter**: common. **Migration**: common. Least concern. Protected.

Population trends: The population is between 9,000 and 18,000 pairs. It decreased by 20–50% between the mid-1970s and mid-1990s. The number of wintering birds is estimated to be between 6,000 and 12,000 individuals.

Distribution: Nationwide. May occur less commonly in LB, TR and SO counties.

Timing: All year round. Breeding occurs from mid-April until the beginning of June, peaking at the end of April and beginning of May.

Black Woodpecker *Dryocopus martius*

Datel cerny   Tesar cierny   Schwarzspecht

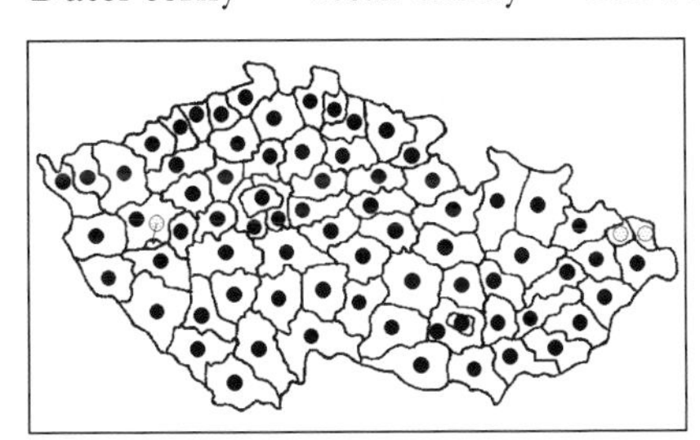

Black Woodpecker is a fairly common breeder, distributed across the country, except in treeless areas. This species is rather scarce in lowlands, but does occur in old riverine forest in counties such as PR, OL, KM, HO and BV. Its main range extends from the highlands up to 1000 m in the mountains. It has been recorded up to 950 m in the Orlicke hory mountains (RK), to 1000 m in the Krkonose (SE, TU) and Jizerske hory (LB, JN) mountains, to about 1050 m in the Jeseniky mountains (BR, SU), and to 1200 m in the Sumava (CK, PT, KT) and Beskydy (FM, VS) mountains. This species is usually found in larger woodlands, but may also occur in relatively small forest areas and hedgerows in farmland. It prefers mixed and coniferous forest (but not too dense) with mature trees. Nest cavities are often placed in beech, fir, pine or oak, from 8–12 m above ground. Hundreds of breeding pairs can be found in the Sumava mountains, about 100 pairs around Trebon (JH), 80–100 pairs in the Beskydy mountains, and 70–95 pairs in the Jeseniky mountains. Regular breeding also occurs in forest at the edge of towns such as Praha (AA), Brno (BM), Breclav (BV) and Zlin (ZL). During the 1970s, breeding density was 3 pairs per km^2 in spruce forest near Milevsko (TA), and 1 individual per km^2 in pine-spruce forest around the Nova reka (JH) river, and, during the 1980s, it was 20 and 13 pairs per km^2 respectively in beech forest in the Krusne hory mountains (CV, KV, MO, TP) and in the foothills of the Jizerske hory mountains (LB, JN), 16 pairs per km^2 in mature spruce forest in the Cesky les mountains (DO, TC), and 2.5–3.2 pairs per km^2 in a beech dominated forest at 550 m in the Chriby hills (UH). It was 0.8–1 pair per km² at about 900 m in the Beskydy mountains at the beginning of the 1990s. It has been suggested that Black Woodpecker has been extending its range into lowlands and habitats at the edges of towns over the last few decades (Stastny *et al.* 1996).

Status: Resident. **Breeding season:** local. **Winter:** common. **Migration:** common. Least concern. Protected.

Population trends: The population is between 3,000 and 6,000 pairs, and has been stable during the past 20 years. The number of wintering birds is estimated to be between 3,000 and 6,000 individuals.

Distribution: Nationwide.

Timing: All year round. Breeding occurs during April and May, peaking in the second half of April.

Great Spotted Woodpecker *Dendrocopos major*

Strakapoud velky   Datel velky   Buntspecht

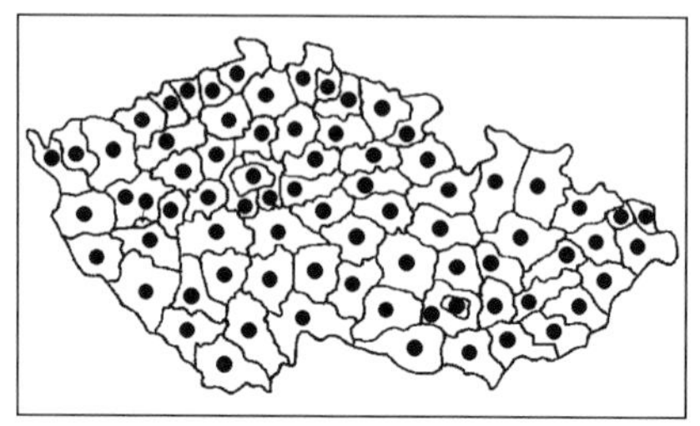

This is the most common woodpecker in the Czech Republic, distributed from lowlands up to about 900 m in the Beskydy mountains (FM, VS), from 1000–1100 m in the Jizerske hory (LB, JN), Orlicke hory (RK), Jeseniky (BR, SU) and Krkonose (SE, TU) mountains, and to 1300 m in the Sumava (CK, PT, KT) and Krusne hory (CV, KV, MO, TP) mountains. Typical habitats include mature woodland of any type, although it is probably more common in mixed forest than in dense coniferous plantations. It is commonly around human habitations, found in gardens, avenues, parks, cemeteries, in groups of trees scattered in farmland, hedgerows and in growths along rivers. Nest holes are usually located in oak, alder, beech, spruce or elm, from 5–15 m above ground. It also uses nest boxes. At the beginning of 1970s, breeding density was 3–23 individuals per km², in growths dominated by mature oak, around ponds (JH) and 26–45 pairs per km² 20 years later; it was 8–22 pairs per km² in spruce forest around Milevsko (TA), 28–33 pairs per km² in riverine forest in KM county, and 22–29 pairs per km² in parks in Praha (AA) during the 1970s. During the 1980s, it was 26 pairs per km² in fir-beech forest in the Novohradske hory mountains (CK, CB), 27 and 108 pairs per km² respectively in riverine forest in sw. Bohemia and OL county, 5 pairs per km² in acid-rain-damaged forest in the Krusne hory mountains, 21, 2 and 10 pairs per km² respectively in various types of forest in TC county, in the Cesky les mountains (DO, TC), and around Tabor (TA), 48 pairs per km² in oak forest in MO county, 55–60 pairs per km² in oak-elm forest at the edge of Praha (AA), 20 pairs per km² in beech forest in the Cesky raj cliffs (MB), Jizerske hory and Krusne hory mountains, 10–58 pairs per km² in various parks in sw. Bohemia, 13 individuals per km² in windbreaks around Breclav (BV), 6–14 pairs per km² in mature mixed forest at 240 m in UH county, and 4–9 pairs per km² in farmland with windbreaks and hedgerows at 180 m in UH county. At the beginning of the 1970s, winter density was 20 individuals per km² in parks and orchards in Brno (BM); and it was 18 individuals per km² in pine plantations, and 4–13 individuals per km² in a beech forest in the Cesky les mountains (TC) in the mid-1970s. By the end of the 1970s, 0–25 individuals per km² were found in primeval beech and fir forest at about 900 m in VS county; 8–15 individuals per km² were recorded in mixed woodland at 280 m in UH county, and 4–7 individuals per km² in poplar-dominated windbreaks and hedgerows in farmland at 180 m in UH county at the end of the 1980s. The breeding population belongs to the *pinetorum* race, but in winter numbers are augmented by birds of the nominate *major* race from n. and ne. Europe. In the winters of 1929–1930, 1935–1936, 1956, and 1974–1975, larger invasions of the nominate race were recorded (Hudec *et al.* 1977).

Status: Resident. **Breeding season:** common (*pinetorum*), rare (*major*). **Winter:** common (*pinetorum*), uncommon (*major*). **Migration:** common (*pinetorum*), uncommon (*major*). Protected.

Population trends: The breeding population is between 200,000 and 400,000 pairs, and the wintering population between 150,000 and 300,000 individuals. The population has been stable for the past 20 years.

Distribution: Nationwide.
Timing: All year round. Breeding occurs from mid-April until the beginning of June, peaking towards the end of April and early May.

Syrian Woodpecker *Dendrocopos syriacus*

Strakapoud jizni Datel hnedkavy Blutspecht

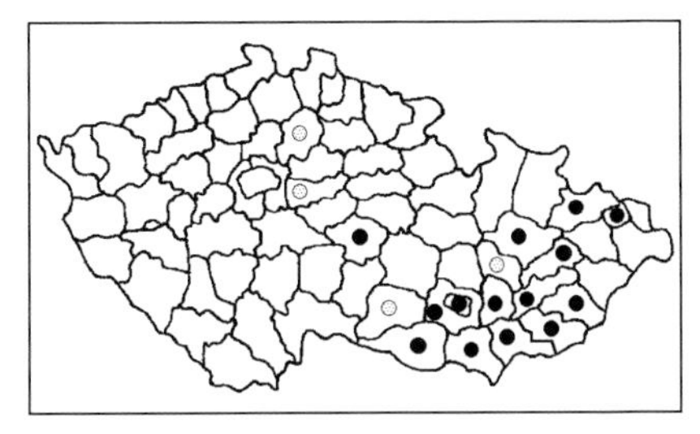

Syrian Woodpecker has occurred in the Czech Republic since 1952, when 1 individual was observed in Lednice (BV). Two years later more birds were seen in Breclav (BV). In 1955, this species colonized BV, ZN and BO counties and, in 1956, it was recorded in Brno (BM). In 1962, it was recorded in HO county, 2 years later in ZL county, during 1966 in SU county, and a year later in OP county. In the west of the Czech Republic it was recorded for the first time in 1959 in PU county, and in 1962 in ME county. Since then, occasional breeding of 1 pair has been recorded in Bohemia, but it is still a rare visitor and breeder in that part of the country. Range expansion in the Czech Republic appears to have stopped in the mid-1980s (Stastny *et al.* 1996). Syrian Woodpecker is distributed mostly in the lowlands of s. Moravia. Areas with the regular occurence of several pairs include the Palava hills (BV), with 10–20 pairs, Lednicke ponds (BV), with 5–10 pairs, Pohorelicke ponds (BV), with 1–2 pairs, the area between Bozice-Hodonice-Hradek and Lechovice (ZN), with up to 5 pairs, Kyjov (HO), with about 10 pairs, Brno (BM), with dozens of pairs, and parkland-type habitats around Uherske Hradiste (UH), with up to 20 pairs. This species prefers open habitats with orchards, gardens, parks, avenues, hedgerows and deciduous woodland. It does not generally occur in large deciduous or in coniferous woodlands, unlike Great Spotted. Nest holes are placed in apple, willow, poplar or cherry, from 1.5–9 m above ground. Hybrid Syrian X Great Spotted Woodpeckers have been recorded.
Status: Resident. **Breeding season**: uncommon/local. **Winter**: uncommon/local. **Migration**: uncommon/local. Endangered. Protected.
Population trends: Between 1953 and 1989 the breeding population was 70–120 pairs; from 1990 to 1994 it was 300–400 pairs. In 5 s. Moravian counties, BM, BO, ZN, BV, and HO, it ranges from 220–230 pairs. The number of wintering birds is estimated to be up to 200 individuals.
Distribution: Regular breeding occurs in the following counties: ZN, BV, HO, UH, BM, BO, VY, KM, ZL, PV, OL, VS, PR and OV. Occasional breeding has been recorded in OP, BR, MO, UO, KO, HB, SU and HK counties, but may occur in other counties as well.
Timing: All year round. Breeding starts in mid-April, with the peak during May.

Syrian Woodpecker

Middle Spotted Woodpecker *Dendrocopus medius*

Strakapoud prostredni Datel prostredny Mittelspecht

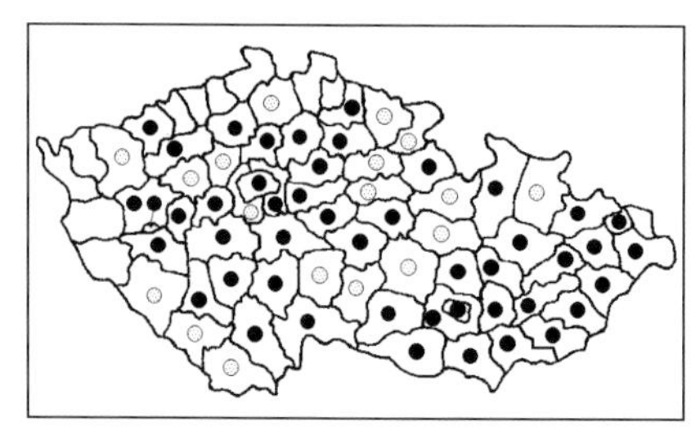

Middle Spotted Woodpecker is rather an uncommon species with patchy distribution across the country. It is most commonly found in lowlands, up to about 500 m in highlands and in the foothills of mountains, but has also been found at 760 m in the Ceskomoravska vysocina highlands (HB, JI, PE, ZR), at 900 m in the Sumava mountains (CK, PT, KT), and at 1300 m in the Krkonose mountains (SE, TU). It is most common in central Bohemia, s. Moravia and central Moravia. It usually breeds in oak-dominated deciduous woods, particularly favouring riverine forest, stands of mature oaks around fishponds, oak-dominated wooded pastures and, less commonly, mixed forest. Outside the breeding season, it occurs more commonly in larger parks, gardens and stands of trees in farmland. Nest holes are usually located in oaks, less commonly in other species of tree such as willow, elm, beech, spruce or apple, and from 2–10 m above ground. Numbers of breeding pairs at some sites are as follows: around Trebon (JH), up to 50 pairs, between the villages of Majdalena and Stara Hlina (JH), up to 10 pairs, the Palava hills (BV), dozens of pairs, riverine forest s. of Lanzhot (BV), at least 50 pairs, Lednicke ponds (BV), at least 15–20 pairs, and Pohorelicke ponds (BV), 2–3 pairs. The highest numbers of breeding pairs seem to be in oak and riverine forest in HO and BV counties (Chytil in Stastny *et al.* 1996). Breeding density was 2–9 individuals per km^2 in oak stands along ponds around Trebon (JH), and 0.9–1.2 pairs per km^2 in mixed forest in BO county during the 1970s and beginning of the 1980s. During the 1980s, it was 0–100 individuals per km^2 in a riverine forest in OL county, 4 pairs per km^2 in beech-lime forest in sw. Bohemia, and 1–2.5 pairs per km^2 in pastures with mature solitary trees, mostly oak, at 420 m in the Bile Karpaty mountains (UH, HO, ZL). The availability of suitable trees for nest holes may limit its density and distribution among counties.

Status: Resident. **Breeding season:** uncommon/local. **Winter:** local/common. **Migration:** local/common. Vulnerable. Protected.

Population trends: The population was between 1,000 and 2,000 pairs from the mid-1970s to the end of the 1980s. Based on the records of breeding pairs from HO and BV counties, it was estimated to be between 3,000 and 6,000 pairs in the period from 1990 to 1994. The number of wintering birds ranges from 1,200 to 2,500 individuals.

Distribution: It is rather an uncommon breeder in CB, ST, PI, DO, PJ, LT, HB, SU, FM and NJ counties.

Timing: All year round. Breeding extends from the end of April to the end of May, peaking at the end of April and beginning of May.

White-backed Woodpecker *Dendrocopus leucotos*

Strakapoud belohrbety Datel bielochrbty Weißrückenspecht

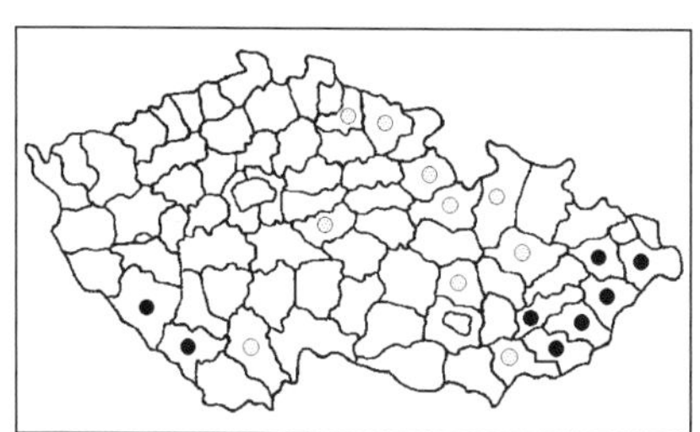

White-backed Woodpecker's range is mainly confined to the highlands and mountains in the east of the country, the Beskydy mountains (FM, VS), Hostynske vrchy hills (ZL, KM), Javorniky hills (ZL, VS) and Bile Karpaty mountains (HO, UH, ZL). Regular breeding in Bohemia occurs in the Sumava (CK, PT, KT) and Krkonose (TU, SE) mountains, and recently regular breeding of at least 10 pairs has been confirmed in the Chriby hills (KM, UH). It is distributed from about 470 m up to 1300 m. It is found in mature beech woodland or beech-dominated mixed forest. Nest holes are usually made in a beech, less commonly in spruce or larch, and from 3–10 m above ground. Breeding density in the Beskydy mountains was 4 pairs per km^2 at the end of the 1970s, and 5 pairs per km^2 during the 1980s, and at the beginning of the 1990s, it was

0.4–0.6 pairs per km2 between 900 and 1276 m in the Beskydy mountains, and 0.18 pairs per km2 in mature beech forest in the Hostynske vrchy hills. The total number of pairs in the Beskydy mountains may reach 160 pairs, about 10–25 in the Sumava mountains, and 1–2 in the Krkonose mountains. The main threat to this species is probably a loss of mature (over 100-year-old) beech-dominated woodland through antipathetic forest management. The population belongs to the *leucotos* race.
Status: Resident. **Breeding season:** uncommon/local. **Winter:** uncommon/local. **Migration:** uncommon/local. Endangered. Protected.
Population trends: The population is between 150 and 250 pairs, and has been stable over the past decade.
Distribution: Except for the abovementioned counties, where it breeds, stragglers have also been recorded in SU, BK, KT, RK, ZN, OL, BK and KH counties. Young birds may move dozens of kilometres from the nest sites in autumn.
Timing: All year round. Breeding extends from the end of April to the end of May.

Lesser Spotted Woodpecker *Dendrocopus minor*

Strakapoud maly Datel maly Kleinspecht

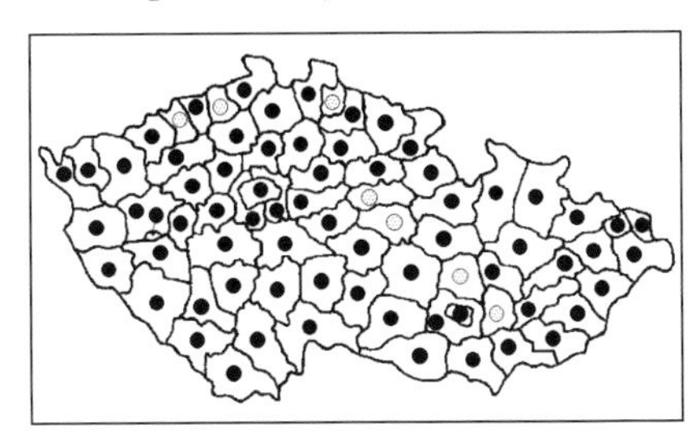

Lesser Spotted Woodpecker is a fairly common breeder in some areas, but rather scarce as a whole in the Czech Republic. It is found in lowlands and highlands, up to 300–400 m in the Ceskomoravska vysocina highlands (HB, JI, PE, ZR), up to 600 m in the Cesky les mountains (DO, TC), to 650 m in the Jeseniky mountains (BR, SU), to 800 m in the Beskydy mountains (VS, FM), and 800–900 m in the Sumava (CK, PT, KT) and Krkonose (SE, TU) mountains. Lesser Spotted Woodpecker frequents smaller deciduous and mixed oak- and beech-dominated forest, riverine forest, larger orchards, gardens, parks, and avenues in open habitat. In winter, it can be seen more commonly around human settlements and is often found in thickets with dense undergrowth around rivers and ponds. It does not usually occur in dense forest or coniferous plantations. Nest holes are usually placed in beech, aspen or willow, 3–7 m above ground. At the beginning of the 1970s, breeding density was 2 individuals per km2 in the Ceske Stredohori highlands (UL, LT), 7 pairs per km2 in a city park in Vizovice (ZL) at the end of the 1970s, and 10–30 pairs per km2 in riverine forest in PR and KM counties during the second half of 1970s. During the 1980s, it was 6 pairs per km2 in beech forest in the foothills of the Jizerske hory mountains (JN, LB), 10 pairs per km2 in forest in RK county, 0–50 individuals per km2 in forest along the Morava river (OL), and 9 pairs per km2 in growths around Strakonice (ST). In parkland around a castle (ST) it was 10 pairs per km2, and in a fir-beech forest at about 733–825 m in the Novohradske hory mountains (CK, CB) 2 pairs per km2 at the beginning of 1990s. At the beginning of the 1970s, winter density was 0.6 individuals per km2 in parks and gardens in Brno (BM); in the mid-1980s, 1–2 individuals per km2 in farmland with windbreaks and hedgerows at 180 m in farmland in UH county, and 2–3.5 individuals per km2 in mixed forest at 240 m in UH county. The population belongs to the *hortorum* race.
Status: Resident. **Breeding season:** uncommon/local. **Winter:** local/common. **Migration:** local/common. Near threatened. Protected.
Population trends: The population is between 2,000 and 4,000 pairs and has been stable for the past 20 years. The number of wintering birds ranges from 3,000–6,000 individuals.
Distribution: Scattered nationwide. Breeding may be rather scarce in VS, SY, ZR, TR, ZN, PE, NA, LB, CV and KT counties
Timing: All year round. Breeding extends from the end of April to the beginning of June, peaking in mid-May.

Three-toed Woodpecker *Picoides tridactylus*

Datlik triprsty Dubnik trojprsty Dreizehenspecht

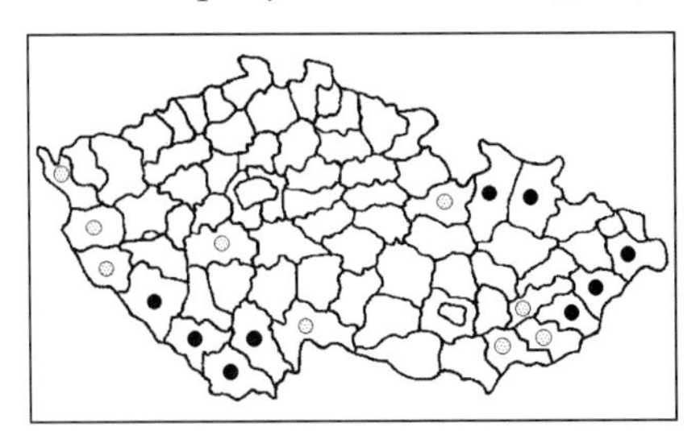

Three-toed Woodpecker occurs regularly in a few areas of the Czech Republic. It is found in the Beskydy mountains (VS, FM), the Vsetinske vrchy (VS) and Javorniky (ZL, VS) hills, and the Jeseniky mountains (BR, SU) in Moravia. In Bohemia, it occurs in the Novohradske hory (CK, CB), and Sumava (CK, PT, KT) mountains. Probable breeding has been reported from several other areas. This species occurs from about 450 m up to 1300 m in the mountains. It is closely associated with mature spruce plantations, or spruce-dominated mixed woods where dead trees are available. Forests severely damaged by acid-rain seem to provide optimal habitats. Nest holes are made in a spruce or fir, 3.5–6 m above ground. Nest boxes are occasionally used. During the 1980s, breeding density was 6 pairs per km^2 in mature spruce forest in the Sumava mountains (CK, PT, KT); 1–1.2 pairs per km^2 from 900–1270 m in the Beskydy mountains (FM, VS), and 7 pairs per km^2 in fir-beech forest in the Novohradske hory mountains (CK, CB) at the beginning of the 1990s. The Sumava mountains hold a few hundred pairs, and the Beskydy mountains about 50–80. In winter, solitary birds may appear at lower altitudes, even in lowland areas. The Czech population belongs to the *alpinus* race.

Status: Resident. **Breeding season:** uncommon. **Winter:** uncommon. **Migration:** uncommon. Endangered. Protected.

Population trends: The breeding population is between 300 and 500 pairs, and has been stable over the past 20 years. The winter population is estimated to be between 150 and 300 individuals.

Distribution: Outside the breeding season, it was recently observed in HO, JH, DO, UO, RO and CH counties.

Timing: All year round. Breeding extends from mid-April to mid-June.

PASSERIFORMES

Includes 401 species in 34 families recorded in the w. Palearctic. In the Czech Republic, 146 species belonging to 24 families have occurred. Three regular breeders, 1 winter visitor and 2 accidentals occur from the family **Alaudidae.** Three regular breeders belong to the family **Hirundinidae.** The family **Motacillidae** includes 7 regularly breeding species, 2 vagrants and one accidental. A regular winter visitor belongs to the family **Bombycillidae.** A resident breeder is in the family **Cinclidae,** and another regular breeder comes from the family **Troglodytidae.** Two regular breeders and an accidental belong to the family **Prunellidae.** Fifteen regular and irregular breeders and 6 accidentals occur from the family **Turdidae.** The family **Sylviidae** includes 19 regular breeders, 3 migrants or vagrants and 9 accidentals. Four regularly breeding species belong to the family **Muscicapidae.** A resident, which is a local regular breeder, belongs to the family **Timaliidae,** while another regular breeder is a member of the family **Aegithalidae.** The family **Paridae** is represented by 6 regularly breeding residents and a vagrant. The family **Sittidae** includes one resident breeder. A species from the family **Tichodromadidae** is a vagrant to the Czech Republic. Two resident breeders come from the family **Certhiidae.** One regular breeder occurs from the family **Remizidae** and one from **Oriolidae.** Two regular breeders and 2 accidentals occur from the family **Laniidae.** Family **Corvidae** is represented by 7 breeding species and one accidental. A regularl breeder and a vagrant come from the family **Sturnidae.**

Two regular breeders and a vagrant are representatives of the family **Passeridae.** Eleven regular breeders, 6 migrant and vagrants and one accidental belong to the family **Fringillidae.** Four regular breeders, 2 vagrants and 8 accidentals belong to the family **Emberizidae.**

Crested Lark *Galerida cristata*

Chocholous obecny Pipiska chochlata Haubenlerche

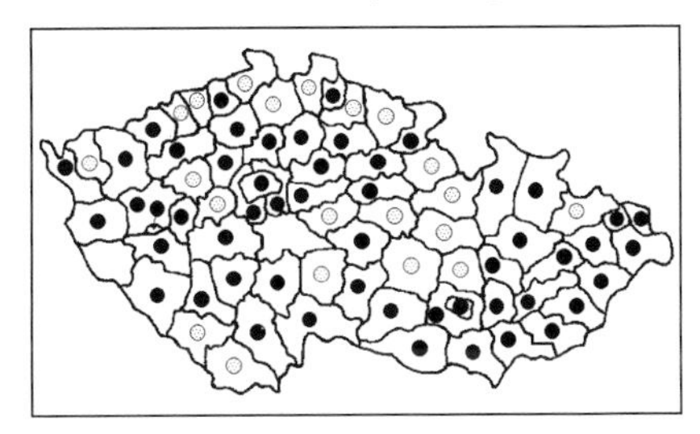

This is a regular, but quite uncommon breeder in the Czech Republic, scattered from lowlands up to 550 m in the Krkonose mountains (SE, TU), to 580 m in the Ceskomoravska vysocina highlands (HB, JI, PE, ZR), to 650 m in the Jeseniky mountains (BR, SU), and to 740 m in the Kasperske hory mountains (KT). It is more abundant in lowlands than at higher altitudes. It normally occurs at drier sites in man-modified areas such as sandpits, railway yards, refuse dumps, pastures, vineyards and the edges of cultivated fields around villages, but also inhabits grassy areas between apartment blocks in towns such as Praha (AA), Prerov (PR), Plzen (PM), Ceske Budejovice (CB), Zlin (ZL) and

Crested Lark

others, where nests are placed on the flat roofs of apartment buildings. In winter, Crested Larks frequent towns, villages and farms. The density of Crested Larks was 1 individual per km^2 at steppes with growths of trees in the Ceske Stredohori highlands (LT, UL) at the end of the 1960s and beginning of the 1970s, 26–50 individuals per km^2 between apartment blocks in Tachov (TC) from the mid-1970s until the end of the 1980s, and 0.4–15 individuals per km^2 in wasteland around Mlada (NB) in the mid-1990s. The main factors in the population decline are probably habitat destruction and loss of prey due to the intensification of agriculture. The population belongs to the nominate *cristata* race.
Status: Resident. **Breeding season:** local/common. **Winter:** local/common. **Migration:** local/common. Endangered. Protected.
Population trends: The breeding population is estimated to be between 1,100 and 2,200 pairs. It has decreased by at lest 50% during the past 20 years. The wintering population is somewhere between 1,000 and 2,000 individuals.
Distribution: Nationwide, density varying from county to county. Breeding and winter distribution follows the same pattern.
Timing: All year round. Breeding extends from mid-March to the end of July, peaking between mid-April and the beginning of June.

Wood Lark *Lullula arborea*

Woodlark Skrivan lesni Skovranik stromovy Heidelerche

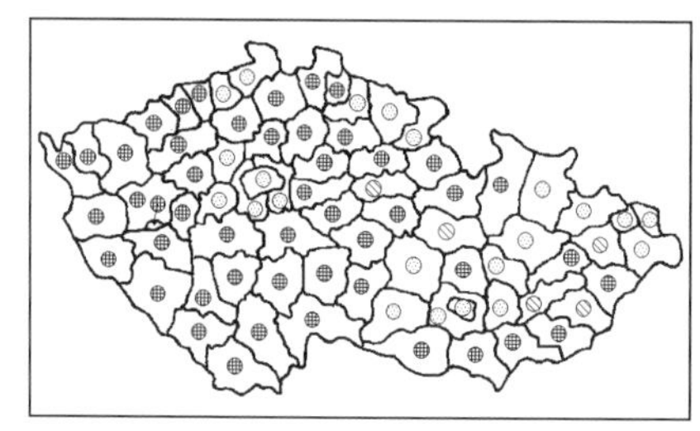

Wood Lark is an uncommon breeder across the country. It occurs from lowlands up to 880 m in the Krkonose (SE, TU) and Jeseniky (BR, SU) mountains, to 900 m in the Krusne hory mountains (CV, KV, MO, TP), and to 1000 m in the Sumava mountains (CK, PT, KT). It is usually found in drier places such as pastures and on the slopes of hills with low grass, bushes and solitary trees, pine plantations with clearings and sand dunes, edges of and clearings in deciduous and mixed forest and, occasionally, in mature vineyards and orchards. In suitable habitats, this species may also occur at the edges of towns. Nests are placed on the ground, usually where the terrain is broken, and often near a tuft of grass. Flocks of varying size can be found during migration in fields and wet meadows. At the end of the 1980s, density was 7–20 pairs per km^2 in hedgerows in farmland (ST); and at the beginning of the 1990s, 11 pairs per km^2 near Holysov (DO) and 1–15 individuals per km^2 in various habitats with sandy soils around Mlada (NB). Habitat loss and degradation are the most likely cause of Wood Lark's disappearance from many counties where it was once quite a common breeder.
Status: Migrant and summer visitor. **Breeding season:** uncommon. **Winter:** rare. **Migration:** local. Occasionally wintering. Endangered. Protected.
Population trends: The breeding population is between 600 and 1,100 pairs. The population has been declining since the early 1960s, and has decreased by 20–50% over the past 20 years. In winter, up to 10 individuals may be recorded.
Distribution: Found on migration nationwide. It is a more common breeder in the west of the country, particularly in the following counties: CK, KT, CB, PJ, PS, MO, DC, CL, PB and UO.
Timing: Spring migration occurs from mid-February to the end of April, peaking during the first half of March. Autumn migration occurs from mid-September, mainly in October, and continues to the beginning of November. Breeding extends from the end of March to the beginning of July, with peaks at the end of April and end of May.

Sky Lark *Alauda arvensis*

Skylark, Eurasian Skylark Skrivan polni Skovranok polny Feldlerche

Although Sky Larks occur in the Czech Republic all year round, the majority of the population is migratory, and the number of birds recorded in December and January is usually low.

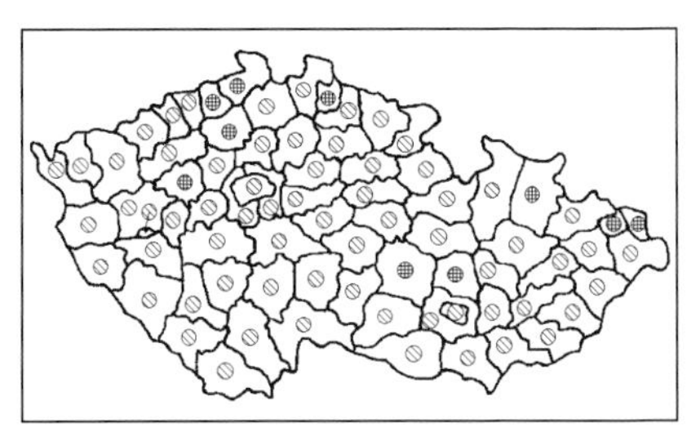

This is a common breeder across the country, from lowlands up to all mountain peaks. Sky Lark is more abundant in lowlands than at higher altitudes. It frequents a variety of drier, and usually treeless, habitats in open country such as fields, pastures, meadows with low grass, and alpine meadows. As a breeder, it may occasionally be found in wet habitats. Nests are usually placed in short and dense vegetation. At the end of the 1970s, breeding density in wasteland with a variety of vegetation, in a coal mining area in MO county, was 7–80 pairs per km^2, in meadows it was 42 individuals per km^2 and in cornfields 40–50 pairs per km^2 around Trebon (JH), at an airfield with a grass runway in KV county it was 130–145 pairs per km^2, and 21–116 individuals per km^2 in farmland in the foothills of the Krkonose mountains (SE, TU). It was 42–49 pairs per km^2 in meadows at about 160 m in HO county at the beginning of the 1980s; and in the mid-1980s, 35–45 pairs per km^2 in farmland at 180 m in UH county, 8 pairs per km^2 in the Jizerske hory mountains (LB, JN), and 10 pairs per km^2 at peatbogs in the Krkonose mountains at 1410 m. On passage, flocks of hundreds of birds can be seen. Agricultural intensification is the major threat to this species. As a breeder, Sky Lark prefers farmland and meadows with short vegetation, but up to 75% of nests may be destroyed owing to farm practices in spring (Stastny *et al.* 1987). The breeding population belongs to the nominate *arvensis* race.

Status: Resident. **Breeding season**: common. **Winter**: local. **Migration**: common. Protected.

Population trends: The breeding population is estimated to be between 800,000 and 1,600,000 pairs, and over the past 20 years has declined by 20–50%. The number of wintering birds, 4,000–8,000 individuals, probably includes birds on spring passage.

Distribution: Nationwide.

Timing: Spring arrival occurs from mid-February until the end of March, with the majority of birds arriving at the end of February and beginning of March. Autumn departure starts in September and continues through the beginning of November, peaking during the second half of October. Breeding extends from the end of March to the end of July, with peaks during the second half of April and mid-June.

Horned Lark *Eremophila alpestris*

Shore Lark Skrivan ouskaty Uskarik vrchovsky Ohrenlerche

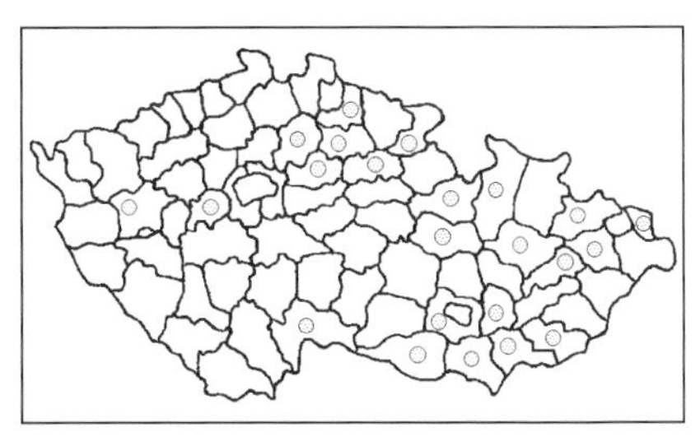

Horned Lark was a quite rare winter visitor to the Czech Republic until the 1950s. Since then, records and numbers have been increasing. This species is usually recorded in e. Bohemia and n. Moravia, although infrequent records come from other parts of the country as well. It is usually found in flocks ranging from a few birds up to 25, and occasionally larger numbers. Horned Lark normally occurs in open habitats such as fields, meadows, pastures, and around roads, railway yards and dumps. Wintering birds belong to the *flava* race.

Status: Migrant and winter visitor. **Breeding season**: rare. **Winter**: uncommon. **Migration**: uncommon. Protected.

Population trends: The wintering population is estimated to be between 100 and 200 individuals. The number of wintering birds and birds on passage has increased by 20–50% over the past 20 years.

Distribution: May occur nationwide. Recent records of flocks of up to 20 individuals come from Zehunsky pond (NB), Mnichovo Hradiste (MB), Prerov (PR), Bohunovice (OL), Podoli (UH), Soutok (BV), and Javornik nad Velickou (HO).

Timing: Birds arrive in mid-November and depart at the beginning of March. Most records are from December–February, and it is rarely seen before mid-November or after mid-March.

Sand Martin *Riparia riparia*

Common Sand Martin Brehule ricni Brehula obycajna Uferschwalbe

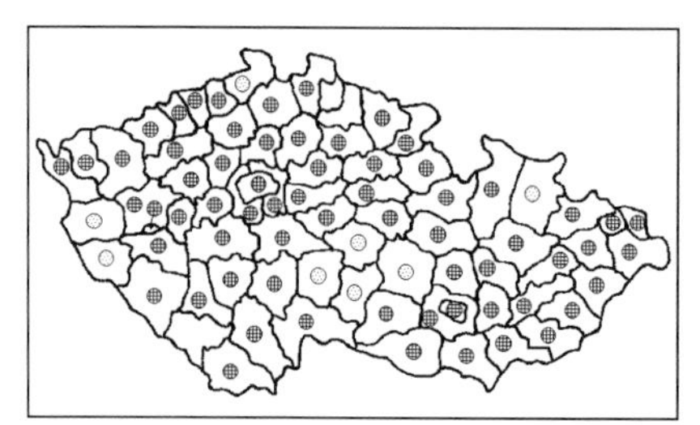

Sand Martin is the least common hirundine occurring in the Czech Republic. It is distributed from lowlands up to 450 m in s. Bohemia, but normally up to about 250 m. This species is a local breeder with strongholds in e. Bohemia, central Bohemia, s. Bohemia, s. Moravia and central Moravia. Breeding colonies are located in open habitats, usually close to open water, for example rivers and gravel pits. Colonies are also found farther from water in sandbanks or mud near county roads, in sandpits and, occasionally, in a variety of often unusual sites in urban habitats. However, these colonies do not exist on a year-to-year basis. The size of breeding colonies ranges from fewer than a dozen pairs up to several hundred. Colonies of more than 500–750 pairs are infrequent, those with thousands of pairs are rare, for example at Strachotin (BV) and Bozice (ZN). The size of the same colonies may vary from year to year. Before autumn departure, flocks of hundreds of Sand Martins roost in reedbeds around larger ponds. Some breeding colonies are destroyed as a result of human activity, for example sand extraction, and the canalization of rivers. However, the population as a whole is not threatened.

Status: Migrant and summer visitor. **Breeding season**: local. **Winter**: does not occur. **Migration**: local/common. Least concern. Protected.

Population trends: The breeding population is estimated to be between 18,000 and 36,000 pairs, and has been stable for the past 20 years.

Distribution: On migration it may occur nationwide in lowlands and highlands. Regular breeding of larger number of pairs is more or less restricted to areas surrounding water in the following counties: fishponds in CB, JH, TA and ST counties, the Vltava river in PZ, AA and ME counties, the Labe river in HK, PU, KO, NB, MB and ME counties, and the Jizera river in MB county. It is also quite common in CH, MO, CL, LN, ZN, BV, TR, HO, BO, KM, PR, OL and OP counties. Occasional breeding may occur elsewhere.

Timing: Spring migration starts in mid-April and continues through early May. Autumn migration occurs from the end of August until the end of September. Birds are rare during the first half of April and the beginning of October. Breeding extends from mid-May until mid-July, peaking at the end of May and beginning of June. Breeding in July is probably a combination of second attempts, where the first failed.

Barn Swallow *Hirundo rustica*

Swallow, Common Swallow Vlastovka obecna Lastovicka obycajna Rauchschwalbe

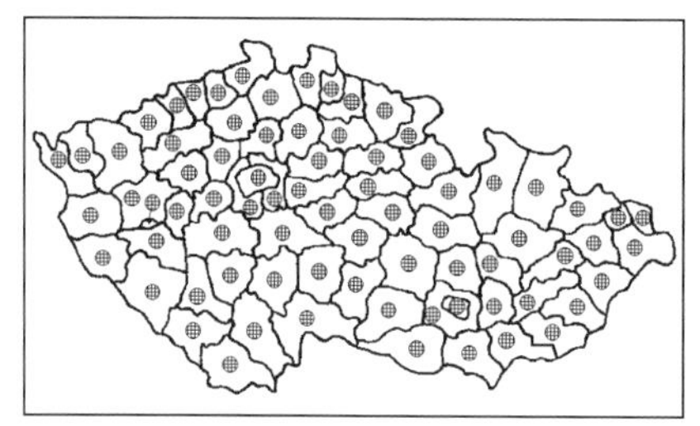

Barn Swallow is a common breeding species throughout the country. It occurs from lowlands up to 700 m in the Orlicke hory mountains (RK), to 800 m in the Jizerske hory mountains (JN, LB), up to 900 m in the Sumava mountains (CK, PT, KT), to about 1000 m in the Krusne hory mountains (CV, KV, MO, TP), and to about 1300 m, occasionally to 1400 m, in the Krkonose mountains (SE, TU). It is more common in lowlands than at higher altitudes. Breeding pairs are found in human habitations such as farms, barns, and in any type of building that offers suitable nest sites. However, changes in barn-building practices have caused the loss of nest sites across the country. Breeding density was 5–44 pairs per km^2 in urban habitats in Bor u Tachova (TC) and Tachov (TC) in the 1980s, and 18 individuals per km^2 around Milovice (MB) at the beginning of the 1990s. It was 14–22 pairs per km^2 at farms at about 200 m in UH county at the end of the 1970s, but only 5–12 pairs at the same farms 10 years later. Before autumn migration, flocks of thousands of birds, often mixed with Sand Martins, roost in the reedbeds around larger ponds

such as, for example, Rezabinec pond (PI), ponds around Ceske Budejovice (CB), Trebon (TR), Ostrava (OV), Hodonin (HO), and Lednice (BV). The breeding population of Barn Swallows is not threatened as a whole, but locally it has become an uncommon species.
Status: Migrant and summer visitor. **Breeding season:** common. **Winter:** does not occur. **Migration:** common. Least concern. Protected.
Population trends: The breeding population is estimated to be between 400,000 and 800,000 pairs. It has decreased by 20–50% over the past 20 years.
Distribution: Nationwide.
Timing: Spring arrival starts at the end of March and continues through mid-April, less frequently at the end of April. Autumn departure occurs between the beginning of September and early October, rarely later. Breeding extends from the beginning of May to the end of July. Second or even third clutches are laid late, usually at nest sites in lowlands. Breeding peaks during the second half of May.

House Martin *Delichon urbica*

Common House Martin Jiricka obecna Beloritka obycajna Mehlschwalbe

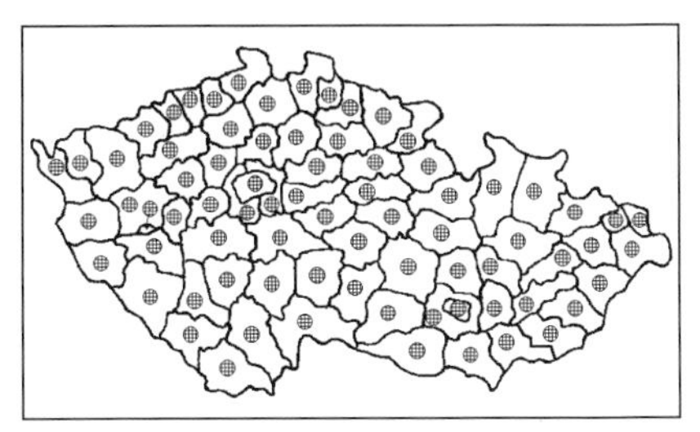

House Martin is a common breeder in the Czech Republic, occurring from lowlands up to 750 m in the Orlicke hory mountains (RK), to 1000 m in the Jeseniky mountains (BR, SU), to 1050 m in Krusne hory mountains (CV, KV, MO, TP), to 1400 m in the Krkonose mountains (SE, TU), and to 1450 m in the Sumava mountains (CK, PT, KT). Breeding birds are found in human habitations in villages as well as towns, where they usually build nests on buildings, occasionally under bridges and on other artificial structures. Nesting on rocks and cliffs is rare. This species nests in colonies of varying size, ranging from a few nests up to 150–200. Solitary nests are found occasionally. In farms, House Martins and Barn Swallows may nest together in loose associations. In the 1980s, breeding density was 40–300 pairs per km^2 in urban habitats in Bor u Tachova (TC) and Tachov (TC); 60–73 pairs per km^2 in 2 villages at about 180 m in UH county in the mid-1980s, and 142–200 individuals per km^2 around Milovice (MB) at the beginning of the 1990s. The breeding population is not threatened, although local decreases have been reported.
Status: Migrant and summer visitor. **Breeding season:** common. **Winter:** does not occur. **Migration:** common. Protected.
Population trends: The breeding population ranges from 600,000 to 1,200,000 pairs and has been stable over the past 20 years.
Distribution: Nationwide.
Timing: Spring migration starts at the beginning of April and continues through early May, peaking in mid-April. Autumn migration occurs between the beginning of September and the beginning of October. The majority of birds depart during the second half of September, but some birds may stay until the end of October. Breeding extends from the beginning of May to the end of August, with peaks during the second half of May, beginning of June, and the beginning of July (second clutches).

Tawny Pipit *Anthus campestris*

Linduska uhorni Labtuska polna Brachpieper

Tawny Pipit is a regular, but rare breeder with patchy distribution in the Czech Republic. It is found in lowlands and highlands up to 350–400 m. Breeding was also recorded at about 740 m in CK county (Stastny *et al.* 1987). Traditional breeding sites are in LN and LT counties in the Ceske stredohori highlands, around the Labe river in KO county, and an area between Zidlochovice (BV) and Znojmo (ZN). Relatively new breeding sites are slag heaps around coal mines in MO county in n. Bohemia. This species was more common until the mid-20th century, when breeding was more widespread. Tawny Pipit nests in open and dry habitats with

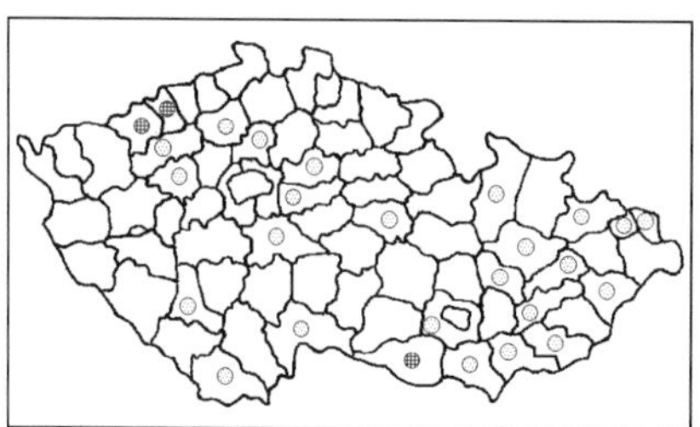

sparse vegetation: stony hillsides, pastures, sandy patches and bare soil. During migration it regularly occurs in farmland. At the beginning of the 1970s, breeding density at slag heaps in MO county was 7–17 pairs per km² (Bejcek and Tyrner 1980). It was 0.4–6 individuals per km² in various habitats around Mlada (NB) in the mid-1990s. The exact causes of its decline are unknown; probably habitat loss is the main reason.

Status: Migrant and summer visitor. **Breeding season:** uncommon. **Winter:** does not occur. **Migration:** uncommon. Critically endangered. Protected.
Population trends: Between 1973 and 1977 the breeding population was between 100 and 200 pairs; more recently 40–80 pairs. It has declined by at least 50% over the past 20 years.
Distribution: On migration it may occur nationwide, although usually in n. Bohemia, central Bohemia, e. Bohemia, s. Moravia and n. Moravia. More or less regular breeding occurs in MO, CV and ZN counties. Recent records of singing males from outside the breeding areas come from Mecichov (ST), Postupice (BN), Zablatsky pond (JH), Stablovice (OP), Branna (SU), and Chorynske ponds (VS).
Timing: Spring migration occurs during April and May, peaking at the end of April. Autumn migration occurs from the second half of August until the end of September, rarely in October. Breeding extends from the end of May to the beginning of July.

Tree Pipit *Anthus trivialis*

Linduska lesni Labtuska horna Baumpieper

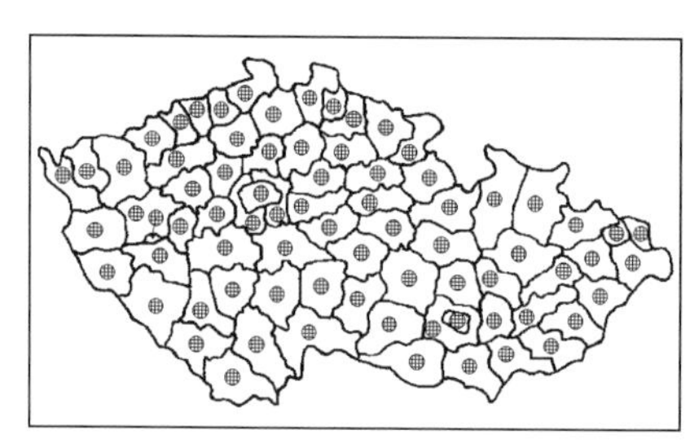

This is the most common *Anthus* species in the Czech Republic. It is distributed from lowlands up to 1100 m in the Orlicke hory mountains (RK), to 1200 m in the Krusne hory mountains (CV, KV, MO, TP), and to 1450 m in the Krkonose (SE, TU) and Jeseniky (BR, SU) mountains. Tree Pipit nests in a wide variety of habitats, typically including clearings and edges of sparse coniferous, mixed and deciduous forest. It is occasionally found in smaller areas of woodland in farmland, and in meadows or pastures. However, the presence of a tree or a tall bush to serve as a song-post for the male is essential. Most nests are found in grass in clearings, thickets, and in meadows surrounding forest. Breeding density data for the 1970s for different habitats was as follows: 53–58 pairs per km² in pine plantations around Trebon (JH), 0–11 pairs per km² in spruce plantations around Milevsko (TA), 20 pairs per km² in beech forest in the Jeseniky mountains, 17–26 pairs per km² in riverine forest in KM and PR counties, and 193 pairs per km² in an abandoned orchard (CV). It was 2–17 pairs per km² in a variety of habitats in the Krkonose mountains in 1984 (Flousek 1991), 21–26 pairs per km² in a mixed mature forest at 180 m in UH county in the mid-1980s, 40 pairs per km² around Tabor (TA), 19–100 pairs per km² in various growths of trees and brushes in farmland (ST), and 42–95 pairs per km² around Tachov (TC) in the 1980s. In acid-rain-damaged spruce forest at various altitudes in the Beskydy mountains (FM, VS) it was 37–115 pairs per km² at the beginning of the 1990s, and in the same type of environment in the Jizerske hory (LB, JN) and Krusne hory mountains it was 0–55 pairs per km² and 20–45 pairs per km² respectively in the 1980s. At the beginning of the 1990s, it was 17–96 individuals per km² in various habitats around Mlada (NB). Tree Pipit may be seen in smaller flocks in meadows and around ponds and rivers before autumn migration begins.
Status: Migrant and summer visitor. **Breeding season:** common. **Winter:** does not occur. **Migration:** common. Protected.
Population trends: The breeding population is estimated to be between 500,000 and 1,000,000 pairs. It has increased by 20–50% over the past 20 years.
Distribution: Nationwide.

Timing: Spring migration occurs from the end of March until the end of April, with the peak in mid-April. Autumn migration extends from the end of August to the beginning of October, but birds are occasionally seen until the end of October. Breeding occurs from the end of April until the beginning of August, peaking in mid-May.

Meadow Pipit *Anthus pratensis*

Linduska lucni Labtuska lucna Wiesenpieper

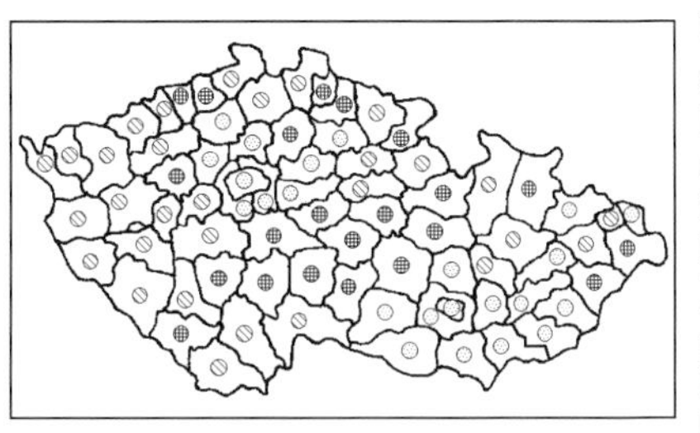

Until the end of the 19th century, Meadow Pipit was a rather scarce breeder in the mountains of n. Bohemia and n. Moravia. During the first decades of the 20th century, this species expanded its range into other mountains, and during the 1930s into the lowlands of the Czech Republic. Even though Meadow Pipit occurs all year round, most of the population is migratory. This species has patchy breeding distribution throughout the country, from lowlands up to mountain peaks. It is more common in the western highlands and mountains than those in the east. Breeding strongholds of this species are mostly mountains in border areas: Novohradske hory (CK, CB), Krusne hory (CV, KV, MO, TP), Jizerske hory (LB, JN), Krkonose (SE, TU), Orlicke hory (RK), Sumava (CK, PT, KT), Beskydy (VS, FM) and Jeseniky (BR, SU), and also the Ceskomoravska vysocina highlands (HB, JI, PE, ZR). When breeding, this species generally prefers open country with wet meadows and peatbogs. In lowlands it will breed in meadows and wetlands around ponds; in mountains, it favours alpine meadows, and stony hillsides with sparse vegetation and dwarf pines. On migration and in winter it can be seen on flooded meadows, around ponds, and in farmland. Breeding density was 33 pairs per km^2 in the Ceskomoravska vysocina highlands in the mid-1970s, and 9 pairs per km^2 in meadows around Trebon (JH) at the beginning of the 1970s. In meadows with dwarf pine at about 1200 m in the Krkonose mountains, it was 36 pairs per km^2 and 18–89 pairs per km^2 in a variety of other habitats in the same mountains during the first half of the 1980s. At commercially exploited peatbogs around Trebon (JH) it was 43 pairs per km^2 at the beginning of the 1980s. In acid-rain-damaged spruce forest at various altitudes in the Beskydy mountains it was 117 pairs per km^2 at the beginning of the 1990s, and in the same type of environment in the Jizerske hory and Krusne hory mountains it was 3–268 pairs per km^2 and 15–155 pairs respectively in the 1980s. Most wintering birds usually stay in small flocks, and are found in s. Bohemia, central Bohemia, e. Bohemia and s. Moravia. Meadow Pipit has been expanding its range in the Czech Republic over recent years.

Status: Resident. **Breeding season**: local/common. **Winter**: uncommon. **Migration**: common. Protected.

Population trends: The breeding population is estimated to be between 30,000 and 60,000 pairs. It has increased by at least 50% over the last 20 years. The number of wintering birds is between 1,500 and 3,000 individuals.

Distribution: During migration it is found nationwide. The highest numbers of wintering birds were recorded in the following counties: KT, CK, JH, PZ, KH, PU, HO, BV, KI and RK.

Timing: Spring migration occurs in March and April, with the majority of birds arriving at the end of March. Autumn migration occurs from August until mid-November. Breeding extends from the beginning of April to mid-July, with peaks at the end of April and beginning of May (first brood), and during the first half of June (second brood).

Red-throated Pipit *Anthus cervinus*

Linduska rudokrka Labtuska cervenohrdla Rotkehlpieper

Until the mid-1940s, Red-throated Pipit was recorded only rarely in the Czech Republic. Since then, the frequency of sightings has been increasing. Migrating birds are usually found in lowlands, with the majority of records from s. and central Moravia. Solitary birds, and occa-

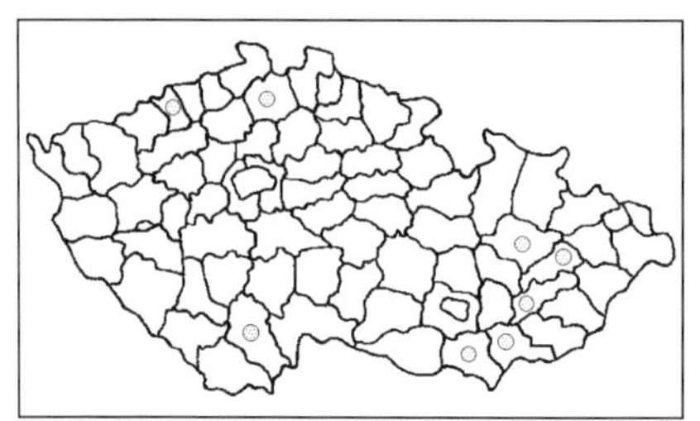

sionally small flocks, occur during migration in wet meadows, in fields and around ponds. This species is recorded more commonly during spring than autumn migration, although birds in non-breeding plumage during autumn may be misindentified as other pipit species.
Status: Migrant. **Breeding season**: rare. **Winter**: does not occur. **Migration**: uncommon. Protected.
Population trends: No data available.
Distribution: May occur nationwide. Recent records come from Zehunsky pond (NB), Dehtar pond (CB), Novozamecky pond (CL), Sumvald (OL), Drevohostice (PR), Tovacov (PR), Lysky (PR), Prerov (PR), Hulin (KM), Kvasice (KM), Vytazniky ponds (HO), and Stara Breclav (BV).
Timing: During spring it occurs from mid-April until the end of May, with most records from the beginning of May. Autumn migration extends from the end of August to the end of October, rarely later. Peak autumn migration is at the beginning of October.

Water Pipit *Anthus spinoletta*

Linduska horska Labtuska vrchovska Wasserpieper

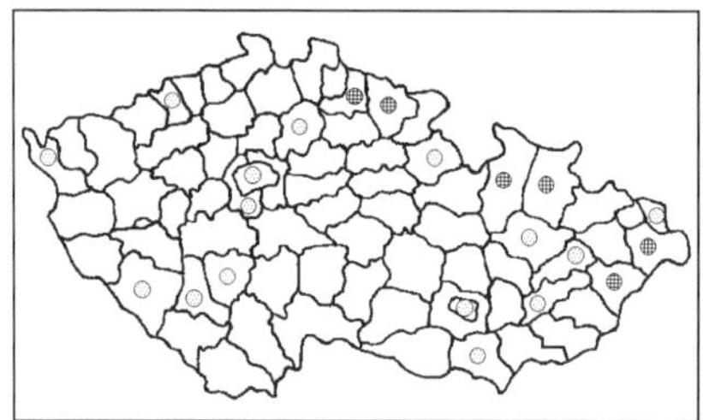

This is a regular breeding species in the Czech Republic, though numbers are low. A few individuals are usually recorded in winter. The breeding range is restricted to higher altitudes in the following mountains: Krkonose (SE, TU), where breeding occurs from about 1000 m up to the peaks, Kralicky Sneznik (UO), with distribution upwards from about 1050 m, Beskydy (FM, VS), where breeding occurs from 600 m, and Jeseniky (BR, SU), from about 950 m upwards, where it occurs in mountains such as Praded, Cervena hora, Vysoka Hole, Serak, Keprnik, and Mravenecnik. It breeds on rocky hillsides, in dwarf pine, and in subalpine meadows above the timberline. Nests are often placed in grass, and close to or under a rock. During migration and in winter this species frequents meadows and fields, usually close to ponds and rivers in both highlands and lowlands. Breeding density was 23 pairs per km^2 at about 1150 m in the Beskydy mountains, 1 pair per km^2 in the Jeseniky mountains, and 1–35 pairs per km^2 in a variety of habitats in the Krkonose mountains during the 1980s and beginning of the 1990s. The density of the breeding population may fluctuate from year to year; about 100–150 pairs were breeding in the Jeseniky mountains in 1985, but only 20–30 in 1993 (Stastny *et al.* 1996). The breeding population belongs to the *spinoleta* race; wintering birds belong to the *littoralis* race, as discovered after trapping birds in winter (Stancl and Stanclova 1987).
Status: Migrant and summer visitor. **Breeding season**: uncommon/local. **Winter**: uncommon. **Migration**: local. Endangered. Protected.
Population trends: Between 1973 and 1977 the breeding population was estimated to be between 250 and 350 breeding pairs and, more recently, between 260 and 380 pairs. Ten to 25 individuals may winter.
Distribution: On migration it may occur nationwide. Recent records of passage birds outside breeding areas come from the Sumava mountains (CK, KT, PT), Zehunsky pond (NB), Skalsky pond (PI), Rezabinec pond (PI), Sumvald (OL), Kojetin (PR), Pravcice (KM), Ladna (BV), Brno (BM), Lednicke ponds (BV), and Stara Breclav (BV).
Timing: Spring migration occurs from mid-March until the end of April, peaking during the first half of April. Autumn migration occurs between the second half of August and the beginning of October. Breeding extends from the end of April to mid-July.

Yellow Wagtail *Motacilla flava*

Konipas lucni Trasochvost zlty Schafstelze

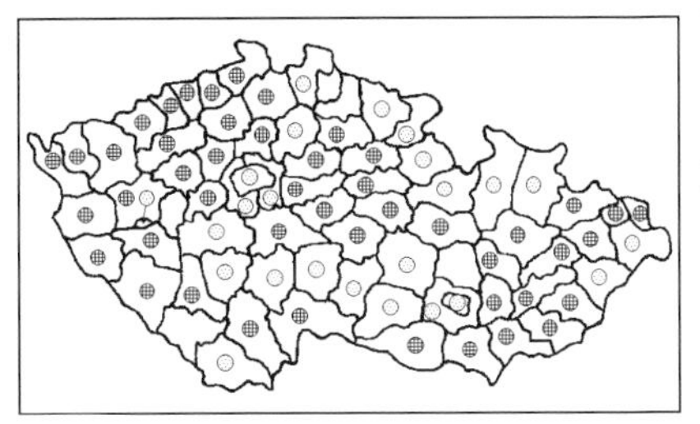

Yellow Wagtail is a regular but uncommon breeder in the Czech Republic. It is a typical lowland species, although regular breeding has been recorded at 400–450 m around Trebon (JH), at 650 m around Tachov (TC), and accidental breeding at 720 m in the Orlicke hory mountains (RK). There are several main areas where this species breeds regularly in higher numbers: in the foothills of the Krusne hory mountains (CV, KV, MO, TP), in TC county, around the Labe river in HK, PU, KO, NB and ME counties, in fishpond areas in CB and JH counties in s. Bohemia, in BV, HO, UH and BO counties in s. Moravia, in KM, PV and PR counties in central Moravia, and in OL, OP, OV and KI counties in n. Moravia. Breeding birds require open habitat with marshes, wet meadows or flooded areas around rivers, canals and ponds. Breeding on slag heaps around coal mines has been recorded in CV and MO counties in n. Bohemia. On migration, this species may occur nationwide around any open water area and in meadows and fields. At the beginning of the 1970s, breeding density was 8 individuals per km^2 in wet meadows in CV county, and 20 pairs per km^2 at dumps around coal mines in MO county. An unusually high density, 160 pairs per km^2, was recorded at a drained man-made area of water in KI county in the mid-1980s. Breeding density was 12–15 pairs per km^2 at wet meadows at 160 m in HO county at the beginning of the 1980s, and 3–5 pairs per km^2 at meadows and around a gravel pit in Ostrozska Nova Ves (UH) in the mid-1980s. Six races have been recorded in the Czech Republic: nominate *flava*, including the breeding population; *cinereocapilla,* a rare visitor, although probable breeding of 1 pair was recorded near Kojetin (PR) in 1992; *beema* (5 individuals recorded at Zahlinicke ponds (KM) in 1974, and at Tovacovske ponds (PR) in 1985); *thunbergi*, a regular spring and autumn migrant, with 1 pair breeding in CL county in 1972; *feldegg,* a regular spring and autumn migrant and rare breeder, with breeding recorded in TR county in s. Moravia and KM county in central Moravia in the 20th century (Hudec *et al.* 1983), and possibly occurring in KI county in 1985; *flavissima*, an adult male recorded in SY county, the only record for the Czech Republic. The exact causes of Yellow Wagtail's decline are unknown, but are most likely attributable to agricultural intensification and habitat loss.

Status: Migrant and summer visitor. **Breeding season:** uncommon (*flava*), rare (*cinereocapilla*, *beema*, *thunbergi*, *feldegg*, *flavissima*). **Winter:** does not occur. **Migration:** common (*flava*), rare (*beema*, *flavissima*), uncommon (*cinereocapilla*, *feldegg*). Endangered. Protected.

Population trends: The breeding population is between 600 and 1,200 pairs, a decline of 20–50% over the past 20 years.

Distribution: On migration it may occur nationwide.

Timing: Spring migration occurs between the end of March and the end of April, peaking during the first half of April. Autumn migration occurs between mid-August and the end of September. Breeding extends from the end of April to mid-July, with peaks during the first half of May, the end of June and beginning of July.

Citrine Wagtail *Motacilla citreola*

Yellow-hooded Wagtail Konipas citronovy Trasochvost zltohlavy Zitronenstelze

Although there are 3 records of Citrine Wagtails from the end of the 19th and beginning of the 20th centuries, the first record accepted by CFC is from 1964. Since then, 14 additional observations of 16 birds have been reported, mostly of single birds, once a flock of 3. Unexpected breeding was recorded in KI county in 1977. Since 1991, singles, usually males, have been recorded 10 times. Citrine Wagtail occurs in similar habitats to the Yellow Wagtail.

Status: Vagrant. **Breeding season:** rare. **Winter:** does not occur. **Migration:** rare. Protected.

Population trends: There has been an increase in records during the past decade.

Distribution: May occur nationwide. Most recent records come from Tovacovske ponds (PR), and 3 from Valasske Mezirici (VS).

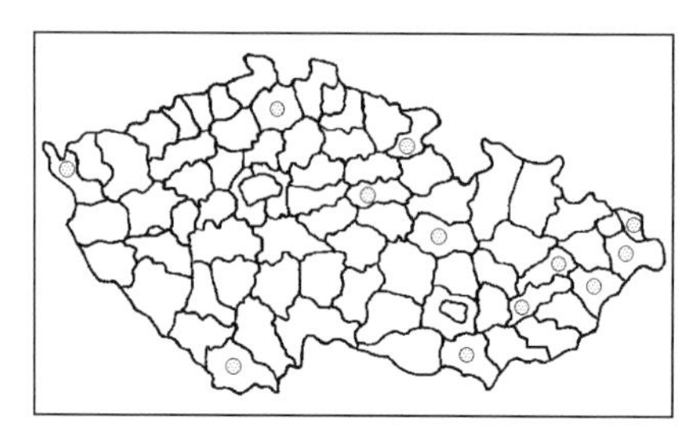

Timing: From April until September. Most records are from April and May.

Grey Wagtail *Motacilla cinerea*

Konipas horsky Trasochvost horsky Gebirgstelze

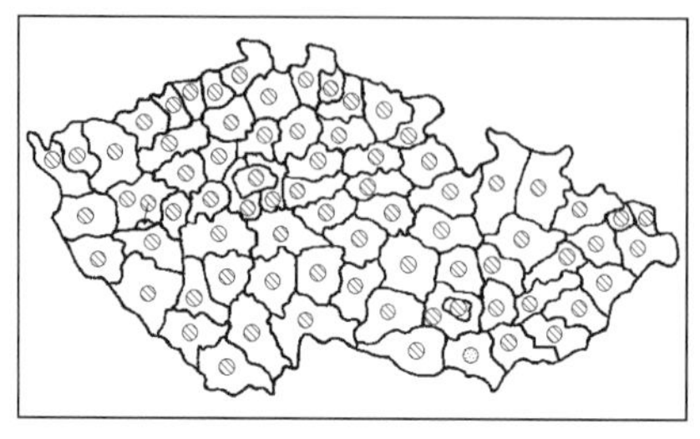

Grey Wagtail is quite common in the highlands and mountains, and is a scarce breeding bird in the lowlands. It occurs regularly from 450–500 m up to 1000 m in the Orlicke hory mountains (RK), to 1200 m in the Krusne hory mountains (CV, KV, MO, TP), to 1250 m in the Jeseniky mountains (BR, SU), to 1300 m in the Sumava mountains (CK, PT, KT), and to 1400 m in the Krkonose mountains (SE, TU). It breeds on the banks of fast-flowing rivers, streams and brooks. If breeding at lower altitudes occurs, the birds usually seek fast-flowing stretches of river. The majority of nests are built in or on man-made structures, including nest boxes, with others in natural sites such as rocks and between the roots of trees. During migration, it is also found around gravel pits, ponds, lakes, and in flooded meadows. Wintering birds stay at ice-free parts of the larger rivers in lowlands as well as streams in highlands. The density of breeding birds varies from county to county, and at different sites within each county. At the Metuje river (NA) it was 1 pair per 0.3–0.6 km at the end of the 1970s; it was 1 pair per 0.7–0.8 km at Oslava stream (OL), 1 pair per 0.4–0.7 km at various streams in the Orlicke hory mountains (RK), 1 pair per 0.4 km at the Roznovska Becva river (VS), and 1 pair per 0.5–0.7 km at the Velicka river (HO) in the Bile Karpaty mountains in the 1980s. Although Grey Wagtail is a permanent resident, the breeding population is migratory, and wintering birds come from other populations from in Europe.
Status: Resident. **Breeding season:** local/common. **Winter:** local. **Migration:** common. Protected.
Population trends: The breeding population is between 20,000 and 40,000 pairs. No changes have been recorded during the past 20 years. The number of wintering birds ranges from 500 to 1,000 individuals.
Distribution: Found on migration nationwide. As a breeder it occurs less commonly in the following counties: LN, LT, MB, NB, HK, SY, PV, ZN, BV, VY, NJ, KI and OV. High wintering numbers have been recorded in the following counties: KV, MO, UL, PJ, PM, BE, KL, PB, PI, PT, CK, JH, PZ, PH, HK, RK, BN, JI, ZR, SU, PR and VS.
Timing: Spring migration occurs in March, peaking during the middle of the month. Autumn migration occurs during September and October. Breeding extends from April to mid-July, with peaks in mid-April and at the end of June.

White Wagtail *Motacilla alba*

Pied Wagtail Konipas bily Trasochvost biely Bachstelze

This is the most common of the 4 wagtail species occurring in the Czech Republic. White Wagtail is distributed from lowlands up to the mountains: in the Orlicke hory mountains (RK) up to 1000 m, in the Krusne hory mountains (CV, KV, MO, TP) up to 1250 m, in the Jeseniky mountains (BR, SU) up to 1450 m, and up to 1500 m in the Krkonose mountains (SE, TU). It is found on banks of rivers, streams, brooks, ponds, lakes, and often at industrial complexes

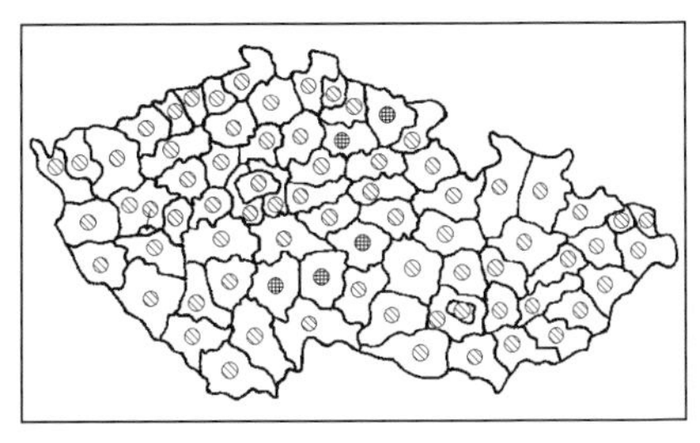

in open country. However, breeding birds are often found near human habitations. During migration, it can be found in fields and meadows. In winter, it frequents farmland and ice-free parts of rivers. It uses a wide variety of nest sites, ranging from the natural to the artificial, for example bridges, buildings and nest boxes. During the 1970s, breeding density was 5.5–25.5 pairs per km^2 around fishponds in JH county, 32.5 pairs per km^2 around a brook in CV county, and 11–21 pairs per km^2 in villages in TC county. In various habitats in the towns of Bor u Tachova and Tachov (TC), breeding density was 6–55 pairs per km^2 in the 1980s and at the beginning of the 1990s. It was 8–13 pairs per km^2 in a village at 170 m in UH county, and 20–23 pairs around a farm at the same altitude and in the same county in the mid-1980s. A 1-km bank of the Roznovska Becva (VS) river was occupied by 1.5 pairs in the 1980s, and a 1-km stretch of the Velicka river (HO) in a forested area by 0.8 pairs at the beginning of the 1980s. Different habitats around Mlada (NB) hosted 1–42 individuals per km^2 in the mid-1990s. The breeding population is migratory, and the origin of wintering birds is unknown. The population belongs to the *alba* race. Individuals, apparently of the British *yarrellii* race, have been recorded several times. However, Cerny (in Hudec *et al.* 1983) suggested that these are probably aberrant melanistic individuals of the *alba* race.

Status: Resident. **Breeding season**: common. **Winter**: local. **Migration**: common. Protected.

Population trends: The breeding population is estimated to be between 100,000 and 200,000 pairs. It has been stable over the past 20 years. In winter from 700 to 1,400 individuals may be recorded.

Distribution: Migrating and breeding birds are found nationwide. Higher densities of wintering birds have been recorded in the following counties: PT, ST, DO, JH, CB, CK, PJ, BE, KV, CV, LN, UL, DC ,LB, PB, PZ, AA, SE, MB, PU, RK, SY, UH, PR, VS, FM and OP.

Timing: Spring migration starts at the end of February and continues until the end of March, peaking during the first half of March. Autumn migration occurs in October. Breeding extends from the beginning of April to the end of July, with peaks at the end of April and beginning of June.

Bohemian Waxwing *Bombycilla garrulus*

Waxwing Brkoslav severni Chochlac seversky Seidenschwanz

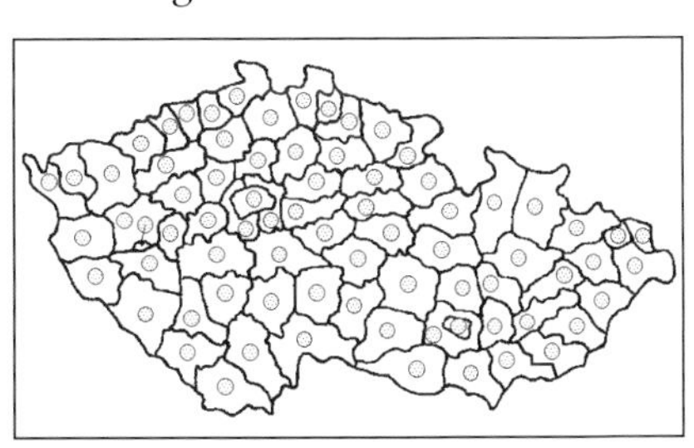

This species is an annual winter visitor to the Czech Republic. Periodically, its occurrence resembles an invasion, and high numbers are recorded. Between 1843 and 1976, 50 such invasions have been recorded (Hudec *et al.* 1983). Even though Bohemian Waxwings can be scattered nationwide, they normally occur in both lowlands and highlands in mature gardens and orchards, not too dense deciduous and mixed forest, larger parks, open country with groups of trees, and sites around rural settlements. Bohemian Waxwings occur in flocks ranging from fewer than a dozen birds up to several hundred. Singles are rare, as are flocks of more than a thousand. Although possible breeding has been reported several times in the 19th and 20th centuries, it has never been documented.

Status: Migrant and winter visitor. **Breeding season**: rare. **Winter**: local. **Migration**: local. Vulnerable. Protected.

Population trends: The number of wintering birds is estimated to be between 3,000 and 15,000 individuals annually. However, it is higher during invasions.

Distribution: May occur nationwide. High numbers of wintering birds have been recorded in the following counties: CK, PS, CH, SO, KV, KL, BN, LB, JN, TU, KO, KH, SY, BO, UH, KM, ZL, VS, PR, OL, FM and OP.

Timing: It occurs from October until the beginning of May. The first birds arrive in mid-

October, but mostly during November when numbers are highest. Departure occurs mostly from March through the first half of April.

Dipper *Cinclus cinclus*

White-throated Dipper   Skorec vodni   Vodnar obycajny   Wasseramsel

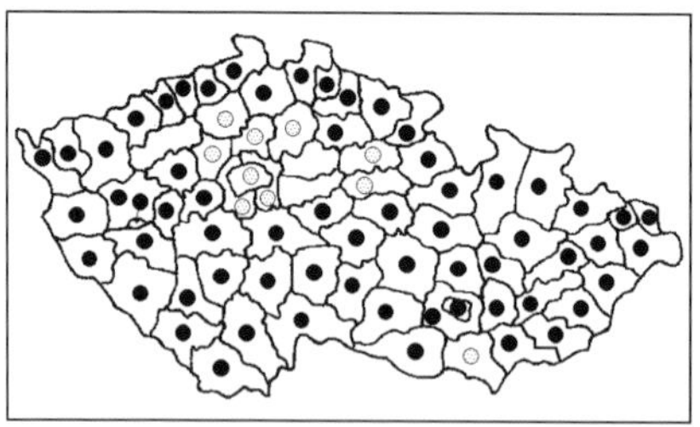

Dipper is a typical high-altitude species in the Czech Republic. It occurs from 300–350 m, up to 630 m in the Bile Karpaty mountains (HO, UH, ZL), to 750 m in the Orlicke hory mountains (RK), to 900 m in the Krusne hory mountains (CV, KV, MO, TP), to 1000 m in the Jizerske hory mountains (LB, JN), to 1050 m in the Jeseniky mountains (BR, SU), to 1100 m in the Sumava mountains (CK, PT, KT), and up to 1300, occasionally 1400 m, in the Krkonose mountains (SE, TU). It occasionally breeds at lower altitudes such as 200–250 m, and nests have also been found at 150 m. Birds are always found at fast-flowing streams with rock or gravel, or at brooks or rivers with the same conditions. Nests are placed in natural as well as artificial sites, such as bridges, frequently within 1 m of the water. Dipper stays within the same territory all year round; when the stream is iced over, they move to ice-free areas. After the breeding season, they can be found farther afield, particularly young birds, usually never farther than 100 km from natal sites. Each breeding pair occupied 0.5–0.7 km of a stream in BK county at the beginning of the 1960s (Balat 1964). At the Velicka river (HO) in the Bile Karpaty mountains at about 480 m, there was 1 breeding pair per 0.9–1.1 km during the early 1980s. At various rivers in the Orlicke hory mountains (RK), at 300–600 m, at the end of the 1980s, 1 pair occupied about 7.25 km. In the Labske piskovce rocks (DC), 1 pair occupied about 1.6 km of a stream in the mid-1980s; at the Svratka river (ZR), 1 pair was found about every 2 km; and at various streams in the Ceskomoravska vysocina highlands (HB, JI, PE, ZR) at the end of the 1980s, 1 pair was found every 5.6 km along each stream. The population belongs to the *aquaticus* race. The dark-bellied *cinclus* race is recorded occasionally. However, Hudec *et al.* (1983) believe that individuals with dark bellies occur in the nominate *aquaticus* race, especially at higher altitudes.

Status: Resident. **Breeding season:** local/common. **Winter:** local/common. **Migration:** local/common. Conservation-dependent. Protected.

Population trends: The breeding population is between 1,000 and 2,000 pairs, and has been stable for the past 20 years. The number of wintering birds ranges from 1,800 to 3,500 individuals.

Distribution: In autumn and winter it may occur nationwide.

Timing: Breeding starts from mid-March and continues until the end of June, peaking in April.

Wren *Troglodytes troglodytes*

Winter Wren   Strizlik obecny   Oriesok obycajny   Zaunkönig

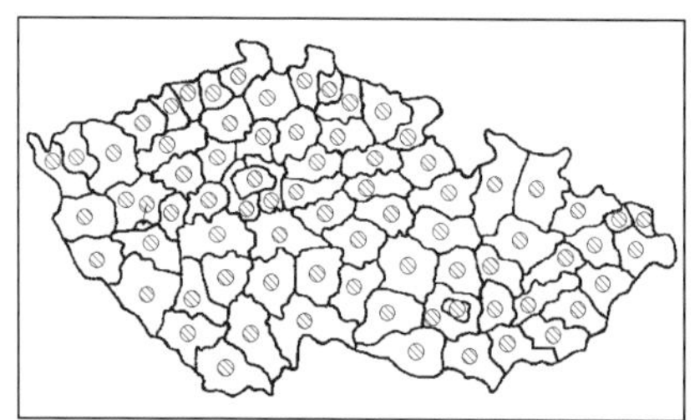

Wren is common throughout the country. It is found from lowlands up to 800 m in the Krusne hory (CV, KV, MO, TP) and Cesky les (DO, TC) mountains, to 950 m in the Orlicke hory mountains (RK), to 1100 m in the Jizerske hory mountains (LB, JN), to 1200 m in the Beskydy mountains (VS, FM), and to 1300 m in the Sumava (CK, PT, KT), Krkonose (SE, TU) and Jeseniky mountains (BR, SU). It is less common in lowlands than in highlands and mountains. It exploits a wide range of natural and man-made habitats, but favours any type of forest with scrub undergrowth, dense thickets and scrub around rivers and brooks, and mature parks and gardens. It also breeds in parks inside large

towns such as Praha (AA), Brno (BM), Olomouc (OL), Ostrava (OV), Plzen (PM) and Karlovy Vary (KV). After the breeding season, and occasionally in winter, Wrens quite often frequent reedbeds around ponds. Nests are commonly found among the roots of trees on the banks of brooks and rivers. At the end of the 1970s, breeding density in a spruce plantation was 10–56 pairs per km^2 near Milevsko (TA), 6 pairs per km^2 in a village, and 3 pairs per km^2 in a young deciduous forest in TC county, and 32–52 pairs per km^2 in Praha's (AA) parks. At the beginning of the 1980s, it was 9–12 pairs per km^2 in young forest and in ditches in farmland at about 170 m, 10–15 pairs per km^2 around a river with mature stands of trees in UH county, and 30–40 pairs per km^2 in riverine forest (KM). In the 1980s, in beech forest in the Jizerske hory mountains, it was 26 pairs per km^2, in fir-beech forest in the Beskydy mountains it was 22–28 pairs per km^2, in the Novohradske hory mountains (CB, CK) it was 97 pairs per km^2, and 56–124 pairs per km^2 in growths around a brook (CK). In various habitats around Mlada (NB) it was 9 individuals per km^2 at the beginning of the 1990s. At the beginning of the 1990s, in acid-rain-damaged forest in the Beskydy mountains it was 13–63 pairs per km^2, and in the Krkonose mountains it was 10–17 pairs per km^2. In the 1980s, breeding density in parks in Bor u Tachova (TC) was 28 pairs per km^2, in Chodova Plana (TC) it was 13 pairs per km^2, and in Blatna 10 pairs per km^2. Winter density was 1–3 individuals per km^2 in mixed forest with spruce stands at about 190–210 m in UH county during the 1980s. The breeding population is partly migratory, and remaining birds are joined by individuals from n. Europe.
Status: Resident. **Breeding season**: common. **Winter**: common. **Migration**: common. Protected.
Population trends: The breeding population is between 100,000 and 200,000 pairs, and it has been relatively stable for the past 20 years. However, severe winters may significantly decrease local populations. The wintering population is estimated to be between 70,000 and 140,000 individuals.
Distribution: Nationwide. Winter distribution is generally consistent with breeding distribution, although birds from higher altitudes usually move to lowlands.
Timing: Breeding extends from mid-April to the end of July.

Hedge Accentor *Prunella modularis*

Dunnock   Pevuska modra   Vrcharka modra   Heckenbraunelle

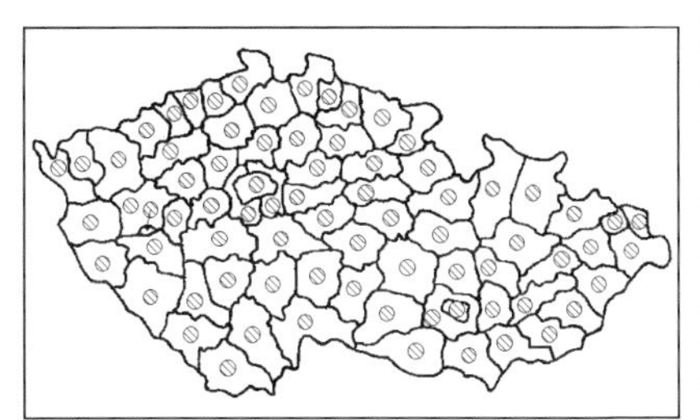

Hedge Accentor is a common breeding species throughout the country, although its density varies from county to county, depending on the availability of suitable habitat. It is distributed from lowlands up to the dwarf-pine zone in mountains. In winter, this species is more common in lowlands, and at lower altitudes in highlands. It is found in coniferous and mixed woodland with dense scrub undergrowth, especially at woodland edges and in clearings, a variety of scrub habitats around rivers, brooks, ditches and in gardens and parks. It is commonly found in old cemeteries, hedgerows and in woodland on farms. An important habitat requirement seems to be dense secondary growth. Nests are usually built in spruce, juniper, raspberry bushes, and European elder, 0.5–1.5 m above ground. During migration it frequents growths around rivers. Wintering birds are often found in dense undergrowth around farms and other human habitations. At the beginning of the 1970s; breeding density was 19–30 pairs per km^2 in coniferous forest around Trebon (JH), in spruce plantation near Milevsko (TA) it was 10–22 pairs per km^2 at the end of the 1970s; in spruce plantations at 790 m in MO county it was 15 pairs per km^2 at the beginning of the 1970s, and in Praha's parks (AA) it was from 24–38 pairs per km^2 at the end of the 1970s. It was 12–19 pairs per km^2 in woodland and ditches in farmland at 180 m in UH county at the beginning of the 1980s; and it was 10 pairs per km^2 in beech forest in the Krusne hory mountains (CV, KV, MO, TP), 70 pairs per km^2 in fir-beech forest in the Beskydy mountains (FM, VS), 12 pairs per km^2 in oak forest in MO county, 152 pairs per km^2 in pine thickets (JH), 37 pairs per km^2 in riverine forest (ST), 240 pairs per km^2 in growths around brooks (ST), and 125 pairs per km^2 in the same habitat in CK county in the 1980s. In

acid-rain-damaged forest at various altitudes in the Krusne hory mountains it was 13–133 pairs per km^2 and 7–105 pairs per km^2 in Jizerske hory mountains (LB, JN) in the 1980s; in the Beskydy mountains (FM, VS) it was 30–77 pairs per km^2 and in the Krkonose mountains (SE, TU) it was 10–42 pairs per km^2 at the beginning of the 1990s. In city parks in Bor u Tachova (TC) it was 28 pairs per km^2, in Chodova Plana (TC) 33 pairs per km^2, and 4–10 pairs in Ostrava (OV). The breeding population is partly migratory, and remaining birds are joined by individuals from n. Europe.
Status: Resident. **Breeding season**: common. **Winter**: local. **Migration**: common. Protected.
Population trends: The breeding population is between 200,000 and 400,000 pairs, and has increased by 20–50% over the past 20 years. The number of wintering birds ranges from 600 to 1,200 individuals.
Distribution: Nationwide. Winter and breeding distribution are similar, although it may be rather scarce in the following counties: DC, CL, KT, TU, CR, HB, JI, BR, BK, ZN and VS.
Timing: Spring arrival occurs in March and April, peaking at the end of March and beginning of April. Autumn departure occurs from the beginning of September until the end of October. Breeding starts in mid-April, and continues until mid-July, with peaks at the end of April, beginning of May and the end of June.

Alpine Accentor *Prunella collaris*

Pevuska podhorni Vrcharka cervenkava Alpenbraunelle

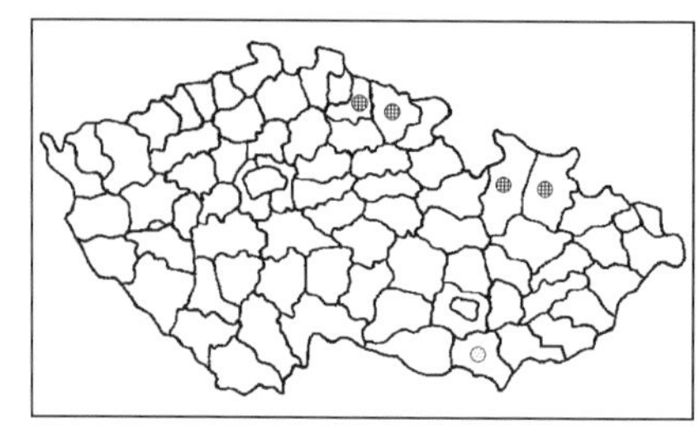

Alpine Accentor is a regular but rare breeding bird in the Czech Republic, which is this species' most northerly breeding area in Europe. The breeding population, of about 10–15 pairs, is found at Mt Snezka (1610 m), Mt Studnicni hora (1554 m), and Labsky dul and Kotelni Jamy canyons in the Krkonose mountains (SE, TU). In the Jeseniky mountains (BR, SU), the breeding population occurs at altitudes of about 1370 m, with a total of about 5 pairs. However, breeding has also been recorded in a few other areas such as the Orlicke hory mountains (RK) and the Kralicky Sneznik mountains (UO). It prefers rocky and grassy mountain slopes, regularly above the dwarf-pine zone. Nests are usually placed in crevices in rocks. Birds from the population in the Krkonose mountains are threatened by domestic cats kept as pets in the mountain cabins (Sedlacek *et al.* 1988). Alpine Accentor is more common in the mountains of Slovakia, where the breeding population is estimated to be between 300 and 400 pairs (Murin *et al.* 1994).
Status: Migrant and summer visitor. **Breeding season**: uncommon. **Winter**: does not occur. **Migration**: uncommon. Critically endangered. Protected.
Population trends: The breeding population is between 15 and 20 pairs, and was stable between the beginning of the 1970s and late 1980s.
Distribution: Breeding is restricted to 4 counties. Birds on migration, and non-breeding individuals during summer, may occur in other counties as well; recent records come from the Palava hills (BV), which are at about 550 m.
Timing: Birds arrive at the breeding grounds from the end of March until mid-April, but have occasionally been observed on passage during the second half of April outside breeding areas. Departure from the breeding grounds occurs from the end of September to early October. Breeding extends from the beginning of May to the end of June, peaking during the second half of June.

Robin *Erithacus rubecula*

European Robin Cervenka obecna Cervienka obycajna Rotkehlchen

This is one of the county's most common passerines. Robin occurs from lowlands up to 800–1000 m in the Krusne hory mountains (CV, KV, MO, TP), up to 1090 m in the Orlicke hory mountains (RK), up to 1100 m in the Jizerske hory mountains (LB, JN), up to 1250 m

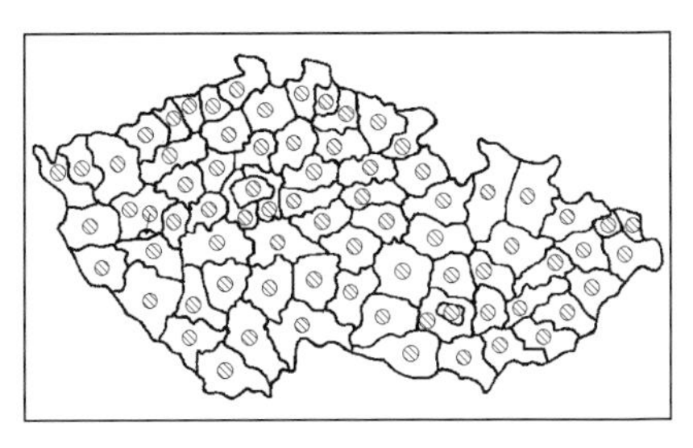

in the Krkonose (SE, TU) and Kralicky Sneznik (UO) mountains, up to 1275 m in the Beskydy mountains (FM, VS), and up to 1400 m in the Jeseniky mountains (BR, SU). It frequents a variety of habitats: any type of forest with dense scrub, old parks and gardens, hedgerows, and dense vegetation around any type of open water, particularly rivers. During winter, Robins can be found more commonly close to human habitation such as farms, parks, gardens, cemeteries, and near villages in ditches and brooks with dense cover. Migrating birds often occur in larger numbers in scrub around rivers. Nests are commonly placed on a slope, in a riverbank or in bushes, as well as on man-made structures. The following data reflect the situation in various counties in the 1970s and at the beginning of the 1980s. Breeding density was 4–8 pairs per km^2 in riverine forest, 10.5–80 pairs per km^2 in a beech–hornbeam-dominated forest, 14–33 pairs per km^2 in beech forest, 13–21 pairs per km^2 in pine forest, 5–33 pairs per km^2 in a spruce plantation at intermediate altitudes, 7–59.5 pairs per km^2 in a spruce plantation in the mountains, 52–88 pairs per km^2 at an old cemetery in Praha (AA), and 10–20 pairs per km^2 in Praha's parks (AA). In the 1980s, breeding density in hedgerows in TC county was 47–132 pairs per km^2 and 35 pairs per km^2 in ST county, and in city parks in Bor u Tachova (TC) it was 28 pairs per km^2 and in Chodova Plana (TC) 33 pairs per km^2. At the beginning of the 1980s, it was 11–16 pairs per km^2 in mixed forest at 180 m, and 15–38 pairs per km^2 in hedgerows and around oxbows in farmland at 170 m in UH county; and during the 1980s, it was 28–53 pairs per km^2 in spruce forest in the Sumava mountains (CK, PT, KT), and 27–51 pairs per km^2 in the Cesky les mountains (DO, TC), in beech forest it was 26 pairs per km^2 in the Jizerske hory mountains, and 26 pairs per km^2 at the Cesky raj cliffs (MB), in an oak forest it was 36 pairs per km^2 in MO county, in riverine forest it was 68 pairs per km^2 in ST county, and 100 individuals per km^2 in OL county, in pine forest it was 16 pairs per km^2 in the Cesky les mountains and 55–120 pairs per km^2 in TA county. In acid-rain-damaged forest in the Krusne hory mountains it was 7–60 pairs per km^2, and 5–38 pairs per km^2 in the Jizerske hory mountains in the 1980s, and at the beginning of the 1980s, in the Beskydy mountains, it was 70–113 pairs per km^2, and in the Krkonose mountains it was 2–33 pairs per km^2. Robins are often dominant species in mountain forest. Although this species is a permanent resident, the breeding population is mostly migratory.

Status: Resident. **Breeding season:** common. **Winter:** local/common. **Migration:** common. Protected.

Population trends: The breeding population is estimated to be between 500,000 and 1,000,000 pairs and it has been stable for the past 20 years. The wintering population ranges from 1,000 to 2,000 individuals.

Distribution: Nationwide. Winter distribution more or less corresponds to breeding distribution, although Robins may occur rarely in the following counties: DC, CL, PE, HB, ZR, BR and SY. Wintering birds are more commonly found in lowlands than at higher altitudes.

Timing: Spring migration starts during early March and continues until the beginning of April, peaking during the second half of March. Autumn migration occurs between mid-September and the end of October. Breeding extends mid-April to the beginning of July, peaking at the end of April and beginning of May.

Thrush Nightingale *Luscinia luscinia*

Slavik tmavy   Slavik velky   Sprosser

Even though it is a regular migrant and recorded annually, Thrush Nightingale is a rare species in the Czech Republic. Passage and breeding birds usually occur in lowlands, around rivers and ponds with dense vegetation, in riverine and flooded woodlands, and in other wetland areas. However, migrating birds may also be found in drier habitats, such as mature gardens or parks. Despite the fact that individual birds have been recorded quite regularly in June, breeding was only first documented in 1989, when a nest with a clutch was found in s. Bohemia. Two years later, a nest with nestlings was found, again in s. Bohemia, at Velky Tisy

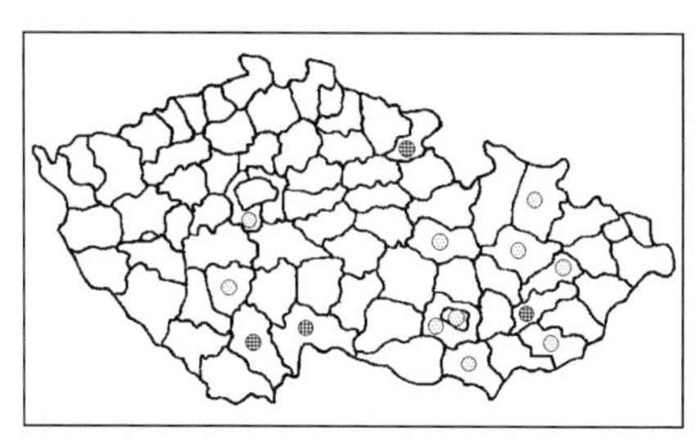

pond (JH). Probable breeding attempts have been reported from s. Moravia from the end of the 1980s, but nesting not confirmed. Singing males during the breeding season have been reported from other sites in Moravia as well. Breeding in Moravia was first reported from KM county in 1996. Thrush Nightingale is a breeding species in Slovakia, where the population is estimated to be between 1,000 and 1,500 pairs (Murin *et al.* 1994).

Status: Migrant and accidental summer resident. **Breeding season:** rare. **Winter:** does not occur. **Migration:** local. Critically endangered. Protected.

Population trends: No data available.

Distribution: On migration it may occur nationwide. Between 1989 and 1996, there were 2 breeding records from CB and JH counties in s. Bohemia, and 1 record from KM county in central Moravia. A female with brood patch was captured in Praha-Litoznice (PZ) in June 1996. A hybrid pair, female Thrush Nightingale X male Rufous Nightingale nested in NA county in 1997. Recent records of solitary singing males, or records of trapped and banded birds in May, June and August, come from Velky Tisy pond (JH), Ceske Budejovice (CB), Kluky (PI), Rezabinec pond (PI), Cerny pond (SY), Novy pond near Opatov (SY), Bobrovnik (BR), Slezske Pavlovice (BR), Dolni Moravice (BR), Hlusovice (OL), Hanusovice (OL), Prerov (PR), Tovacov (PR), Hulin (KM), Kunovice (UH), Soutok (BV) and Lednicke ponds (BV).

Timing: Spring migration occurs at the end of April and during May, peaking at the beginning of May. Autumn migration occurs from the end of August until mid-September, peaking at the end of August.

Rufous Nightingale *Luscinia megarhynchos*

Nightingale, Common Nightingale   Slavik obecny   Slavik obycajny   Nachtigall

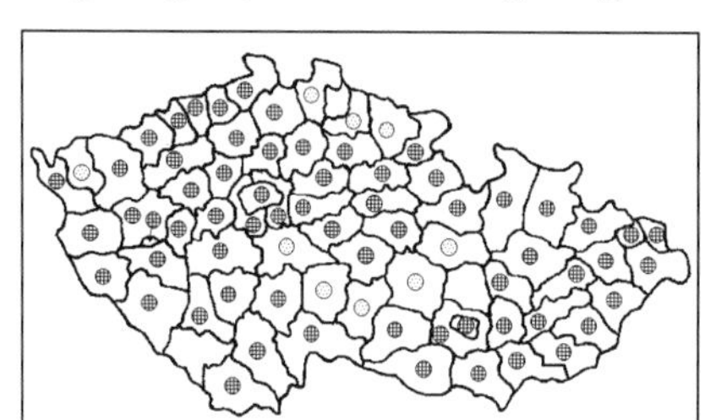

Rufous Nightingale was quite a common breeder in the Czech Republic in the 19th century and until the 1920s. Between the 1920s and 1950s its population declined. Since the early 1960s, the population has been increasing, and Rufous Nightingale has expanded its range into new nesting areas such as TC and CB counties, and around Sluknov (DC). This expansion is still continuing. This is a typical lowland species, with breeding distribution up to 400–500 m in Ceske Stredohori (LT, LN), and up to 480 m in TC county. Singing males have been recorded up to 600 m. Rufous Nightingale is a local breeder, with high numbers in n. Bohemia, central Bohemia, e. Bohemia, s. Moravia and central Moravia. It favours moist habitats, such as dense scrub around brooks and rivers, edges of less dense deciduous forest, but avoids flooded riverine forest. It frequently occurs at drier places such as mature parks and gardens, edges of vineyards surrounded by hedges, hill-sides with scrub that open to meadows, areas of sparse deciduous forest in highlands, hedgerows in farmland, and cemeteries. It occurs quite commonly in larger parks in towns. Breeding density at Trojsky ostrov islet in Praha (AA) was 29 pairs per km^2 in 1979, and 190 pairs per km^2 around Lenesicky pond (LN) at the beginning of the 1990s. Six singing males were recorded around a 1.5-km brook near Cesky Brod (PH) in 1973. In hedges around vine-yards near Podoli (UH), 3 singing males were recorded along a 1-km transect, and 2 singing males along a 1-km transect in scrub around the Olsava river (UH) in the mid-1980s. In June 1998, there were 2 and 6 singing males respectively along the abovementioned transects. The breeding population is not threatened.

Status: Migrant and summer visitor. **Breeding season:** uncommon/local. **Winter:** does not occur. **Migration:** local/common. Least concern. Protected.

Population trends: The breeding population is estimated to be between 6,000 and 12,000 pairs, and has increased by 20–50% over the past 20 years.

Distribution: On migration it may occur nationwide. The stronghold of the breeding population is in the following counties: LN, MO , LT, KL, PZ, PH, AA, MB, NB, ME, KO, PU, KH, ZN, BV, HO, BO, VY, KM, PR, UH, OV and KI.
Timing: Spring migration starts at the beginning of April and continues until the beginning of May, with the peak in mid-April. Autumn migration occurs between mid-August and the beginning of September. Single birds can be recorded until the end of September. Breeding occurs between early May and mid-June, with the majority of eggs laid during mid- to late May.

Bluethroat *Luscinia svecica*

Slavik modracek   Slavik modrak   Blaukehlchen

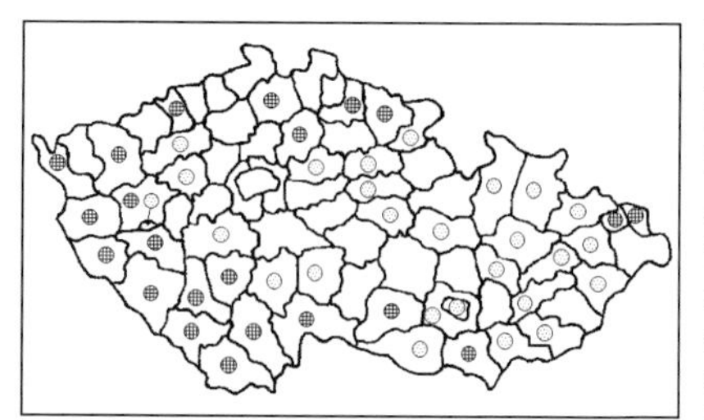

Bluethroat is a regular but rare breeder in the Czech Republic. Even though an expansion of range has been happening since the 1970s, it is still a localized breeder. Two races occur: *cyanecula* and *svecica*. *L. s. cyanecula* first bred near Klatovy (KT) in 1982, then in s. Bohemia in 1984, in n. Moravia in 1987, and in s. Moravia in 1989. Regular nesting of this race is confined to lowland areas, as well as at higher altitudes in counties such as CK, PT and KT. It breeds in wetland habitats such as meadows, marshes, edges and surrounds of ponds with growths of reed and willow. Nests are built in emergent vegetation, reedbeds or willow scrub. Strongholds include fishponds around Trebon (JH), with up to 55 pairs, Maly and Velky Tisy pond (JH), with 30–40 pairs, and ponds around Ceske Budejovice (CB). Other places with high numbers of breeding birds include Postrekov (DO), Mlada Boleslav (MB), ponds around Jindrichuv Hradec (JH) and Ostrava (OV). Breeding density in reedbeds around several ponds in s. Bohemia was 10–80 pairs per km^2 at the end of the 1980s. *L. s. svecica* first bred (3 nests) in the Krkonose mountains (SE, TU) in 1978. Breeding occurs from 1300 m and to higher altitudes, as for example in Pancavska and Labska louka peatbogs, with about 10 pairs, and Upska raselina peatbog, with 15–20 pairs. Between 1978 and 1980 the breeding population was 6–11 pairs, and between 1983 and 1986 it was 13–18. Eighteen nests were found in 1988, and 14 nests in 1989. Breeding density at several sites was 21–35 females per km^2 at the end of the 1980s. Bluethroat breeds in peatbogs with dwarf pine. The Krkonose mountains is the only area in the country where *svecica* breeds, although a singing male was also recorded in the Jeseniky mountains (BR, SU) in 1989. On migration, both races can be found in reedbeds and willows around ponds and rivers.
Status: Migrant and summer visitor. **Breeding season:** uncommon/local (*cyanecula*), uncommon (*svecica*). **Winter:** does not occur (both races). **Migration:** local (*cyanecula*), uncommon (*svecica*). Endangered (both races). Protected.
Population trends: The breeding population of *L. s. cyanecula* was 90–140 pairs between 1980 and 1993. Since 1994 it has been 190–210 pairs. Over the past 20 years the population has increased by more than 50%. The breeding population of *L. s. svecica* has been 25–30 pairs since 1994.
Distribution: On migration it may occur nationwide in suitable habitat. Singing males of the race *L. s. cyanecula* have been recorded during the breeding season in the following counties, and these are where breeding is also most likely to occur: PU, CL, CH, KM, HO, PR, BR and OL. It has been expanding its range during the last 15 years.
Timing: Spring migration extends from late March to the end of April, peaking at the beginning of April. Autumn migration occurs between mid-August and the end of September, peaking at the beginning of September. Breeding occurs from late April until early July.

Black Redstart *Phoenicurus ochruros*

Rehek domaci Zltochvost domovy Hausrotschwanz

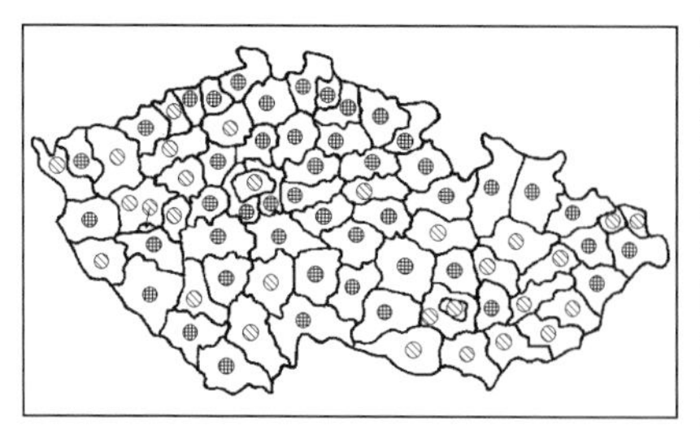

Black Redstart is common throughout the country. It occurs from lowlands up to the peaks of mountains: in the Krkonose mountains (SE, TU), breeding was recorded at Mt Snezka at 1600 m. Normal breeding habitats in rural areas include quarries, rocky slopes with sparse vegetation, and rocks in mountains. Black Redstarts generally avoid woodland, meadows and farmland, unless there are at least some solitary buildings that can provide suitable nesting places. In urban areas, this species nests around farms, factories and warehouses, in villages and even in large cities. Nests are usually placed on rafters under roofs, in holes in walls, on window ledges, and on a variety of artificial structures. In rural areas, nests are placed in piles of stones or in rocks. After breeding and before migration, this species occurs at forest edges, in hedges and in growths around rivers, where it feeds on berries, particularly elderberries. Breeding density was 59 individuals per km^2 in rocky slopes in the Ceske Stredohori highlands (LT, UL), and 20–40 individuals per km^2 in Brno (BM) at the beginning of the 1970s, 30 pairs per km^2 in a part of Praha (AA), and 11–16 pairs per km^2 in 2 villages in TC county at the end of the 1970s. It was 13–15 pairs per km^2 in a village in UH county at the beginning of the 1980s, and 17 pairs per km^2 in a village in VS county in the mid-1980s. In Bor u Tachova (TC), breeding density has varied between 27 and 67 pairs per km^2, being higher in industrial areas of the town. Although this is a migratory species, a few individuals may occur during winter. They are usually found around farms, or in towns and villages in the lowlands. Wintering Black Redstarts have been recorded only for the past 3 or 40 years. The breeding population belongs to the *gibraltariensis* race.

Status: Migrant and summer visitor. **Breeding season**: common. **Winter**: uncommon. **Migration**: common. Protected.

Population trends: The breeding population is between 200,000 and 400,000 pairs. It has increased by 20–50% over the past 20 years. The wintering of 5–10 individuals is reported annually.

Distribution: Nationwide.

Timing: Spring arrival starts at the beginning of March and continues through mid-April, peaking at the end of March. Autumn departure occurs from September until the beginning of November, peaking in mid-October. Breeding extends from mid-April to the beginning of July, peaking at the end of April and beginning of May.

Common Redstart *Phoenicurus phoenicurus*

Redstart Rehek zahradni Zltochvost horny Gartenrotschwanz

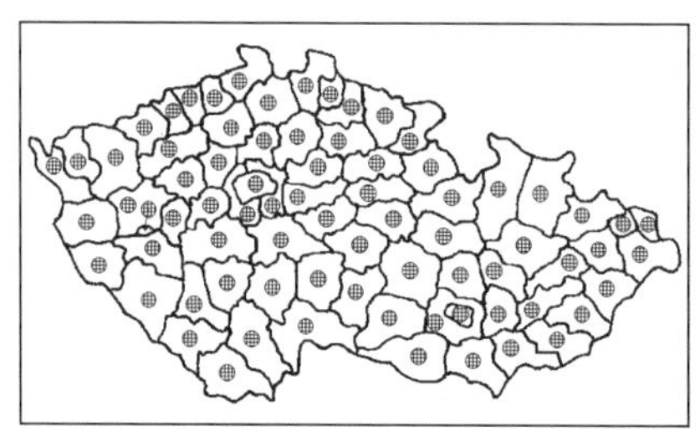

Common Redstart is a regular but rather local breeder in the Czech Republic. It occurs throughout the country, densities varying from county to county. It is found from the lowlands up to 840 m in the Cesky les mountains (DO, TC), to about 1050 m in the Krkonose (SE, TU) and Sumava (CK, PT, KT) mountains, to 1100 m in the Orlicke hory (RK) and Krusne hory (CV, KV, MO, TP) mountains, to 1200 m in the Beskydy mountains (FM, VS), and to 1400 m in the Jeseniky mountains (BR, SU). Its breeding habitats include the edges of and clearings in open deciduous and mixed, pine-dominated, forest, mature growths around rivers, avenues with old trees, woodland on farms, wooded pastures, and larger gardens and parks. Most nests are placed in cavities or artificial nest boxes, but also among tree roots, and in piles of wood. Birds nesting around human habitations build nests in holes in buildings, and under roofs. Breeding density was 8–10 pairs per km^2 in 2 villages in Cesky les mountains, and 10 pairs per km^2 at Trojsky ostrov islet in Praha (AA) at the end of the 1970s. During the 1980s, in spruce and spruce-beech forest in the Krkonose mountains, it was 2–4 pairs per km², in mature pine growths near Tabor (TA), 20 pairs per km², in riverine forest near Strakonice (ST), 23 pairs per km², at various sites in beech-dominated forest in the Beskydy mountains, 0–19 pairs per km². In mature parks around Libejovice (ST) and Blatna (ST) castles, it was 8–14 pairs per km² at the beginning of the 1990s. Breeding density in different habitats in Brno (BM) was 5–60 pairs per km² in the mid-1990s (Martisko and Martiskova 1996). A breeding density of 5–7 pairs per km² in gardens around a village (UH) at 170 m was recorded at the beginning of the 1980s. Ten years later, breeding was not recorded in that area. The disappearance of this species has been seen as a direct result of habitat destruction. The decrease in breeding populations in the Czech Republic is directly linked to habitat loss, particularly of mature trees. However, habitat degradation and the use of pesticides in the wintering grounds may contribute to the decline in this species (Tucker and Heath 1994).

Status: Migrant and summer visitor. **Breeding season:** local/common. **Winter:** does not occur. **Migration:** common. Least concern. Protected.

Population trends: The breeding population is between 30,000 and 60,000 pairs. It has declined by 20–50% between the end of the 1970s and end of the 1980s. However, since the early 1990s, numbers have been increasing locally, and the overall decline in the population has probably stopped.

Distribution: Nationwide. As a breeder, this species may occur rarely in the following counties: ZN, VY, ZL, TR, OL, BK, PB, CL, LT, LN and MB.

Timing: Spring migration occurs from the end of March until the end of April, peaking during the first half of April. Autumn migration occurs between mid-August and mid-October, peaking during the second half of September. Breeding extends from mid-April to mid-June, peaking at the beginning of May.

Whinchat *Saxicola rubetra*

Brambornicek hnedy   Prhlaviar cervenkasty   Braunkehlchen

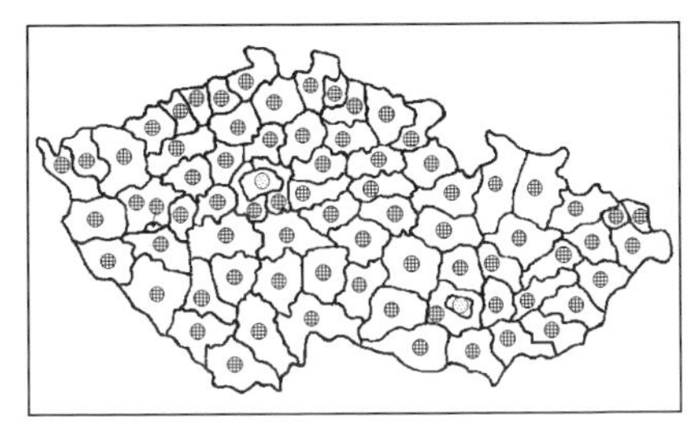

Whinchat is a regular and still rather uncommon breeder in some counties of the Czech Republic, even though its numbers have increased. This species was a common breeder during the 19th century, occurring in wet meadows in lowlands. The drainage of meadows has probably been the cause of its decline in, and partial extirpation from, lowlands. Today, Whinchats have a patchy distribution in the lowlands, and are most common in highlands and mountains at altitudes of 600–900 m. As a breeder, it has been recorded up to 1050 m in the Krusne hory mountains (CV, KV, MO, TP), to 1150 m in the Beskydy mountains (FM, VS), to 1400 m in the Krkonose mountains (SE, TU), and to 1490 m in the Jeseniky mountains (BR, SU). It prefers wet meadows with scattered scrub and hedges, growths around canals, rivers and ditches, fringes of wetlands, and peatbogs in the mountains. Nests are built on the ground, in relatively dense grass or vegetation. At the beginning of the 1970s, 9 individuals per km² were recorded in meadows around a lake at 790 m in MO county, 17–22 pairs per km² on slag heaps around coal mines in MO county, and 1 individual per km² around Rozvadov (TC) at the end of the 1970s. In the 1980s, breeding density around ponds in TC county was 9 pairs per km², at a peatbog (JH) 10 pairs per km², in various growths around a brook (CK) it was 0–71 pairs per km². In clearings in acid-rain-damaged forest at various altitudes in the Beskydy mountains it was 23 pairs per km² at the beginning of the 1990s, and in the same type of environment in the Jizerske hory (LB, JN) and Krkonose mountains it was 13 pairs and 1 pair per km² respectively in the 1980s. It was 5–37 individuals per km² in various habitats around Mlada (NB) at the beginning of the 1990s. Expansion of this species' range in the Czech Republic has been continuing for the past 25 years.

Status: Migrant and summer visitor. **Breeding season:** uncommon/local. **Winter:** does not occur. **Migration:** common. Least concern. Protected.

Population trends: The breeding population is between 10,000 and 20,000 pairs. It has increased by 20–50% over the past 20 years.
Distribution: Nationwide. It may be less common in the following counties: LN, LT, BE, PB, PH, RA, MB, KO, HK, PU, VY, BK, ZN, BV, ZL and OP.
Timing: Spring migration starts at the beginning of April and continues until the beginning of May, peaking at the end of April. Autumn migration occurs between late August and early October. Birds are rare at the end of March and during the second half of October. Breeding extends from the beginning of May to the beginning of July, peaking in mid-May.

Common Stonechat *Saxicola torquata*

Stonechat Brambornicek cernohlavy Prhlaviar ciernohlavy Schwarzkehlchen

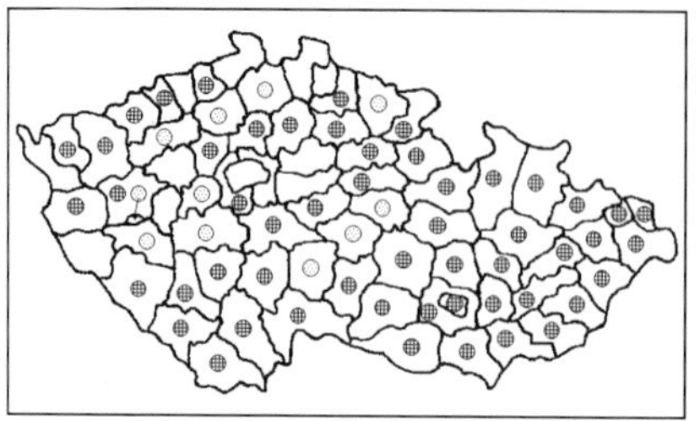

This is a regular but generally rare breeder in most of the country, except for s. Moravia and central Moravia where it is fairly common. During the 19th century, Common Stonechats were more common in highlands than lowlands. At the beginning of the 20th century, Common Stonechat expanded its range into lowlands, where wet meadows were transformed into arable fields, and road and railway construction took place. It occurs less commonly in the west of the Czech Republic, where it has a patchy distribution, and frequents drier and warmer lowlands and highlands up to 600 m, such as in the Ceskomoravska vysocina highlands (HB, JI, PE, ZR). However, it has also been found during the breeding season at about 750 m in the Sumava mountains (CK, PT, KT), at 1170 m in the Beskydy mountains (FM, VS), and at 1350 m in the Krkonose mountains (SE, TU). Breeding pairs prefer open dry areas with pastures and meadows, hillsides with scattered trees and scrub, poles and other artificial structures, fringes of infertile soil, vineyards, edges of old orchards, roadsides, railway sidings and, occasionally, riverbanks, ditches and canals. Nests are usually placed on the ground on a grassy slope. In the mid-1980s, breeding density was 40 individuals per km^2 in windbreaks (BV), 10–15 pairs per km^2 at about 490 m in the Bile Karpaty mountains (HO, UH, ZL), and 8–10 pairs around ditches and railways in farmland (UH) at about 170 m. It was 10 pairs per km^2 in clearings in acid-rain-damaged forest in the Beskydy mountains, and 3–4 individuals per km^2 in various habitats around Mlada (NB) at the beginning of the 1990s. On passage, birds frequently occur in fields and meadows. Common Stonechats are often found perching on telegraph wires near railways and roads. The accidental wintering of a solitary bird was recorded in 1991 and 1995 (Belka 1996). This species is more common in Slovakia, where the breeding population is estimated to be between 20,000

Common Stonechat

and 40,000 pairs (Murin *et al.* 1994). The breeding population is of the *rubicola* race.
Status: Migrant and summer visitor. **Breeding season:** uncommon/local. **Winter:** does not occur. **Migration:** local/common. Conservation-dependent. Protected.
Population trends: The breeding population is between 2,500 and 5,000 pairs. Local declines in the breeding population during the 1970s has now stopped, and numbers have been increasing for the past 10 years.
Distribution: On migration found nationwide. Regular breeding of large numbers of pairs occurs in the following counties: ZN, BV, BO, HO, UH, VY, KM, ZL, PR, VS and OL. It is a rather uncommon and local breeder in the following counties: CK, PT, CB, PI, JH, KT, SO, KV, CV, UL, KL, PZ, PE, ME, MB, HK, NA, PU, BM, SY, BK, SU, BR, FM, OP and ZR. Occasional breeding elsewhere is possible.
Timing: Spring migration occurs during March and April, peaking during the second half of March. Autumn migration occurs in September and October, peaking during the first half of October. Birds are rare at the end of February and in November. Breeding extends from the beginning of April to the beginning of July, with peaks during the second half of April and beginning of June.

Northern Wheatear *Oenanthe oenanthe*

Wheatear Belorit sedy Skaliarik sivy Steinschmätzer

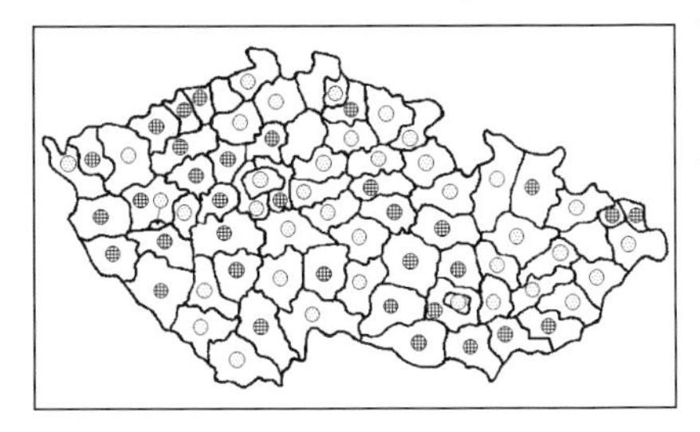

This is a regular but rather uncommon breeder in the Czech Republic, where the population has been declining since the mid-1940s. Over the following 25 years, Northern Wheatears disappeared from many traditional breeding sites. Today, breeding pairs are scattered across the country. It occurs near slag heaps around coal mines in CV and MO counties in n. Bohemia, KL county in central Bohemia, and OV and KI counties in n. Moravia. Northern Wheatears are found from lowlands up to 800 m in the Krusne hory mountains (CV, KV, MO, TP), to 900 m in the Sumava mountains (CK, PT, KT), to 1490 m in the Jeseniky mountains (BR, SU), and to about 1500 m in the Krkonose mountains (SE, TU). Breeding habitat is open country with stony or poor soils and sparse vegetation, stony hillsides, sandpits and gravel pits, and construction sites in urban or village areas. Nests are most commonly placed in a pile of rocks, in stony walls, and in cavities in earth and sand banks. Nesting in ruins and in buildings and other artificial constructions has also been reported. Breeding density at slag heaps in MO county was 4–33 pairs per km² during the 1970s, depending on the cover offered by vegetation: places with denser vegetation had a higher density of breeding pairs (Bejcek and Tyrner 1980). It was 3 individuals per km² in steppe with trees in the Ceske Stredohori highlands (LT, UL) at the beginning of the 1970s, and 0.5 pairs per km² in areas with sandy soil and young growths of pine with clearings near Bzenec (HO) in the mid-1980s. During migration, Northern Wheatears occur in farmland, meadows, and in urban areas as well. The exact causes of its decline are unknown, but are probably the loss of natural habitat with suitable natural nest sites. This species occurs more commonly in Slovakia, where the breeding population is estimated to be between 6,000 and 9,000 pairs (Murin *et al.* 1994). Birds occurring in the Czech Republic belong to the nominate *oenanthe* race.
Status: Migrant and summer visitor. **Breeding season:** uncommon/local. **Winter:** does not occur. **Migration:** local/common. Endangered. Protected.
Population trends: The breeding population is between 500 and 1,000 pairs. It has declined by 20–50% over the past 20 years.
Distribution: During migration found nationwide. Higher densities of breeding pairs have been recorded in the following counties: CV, MO, KL, PB, PH, ME, KI and OV.
Timing: Spring arrival occurs from late March until the end of April, with the main influx during the first half of April. Autumn departure starts during late August and continues to mid-October, peaking in mid-September. Occasional birds are recorded until mid-November. Breeding extends from the beginning of April to mid-June, with the majority of eggs laid during mid-April.

Ring Ouzel *Turdus torquatus*

Kos horsky Drozd kolohrivec Ringdrossel

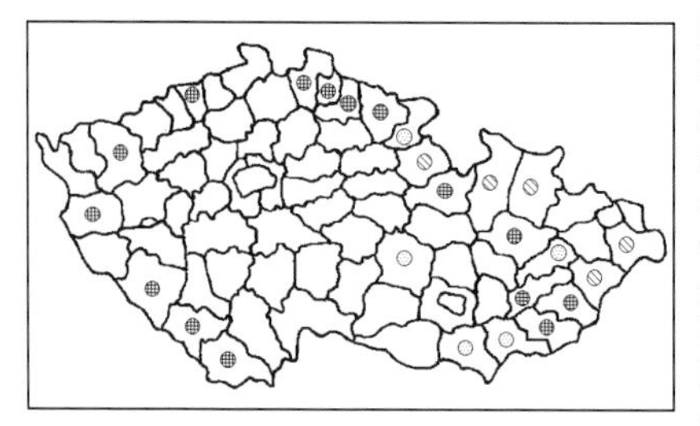

Ring Ouzel occurs in mountains bordering the Czech Republic. Strongholds are in the Krkonose mountains (SE, TU), with 200–250 breeding pairs, the Sumava mountains (CK, PT, KT), with hundreds of breeding pairs, the Beskydy mountains (FM, VS), with 600–900 breeding pairs, and the Jeseniky mountains (BR, SU), with tens of breeding pairs. It breeds from about 400 m in the Vsetinske vrchy hills (VS), from 450–470 m in the Bile Karpaty mountains (UH, HO, ZL), from 550 m in the Beskydy mountains, from 700 m in the Orlicke hory mountains (RK), from 750 m in the Jeseniky mountains, and from 800 m in the Krkonose, Sumava and Novohradske hory (JH, CB) mountains. The majority of breeding pairs in most of the mountains occur between 800 and 1000 m, up to 1200 m in the Sumava and to 1500 m in the Krkonose mountains. It is found in coniferous, spruce-dominated forest, less commonly in mixed forest or growths of dwarf pine. It prefers forest with scrub, opening to pastures and meadows. Most nests are placed in spruce, a few in rocks. In the 1980s, density in a spruce forest was 8 individuals per km^2, and 16 individuals per km^2 in mixed forest in the Sumava mountains; in a mature spruce forest in the Bile Karpaty mountains it was 10–33 pairs per km^2. It was 3–13 pairs per km^2 in spruce forest at about 1150 m in the Beskydy mountains at the beginning of the 1990s. Outside the breeding season, Ring Ouzels can be found at lower altitudes. Although this is a migratory species, dozens of individuals may stay during winter. The majority of the breeding population belongs to the nominate *alpestris* race. Birds breeding in the Krkonose mountains are of the *torquatus* race.

Status: Migrant and summer visitor. **Breeding season**: uncommon/local (*alpestris*), rare (*torquatus*). **Winter**: uncommon (both races). **Migration**: local (*alpestris*), uncommon (*torquatus*). Vulnerable. Protected.

Population trends: The breeding population is between 1,500 and 2,500 pairs. It has been stable for the past 20 years. Occasionally 100–200 individuals may winter.

Distribution: On migration it may occur nationwide. The breeding population is restricted to about 20 counties. Breeding and wintering ranges more or less overlap.

Timing: Spring migration occurs in March and April, with the majority of birds arriving in mid-April. Autumn migration occurs from mid-August until the beginning of October. Breeding extends from the beginning of May to the end of June.

Blackbird *Turdus merula*

Common Blackbird, Eurasian Blackbird Kos cerny Drozd cierny Amsel

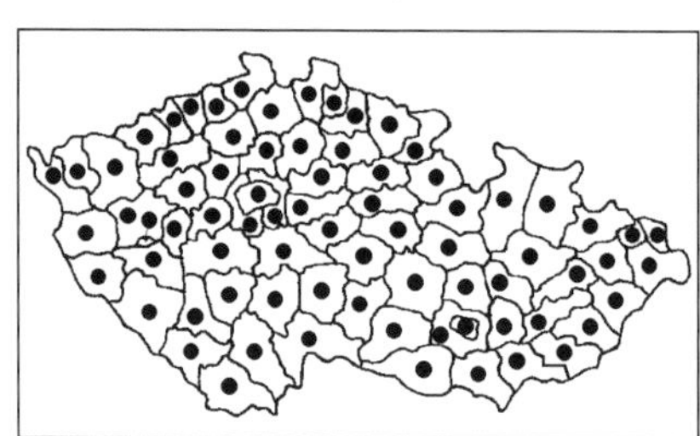

Blackbird is one of the commonest birds species in the Czech Republic. Breeding pairs are found throughout the country from lowlands up to 800 m in the Cesky les mountains (DO, TC), to 1050 m in the Krusne hory mountains (CV, KV, MO, TP), to 1100 m in the Orlicke hory (RK) and Jeseniky (BR, SU) mountains, to 1200 m in the Sumava mountains (CK, PT, KT), and to 1270 m in the Krkonose (SE, TU) and Beskydy (FM, VS) mountains. It originally inhabited woodland, but during the past 100–150 years has colonized urban habitats (Hudec *et al.* 1983). Hence, 'urban' and 'rural' populations can be separated, and their breeding biology may differ. The 'urban' populations of Blackbird usually start to nest earlier and have up to 3, occasionally 4 clutches per year, while pairs inhabiting woodland outside human habitations usually have fewer. Today, Blackbird exploits a wide range of natural and man-made habitats: any type of forest, hedges, windbreaks, scattered scrub in farmland, growths along rivers and around ponds, gardens, orchards, cemeter-

ies, parks, and town centres and villages. Nests are mostly found in trees and scrub, less commonly on buildings and other artificial structures, although in urban habitats these may be common nest sites. The majority of nests in trees are in spruce. During the 1980s, breeding density in spruce and pine forest in TC, TA, and JH counties was 30–430 pairs per km^2, in oak forest in MO and NA counties it was 24–27 pairs per km^2, in riverine forest in KM, PR and OL counties it was 9–60 pairs per km^2, in deciduous forest in ST and PI counties it was 19–68 pairs per km^2, and in various hedgerows in TA and ST counties it was 20–240 pairs per km^2. It was 19–32 pairs per km^2 in mature mixed forest, and 29–45 pairs per km^2 in gardens around Podoli (UH) at about 190–210 m at the end of the 1980s. In spruce and spruce-beech forest at about 1150 m in the Beskydy mountains (FM, VS), it was 10–20 pairs per km^2 at the beginning of the 1990s. It was 19–525 pairs per km^2 in parks and gardens in Praha (AA) during the 1970s; 168–182 pairs per km^2 in a park in Ostrava (OV), and 13–140 pairs per km^2 in various habitats in Tachov (TC) in the 1980s; and 35–68 pairs per km^2 at several cemeteries with mostly young conifers and occasionally mature deciduous trees in UH county at the end of the 1980s. The density of wintering birds is higher in urban areas than in natural habitats: it was 0–1 individual per km^2 in fir-beech forest at 900 m in VS county at the end of the 1970s and beginning of the 1980s, 0–2 individuals per km^2 around fishponds in JH county in the mid-1980s, 5–19 individuals per km^2 in beech forest at about 850 m in TC county and 82–100 individuals per km^2 in Brno (BM) at the beginning of the 1970s; 8–26 individuals per km^2 in mixed forest at about 230 m in UH count and 67–90 individuals per km^2 in city parks in Uherske Hradiste (UH) at the beginning of the 1980s. Although this species is a permanent resident, part of the population, mostly young birds, is migratory.
Status: Resident. **Breeding season:** common. **Winter:** common. **Migration:** common. Protected.
Population trends: The breeding population is between 2,000,000 and 4,000,000 pairs. It has been stable for the past 20 years. The wintering population is between 1,000,000 and 2,000,000 individuals.
Distribution: Nationwide.
Timing: Spring arrival occurs from March to April, and autumn departure from September to October. Breeding extends from mid-March to mid-July, peaking during the first half of April. The 'urban' population may start to nest at the end of February, and continue after July.

Fieldfare *Turdus pilaris*

Drozd kvicala Drozd cvikotavy Wacholderdrossel

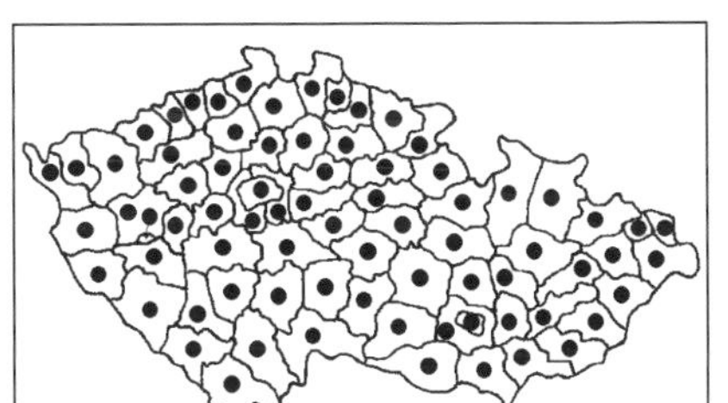

Fieldfare became a breeding bird in the Czech Republic in the middle of the 19th century, when it was expanding its range in Europe. Breeding was first documented in n. Bohemia in 1840, in e. Bohemia in 1845, in ne. Moravia in 1850, in s. Bohemia during 1860–1880, and in central Moravia during 1880–1910. Between 1910 and 1950, several regressions occurred, and Fieldfares disappeared from previously colonized areas (Hudec *et al.* 1983). Since the 1950s, Fieldfare has once again been expanding its range, and increasing in numbers. This species is distributed throughout the country from lowlands up to 660 m in the Cesky les mountains (DO, TC), to 750–820 m, and occasionally higher, in the Krkonose mountains (SE, TU), to 900 m in the Krusne hory mountains (CV, KV, MO, TP), to 750–1000 m in the Orlicke hory mountains (RK), and to 1300 m in the Sumava mountains (CK, PT, KT). Fieldfares are most abundant in highlands between 300 and 600 m, where they exploit a wide range of habitat, include human settlements. However, typical breeding habitats include edges of coniferous, deciduous and mixed forest, which are surrounded by wet meadows and pastures, growths around rivers, windbreaks and woodland in farmland. This species usually nests in colonies ranging from a few individuals, up to 60–80 pairs. Solitary breeding is less common. Most nests are found in deciduous trees, usually 4–15 m above ground. During the 1980s, breeding density in woodland in farmland (TC) was 10–80 pairs per km^2, in growths around a brook and oak avenues it was 120 and 130 pairs per km^2 respectively, and in growths around a brook in county CK it was 80–290 pairs per km^2. It was 60–110 pairs per km^2 in several windbreaks in farmland at about 210 m in UH county at the beginning of the 1980s. In urban habitats, including parks around castles in w. Bohemia, breeding density ranged from 8 to 272 pairs per km^2 during the 1980s and at the beginning of the 1990s. Because of the local fluctuation in the numbers of nesting colonies and individuals, birds may disappear and recolonize sites, often on a year-to-year basis. The following densities were recorded in winter: 27 individuals per km^2 in pine forest in TC county during the 1970s, 1 individual per km^2 in growths along a river in JH county in the mid-1980s, 34 individuals and 2–6 individuals per km^2 in human settlements in TC and VS counties in the mid-1970s and at the end of the 1970s respectively, 0.4 individuals per km^2 in Brno (BM) at the beginning of the 1970s, and 10–15 individuals per km^2 in gardens in a village at 170 m in UH county at the beginning of the 1980s. The breeding population is mostly migratory, and the remaining wintering individuals are joined by populations from n. Europe. In winter, flocks of Fieldfares commonly occur in gardens, orchards, parks and avenues, and are joined by Redwings and Blackbirds.

Status: Resident. **Breeding season:** local/common. **Winter:** common. **Migration:** common. Protected/not hunted all year round.

Population trends: The breeding population is between 70,000 and 140,000 pairs, and has increased by 20–50% over the past 20 years. The number of wintering birds fluctuates between 1,000,000 and 2,000,000 individuals.

Distribution: On migration and when wintering birds are found nationwide. As a breeder, found nationwide, being less common in the following counties: JC, NB, ME, AA, PB, PZ, CR and ZN.

Timing: Spring migration occurs from the beginning of February until early April, peaking in March. Autumn migration starts at the end of September and continues until the end of October, with the main influx towards the end of October. Breeding occurs from the beginning of April until the end of June, peaking from mid-April to the end of the month.

Song Thrush *Turdus philomelos*

Drozd zpevny Drozd plavy Singdrossel

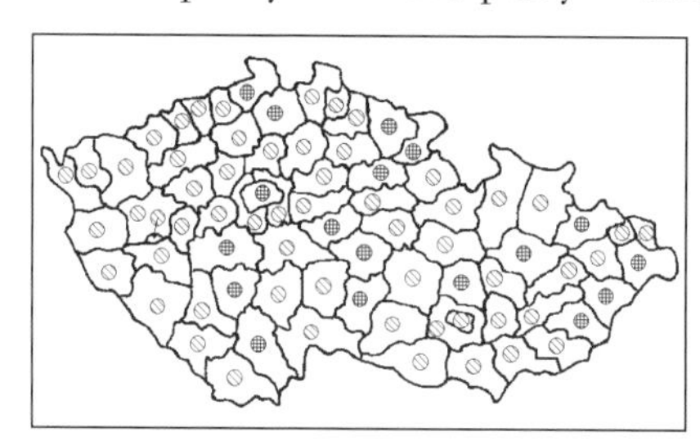

This is a common species throughout the Czech Republic. Song Thrush is found from lowlands, up to 800 m, but occasionally up to 1300 m, in the Jeseniky mountains (BR, SU), to 1025 m in the Orlicke hory mountains (RK), to 1225 m in the Krkonose mountains (SE, TU), to 1270 m in the Beskydy mountains (FM, VS), and to 1300 m in the Sumava mountains (CK, PT, KT). Originally, Song Thrush inhabited forest, but during the 20th century part of the population has colonized urban areas. It occurs in any type of forest, including coniferous plantations, hedges, windbreaks and woods in farmland, growths around open water, gardens, orchards, parks and cemeteries. The majority of nests are built in trees such as spruce, hornbeam and oak, and in scrub of plants such as European elder and hawthorn; nests are occasionally placed on buildings and on other artificial structures. Nests are usually built 1–2 m above ground. In the mid-1970s, breeding density was 10–33 pairs per km^2 in spruce plantations around Milevsko (TA). During the 1980s, in various spruce growths in TA county it was 34–55 individuals per km^2, in growths of pine in JH and TA counties it was 30 and 10 pairs per km^2 respectively, in growths of pine in TC county it was 20 pairs per km^2, and in mixed conifers it was 101 pairs per km^2 in the same county. During the 1980s, in fir-beech forest in the Beskydy mountains it was 4–9 pairs per km^2, in acid-rain-damaged spruce and spruce-beech forest in the Krkonose mountains it was 5–17 pairs per km^2, in riverine forest in central and n. Moravia it was 18–187 pairs per km^2. It was 14–27 pairs per km^2 in mixed, 40-year-old forest at 230 m around Podoli (UH), and 4–7 pairs per km^2 at several cemeteries with young conifers (UH) at the beginning of the 1980s. Density in spruce and mixed forest at about 1150 m in the Beskydy mountains (FM, VS) was 13–20 pairs per km^2 at the beginning of the 1990s. In urban habitats, including parks

around castles in w. Bohemia, breeding density ranged from 28 to 73 pairs per km^2 during the 1980s and beginning of the 1990s. Density in parks in Praha (AA) was 12–530 pairs per km^2 in the mid-1970s, and in a park in Ostrava (OV) it was 84–117 pairs per km^2 in the mid-1980s. Even though Song Thrush is a typical migratory species, the number of wintering individuals has been increasing over the past few decades. In winter it usually occurs around human habitations.
Status: Resident. **Breeding season**: common. **Winter**: uncommon/local. **Migration**: common. Protected.
Population trends: The breeding population is between 400,000 and 800,000 pairs, and has been stable for the past 20 years. The number of wintering birds is estimated to be between 600 and 2,000 individuals.
Distribution: Migrating and breeding birds are found nationwide. High numbers of wintering birds have been reported from the following counties: CK, PT, KT, PJ, PS, CH, SO, KV, MO, PT, UL, LT, KL, SE, MB, KO, PU, RK, JH, BN, TA, CR, OP, KI, PV, KM, BV and HO.
Timing: Spring migration starts at the end of February and continues until the beginning of April, peaking during early–mid-March. Autumn migration occurs between the beginning of September and early November, peaking during the second half of October. Breeding occurs between the beginning of April and the beginning of July, peaking during mid-April.

Redwing *Turdus iliacus*

Drozd cvrcala Drozd cervenkavy Rotdrossel

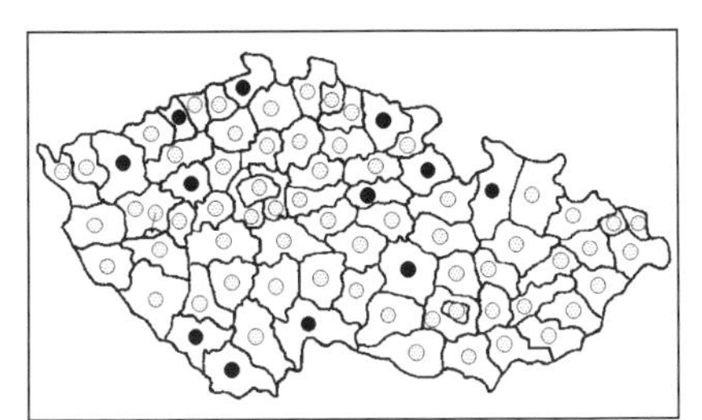

Redwing is predominantly a common wintering species, although the number of breeding birds seems to be increasing in the Czech Republic. Breeding pairs are scattered across the country, mostly in highlands and mountains. It occurs more or less at the same altitudes as Fieldfare in mountains, although in the Krkonose mountains (SE, TU) it has been recorded up to 1400 m. It breeds in coniferous and birch forest with a scrub undergrowth, close to streams and wet meadows. Most nests are placed in willows, 1.5–14 m above ground. Nesting pairs are also found in colonies of Fieldfares. More or less regular breeding has been recorded in CK and TU counties. As a migrant and wintering species, Redwing is found in both lowlands and highlands, where it frequents deciduous forest, hedgerows, avenues, and windbreaks in farmland, as long as there are plenty of berry-bearing trees and shrubs. It is often found in mixed flocks with Fieldfares.
Status: Migrant and winter visitor. **Breeding season**: uncommon. **Winter**: uncommon. **Migration**: common. Critically endangered. Protected.
Population trends: The number of breeding pairs fluctuate annually between 1 and 10. During the 1970s it was 1–5 pairs annually. The wintering population is estimated to be between 100,000 and 200,000 individuals. Both the number of breeding as well as wintering birds has increased by 20–50% over the past 20 years.
Distribution: On migration and wintering found nationwide. High densities of wintering birds have been reported from the following counties: LB, JN, SE, TU, MB, LT, DO, PT, JH, PH, UO and UH. Breeding has been recorded in about 10 counties to date.
Timing: Spring migration occurs from the beginning of March until the end of April, peaking during late March. Autumn migration starts at the end of September and continues until the end of November, peaking at the end of October and beginning of November. Breeding extends from the beginning of May to early July.

Mistle Thrush *Turdus viscivorus*

Drozd bravnik Drozd trskotavy Misteldrossel

This species occurs across most of the Czech Republic, although it is missing in some local lowland areas. It is found from lowlands up to 800 m in the Krusne hory mountains (CV, KV,

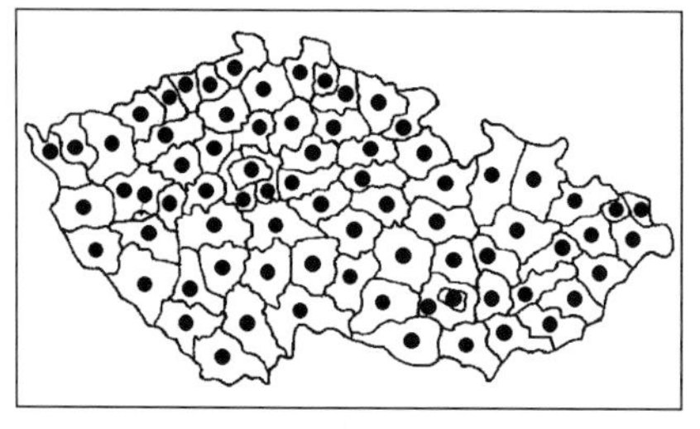

MO, TP), to 1200 m in the Beskydy mountains (FM, VS), to 1300–1400 m in the Sumava (CK, PT, KT) and Jeseniky (BR, SU) mountains, and to 1500 m in the Krkonose mountains (SE, TU). Mistle Thrush is most common at mid- and high altitudes. Reports suggest that in some counties, such as in JI, its population has been declining, but in others, such as BM and BO, increasing. It prefers not too dense coniferous/deciduous forest, opening to meadows, pastures, and farmland. Unlike Blackbird and Song Thrush, this species has not invaded human habitations. Most nests are placed in spruce and pine, most commonly 1–4 m above ground. In the 1980s, breeding density in spruce plantations in the Sumava mountains was 9 pairs per km^2, in the Novohradske hory mountains (CB, CK) it was 3 pairs per km^2, in fir-beech forest in the Beskydy mountains it was 4–9 pairs per km^2, in acid-rain-damaged spruce forest in the Krkonose mountains it was 2–4 pairs per km^2, and in similar habitat in the Jizerske hory mountains (LB, JN) it was 3–5 pairs per km^2. In mature spruce forest around Tachov (TC) it was 19 individuals per km^2, and in hedgerows and windbreaks (ST) 10 pairs per km^2 in the 1980s. At the beginning of the 1990s, in spruce and spruce-beech forest at about 1100 m in the Beskydy mountains, it was 7–20 pairs per km^2, in acid-rain-damaged spruce forest in the same mountains it was 3 pairs per km^2, and in mature oak forest (NB) it was 4 individuals per km^2. Most of the breeding population is migratory, and the remaining wintering individuals are joined by birds from n. Europe. In winter, Mistle Thrush is more common in lowlands than at higher altitudes, particularly in e. Bohemia and s. Moravia. Usually small flocks or solitary birds are found in mixed or deciduous forest, avenues, windbreaks, and woods in farmland. They can frequently be seen in stands of oaks. The density of wintering birds was 0–1 individual per km^2 in a mountain village at 730 m in VS county at the end of the 1970s and beginning of the 1980s, 0–19 individuals per km^2 in pine forest in JH county at the beginning of the 1970s, and 3 individuals per km^2 in mixed forest at about 250 m in UH county at the beginning of the 1980s.
Status: Resident. **Breeding season**: local/common. **Winter**: common. **Migration**: common. Protected.
Population trends: The breeding population is between 35,000 and 70,000 pairs, and has been stable for the past 20 years, although year-to-year fluctuation is possible. The wintering population is estimated to be between 3,000 and 7,000 individuals.
Distribution: Migrating and breeding birds are found nationwide. Wintering birds have been reported from all except the following counties: SO, CV, UL, DC, ME and PZ.
Timing: Spring migration starts in mid-February and continues until the end of March, with peaks in late February and mid-March. Autumn departure of the breeding population occurs in September and October, with the majority leaving in October. Breeding extends from the last decade of March to the end of June, peaking in April.

Grasshopper Warbler *Locustella naevia*

Common Grasshopper Warbler Cvrcilka zelena Svrciak zelenkavy Feldschwirl

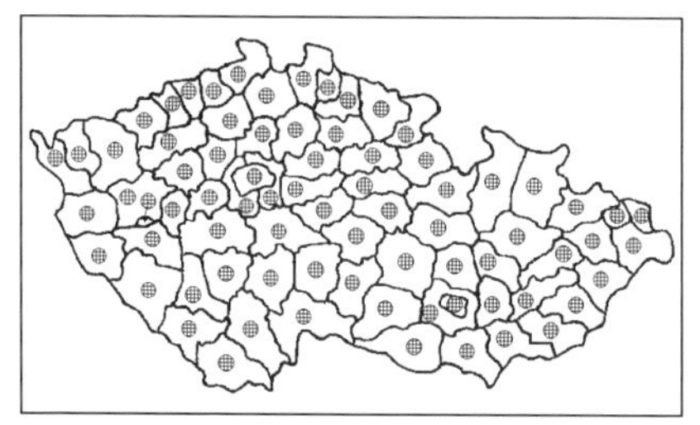

This is the most common of the 3 *Locustella* warblers occurring in the Czech Republic. Breeding pairs of Grasshopper Warbler are distributed throughout the country, being more common in lowlands and highlands than in mountains. This species occurs up to 600 m in the Ceskomoravska vysocina highlands (HB, JI, PE, ZR), to 950 m in the Sumava (CK, PT, KT) and Orlicke hory (RK) mountains, to about 1000 m in the Krkonose (SE, TU) and Krusne hory (CV, KV, MO, TP) mountains, and to 1100 m in the Beskydy mountains (FM, VS). At the end of the 1940s, the density of this species, particularly in lowlands, had decreased as a result of changes in agricultural practice, marsh drainage and habitat destruction. However, Grasshopper Warbler has started to occu-

py new habitats, expanding its range to higher altitudes, and the density has been increasing over the past 30–35 years. It breeds in wet meadows with tall, dense grasses, and scattered bushes and trees, at the edges of ponds, in ditches and, less commonly, growths around brooks and rivers. As a breeder, it may also be found far from marsh areas, at the edges of clearings in woods, or at slag heaps in coal mining areas in MO and OV counties. Nests are placed in grass, or a few centimetres above ground in dense brush. In many counties, the breeding range of Grasshopper Warbler and River Warbler overlaps, and both species can be found at the same sites. Breeding density varies among counties as well as among habitats: during the 1970s, it was 4 and 10–25 individuals per km^2 in meadows around Trebon (JH) and Chomutov (CV) respectively, and 30 pairs per km^2 at slag heaps in MO county; in farmland in s. Bohemia it was 10 pairs per km^2, in reedbeds around ponds in s. Bohemia it was 10–80 pairs per km^2, in growths around a brook (ST) it was 60 pairs per km^2, in pine thickets around Trebon (JH) it was 18 pairs per km^2, and in peatbogs with varying densities of vegetation around Trebon (JH) it was 6–10 pairs per km^2. In parkland around a castle (TC) it was 2 pairs per km^2 at the beginning of the 1980s, and in dry habitat near Mlada (NB) it was 4 individuals per km^2 at the beginning of the 1990s. In clearing in acid-rain-damaged forest at about 1100 m in the Beskydy mountains it was 47 pairs per km^2 at the beginning of the 1990s.
Status: Migrant and summer visitor. **Breeding season:** local/common. **Winter:** does not occur. **Migration:** common. Protected.
Population trends: The breeding population is between 15,000 and 30,000 pairs, and has increased by 20–50% over the past 20 years.
Distribution: Nationwide. As a breeder it may occur less commonly in the following counties: LB, VY, PV, BK, ZN and OP.
Timing: Spring migration occurs from mid-April until mid-May, peaking during early May. Autumn migration starts in late July and continues until early September, peaking in the second half of August and beginning of September. Birds are rare after early September. Breeding extends from the beginning of May to early July.

River Warbler *Locustella fluviatilis*

European River Warbler, Eurasian River Warbler Cvrcilka ricni Svrciak riecny Schlagschwirl

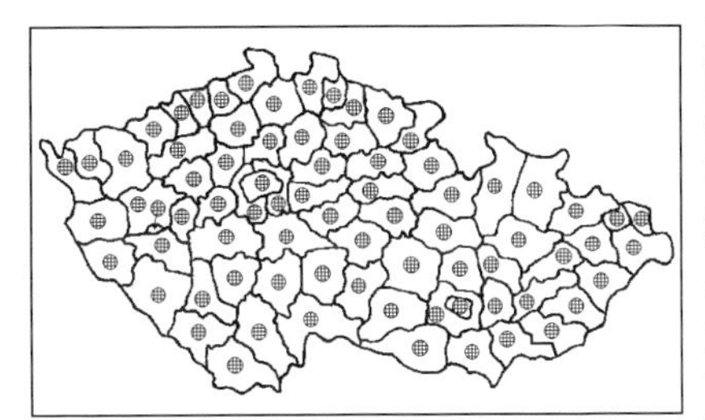

River Warbler is distributed throughout the country, but although it may be locally a fairly common species, it is rather scarce in some areas. It occurs from lowlands up to about 450 m in OP and OV counties in n. Moravia, to 500 m in JH, CB, CK and TA counties in s. Bohemia, to 650 m in the Ceskomoravska vysocina highlands (HB, JI, PE, ZR), to 680 m in the Krkonose mountains (SE, TU), to 700 m in the Doupovske hory mountains (KV), to 735 m in the Sumava mountains (CK, PT, KT), and occasionally up to 850 m in the Orlicke hory mountains (RK). It may be found more commonly around rivers in lowlands, such as the Labe (HK, PU, KO, NB), Vltava (BN, PZ), Odra (NJ, OV, KI), Dyje (BV) and Morava (OL, PR, KM, UH, HO). During the first half of the 20th century, distribution of River Warbler in the Czech Republic was more restricted. However, since about the 1950s, it has been expanding its range into previously unoccupied areas, including habitat at higher altitudes. Typical breeding habitat includes riverine forest and clearings with dense scrub undergrowth and thickets, willow and alder along rivers, brooks and ditches, and usually the edges of any type of secondary woodland. It inhabits a range of sites, from wetland to completely dry areas with growths of nettles. Occasionally, it may be found in larger parks and old abandoned gardens. Nests are often built in nettles, tufts of grass, and at the base of bushes in thick grassland. Breeding density in various types of growths along rivers near Trebon (JH) was 3–220 individuals per km^2 in the 1970s. During the 1980s, in growths along brooks in CK and ST counties, it was 116 and 100 pairs per km^2 respectively, 10 and 3 pairs per km^2 respectively in hedgerows and in marshes near ponds around Tachov (TC), and 4 pairs per km^2 in farmland in s. Bohemia. In riverine forest in cen-

tral and n. Moravia breeding density ranged from 30–80 individuals per km^2 in the 1980s, and 18–25 pairs per km^2 in growths along the Olsava river (UH) at the beginning of the 1980s.
Status: Migrant and summer visitor. **Breeding season**: local/common. **Winter**: does not occur. **Migration**: local/common. Protected.
Population trends: The breeding population is between 10,000 and 20,000 pairs, and has been stable for the past 20 years, although year-to-year fluctuation is possible.
Distribution: Nationwide. As a breeder it may be rather scarce in the following counties: SO, LB, ZN, FM, LN, LT, CL and UO.
Timing: Spring migration starts at the end of April and continues until the end of May, peaking during early May. Birds are rare at the beginning of April. Autumn migration occurs from mid-August until early September. Breeding starts during mid-May and continues to the end of June

Savi's Warbler *Locustella luscinioides*

Cvrcilka slavikova Svrciak slavikovity Rohrschwirl

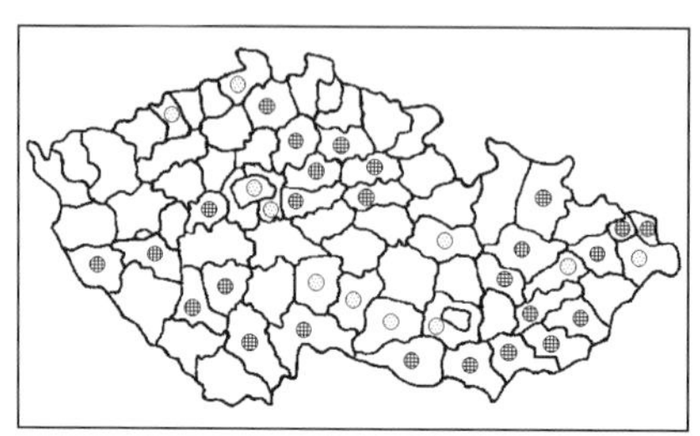

As a breeder, Savi's Warbler is a relatively new member of the Czech avifauna. Breeding was first documented in BV county in s. Moravia in 1946, and the following year there were breeding records from 18 different sites in the same county. In 1947, breeding also occurred at Velky Tisy pond (JH), at Bohdanecsky pond (PU) in 1948, at Novozamecky pond (CL) between 1947 and 1949, and at ponds near Ostrava (OV) in 1951. Breeding in w. Bohemia was first documented during the second half of the 1980s. There are 5 major areas where this, the rarest of the *Locustella* warblers, breeds regularly in the Czech Republic: fishponds in the lowlands of e. Bohemia, s. Bohemia, s. Moravia, central Moravia and n. Moravia. Breeding is more or less restricted to altitudes below about 500 m. On migration, it may occur at higher altitudes and in different habitats from those used during breeding. Typical breeding sites are the edges of ponds, marshes, canals and slow-running rivers with reedbeds and dense sedge undergrowth. Occasionally, it may nest in growths of sedges with scattered bushes, usually willows, or in small reedbeds. Nests are placed up to about 0.5 m above ground or water, in sedges or reeds. Sites with high breeding densities include Lednicke ponds (BV), Novozamecky pond (CL), Bohdanecsky pond (PU), Velky Tisy pond (JH), Rozmberk pond (JH), Opatovicky pond (JH) and Zehunsky pond (NB). Breeding density may vary significantly from place to place, depending on the extent and density of reedbed. At Nesyt pond (BV), during the 1970s, it was 280 pairs per km^2, but at Kobylske jezero (BV) lake only 2. At various ponds in s. Bohemia it was 10–60 pairs per km^2 during the 1980s, while it was 120–180 individuals per km^2 in reedbeds at Nesyt pond (BV) at the end of the 1980s.
Status: Migrant and summer visitor. **Breeding season**: uncommon. **Winter**: does not occur. **Migration**: local. Vulnerable. Protected.
Population trends: The breeding population is between 400 and 700 pairs, and has been stable for the past 20 years.
Distribution: On migration it may occur nationwide. Breeding is more or less restricted to about 20 counties in the lowlands, but breeding pairs may occur in suitable habitats in other counties as well.
Timing: Spring arrival starts in mid-April and may continue until the end of May, peaking during late April. Autumn migration occurs between the beginning of August and mid-September, with the peak at the end of August. Breeding starts at the end of April, peaking during early–mid-May, and continues until the end of June.

Moustached Warbler *Acrocephalus melanopogon*

Rakosnik tamaryskovy Sasiniarik tenkozoby Mariskensänger

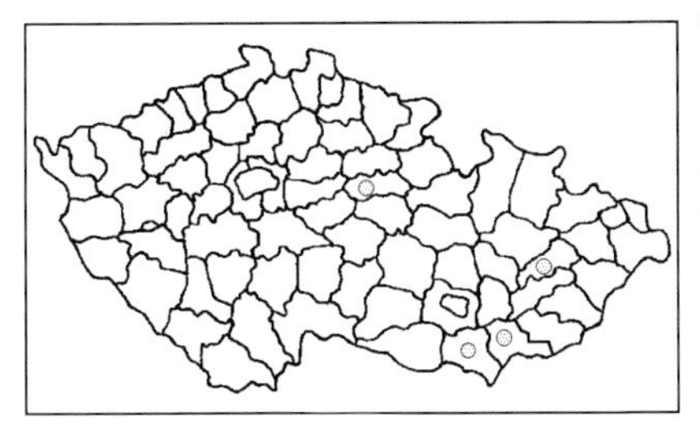

This is the rarest *Acrocephalus* species in the Czech Republic, being recorded for the first time in 1961. Reedbeds surrounding larger fishponds in s. Moravia are the most likely places to find Moustached Warbler. Occasionally it is reported from other places as well. Because of its inconspicuous vocalizations, it is quite easy to overlook Moustached Warblers, and most of the Czech records are of birds that were trapped and banded.
Status: Vagrant. **Breeding season:** rare. **Winter:** does not occur. **Migration:** uncommon. Protected.
Population trends: Up to 10 birds are seen or trapped and banded annually. This number has been increasing over the past 20 years.
Distribution: May occur nationwide. It has been recorded in the following counties: PU, PR, HO and BV. Most recent records are from Tovacovske ponds (PR), and Lednicke ponds (BV). Six individuals were banded at Nesyt pond (BV) between the beginning of August and October 1997.
Timing: It typically occurs from early May until the end of August, with most records from August.

Aquatic Warbler *Acrocephalus paludicola*

Rakosnik ostricovy Trsteniarik vodny Seggenrohrsänger

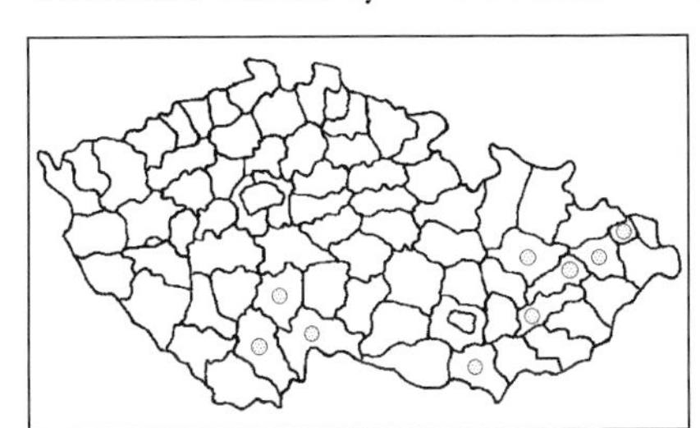

Although Aquatic Warbler occurs regularly on migration, it is an uncommon species in the Czech Republic. Regular breeding at several sites was recorded at the end of the 19th and the beginning of the 20th centuries, but since about the 1940s, although a few breeding attempts have been observed, successful nesting has not been recorded. However, singing males are seen quite regularly during the breeding season. On migration, Aquatic Warbler usually occurs at larger fishponds, and at marshes with scattered sedge surrounding ponds. Recently, it has been regular on migration at Tovacovske ponds (PR) and Zahlinicke ponds (KM) in central Moravia. A dearth of suitable breeding habitat is probably the major factor restricting breeding in the Czech Republic.
Status: Migrant. **Breeding season:** rare. **Winter:** does not occur. **Migration:** uncommon. Conservation-dependent. Protected.
Population trends: Up to 25 birds are observed or banded annually.
Distribution: May occur nationwide. Recent records come from Horusice (TA), Velky Tisy pond (JH), Koclirov pond (JH), Nakri (CB), Korensky pond (CB), Tovacovske ponds (PR), Zahlinicke ponds (KM), and Lednicke ponds (BV).
Timing: Spring migration occurs between the end of April and the end of May. Autumn migration extends from late July to the end of September. Most of the recent records are from between late April and late May, and late August and late September.

Sedge Warbler *Acrocephalus schoenobaenus*

Rakosnik prouzkovany Trsteniarik maly Schilfrohrsänger

Sedge Warbler is local throughout the country. It occurs from lowlands up to 380 m in the foothills of the Krkonose mountains (SE, TU), to 400 m at ponds around Trebon (JH), to 510 m at ponds around Plana (TC), to about 600 m at ponds in JI county, and to 730 m around Lipno reservoir (CK). Areas where it breeds in higher densities include fishponds in e.

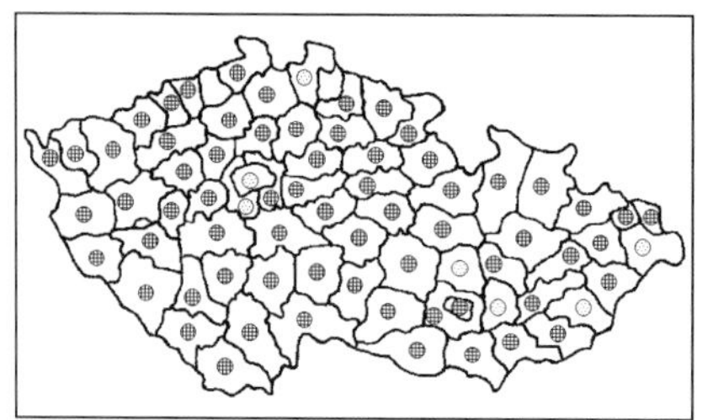

Bohemia, s. Bohemia, s. Moravia, central Moravia and n. Moravia. A variety of waterside habitats, such as edges of ponds, marshes, flooded meadows, and ditches with abundant aquatic vegetation, are utilized for breeding. However, breeding in drier habitats such as meadows with clumps of willow, crops of oilseed rape, and in cornfields is not uncommon. On migration, Sedge Warbler can also be found in shrubs around rivers, ditches, and railroads, and at the edges of riverine forest; and especially in areas with European elder during autumn migration. Nests are built in sedge, reeds, grass, nettles and in shrubs in tall grass. Breeding densities in the 1970s were as follows: 1,300 pairs per km^2 in mixed reeds and sedge around Kanov pond (JH), 60 pairs per km^2 in a strip of reeds around Opatovicky pond (JH), 70 pairs per km^2 in willow stands around Rozmberk pond (JH), 70 pairs per km^2 around Dolni Pocernice gravel pit (PH), and 610 pairs per km^2 in reeds around Nesyt pond (BV). In reedbeds at various ponds in s. Bohemia, it was 210–1,115 pairs per km^2 in the 1980s. Breeding density at Nesyt pond (BV) was 530 pairs per km^2 in sedges and reedbeds in 1987, and 860 pairs per km^2 in the same habitat in 1988. Local breeding densities may fluctuate from year to year, and also vary among habitats.

Status: Migrant and summer visitor. **Breeding season**: local/common. **Winter**: does not occur. **Migration**: common. Protected.

Population trends: The breeding population is between 40,000 and 80,000 pairs, and has been stable for the past 20 years.

Distribution: On migration found nationwide. Breeding pairs are scattered nationwide with the strongholds in the following counties: CB, ST, JH, HK, PU, JC, NB, KO, PH, BV, HO, KM, NJ and OV.

Timing: Spring migration starts at the beginning of April and continues until the end of May, peaking during mid- to late April. Autumn migration occurs between mid-August and early October, peaking during the first half of September. Breeding extends from the beginning of May to mid-July, peaking during mid- to late May.

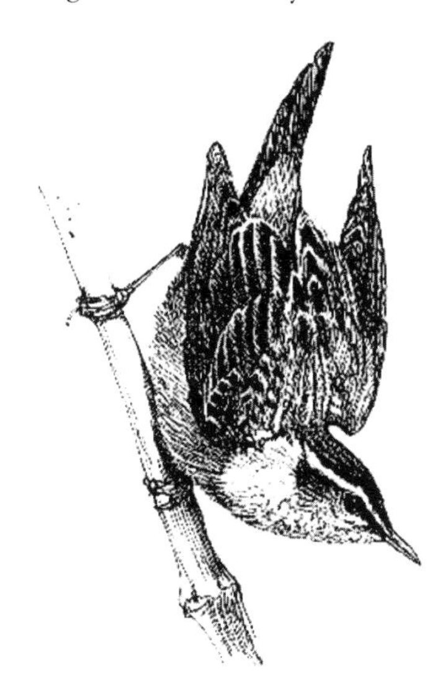

Sedge Warbler

Marsh Warbler *Acrocephalus palustris*

Rakosnik zpevny Trsteniarik obycajny Sumpfrohrsänger

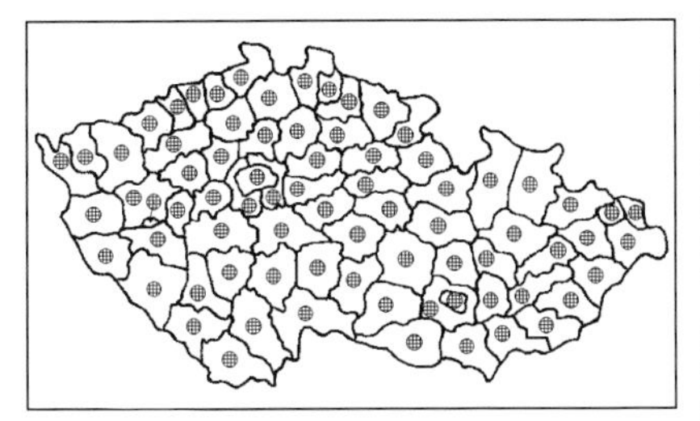

Marsh Warbler is the most common *Acrocephalus* species breeding in the Czech Republic, having expanded its range over the past 30–35 years. It is distributed widely, from lowlands up to about 590 m in the Bile Karpaty mountains (UH, HO, ZL), to 620 m in the foothills of the Krkonose mountains (SE, TU) and in the Ceskomoravska vysocina highlands (HB, JI, PE, ZR), to 700 m in Orlicke hory mountains (RK), to 800 m in the Sumava mountains (CK, PT, KT), and to 820 m in the Krusne hory mountains (CV, KV, MO, TP). Nevertheless, it is most common in lowlands and at lower levels in the highlands. Marsh Warbler is not so restricted to waterside habitats as other species of the same genus, and exploits a wide range of breeding sites. It is typically found in bushes and vegetation around rivers, canals, ditches, meadows with willow scrub, dumps with nettles, and in emergent vegetation at the edges of ponds. As a breeder, this species is also attracted to drier areas such as cultivated fields, bushes on hillsides, the edge of woodland surrounded by meadows, and human habitations, where it is found in abandoned orchards and parks. Marsh Warbler and Reed Warbler breed in the same habitats at some sites. Nests are usually built in nettles, or nettle-dominated areas of vegetation up to 0.5 m above ground. On autumn migration, Marsh Warbler is commonly found in riverine forest with growths of European elder. Local breeding densities vary a great deal, dictated by the range of habitats used. During the 1970s, there were 35 pairs per km^2 in growths along a brook in CV county, 3 individuals per km^2 in meadows with sparse willows around Trebon (JH), 410 pairs per km^2 in growths along the Zlata Stoka river (JH), and 30 pairs per km^2 at dumps with 20-year old scrub around coal mines in MO county. Breeding density in various habitats in Praha (AA) was 10–127 pairs per km^2 in the 1970s. In the 1980s, it was 3–5 pairs per km^2 in farmland in s. Bohemia, 25–129 pairs per km^2 at the edges of ponds in s. Bohemia, 10–240 and 216–700 pairs per km^2 respectively in mixed vegetation around Strakonice (ST) and in CK county. In the mid-1980s, breeding density was 180–195 pairs per km^2 in nettles around the Olsava river at 170 m in UH county, and 35–50 pairs per km^2 around the edge of Nesyt pond (BV) at the end of the 1980s. The breeding population fluctuated from year to year during the 1980s.

Status: Migrant and summer visitor. **Breeding season:** local/common. **Winter:** does not occur. **Migration:** common. Protected.

Population trends: The breeding population is between 80,000 and 160,000 pairs, and has declined by 20–50% over the past 20 years.

Distribution: Nationwide. It may occur less commonly in the following counties: ZN, TR, ZR, BK, SO and LB.

Timing: Spring migration starts in mid-April and continues until the end of May, peaking during early to mid-May. Autumn migration occurs in August and September, with the peak during mid-August. Birds are rare at the beginning of October. Breeding extends from mid-May to the beginning of July, peaking during early June.

Reed Warbler *Acrocephalus scirpaceus*

European Reed Warbler, Eurasian Reed Warbler

Rakosnik obecny Trsteniarik bahenny Teichrohrsänger

Although Reed Warbler is distributed throughout the country, it mainly occurs in fishpond areas. As a breeder, it can be found from lowlands up to 400–500 m at ponds around Ceske Budejovice (CB) and Trebon (JH), to 480 m in the foothills of the Krkonose mountains (SE, TU), to 510 m around Plana (TC), to 590 m at ponds around Bohdalov and Nove Veseli (ZR), and to 730 m around Lipno reservoir (CK). The range of its breeding habitats is not so wide as those used by Marsh Warblers: breeding is more or less restricted to reedbeds in aquatic, as well as semi-terrestrial, habitats. It often uses quite small areas of reed, for example around railroads, roads and ditches. Nests are usually placed in reeds, occasionally in other plants

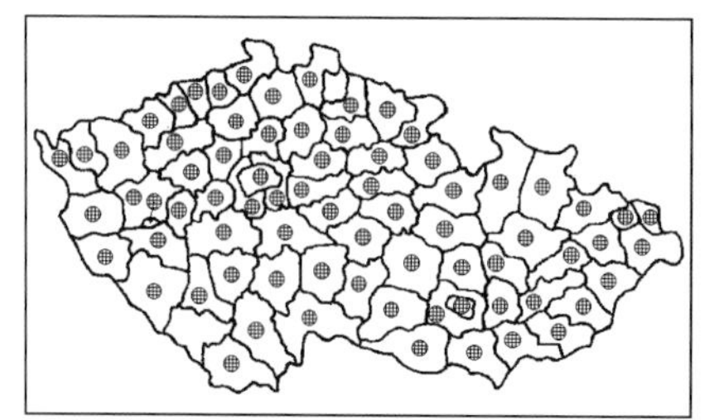

such as reedmace, or in shrubs, 0.25–1.0 m above water level or above the ground. On migration, this species also occurs around rivers and ditches, in abandoned orchards, and at dumps with vegetation or brush. Higher breeding densities of Reed Warblers are found in strips and small areas of reedbed than in large stands. At the beginning of the 1970s, breeding density was 740 pairs per km^2 at Opatovicky pond (JH), 190–380 pairs per km^2 at Nesyt pond (BV), and 90 pairs per km^2 at several ponds around Sedlcany (BN) at the end of the 1970s. It was 280–1,440 pairs per km^2 in reedbeds around Rozmberk pond (JH) in the 1980s, and 30–110 pairs per km^2 at Vrbenske ponds (CB) at the end of the 1980s and beginning of the 1990s. Breeding density was 420 and 580 pairs per km^2 respectively in 1987 and 1988 at Nesyt pond (BV), and 210–440 pairs per km^2 in reedbeds around Ostrozska Nova Ves gravel pit (UH) in the mid-1980s.

Status: Migrant and summer visitor. **Breeding season:** local/common. **Winter:** does not occur. **Migration:** common. Protected.

Population trends: The breeding population is between 50,000 and 100,000 pairs, and has been relatively stable for the past 20 years.

Distribution: On migration found nationwide. As a breeder, it may be rather scarce in the following counties: SO, JN, LB, SY, BK, OP, FM and VS. High breeding densities can be found at fishponds in the following counties: JH, CB, PU, HK, PU, PH, KO, BV, HO, OV and KI.

Timing: Spring migration starts during mid-April and continues until mid-May, peaking at the end of April and beginning of May. Autumn migration occurs between mid-August and the end of September, peaking from early to mid-September. Individual birds are seen occasionally until mid-October. Breeding extends from late May to late July, peaking from early to mid-June.

Great Reed Warbler *Acrocephalus arundinaceus*

Rakosnik velky   Trsteniarik velky   Drosselrohrsänger

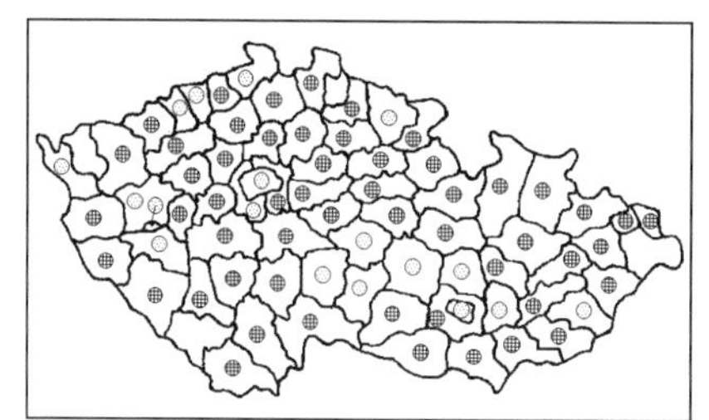

Breeding pairs of Great Reed Warbler are scattered across the country, from lowlands up to 360 m in the foothills of the Krkonose mountains (SE, TU), to 510 m around Plana (TC), and to 640 m at ponds in ZR and PB counties. The majority of the breeding population occurs at fishponds in lowlands. As a breeder, this species is usually restricted to mature growths of reeds and reedmace. It can be found around fishponds, gravel pits, larger oxbows, lakes and canals. On migration, it also occurs at the shrubby edges of riverine forest in farmland. Nests are almost exclusively placed in growths of reed and reedmace, 0.25–0.75 m above water level. Breeding density may vary widely from place to place. It was 160 pairs per km^2 at Opatovicky pond (JH) at the beginning of the 1970s, and 60 pairs per km^2 at Velky Panensky pond (JH) in the mid-1970s; it was 40–70 pairs per km^2 at 3 ponds in s. Bohemia in the 1980s; and it was 210 pairs per km^2 at Nesyt pond (BV) at the beginning of the 1970s, and 90 pairs per km^2 at the same place in 1987. Generally, breeding densities at several sites in s. Bohemia and s. Moravia were higher until the beginning of 1970s than in the following 20 years when a decrease was recorded. It is likely that the falls in population levelled off at the beginning of the 1990s. The main cause of Great Reed Warbler's decline in the Czech Republic is probably the degradation and fragmentation of breeding habitats, and the reduced diversity of prey due to insecticide usage.

Status: Migrant and summer visitor. **Breeding season:** local. **Winter:** does not occur. **Migration:** common. Endangered. Protected.

Population trends: The breeding population is between 1,500 and 3,000 pairs, and has declined by at least 50% over the past 20 years.

Distribution: On migration found nationwide. Strongholds of the breeding population are in the following counties: CB, JH, PU, BV, HO, OV, LN (10 pairs at Lenesicky pond in 1999)

and KI. As a breeder, it is rather scarce in the following counties: DO, KV, UL, LT, PS, CK, PT, SO, DC, BN, PV, ZL, OP, RA, LB, TU, PE, SY, UO, BK, BR, OL, VS and FM.
Timing: Spring migration occurs between mid-April and mid-May, peaking during late April and early May. Spring migration starts at the beginning of August and continues to the end of September, peaking during early to mid-September. Birds are rarely seen during October. Breeding extends from the beginning of May to mid-July, peaking during late May and early June.

Icterine Warbler *Hippolais icterina*

Sedmihlasek hajni   Sedmohlasok obycajny   Gelbspötter

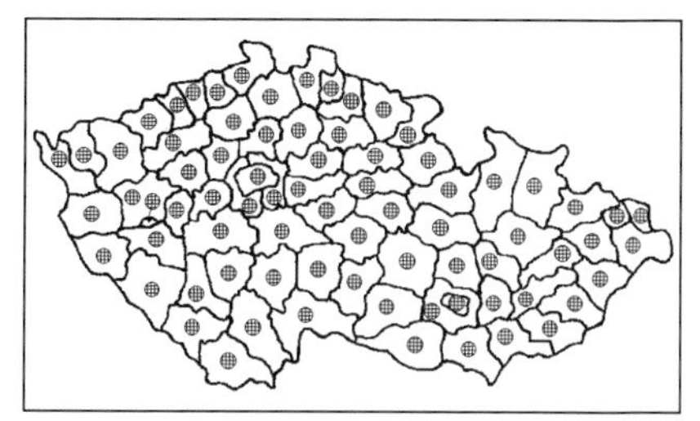

Icterine Warbler occurs throughout the country from lowlands up to about 800 m in most mountain areas such as Krkonose (SE, TU), Sumava (CK, PT, KT), Krusne hory (CV, KV, MO, TP), Jeseniky (BR, SU), and the Ceskomoravska vysocina highlands (HB, JI, PE, ZR). However, Icterine Warbler is more common in lowlands than at higher altitudes, where it is usually found around human habitations, brooks and rivers. Typical breeding habitats include larger orchards, parks, sparse poplar, birch or alder-dominated forest with scrub undergrowth and clearings, riverine forest, and growths of trees and bushes around rivers and other areas of open water. Occasionally it inhabits mixed forest, but it avoids coniferous and dense woodland. It is a regular breeder in the larger parks of many towns. Most nests are placed in European elder, 1.5–2.5 m above the ground. Breeding density varies from county to county, and among habitats. In the 1970s, it was 0.5 pairs per km^2 in deciduous, oak-dominated forest in the Ceske stredohori highlands (UL, LT), 90 individuals per km^2 in growths along the Zlata stoka river (JH) and 2 individuals per km^2 in a suburb of Brno (BM). In riverine forest in PR and OL counties it was 10–20 pairs per km^2 and 18–100 individuals per km^2 respectively, and 9 pairs per km^2 in ST county in the 1980s. During the 1980s, in various types of growth around Tachov (TC) and Strakonice (ST), it was 10 and 40–120 pairs per km^2 respectively, in windbreaks in farmland (BV) it was 180 individuals per km^2, and 11 pairs per km^2 in growths along brooks (CK). Higher densities seem to occur in city parks: during the 1970s, in Cesky Brod (KO), there were 62–93 pairs per km^2, 41 pairs per km^2 in Lesna near Zlin (ZL), 35–50 pairs per km^2 in Vizovice (ZL), and 76–114 pairs per km^2 in Vsetin (VS). During the 1980s, there were 65 pairs per km^2 in Ostrava (OV), 0–58 pairs per km^2 in Tachov, and 20 pairs per km^2 in Bor u Tachova (TC) and Chodova Plana (TC). Breeding density was 73–90 pairs per km^2 in a small area of deciduous forest at about 170–200 m in UH county at the end of the 1970s, but only 30–50 pairs per km^2 in the same habitat 10 years later.
Status: Migrant and summer visitor. **Breeding season:** common. **Winter:** does not occur. **Migration:** common. Protected.
Population trends: The breeding population is between 50,000 and 100,000 pairs, and has been stable for the past 20 years.
Distribution: Nationwide. As a breeder it may be less common in the following counties: TC, SO, ZN, PE and BK
Timing: Spring migration occurs from late April until the end of May, peaking during early May. Autumn migration starts at the beginning of August, peaking from mid- to late August, and continues until the beginning of September. Breeding extends from mid-May to early July, peaking at the end of May and beginning of June.

Barred Warbler *Sylvia nisoria*

Penice vlasska   Penica jaraba   Sperbergrasmücke

Barred Warbler is a regular but quite uncommon breeder in the Czech Republic. It occurs mainly in lowlands, although it has been recorded up to 400 m in the Jeseniky mountains (BR, SU), and to 650 m in the Krkonose mountains (SE, TU); it also breeds in shrubs in the Ceske Stredohori highlands (LN, LT, MO, UL). This species was expanding its range in the Czech

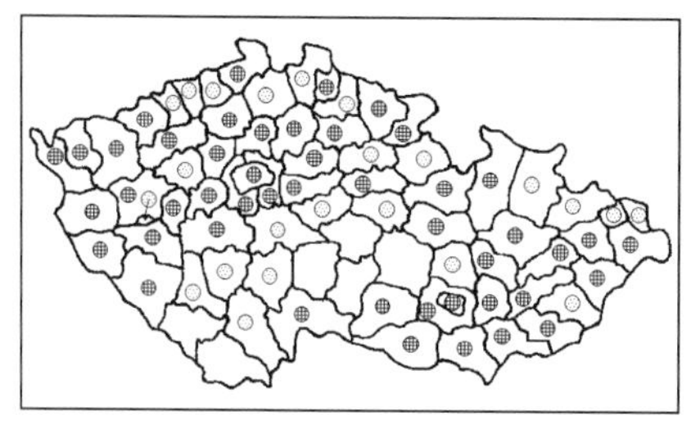

Republic at the beginning of the 20th century, and was more common in the middle of the 1900s than it is now. The breeding population has been declining since about the 1960s (Stancl and Stanclova 1984–85). However, this decline probably stopped at the beginning of the 1990s, and locally the numbers have been increasing. Typical breeding habitats include the edges of deciduous forest and clearings, always dominated by dense scrub, sunny hillsides and pastures with dense thorny bushes, particularly buckthorn and hawthorn, hedgerows around vineyards and along farmland roads, old abandoned orchards, and growths around ditches. It is also found in thickets around brooks and fishponds, although Barred Warbler is not usually attracted to habitats near water. Generally it avoids forest. Nests are built in blackthorn or roses, up to 2 m above ground. It often breeds in close proximity to Red-backed Shrike. Breeding density was 10–44 pairs per km^2 at slag heaps with scrub around coal mines in MO county at the beginning of the 1970s, 25 pairs per km^2 at 420 m on shrubby hillsides in the Bile Karpaty mountains (HO, UH, ZL) in the mid-1980s, and 5 individuals per km^2 around Mlada (NB) at the beginning of the 1990s. Some of the sites where dozens of pairs breed regularly include the Palava hills (BV), Lednicke ponds (BV), Pohorelicke ponds (BV), and Soutok, an area s. of the village of Lanzhot (BV). The main factors in Barred Warbler's decline are probably habitat degradation and the reduction of food availability through the removal of hedges and bushes.

Status: Migrant and summer visitor. **Breeding season:** local. **Winter:** does not occur. **Migration:** local. Vulnerable. Protected.

Population trends: The breeding population is estimated to be between 1,500 and 3,000 pairs. It has declined by 20–50% over the past 20 years but is now considered stable.

Distribution: On migration it may occur nationwide. Counties with the regular breeding of good numbers include: BV, BO, PR, UH, PJ, LN and JC.

Timing: Spring arrival starts during mid-April and continues until mid-May, peaking during early May. Autumn migration occurs between the beginning of August and mid-September. Breeding starts at the beginning of May, peaking at the end of May and beginning of June, and continues until mid-June.

Lesser Whitethroat *Sylvia curruca*

Penice pokrovni   Penica popolava   Klappergrasmücke

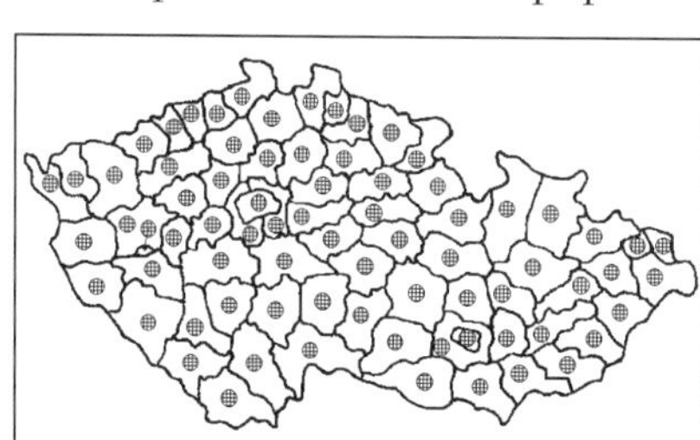

Although Lesser Whitethroat is distributed throughout the country, it may be rather scarce in some counties. This species occurs from lowlands up to 800–1000 m in the Krusne hory mountains (CV, KV, MO, TP), to 1025 m in the Orlicke hory mountains (RK), to 1100 m in the Sumava mountains (CK, PT, KT), to 1150 m in the Krkonose mountains (SE, TU), to 1270 m in the Beskydy mountains (FM, VS), and to 1350 m in the Jeseniky mountains (BR, SU). It is found in young scrub in clearings or at the edges of all types of forest, in thickets and bushes around rivers, brooks and ponds, in woods in farmland, and in parks, cemeteries, and mature gardens, where it breeds in currant or gooseberry bushes, in spruce, blackthorn or European elder, usually up to 2 m above ground. At high altitudes it frequents dwarf pine. On migration it occurs elsewhere, quite frequently in reedbeds. At the beginning of the 1970s, breeding density was 28 pairs per km^2 in hedgerows around Trebon (JH), 38 and 177 individuals per km^2 respectively in deciduous oak-dominated forest and on steppes with growths of trees in the Ceske stredohori highlands (UL, LT), and 210–339 individuals per km^2 in growths along riverbanks and orchards in CV county. In the 1980s, in hedgerows in TC county, it was 20–270 pairs per km^2, in various types of growth in ST county it was 40–240 pairs per km^2, in various biotopes around Milevsko (TA) it was 8–168 pairs per km^2, in pine thickets around Trebon (JH) it was 9 pairs per km^2, and in farmland in s. Bohemia

it was 6–13 pairs per km². At the beginning of the 1980s, it was 110–130 pairs per km² in hedges around vineyards and in old, abandoned orchards with shrub in farmland at about 180 m in UH county. The density had decreased by about 50% at the end of the 1980s, after hedges had been cleared. In dwarf pines at about 1170 m in the Beskydy mountains (FM, VS) breeding density was 10 pairs per km² at the beginning of the 1990s; and it was 10–97 pairs per km² in various types of growth in Praha (AA) during the 1970s, 24 pairs per km² in a park in Ostrava (OV), and 15–86 pairs per km² in various habitats in Tachov (TC) during the 1980s.
Status: Migrant and summer visitor. **Breeding season**: common. **Winter**: rare. **Migration**: common. Protected.
Population trends: The breeding population ranges from 50,000 to 100,000 pairs. It has declined by 20–50% over the past 20 years. The unusual wintering of 3 individuals has been recorded during the past 30 years.
Distribution: Nationwide.
Timing: Spring migration occurs from early April until early May, peaking during the second half of April. Autumn migration starts at the beginning of August and continues until the end of September, peaking during early to mid-September. Birds are occasionally seen until mid-October. Breeding extends from the end of April to the end of June, peaking during mid-May.

Common Whitethroat *Sylvia communis*

Whitethroat Penice hnedokridla Penica hnedokridla Dorngrasmücke

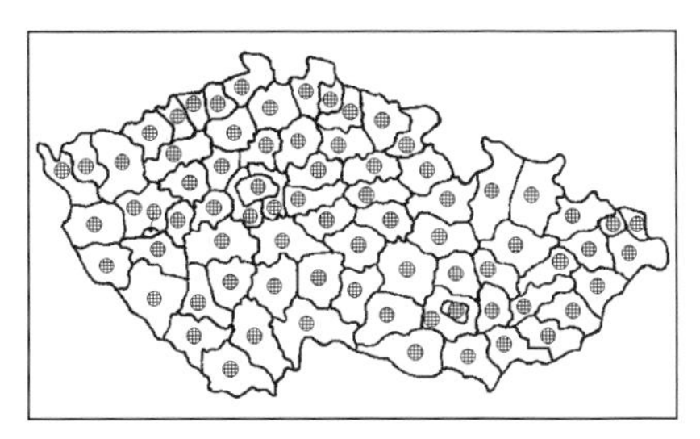

Common Whitethroat is distributed throughout the country, from lowlands up to 1000 m in the Krusne hory mountains (CV, KV, MO, TP), to 1025 m in the Orlicke hory mountains (RK), to 1100 m in Sumava mountains (CK, PT, KT), to 1170 m in the Beskydy mountains (FM, VS), to 1360 m in the Krkonose mountains (SE, TU), although breeding occurs at 1000 m and 1450 m in the Jeseniky mountains (BR, SU). Nevertheless, it is more common in lowlands and highlands than at higher altitudes. Found at the edges of forest and clearings with tall vegetation and low shrubs, thickets and bushes along ditches, hedgerows in farmland and around country roads, avenues, usually more or less dry pastures, meadows with bushes and young trees, and vineyards. It is also found close to human settlements in parks, orchards and gardens. On migration, this species frequents reedbeds around fishponds, and growths around rivers. Nests are normally built in nettles, blackberry bushes or roses, up to 0.5 m above ground. During the 1970s, breeding density in various habitats around Trebon (JH) was 28–55 pairs per km², 9–51 pairs per km² in parks and other growths in Praha (AA), 5 pairs per km² in avenues in the Cesky les mountains (TC), and 10–33 pairs per km² at shrub-covered slag heaps around coal mines in MO county. In the 1980s, in various types of growth in TC and ST counties it was 20–200 and 10–640 pairs per km² respectively, in various biotopes around Milevsko (TA) it was 32–156 pairs per km², in pine thickets around Trebon (JH) it was 30 pairs per km², in young growths along a brook in CK county it was 100 pairs per km², and in farmland in s. Bohemia it was 9–21 pairs per km². At the beginning of the 1980s, it was 20–50 pairs per km² in hedgerows around vineyards, along railways and in old abandoned orchards around Podoli (UH) at about 180 m. In acid-rain-damaged spruce forest and clearings at about 1140 m in the Beskydy mountains it was 35 and 60 pairs per km² respectively, and in various habitats around Mlada (NB) it was 12–58 individuals per km² at the beginning of the 1990s. The density was 3–12 pairs per km² in parkland around several castles in w. Bohemia during the 1980s. The decline in breeding pairs stopped in the mid-1980s, and the population began to rise.
Status: Migrant and summer visitor. **Breeding season**: common. **Winter**: does not occur. **Migration**: common. Protected.
Population trends: The breeding population is between 90,000 and 180,000 pairs, and has declined by 20–50% over the past 20 years.
Distribution: Nationwide. As a breeder it may be less common in the following counties: SO, LB, KV, BK and ZN.

Timing: Spring migration occurs from the beginning of April until early May, peaking during late April. Autumn migration starts at the beginning of August and continues until the beginning of October, peaking during early September. Breeding extends from the beginning of May, rarely late April, until early July.

Garden Warbler *Sylvia borin*

Penice slavikova   Penica slavikovita   Gartengrasmücke

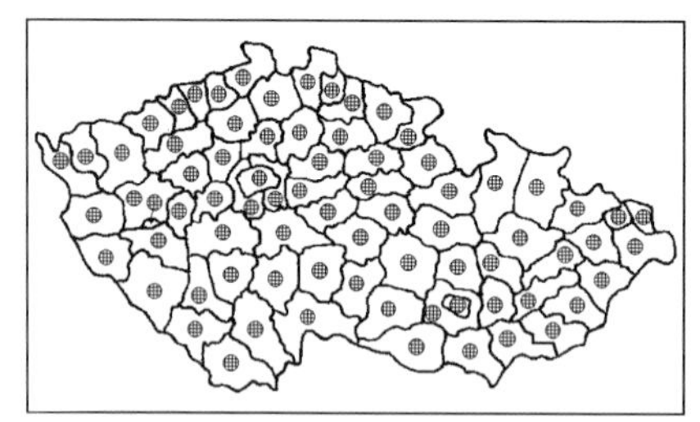

Garden Warbler is one of the 2 *Sylvia* species whose population has been increasing over the past 20 years in the Czech Republic. This species breeds throughout the country, from lowlands up to about 850 m in the Krusne hory mountains (CV, KV, MO, TP), to 900 m in the Beskydy mountains (FM, VS), to 940 m in the Jeseniky mountains (BR, SU), from 990–1020 m in the Orlicke hory mountains (RK), to 1200 m in the Sumava mountains (CK, PT, KT), and to 1250 m in the Krkonose mountains (SE, TU). It is more common in lowlands and highlands than in mountains, where it usually occurs around brooks and streams. Garden Warbler frequents moist, deciduous forest with a shrub undergrowth, clearings, and growths along rivers, brooks and ditches, less commonly in old gardens with shrubs, or in parks, cemeteries, and mixed, conifer-dominated forest. It avoids conifer plantations (except areas of woodland with thickets of conifer) and dense forest. During autumn migration, it often occurs in large numbers at the edges of riverine forest with growths of European elder, and at the edges of fishponds. Nests are usually built in raspberry canes and in hornbeams, 0.2–1 m above ground. During the 1970s, breeding density was 39–126 individuals per km^2 in stands of old trees surrounding fishponds around Trebon (JH), 392 individuals per km^2 in growths around the Zlata Stoka river (JH), and 30–50 pairs per km^2 in growths along riverbanks in CV county. In the 1980s, in a variety of vegetation in TC and ST counties it was 10–50 and 10–560 pairs per km^2 respectively, in the same range of habitat around Milevsko (TA) it was 36–152 pairs per km^2, in pines in JH and TA counties it was 9–30 and 25 pairs per km^2 respectively, in growths along a brook (CK), depending on the density of bushes and trees, it was 100–286 pairs per km^2, and in younger growths around ponds in CB county it was 23–55 pairs per km^2; in riverine forest in OL and ST counties it was 17 individuals per km^2 and 9 pairs per km^2 respectively, in acid-rain-damaged spruce and spruce-beech forest in the Krkonose mountains it was 2–3 pairs per km^2. In several parks in w. Bohemia it was 3–43 pairs per km^2 in the 1980s, and it was 85–115 pairs per km^2 in deciduous woodland and growths around rivers and brooks in farmland at about 180 m in UH county in the mid-1980s. In oak-dominated deciduous forest in NB county it was 8–70 individuals per km^2 at the beginning of the 1990s.
Status: Migrant and summer visitor. **Breeding season**: common. **Winter**: does not occur. **Migration**: common. Protected.
Population trends: The breeding population is between 200,000 and 400,000 pairs, and has increased by 20–50% over the past 20 years.
Distribution: Nationwide.
Timing: Spring arrival starts at the beginning of April, with increasing numbers until early May, and ends during mid-May. Autumn departure starts at the end of July, peaking at the end of August and beginning of September, and continues until the end of September. Birds are rare during early to mid-October. Breeding extends from late April to mid-July, peaking during mid- to late May.

Blackcap *Sylvia atricapilla*

Penice cernohlava   Penica ciernohlava   Mönchsgrasmücke

This is the most common *Sylvia* species in the Czech Republic. Blackcap is distributed from lowlands up to 750 m in the Cesky les mountains (DO, TC), to 1000 m in the Krusne hory

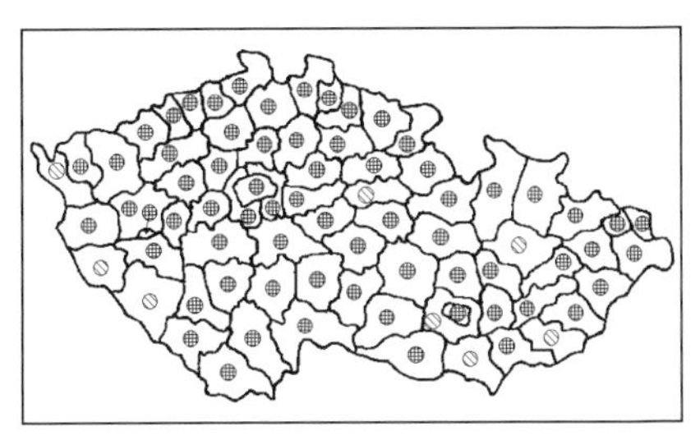

mountains (CV, KV, MO, TP), to 1025 m in the Orlicke hory mountains (RK), to 1180 m in the Beskydy mountains (FM, VS), to 1200 m in the Sumava mountains (CK, PT, KT), to 1360 m in the Krkonose mountains (SE, TU), and to 1400 m in the Jeseniky mountains (BR, SU). This species, which is more common in lowlands than at higher altitudes, utilizes a wide range of woodland habitats: any type of forest with scrub undergrowth, coniferous plantations, dwarf pines in mountains, growths along rivers, hedgerows in farmland, parks, avenues, mature orchards with shrubs, and cemeteries. On migration it can be seen elsewhere; during autumn migration, it is frequently found in riverine forest, where it feeds on elderberries. Nests are usually built in European elder, spruce, hornbeam, and blackberry bushes, 0.5–2.0 m above ground. Breeding density varies among habitats. During the 1980s, it was 10–20 and 10–90 pairs per km^2 in pine forest in TA and JH counties respectively, 10–33 pairs per km^2 in spruce forest around Milevsko (TA), 12–36 pairs per km^2 in oak forest in MO, NA and PI counties, 100–160 pairs per km^2 and 120–470 individuals per km^2 respectively in riverine forest in central and n. Moravia, 75 pairs per km^2 in growths along a brook in CK county, 0–46 pairs per km^2 in fir-beech forest at about 900 m in the Beskydy mountains, and 79–114 individuals per km^2 in spruce forest in the Sumava mountains. Breeding density was 10–80 and 60–120 pairs per km^2 respectively in a range of vegetation in TC and ST counties during the 1980s, 11–146 pairs per km^2 in parks in Praha (AA) during the 1970s, 35 and 15–86 pairs per km^2 respectively in parks in Ostrava (OV) and Tachov (TC) during the 1980s, and 10–125 pairs per km^2 in several parks in w. Bohemia during the 1980s and beginning of the 1990s. It was 101 pairs per km^2 in poplar-dominated windbreaks and hedgerows in farmland in UH county, and 90–120 pairs per km^2 in growths along rivers and brooks in UH county in the mid-1980s. Breeding density in acid-rain-damaged spruce and spruce-beech forest at about 1100 m in the Beskydy mountains was 7–40 pairs per km^2 at the beginning of the 1990s, and in the same habitat in the Krkonose mountains it was 4–28 pairs per km^2 during the 1980s. The breeding population of Blackcap has been increasing steadily.

Status: Migrant and summer visitor. **Breeding season**: common. **Winter**: uncommon. **Migration**: common. Protected.

Population trends: The breeding population is between 600,000 and 1,200,000 pairs. It has increased by 20–50% over the past 20 years. Up to 5 individuals have been recorded in winter.

Distribution: Nationwide.

Timing: Spring migration occurs from early April, rarely late March, until mid-May. Peak spring migration is during the second half of April. Autumn migration starts during mid-August and continues until the end of October, peaking during late September and early October. Breeding extends from late April to the end of June, peaking during the second half of May.

Greenish Warbler *Phylloscopus trochiloides*

Western Greenish Warbler   Budnicek zeleny   Kolibkarik zeleny   Grünlaubsänger

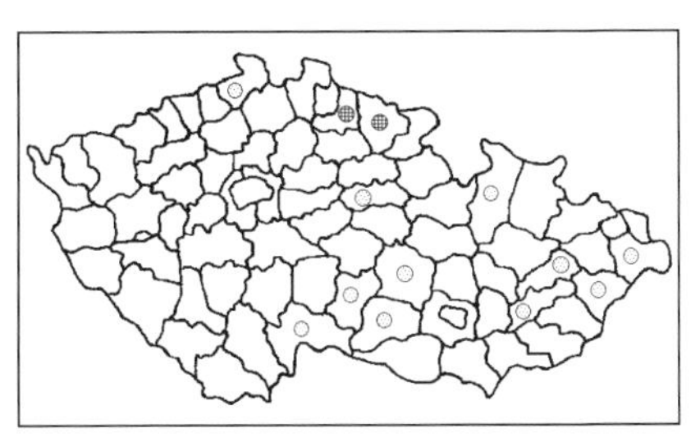

Greenish Warbler is a relatively new species to the Czech avifauna. The first singing male was recorded near Polna (JH) in the Ceskomoravska vysocina highlands in May 1963. Since then, there have been more records, but breeding was not observed until the early 1990s. Breeding distribution of this species is restricted to the Krkonose mountains (SE, TU), where it was recorded for the first time in 1992. Breeding habitats include young spruce with a not too dense undergrowth, and mixed woodland along streams (Flousek 1993). Individual birds, usually singing males, are recorded annually at other places in the country as well, from about 200 m up to 1350 m. Most non-breeding birds have

been seen in spruce or mixed forest with clearings and sparse undergrowth, in growths along brooks and streams, and in parks, usually avoiding dense vegetation. Birds recorded in the Czech Republic belong to the *viridanus* race.
Status: Summer visitor. **Breeding season:** rare. **Winter:** does not occur. **Migration:** uncommon. Critically endangered. Protected.
Population trends: Up to 15 pairs may breed annually, and up to 10 individuals are recorded on passage outside the breeding season. Between 1963 and 1991, 26 individuals were recorded in the country. The number of birds recorded on passage has increased by 20–50% during the last decade.
Distribution: Recent observations, excluding records from the Krkonose mountains, come from Lomnice nad Luznici (JH), Halenkov (VS), Velke Karlovice (VS), Vsetin (VS), and Kromeriz (KM).
Timing: Spring migration occurs from mid-April until mid-May. Autumn departure occurs from mid-July. Breeding occurs during the second half of June and beginning of July.

Western Bonelli's Warbler *Phylloscopus bonelli*

Bonelli's Warbler   Budnicek horsky   Kolibkarik horsky   Berglaubsänger

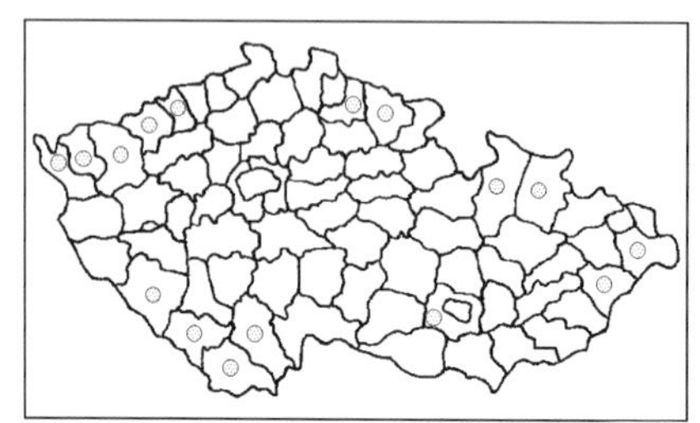

Several dozen records of sightings and breeding of Bonelli's Warblers in the Czech Republic have been published since the end of the 1880s. There are also 14 records of banded birds. However, there is no specimen or sufficient documentation to support any of these records. It is very likely that some of the reported birds were misindentified for other *Phylloscopus* species. The CFC has suggested the revision of all of the records (Hudec *et al.* 1995). Most of the records come from mountains such as the Krusne hory (CV, KV, MO, TP), Krkonose (SE, TU), Sumava (CK, PT, KT), Jeseniky (BR, SU), and Beskydy (VS, FM), where this species is most likely to be found. Records from other non-mountain areas are also available, such as CB, CH and BO counties.
Status: Vagrant. **Breeding season:** rare. **Winter:** does not occur. **Migration:** rare. Protected.
Population trends: No data available.
Distribution: See above.
Timing: This species has been recorded between April and September.

Wood Warbler *Phylloscopus sibilatrix*

Budnicek lesni   Kolibkarik sykavy   Waldlaubsänger

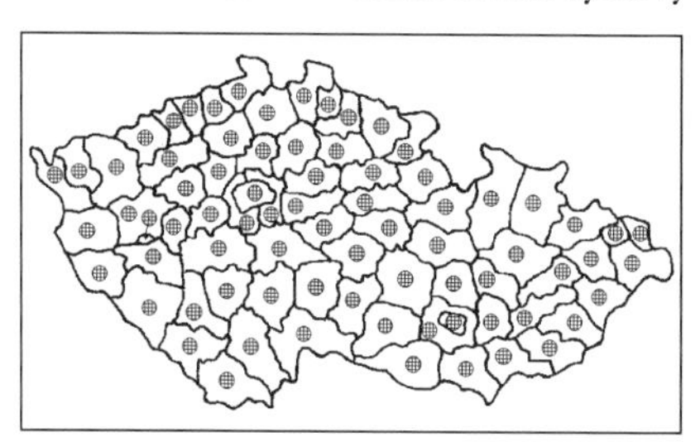

Although Wood Warbler is distributed throughout the country, it is usually absent from treeless areas and from areas with large coniferous plantations. It occurs from lowlands up to 800 m in the Cesky les (DO, TC) and Krusne hory (CV, KV, MO, TP) mountains, to 1000 m in the Jeseniky mountains (BR, SU), to 1025 m in the Orlicke hory mountains (RK), to 1050 m in the Krkonose mountains (SE, TU), to 1160 m in the Beskydy mountains (FM, VS), and to 1200 m in the Sumava mountains (CK, PT, KT). This species inhabits deciduous and mixed, beech-dominated, forest with sparse undergrowth and a closed canopy, but pure stands of beech are usually avoided. Even though it generally dislikes conifers, it may occasionally utilize young pines. It is also found in larger parks. Nests are placed in vegetation on the ground. During migration, Wood Warblers can be found in a range of habitats including orchards, stands of trees in farmland, avenues, and reedbeds around ponds. At the end of the 1970s, density was 10 pairs per km^2 in spruce forest with sparse deciduous trees near Milevsko (TA); 18, 22 and 20 pairs per km^2 respectively in oak

forest in MO, NA and PI counties during the 1980s; and 10–40 pairs per km² in riverine forest in KM county at the beginning of 1980s. It was 9–56 pairs per km² in primeval fir-beech forest at about 900 m in VS county during 1980; 23–37 pairs per km² in spruce-beech forest at about 1140 m in the Beskydy mountains, and 42 pairs per km² in a spruce forest in the Sumava mountains at the beginning of the 1990s. In various parks in w. Bohemia it was 3–42 pairs per km² during the 1980s and beginning of the 1990s, and in larger parks and cemeteries in Praha it was 13–52 pairs per km² in the mid-1970s. Breeding density was 60–83 pairs per km² in hornbeam-dominated forest at about 200 m in UH county, and 75–90 pairs per km² in beech-dominated forest at 450 m in the Bile Karpaty mountains (HO, UH, ZL) at the beginning of the 1980s.
Status: Migrant and summer visitor. **Breeding season:** common. **Winter:** does not occur. **Migration:** common. Protected.
Population trends: The breeding population is between 80,000 and 160,000 pairs, and has been stable for the past 20 years.
Distribution: Nationwide. As a breeder it may be rather scarce in the following counties; LN, LT, CL, PE, ZN, LB, SY and SO.
Timing: Spring migration starts at the end of March, with the main influx during mid- to late April, and continues until mid-May. Autumn migration extends from the beginning of August to early October. It is rarely seen later than early October. Breeding occurs between the beginning of May, rarely late April, and end of June.

Common Chiffchaff *Phylloscopus collybita*

Chiffchaff, Eurasian Chiffchaff   Budnicek mensi   Kolibkarik cipcavy   Zilpzalp

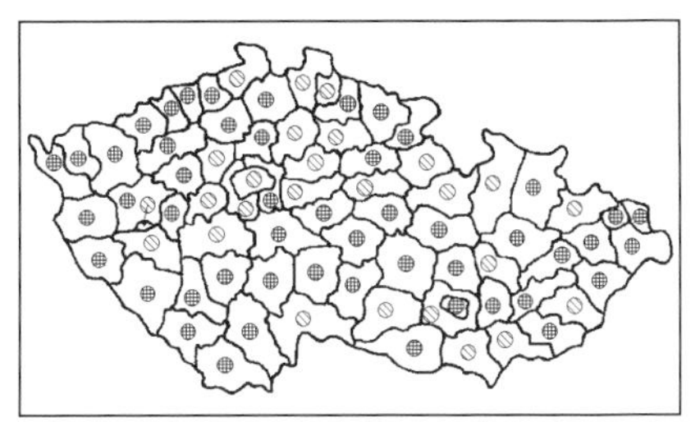

Common Chiffchaff is distributed from lowlands up to about 1200 m in the Krusne hory (CV, KV, MO, TP) and Sumava (CK, PT, KT) mountains, to 1270 m in the Beskydy mountains (FM, VS), and to 1300 m in the Krkonose mountains (SE, TU). This species breeds in a wide range of habitats: any type of forest with clearings and a not too dense canopy. It is also fairly common in spruce plantations. Breeding pairs can be found in small stands of trees and in hedgerows in farmland, in mature orchards with shrubs, parks, mature growths along rivers and around ponds, cemeteries, and dwarf pines in mountains. On migration it occurs elsewhere including human settlements and reedbeds around ponds. Nests are generally placed on the ground, or up to 0.2 m above ground, in grass, at the base of young shrubs and in trees, particularly in spruce and blackberry bushes, and in collected dead wood. Breeding density was 15 pairs per km² in spruce forest around Trebon (JH) at the beginning of the 1970s, and 30–78 pairs per km² in spruce forest near Milevsko (TA) at the end of 1970. During the 1980s, it was 30–50 pairs per km² and 120–267 individuals per km² in riverine forest in central and n. Moravia respectively, and 20–30 pairs per km² in oak forest in MO, NA and PI counties, 36–61 pairs per km², 30–60 pairs per km², and 6–43 pairs per km² in pine forest in JH, TA and TC counties, and 27–55 pairs per km² in spruce plantations in TC county. In acid-rain-damaged spruce and spruce-beech forest in the Krkonose mountains it was 6–14 pairs per km² in the 1980s; and in the same period in a variety of vegetation on farmland in TC, ST and TA counties, it was 50–120, 50–410, and 12–88 pairs per km² respectively, 65 pairs per km² in poplar-dominated windbreaks and in hedgerows in farmland at about 180 m in UH county.The following densities were recorded in various city parks and cemeteries: 62–120 pairs per km² in Cesky Brod (PH) in the mid-1970s, 99–141 pairs per km² in Vizovice (ZL) and 192–279 pairs per km² in Praha (AA) at the end of the 1970s; and 31–183 pairs per km² in w. Bohemia during the 1980s. Three races have been recorded in the Czech Republic: nominate *collybita* (breeding), 2 individuals of the *abietinus* race (trapped in 1944 and 1990 in AA and CL counties respectively), and a singing *brehmii* male (recorded in the Krkonose mountains in 1992).
Status: Migrant and summer visitor. **Breeding season:** common (*collybita*), rare (*abietinus*). **Winter:** uncommon (*collybita*), rare (*abietinus*). **Migration:** common (*collybita*), uncommon

(*abietinus*). Occasionaly winters. Protected.
Population trends: The breeding population is between 800,000 and 1,600,000 pairs. It has been stable for the last 20 years. The number of wintering birds is estimated to be between 40 and 60 individuals, and numbers have been increasing over the past 20 years.
Distribution: Nationwide.
Timing: Spring migration occurs from mid-March until the end of April, peaking during late March. Autumn migration starts at the beginning of August and continues until the end of October, peaking during the first half of October. Breeding occurs from mid-April, peaking during late April until early July.

Willow Warbler *Phylloscopus trochilus*

Budnicek vetsi Kolibkarik spevavy Fitis

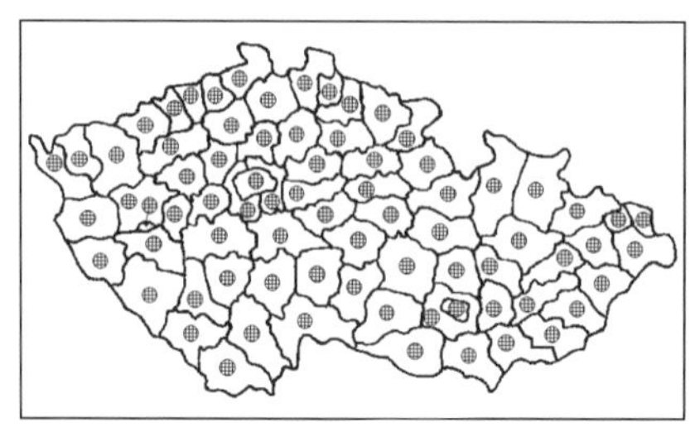

Willow Warbler is common throughout the country, although its density may be lower in counties where suitable habitats are unavailable. It breeds from lowlands up to 1200–1400 m in the majority of mountains. Willow Warbler is often a dominant species in dwarf pine. It usually breeds in young deciduous, mixed or coniferous forest, clearings with plentiful shrub, willow thickets in wet meadows, growths around rivers and ponds, hedgerows, windbreaks, and in despoiled areas with growths of young willow and poplar. As a breeder, it is uncommon in orchards, parks and cemeteries. On migration it occurs in any woodland, growths in farmland, and reedbeds around ponds. Nests are placed on the ground, commonly on slopes, on the banks of rivers, brooks or ditches, concealed in grasses or at the base of young trees and shrubs, especially spruce and blackberry. Breeding density in a young deciduous forest near Praha (AA) was 63–145 pairs per km^2 at the end of the 1970s, in pine forest in TA and TC counties it was 10–125 and 10–240 pairs respectively per km^2, in young growths at peatbogs and a growth of willows around Trebon (JH) it was 55–295 and 170 pairs per km^2, in spruce forest in TC county it was 2–44 pairs per km^2, in oak forest in MO and NA counties it was 24 and 14 pairs per km^2 respectively, and in young deciduous growths around a pond (CB) it was 147–274 pairs per km^2 during the 1980s. It was 40–130 pairs per km^2 in mixed, 40–60 year-old forest with undergrowth at about 200 m in UH county at the beginning of the 1980s. In acid-rain-damaged spruce and spruce-beech forest at 1100 m in the Beskydy moutains (FM, VS) and similar habitats in the Krkonse mountains (SE, TU) it was 13–85 and 5–11 pairs per km^2 respectively during the 1980s and beginning of the 1990s. In parkland around several castles in s. and w. Bohemia it was 42–93 pairs per km^2 during the 1980s and beginning of the 1990s. The breeding population belongs to the *trochilus* race.
Status: Migrant and summer visitor. **Breeding season**: common. **Winter**: does not occur. **Migration**: common. Protected.
Population trends: The breeding population is between 500,000 and 1,000,000 pairs, and has been stable for the past 20 years.
Distribution: Nationwide. As a breeder it may occur less commonly in the following counties: SO, LB, LT and HK.
Timing: Spring arrival starts at the beginning of April, peaking during late April, and continues through early May. Autumn departure extends from the beginning of August to mid-October, peaking during mid- to late September. It is rare after mid-October. Breeding occurs from late April to the end of mid-June, peaking during the first half of May.

Goldcrest *Regulus regulus*

Common Goldcrest Kralicek obecny Kralicek zlatohlavy Wintergoldhähnchen

Goldcrest is a fairly common breeder as well as wintering species throughout the country. It is distributed from lowlands up to the spruce tree-line, for example at 1400–1500 m in the

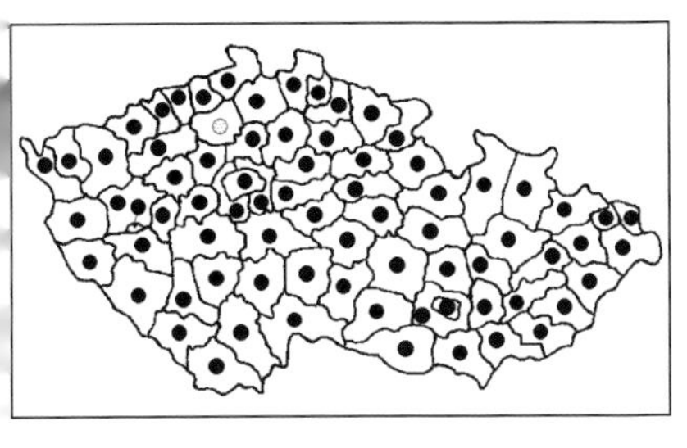

Krkonose (SE, TU) and Jeseniky (BR, SU) mountains. It occurs more commonly than Firecrest at altitudes up to about 800 m; above these, Firecrest is more common. Goldcrest primarily inhabits spruce forest in highlands and mountains, and expanded its range into lowlands during the 19th century as a result of spruce afforestation. Typical breeding habitat is coniferous forest, preferably mature spruces, but occasionally it will breed in mixed woods. Nests are always built in spruce, 2–18 m above ground. In winter, it can be found in more diverse habitats, such as mixed and deciduous woods, parks, orchards, cemeteries, and in growths along rivers. Wintering birds, presumably joined by individuals from n. Europe, usually stay in flocks of varying size, often with other species such as Blue Tit, Great Tit and Coal Tit. At the end of the 1970s, breeding density was 40–70 pairs per km^2 in spruce forest near Milevsko (TA), 75 pairs per km^2 in mature spruce forest near Trebon (JH), and 13–30 pairs per km^2 in primeval fir-beech forest at about 900 m in VS county. During the 1980s, it was 18–105 pairs per km^2 in spruce forest in TC county, 109–176 individuals per km^2 in mature spruce forest in the Sumava mountains (CK, PT, KT), 40 pairs per km^2 in mature spruce forest in the Novohradske hory mountains (CK, CB), 3–70 pairs per km^2 in spruce and mixed forest at about 1100 m in Beskydy mountains (FM, VS), 25–43, 54, and 10–25 pairs per km^2 respectively in pine forest in TC, JH and TA counties, 3 pairs per km^2 in oak forest in NA county, 15–23 pairs per km^2 in mature spruce forest at about 780 m in the Bile Karpaty mountains (HO, UH, ZL), and 6–16 pairs per km^2 in various types of deciduous forest in s. Bohemia. In acid-rain-damaged spruce and spruce-beech forest in the Krkonose mountains it was 7–21 pairs per km^2 during the 1980s. Winter density was 74 individuals per km^2 in pine forest in TC county in the mid-1970s, 4–18 individuals per km^2 in primeval fir-beech forest at about 900 m in VS county at the beginning of the 1980s, and 51–85 individuals per km^2 in spruce forest, and 0–8 individuals per km^2 in pine forest around Trebon (JH) at the beginning of the 1970s. It was 10–25 individuals per km^2 in a mixed 60-year-old forest with undergrowth at 180 m in UH county at the beginning of the 1980s.

Status: Resident. **Breeding season:** common. **Winter:** common. **Migration:** common. Protected.

Population trends: The breeding population is between 200,000 and 400,000 pairs, and has been stable for the past 20 years. The number of wintering birds is between 300,000 and 600,000 individuals.

Distribution: Nationwide. As a breeder it may be less common in the following counties: ST, PI, DO, CH, LT, ME, MB, JC, BR, OL, PV, VY, KM and BV. During winter, it may be rather scarce in the following counties: SO, CV, LN, LT, AA, NB, KO, TR, ZR, SY, BR, BV, VY, BK, PV and KM.

Timing: All year round. Breeding extends from mid-April to the beginning of June.

Firecrest *Regulus ignicapillus*

Kralicek ohnivy Kralicek ohnivohlavy Sommergoldhähnchen

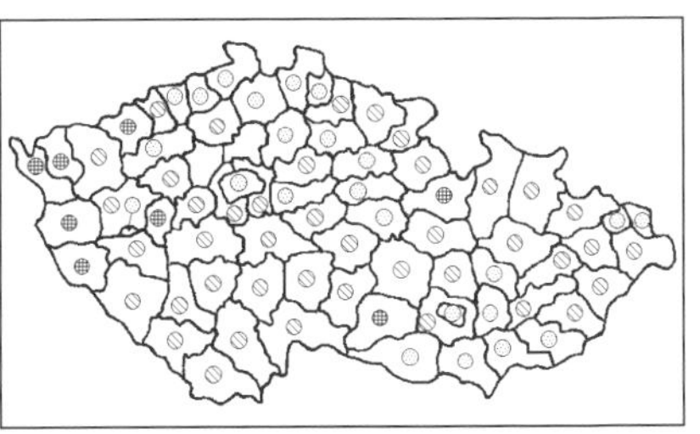

Although Firecrest is a permanent resident in the Czech Republic, the larger part of the breeding population is migratory. This species is distributed from about 190 m up to 1080 m in the Krusne hory mountains (CV, KV, MO, TP), to 1200 m in the Sumava (CK, PT, KT) and Beskydy (FM, VS) mountains, to 1300 m in the Krkonose mountains (SE, TU), and to 1400 m in the Jeseniky mountains (BR, SU). It occurs more commonly at higher altitudes than in lowlands. Breeding Firecrests prefer coniferous forest, but are not restricted to it as much as Goldcrests are. It utilizes the edges of spruce forest as well as mixed forest and larger parks with mature conifers. During the non-breeding season, although Firecrests occur in the same habitats as during the breeding season, they can also be found in mixed forest. Nests are placed in spruce, exceptionally in other conifers, 2–20 m above ground. Breeding density was 11 pairs per km^2 in coniferous forest with stands of beech and oak near Milevsko (TA) at the end of the 1970s, 32 individuals per km^2 in spruce forest in the Sumava mountains, 10–40 pairs per km^2 in spruce forest in TC county, 5 and 2–45 pairs per km^2 respectively in pine forest in JH and TC counties, 8 pairs per km^2 in oak forest in NA county, 5–13 pairs per km^2 in deciduous forest in s. Bohemia. In spruce and mixed forest at about 1100 m in the Beskydy mountains it was 13–27 pairs per km^2, and 1–8 pairs per km^2 in acid-rain-damaged spruce and spruce-beech forest in the Krkonose mountains (SE, TU) during the 1980s and beginning of the 1990s.

Status: Resident. **Breeding season**: local/common. **Winter**: uncommon. **Migration**: local/common. Protected.

Population trends: The breeding population is between 50,000 and 100,000 pairs. It has been stable for the past 20 years. The number of wintering birds is estimated to be between 3,000 and 6,000 individuals.

Distribution: On migration found nationwide. As a breeder, it is virtually absent from the following counties: LT, LN, SO, BV, HO, UH, ZN, KL, DC, CL, CR, PU, HK and JC. In winter, it is rare or does not occur in the following counties: ST, DO, TC, CH, SO, CV, MO, TP, UL, DC, CL, LT, PS, PM, RA, KL, ME, AA, PH, PZ, TA, KH, HB, CR, SU, BR, OV, KI, FM, ZL and ZN.

Timing: All year round. Spring migration occurs from mid-March to the end of April, peaking during early April. Autumn migration starts in mid-September and continues to mid-October. Breeding extends from late April to the beginning of July, peaking at the beginning of May.

Spotted Flycatcher *Muscicapa striata*

Lejsek sedy Muchar sivy Grauschnäpper

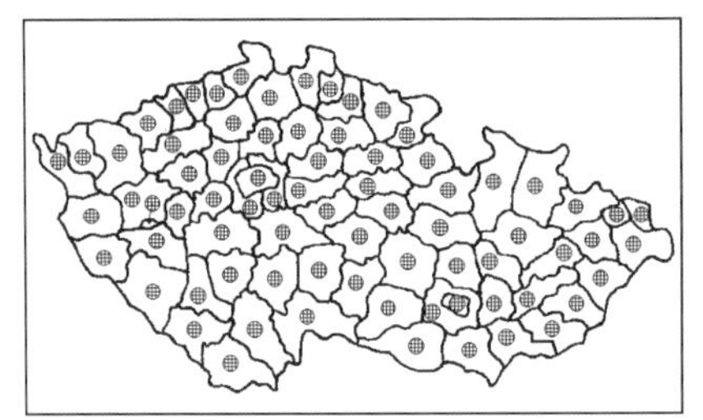

Spotted Flycatcher is a regular but uncommon breeder, distributed throughout the country. It occurs from lowlands up to 700 m in the Krusne hory mountains (CV, KV, MO, TP), to 850 m in the Bile Karpaty mountains (UH, HO, ZL), to 900 m in the Krkonose (SE, TU) and Orlicke hory (RK) mountains, to about 1000 m in the Beskydy (VS, FM) and Jeseniky (BR, SU) mountains, and to 1200 m in the Sumava mountains (CK, PT, KT). This species occurs more commonly in lowlands than at higher altitudes. Typical habitats include the edges of mature, not too dense, deciduous, less often coniferous, forest, avenues, and stands of mature trees along rivers and around ponds. It frequents human habitation, where it utilizes parks, orchards, gardens, and occasionally cemeteries. At higher altitudes, this species exploits mixed woods dominated by spruce. In mountains, at the edge of its altitudinous distribution, it occurs almost exclusively around human settlements. Birds on migration can be found in farmland and along rivers. Nests are more commonly built in trees such as willow, pear, spruce or acacia than on artificial structures such as buildings or in nest boxes; usually 1–3 m above ground. Breeding density in stands of mature oak at ponds around Trebon (JH) was 32–163 individuals per km^2 at the beginning of the 1970s and, 20 years later, only 21–55 individuals per km^2. It was 44 pairs per km^2 in mature trees along the Zlata stoka river around Trebon (JH) in the mid-1970s. Breeding density was 6–8 pairs per km^2 in poplar-dominated windbreaks and in hedgerows in farmland near Uherske Hradiste (UH) at the end of the 1970s; 10 years later, it did not breed in this area, although the habitat had not changed. Density in riverine forest in central and n. Moravia, was 30 pairs per km^2 and 0–27 individuals per km^2 respectively; in ST county it was 27 pairs per km^2, in fir-beech forest in the Beskydy mountains it was 0–19 pairs per km^2, in an oak avenue and in mixed growths along a brook in ST county it was 70 and 120 pairs per km^2 respectively, and 17 pairs per km^2 at a pasture with stands of mature deciduous trees in the Bile Karpaty mountains during the 1980s. In parkland around several castles in s. and w.

Bohemia it was 14–50 pairs per km^2, near Louny (LN) 6 pairs per km^2, and in a park in Ostrava (OV) 28–42 pairs per km^2 during the 1980s and beginning of the 1990s. In parks in Praha (AA) it was 0–24 pairs per km^2 at the end of the 1970s. The exact causes of its decline are unknown, but can probably be attributed to a reduction in available food.
Status: Migrant and summer visitor. **Breeding season**: common. **Winter**: does not occur. **Migration**: common. Least concern. Protected.
Population trends: The breeding population is between 30,000 and 60,000 pairs, and has declined by 20–50% during the past 20 years.
Distribution: Nationwide. As a breeder it may occur less commonly in the following counties: KT, DO, SO, NB and KV.
Timing: Spring migration occurs from mid-April to the end of May, peaking during early May. It is rare before mid-April. Autumn migration starts during late August, and continues until the end of September, peaking during the first half of September. Birds are rare during early October. Breeding extends from mid-May until mid-July, peaking during late May and early June.

Red-breasted Flycatcher *Ficedula parva*

Lejsek maly Mucharik maly Zwergschnäpper

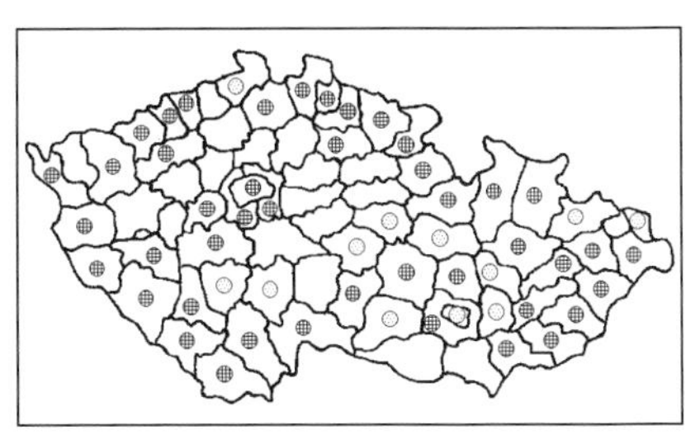

Red-breasted Flycatcher typically occurs at higher altitudes, from about 500 m, up to about 900 m in the Beskydy mountains (FM, VS), up to 950 m in the Orlicke hory (RK), and to 1150 m in the Jizerske hory (LB, JN) and Krkonose (SE, TU) mountains. In the Ceskomoravska vysocina highlands (HB, JI, PE, ZR) it breeds between 500 and 700 m. Occasional breeding is recorded at 200–250 m. Breeding is more or less restricted to mature beech forest, but it may occasionally nest in oak-dominated deciduous or mixed forest. On migration, it can be found in a wider range of habitats including larger parks, orchards, and growths along rivers and brooks. Nests are usually placed in beech, less commonly in hornbeam or oak, 1–6 m above ground. Areas with high numbers of breeding pairs include the Sumava (CK, PT, KT) and Krusne hory (CV, KV, MO, TP) mountains, the Krkonose and Jizerske hory mountains, and the Vsetinske vrchy hills (VS). The breeding population in the Beskydy mountains is estimated to be between 400 and 700 pairs, and in the Jeseniky mountains (BR, SU) between 100 and 150 pairs. Breeding density was 0–43 pairs per km^2 in primeval fir-beech forest at about 900 m in the Beskydy mountains, and 1–4 pairs per km^2 in the Sumava mountains during the 1980s. This is a more common species in Slovakia, where the breeding population is between 5,000 and 10,000 pairs (Murin *et al.* 1994). It may be threatened locally as a result of the clearing of mature beeches.
Status: Migrant and summer visitor. **Breeding season**: local/common. **Winter**: does not occur. **Migration**: local. Vulnerable. Protected.
Population trends: The breeding population is between 800 and 1,400 pairs, and has increased by 20–50% during the past 20 years. However, the 'increase' may be due to greater observer attention than was previously paid.
Distribution: On migration it may occur nationwide. Breeding has been confirmed in about 35 counties. Recent records of birds, on migration and outside the breeding areas, come from Praha-Kunratice (PH), Kluky (PI), Sadek (DO), Pivon (DO), Podhradi (CR), Zarovice (PV), Sardice (HO), Brezova (UH), and Strani (UH).
Timing: Spring migration starts during late April and continues until the end of May, occasionally to early June, peaking during the first half of May. Autumn migration occurs from mid-August until the end of September, peaking at the beginning of September. Birds are rare during early October. Breeding occurs from late May until the end of June, peaking at the end of May.

Collared Flycatcher *Ficedula albicollis*

Lejsek belokrky Mucharik bielokrky Halsbandschnäpper

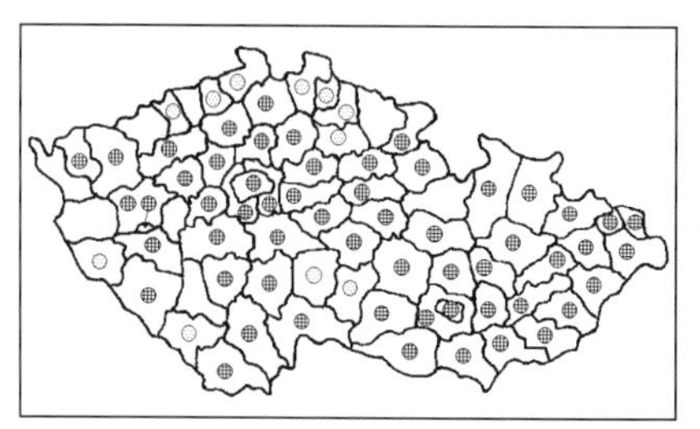

This is a regular and locally common breeder in the Czech Republic. It occurs more frequently in the east of the country. It is found from lowlands up to 600 m in the foothills of the Krkonose (SE, TU) and Jeseniky (BR, SU) mountains, to about 750 m in the Sumava mountains (CK, PT, KT), to 800 m in the Ceskomoravska vysocina highlands (HB, JI, PE, ZR), and to 900 m in the Beskydy mountains (FM, VS). However, it is more common in lowlands, with strongholds in central Bohemia, the southeast part of s. Moravia, and n. Moravia. Hundreds of pairs regularly breed in fishpond areas around Trebon (JH), between Jesenik nad Odrou (NJ) and Ostrava (OV), in the Palava hills (BV), and in the riverine forest area s. of the village of Lanzhot (BV). It breeds in mature deciduous, beech- or oak-dominated forest. It occasionally breeds in mixed woods, larger parks, and close to human habitations, in older orchards and gardens. In s. Moravia, it commonly breeds in pine with scattered stands of deciduous trees, and in s. Bohemia in mature avenues of oaks around ponds. On migration, it occurs elsewhere. Nests are always built in cavities in oak, alder or acacia, or in artificial nest boxes. Breeding density was 123–134 individuals per km^2 and 59–189 individuals per km^2 in mature avenues of oak around ponds near Trebon (JH) at the beginning of the 1970s and in the 1990s respectively. It was 100–210 pairs per km^2 at the end of the 1970s, and 155 pairs per km^2 in the 1980s in n. Moravia, but nest boxes were provided in these areas. In deciduous forest in s. Bohemia it was 20–64 pairs per km^2, in riverine forest in central and n. Moravia it was 30–50 pairs per km^2 and 118–160 individuals per km^2 respectively, and 3–7 pairs per km^2 in poplar-dominated windbreaks and hedgerows in farmland in UH county during the 1980s. In parks around several castles in s. and n. Bohemia it was 10–50 pairs per km^2 during the 1980s and beginning of the 1990s. In deciduous and mixed forest around Nymburk (NB) breeding density was 8–270 individuals per km^2 at the beginning of the 1990s. Hybridization with Pied Flycatcher occurs in areas where these 2 species are sympatric.

Status: Migrant and summer visitor. **Breeding season**: local/common. **Winter**: does not occur. **Migration**: local/common. Protected.

Population trends: The breeding population is between 25,000 and 50,000 pairs, and has been stable during the past 20 years.

Distribution: On migration found nationwide. As a breeder, it may be scarce or missing in the following counties: PJ, DO, LT, NA, SY, HB, ZR, JI, CR, KH, PE, PT, KT, SO, KV, LN, LB, MO, UL, DC, CL, JN, SE, TA and PS.

Timing: Spring arrival starts during early April, and continues until mid-May, peaking during the second half of April. Autumn departure occurs between mid-August and mid-September, with the majority of birds leaving at the end of August. Breeding extends from late April to early June, peaking during mid- to late May.

Pied Flycatcher *Ficedula hypoleuca*

European Pied Flycatcher Lejsek cernohlavy Mucharik ciernohlavy Trauerschnäpper

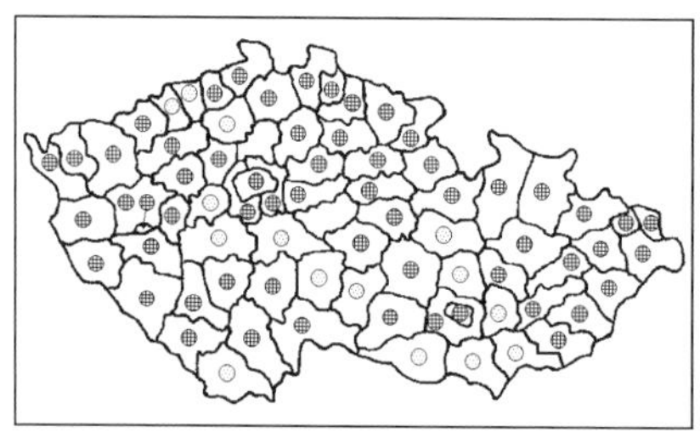

Breeding pairs of Pied Flycatcher are scattered across the Czech Republic, with higher numbers in the north and northwest parts of the country than elsewhere. This species is usually found in highlands and mountains, up to 700 m in the Krusne hory mountains (CV, KV, MO, TP), to 750 m in the Cesky les mountains (DO, TC), to 850 m in the Jeseniky mountains (BR, SU), to 900 m in the Krkonose (SE, TU) and Jizerske hory (LB, JN) mountains, to 1000 m in the Orlicke hory mountains (RK), and to 1100 m in the Sumava mountains (CK, PT, KT). Pied Flycatcher has been expanding its breeding range eastward and southward in the country for about 30 years. It is not so restricted to deciduous forest as Collared Flycatcher, and regularly breeds in mixed and coniferous forest. As a breeder, it also utilizes more commonly than Collared Flycatcher large and mature gardens, orchards and parks. Nests are built in cavities in beech, oak, aspen or lime, or in artificial nest boxes, usually 1–6 m above ground. During the 1980s, breeding density in mature oak forest in Jizerske hory (LB, JN), and around Nachod (NA) was 33 and 5 pairs per km^2 respectively, in riverine forest in n. Moravia it was 10 pairs per km^2, in oak-lime forest in s. Bohemia it was 6 pairs per km^2, and in acid-rain-damaged spruce and spruce-beech forest in the Krkonose mountains (SE, TU) it was 0–5 pairs per km^2. In parkland around castles in s. and n. Bohemia it was 3–30 pairs per km^2 during the 1980s and beginning of the 1990s.

Status: Migrant and summer visitor. **Breeding season:** local/common. **Winter:** does not occur. **Migration:** local/common. Protected.

Population trends: The breeding population is between 10,000 and 20,000 pairs, and has increased by 20–50% during the past 20 years.

Distribution: On migration found nationwide. As a breeder, it may be scarce in the following counties: CB, DO, TC, RO, LT, KL, MB, BN, KH, HB, SY, BK, BV and ZN.

Timing: Spring migration occurs between mid-April and early May, peaking during late April. Birds are rare before mid-April. Autumn migration occurs from mid-August until the end of September, peaking during mid-September. Birds are rare at the beginning of October. Breeding occurs between mid-May and early June.

Bearded Tit *Panurus biarmicus*

Sykorice vousata Fuzatka trstinova Bartmeise

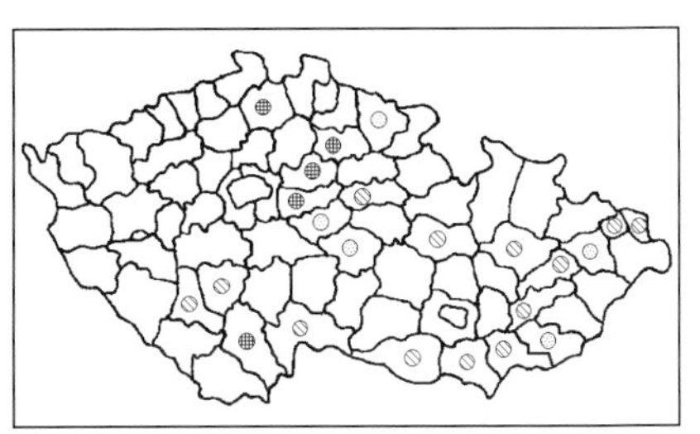

During the 19th, and first half of the 20th centuries, Bearded Tit occurred in the Czech Republic only sporadically. Nesting of a pair was first recorded at the Pohorelicke ponds (BV) in 1951. Since then, Bearded Tit has expanded its range into other areas of the country: in the early 1950s into HO and ZN counties, as well as other sites in BV county; at the end of the 1950s into OV, PU, CL and JH counties. During the 1970s, for unknown reasons, the number of breeding pairs declined, and irregular breeding of Bearded Tits was documented only at a few places in PI, PU, CL and OV counties. Regular breeding, however, occurred at 2 sites in BV county. Since 1983, the breeding population has been increasing again, and Bearded Tit has expanded its range into new, previously unoccupied areas. Breeding of this species is restricted to larger swamps of reed and reedmace with a dense undergrowth of sedge, and a reliable water level. Nests are usually built in reeds, up to 0.75 m above water level. Breeding strongholds are Nesyt pond (BV), where the number of pairs fluctuates from 30 to 70, occasionally more, Zehunsky pond (NB), with about 20 pairs, Pohorelicke ponds (BV), with up to 10 pairs, and Lesnik pond (OV), with 10–15 pairs. Breeding density at Nesyt pond (BV) was 160–230 pairs per km^2 at the beginning of the 1970s. At the same site, it was 110–120 pairs per km^2 in 1987, but only 40–62 pairs per km^2 the following year. Because it needs large areas of reed for breeding, Bearded Tit may be threatened locally by clearance of reed and reedmace. The breeding population belongs to the *russicus* race. A specimen of the *biarmicus* race was collected during the 19th century.

Status: Resident. **Breeding season:** uncommon. **Winter:** uncommon. **Migration:** uncommon. Endangered. Protected.

Population trends: The breeding population between 1973 and 1977 was 15 to 30 pairs; more recently it is 100–300 pairs. The number of breeding pairs fluctuates from year to year. The number of wintering birds was up to 60 individuals at the beginning of the 1980s, and 50–100 individuals between 1990 and 1994.

Distribution: Irregular breeding occurs in CB, JC, PU, SY and KM counties; regular breeding in JH, PI, NB, CL, BV, HO, PR, OV and KI counties. Wintering individuals have been recorded in the following counties: PI, ST, PU OV, OL, KM, BV, SY, and up to 80 individuals at Tovacovske ponds (PR). Because of its expansion over the past 20 years, breeding may occur elsewhere in suitable habitats, up to about 500 m. Regular recent records of 5–20 individuals, and occasionally up to 100, come are from Velky Tisy pond (JH), Kaclezsky pond (JH), Zablatsky pond (JH), Opatovicky pond (JH), Domin pond (CB), Blatec pond (CB), Zrcadlo and Mlynec ponds (JC), Rezabinec pond (PI), Zehunsky pond (NB), Velky Kosir pond near Litomysl (SY), Hvezda pond (SY), Novy pond (SY), Tovacovske ponds (PR), Mutenicke ponds (HO), Hermansky pond (OV), Chomoutov gravel pit (OL), Miloticky pond (HO), Zahlinicke ponds (KM), Lednice-Pastvisko (BV), Lednicke ponds (BV), and Nove Mlyny (BV).

Timing: All year round. Spring arrival of the migratory population occurs between mid-March and the end of April, with the majority arriving at the end of March. Autumn departure occurs from the beginning of September until mid-November. Breeding extends from late March mid-June, peaking at the end of April and end of May.

Long-tailed Tit *Aegithalos caudatus*

Mlynarik dlouhoocasy   Mlynarka dlhochvosta   Schwanzmeise

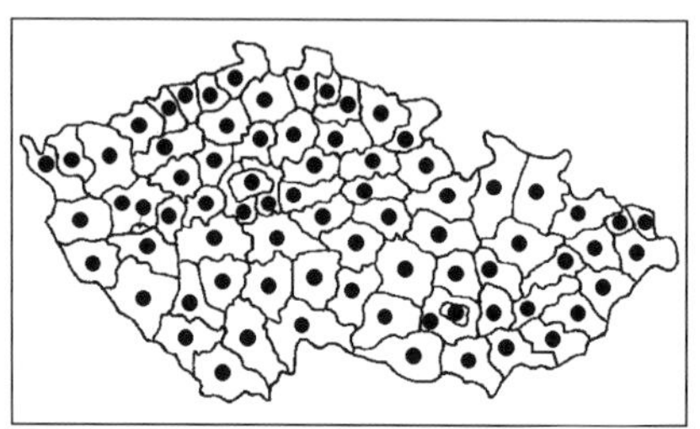

Long-tailed Tit is found throughout the country, normally in both lowlands and highlands. As a breeder, it has been recorded up to 500 m in the Ceskomoravska vysocina highlands (HB, JI, PE, ZR) and in the Krkonose mountains (SE, TU), to 600 m in the Krusne hory mountains (CV, KV, MO, TP), to 750 m in the Cesky les mountains (DO, TC), to 800 m in the Jeseniky mountains (BR, SU), to 860 m in the Orlicke hory mountains (RK), and 1200 m in the Sumava mountains (CK, PT, KT). Typical breeding habitats are not too dense, deciduous and mixed forest with scrub undergrowth, smaller woods and hedgerows in farmland, mature trees with scrub undergrowth along rivers and brooks, and large mature gardens and orchards. Nests are usually built in trees such as spruce, alder, willow, oak, acacia, poplar or hornbeam, less commonly in shrubs such as hawthorn, guelder rose, rose or European elder, 0.1–3 m, and occasionally up to 10 m above ground. In winter, it often associates with Great, Blue and Coal Tits, and frequents the edges of deciduous forest, in groups of trees and in hedgerows in farmland, and in growths along rivers, and in parks and gardens with mature trees. In the 1970s, breeding density was 4 pairs per km^2 in spruce plantations around Trebon (JH), 1 pair per km^2 in oak-dominated deciduous forest, and 4 pairs per km^2 in beech-dominated deciduous forest in the Ceske Stredohori highlands (LN, LT), 3 pairs per km^2 in deciduous forest in NA county, and 6–10 pairs per km^2 in forest along the Ohre river (LN). During the 1980s, it was 119 individuals, 50 individuals, and 19 pairs per km^2 respectively, in growths along brooks in ST, CK and TA counties, 0–19 pairs per km^2 in fir-beech forest in the Beskydy mountains (FM, VS), 76 pairs per km^2 in coniferous, pine-dominated forest around Trebon (JH), and 9 pairs per km^2 in poplar-dominated windbreaks and hedgerows in farmland in UH county. In parkland around castles, and in city parks it was 16 pairs per km^2 in LN county, and 14–19 pairs per km^2 in ZL and VS counties at the end of the 1970s and during the 1980s. Winter density was 50–250 individuals per km^2 in oak stands around ponds near Trebon (JH) at the beginning of the 1970s, 20 individuals per km^2 in pine stands in TC county in the mid-1970s, 10 individuals per km^2 in primeval beech and fir forest at about 900 m in VS county at the end of the 1970s and beginning of the 1980s, 80–110 individuals per km^2 in mixed woods at about 180 m in UH county, and 30–45 individuals per km^2 in poplar-dominated windbreaks and hedgerows in farmland in UH county in the mid-1980s. Both the *caudatus* and *europaeus* races, and their hybrids, occur in the country.

Status: Resident. **Breeding season:** local. **Winter:** common. **Migration:** common. Protected.

Population trends: The breeding population is between 55,000 and 110,000 pairs, and has been stable over the past 20 years. The winter population is between 50,000 and 100,000 individuals.

Distribution: Nationwide. As a breeder, it may be less common in the following counties: KT, TC, LT, ZN, BE and ZR. During winter it infrequently occurs in the following counties: LN, LT, CV, TR, ZR, BR and OP.
Timing: All year round. Breeding occurs from mid-March until mid-June. Breeding peaks during mid-April.

Marsh Tit *Parus palustris*

Sykora babka Sykorka horna Sumpfmeise

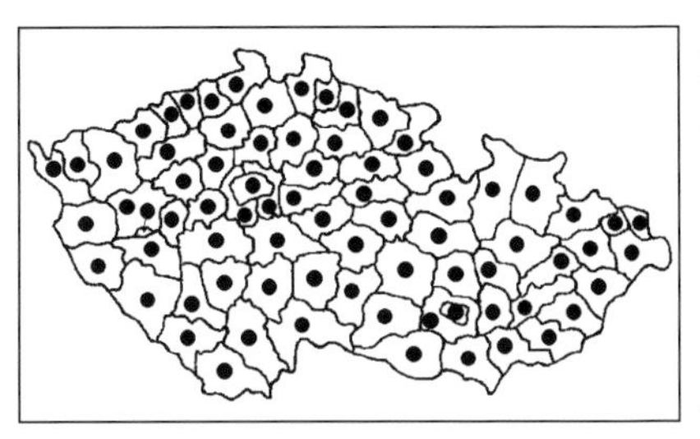

Although Marsh Tit is found throughout the country, it may be a quite uncommon species in some counties. It occurs in lowlands and highlands but, as a breeder, it has been found up to about 700 m in the Krusne hory mountains (CV, KV, MO, TP), to 750 m in the Orlicke hory mountains (RK), to 800 m in the Jeseniky (BR, SU), Krkonose (SE, TU) and Cesky les (DO, TC) mountains, to 1100 m in the Jizerske hory mountains (LB, JN), and to 1200 m in the Sumava mountains (CK, PT, KT). This species frequents deciduous (not too dense), less commonly mixed, moist rather than dry woodland, riverine forest, stands of mature trees with open undergrowth along rivers, large and mature orchards and parks all year round. Nests are usually built in cavities in oak, alder, mountain-ash or acacia, 0.5–5 m above ground. At the end of the 1970s and beginning of the 1980s, breeding density was 20–60 pairs per km^2 in an avenue of oak and growths along a brook (ST), 42 pairs per km^2 in growths along a brook in CK county, 4–9 pairs per km^2 in primeval fir-beech forest at about 900 m in VS county, 1 pair per km^2 in spruce-beech and spruce forest in the Krkonose mountains, 2 pairs per km^2 in spruce forest in the Cesky les mountains, 20 pairs per km^2 in pine forest around Tachov (TC), 26 pairs per km^2 in beech forest at the Cesky raj cliffs (MB), and 10–20 pairs per km^2 in various types of hedgerow in TC county. It was 26 and 25 pairs per km^2 respectively in a city park in Vsetin (VS) and Vizovice (ZL) at the end of the 1970s, and 1–17 pairs per km^2 in parkland around castles in w. and n. Bohemia during the 1980s and beginning of the 1990s. The following winter densities have been recorded: 3 individuals per km^2 in parks and gardens in Brno (BM) at the beginning of the 1970s, 5 individuals per km^2 in pine stands in TC county in the mid-1970s, 7–13 individuals per km^2 around a mountain village (VS) at about 720 m at the end of the 1970s and beginning of the 1980s, and 5–8 individuals per km^2 in mixed woods at about 180 m in UH county in the mid-1980s. The Czech population belongs to the *palustris* race.
Status: Resident. **Breeding season:** common. **Winter:** common. **Migration:** common. Protected.
Population trends: The breeding population is between 60,000 and 120,000 pairs. It declined slightly between the beginning of the 1980s and the 1990s. The number of wintering birds is between 50,000 and 100,000 individuals.
Distribution: Nationwide. As a breeder, it may be locally absent or scarce in the following counties: KV, LT, LN, PE, PB, JI, TR, ZR, ZN, SY and BK. Winter numbers may be low in the following counties: LT, ZN, TR, JI, ZR and BR.
Timing: All year round. Breeding starts during early April and continues until early July. Breeding peaks during late April and early May.

Willow Tit *Parus montanus*

Sykora luzni Sykorka ciernohlava Weidenmeise

Willow Tit has a patchy distribution across the Czech Republic, and is absent from some counties. Over the last 30-odd years, it has been expanding its range into previously unoccupied areas. It occurs in highlands and mountains, rarely in lowlands below 300 m. As a breeder, Willow Tit has been recorded up to 700 m in the Cesky les mountains (DO, TC), to about 800 m in the Jizerske hory (LB, JN), Krusne hory (CV, KV, MO, TP) and Krkonose (SE,

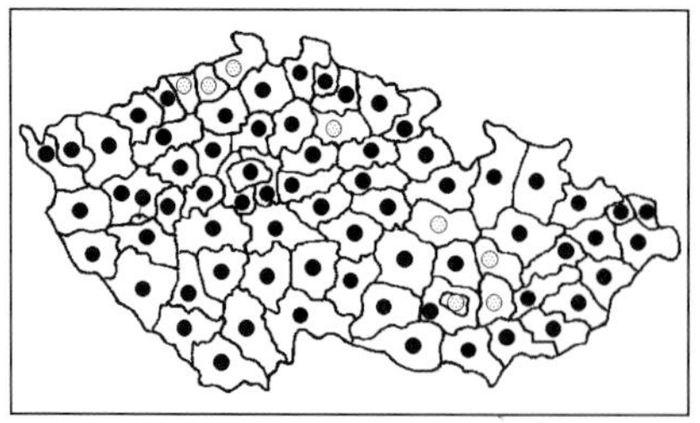

TU) mountains, to 1000 m in the Orlicke hory mountains (RK), to 1200 m in the the Beskydy (FM, VS) and Sumava (CK, PT, KT) mountains, and to 1300 m in the Jeseniky mountains (BR, SU). It is typically found in moist coniferous forest in mountains, and coniferous and mixed forest in highlands, preferring forest with plenty of decaying tree-stumps, and is less common in moist deciduous or mixed forest at lower altitudes. It is often found in willow- or alder-dominated growths along rivers and brooks. It stays in the same habitat all year round, but in winter can also be found in lowlands around open water, particularly in thickets with an undergrowth of nettles. Nests are placed in cavities in spruce, willow, birch or mountain-ash, 0.1–7 m above ground. Breeding density was 15 pairs per km^2 in growths along a brook in CV county, and 1–18 pairs per km^2 in fragments of forest along the Ohre river (LN) at the beginning of the 1970s, and 20 pairs per km^2 in a spruce plantation with stands of deciduous trees near Milevsko (TA) at the end of the 1970s. During the 1980s, it was 6 pairs per km^2 in willows and in thickets in meadows around Trebon (JH), 20–100 pairs per km^2 in various types of growth around Strakonice (ST), 118 pairs per km^2 and 84 individuals per km^2 respectively in growths along brooks in ST and CK counties, 20 pairs per km^2 in coniferous woods in farmland in TC county. In parks around several castles in w. and n. Bohemia it was 3–8 pairs per km^2 during the 1980s and beginning of the 1990s, and 3–13 pairs per km^2 in spruce forest at about 1100 m in the Beskydy mountains at the beginning of the 1990s. Winter density was 0–7 individuals per km^2 in primeval beech and fir forest at about 900 m in VS county at the end of the 1970s and beginning of the 1980s.

Status: Resident. **Breeding season:** local/common. **Winter:** common. **Migration:** common. Protected.

Population trends: The breeding population is between 40,000 and 80,000 pairs, and has been increasing for the past 20 years, with year-to-year fluctuations. The number of wintering birds is between 20,000 and 40,000 individuals.

Distribution: Nationwide. As a breeder, it is uncommon in the following counties: DO, SO, KV, KT, LN, LT, UL, DC, LB, JC, PB, CR, ZR, BK, SY, TR, ZN, BV, BM, HO, UH and VY. Wintering birds may be rather scarce in the following counties: TC, SO, LT, CL, DC, LB, KL, PM, PZ, JC, HK, KO, KH, CR, UO, SY, ZR, JI, TR, ZN, BK, VY and BR.

Timing: All year round. Breeding starts during mid-April and continues until mid-June, and peaks during late April.

Crested Tit *Parus cristatus*

Sykora parukarka Sykorka chochlata Haubenmeise

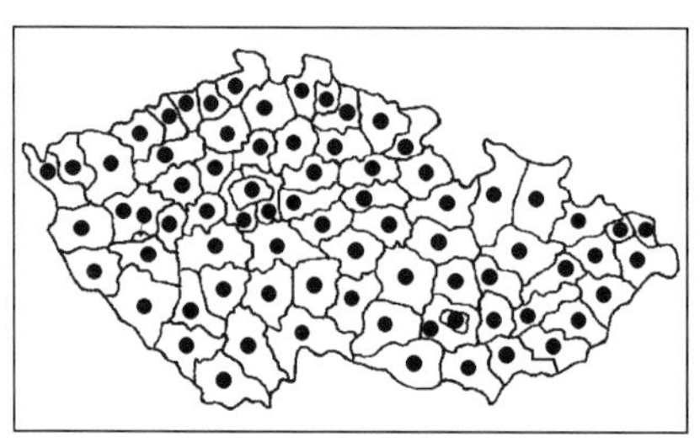

Crested Tit is a typical species of the highlands and mountains, occurring less commonly in lowlands. However, as a breeder it has also been recorded in pines at about 180 m in HO county. It is found up to the spruce tree-line in mountains, but breeding has been recorded at about 1000 m in the Jeseniky (BR, SU) and Krkonose (SE, TU) mountains, and to 1200 m in the Beskydy mountains (FM, VS). Typical habitats include mature spruce or pine, occasionally mixed, conifer-dominated forest. It does not occur in pure deciduous forest or in human settlements such as orchards and gardens. It may be found in larger parks with stands of mature conifers, particularly in winter. Nests are usually built in holes in spruce or pine, and quite often in tree-stumps, 0.1–1 m above ground. Breeding density was 6 pairs per km^2 in spruce forest in TP county at 800 m, and 19–38 pairs per km^2 in mixed conifer forest around Trebon (JH) at the beginning of the 1970s, and 8 pairs per km^2 in a mature spruce plantation near Milevsko (TA) at the end of the 1970s. During the 1980s, it was 3–14 and 1–4 pairs per km^2 respectively in acid-rain-damaged spruce forest in

the Jizerske hory (JN, LB) and Krkonose mountains, 7–9 individuals per km^2 in spruce forest in the Sumava mountains (CK, PT, KT), 1–25 pairs per km^2 in spruce and spruce-dwarf pine in TC county, 25 pairs per km^2 in pine forest in TC county, and 10–20 pairs per km^2 in mature pine forest in TA county. It was 3 pairs per km^2 in castle parkland at Blatna (ST), and 14 individuals per km^2 in mixed forest near Nymburk (NB) at the beginning of the 1990s. Winter density was 35–78 individuals per km^2 in mixed conifer forest around Trebon (JH) at the beginning of the 1970s, 3–11 individuals per km^2 in primeval fir-beech forest at about 900 m in VS county at the end of the 1970s and beginning of the 1980s, and 5 individuals per km^2 in mixed woods with mature spruce stands at 280 m in UH county at the beginning of the 1980s. The exact causes of its decline are unknown.
Status: Resident. **Breeding season:** common. **Winter:** common. **Migration:** common. Protected.
Population trends: The breeding population is between 80,000 and 160,000 pairs, and has declined by 20–50% during the past 20 years. The number of wintering birds is between 40,000 and 80,000 individuals.
Distribution: Nationwide. As a breeder, it is less common in the following counties: UL, LN, LT, HK, TR,VY, ZN, BV, HO, UH and PV. Wintering birds may occur less commonly in the following counties: CV, MO, LN, LT, KL,HK, BN, BR, BV, ZN, TR, ZR and BK.
Timing: All year round. Breeding starts during late March and continues until the end of June, peaking during early to mid-April and early to mid-June.

Coal Tit *Parus ater*

Sykora uhelnicek Sykorka uhliarka Tannenmeise

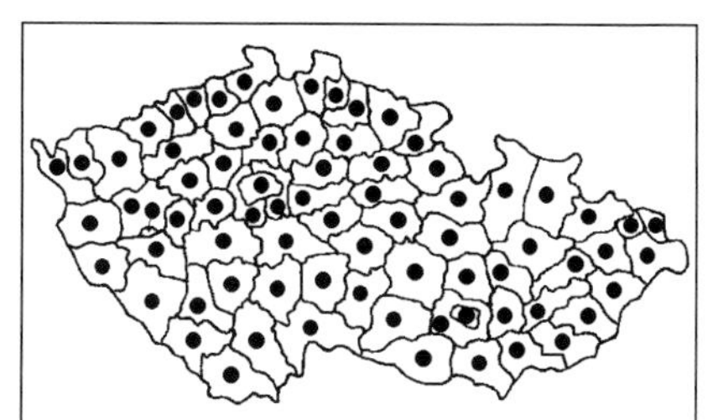

Coal Tit is found throughout the country, its density usually increasing with altitude. It occurs less commonly in lowlands, but breeding has been recorded in pines at about 180 m in HO county. In mountains, it is found up to the spruce tree-line, for example up to 1200 m in the Sumava mountains (CK, PT, KT), to 1250 m in the Beskydy mountains (FM, VS), 1300 m in the Jeseniky mountains (BR, SU), and to 1400 m in the Krkonose mountains (SE, TU), where breeding pairs were found in dwarf pines. Typical habitat all year round is mature coniferous forest; and it occurs less commonly in mixed woods with stands of mature conifers and, rarely, usually in winter, in larger parks and gardens with conifers. It seems to avoid purely deciduous woods. Nests are normally built in holes in spruce, maple, willow, acacia or horse chestnut, in stumps, on the ground, and in stone walls, usually 0–1 m above ground, but commonly up to 5 m above ground. It readily uses nest boxes. Breeding density was 31 pairs per km^2 in spruce forest in TP county at 800 m, and 18–94 pairs per km^2 in mixed conifer forest around Trebon (JH) at the beginning of the 1970s, 10–32 pairs per km^2 in mature spruces near Milevsko (TA), and 10–12 pairs per km^2 in parks in Praha (AA) at the end of the 1970s. During the 1980s, it was 3–14 pairs per km^2 and 5–10 pairs per km^2 respectively in mixed spruce forest in the Jizerske hory (LB, JN) and Krkonose mountains, 50–90 pairs per km^2 and 29–61 pairs per km^2 respectively in pine forest in TA and TC counties, 26–32 individuals per km^2 in the Sumava mountains, 3–20 pairs per km^2 in deciduous and mixed forest, and 0–30 pairs per km^2 in hedgerows in TC and ST counties. It was 43–53 pairs per km^2 in spruce-beech forest and 3–33 pairs per km^2 in spruce forest at about 1150 m in the Beskydy mountains at the beginning of the 1990s. Winter density was 110–120 individuals per km^2 and 19–51 individuals per km^2 respectively in mature spruce forest and pine forest near Trebon (JH) at the beginning of the 1970s, 69 individuals per km^2 in pines in TC county in the mid-1970s, 29–87 individuals per km^2 in primeval beech and fir forest at about 900 m in VS county at the end of the 1970s and beginning of the 1980s, and 10–60 individuals per km^2 in mixed, spruce-dominated mature forest at about 240 m in UH county at the beginning of the 1980s. The exact causes of Coal Tit's decline are unknown, although locally it may be acid-rain damage to forest.
Status: Resident. **Breeding season:** common. **Winter:** common. **Migration:** common. Protected.

Population trends: The breeding population is between 450,000 and 900,000 pairs, and has declined by 20–50% during the past 20 years. The number of breeding pairs may fluctuate both locally and nationwide from year to year. The number of wintering birds is between 300,000 and 600,000 individuals.
Distribution: Nationwide. Breeding pairs may be scarce locally in the following counties: BV, HO, UH, PV, KM, PR, HK, CR, LN, LT and TP. In winter it may occur less commonly in the following counties: KV, CV, LN, LT, KL, ZN, TR, SY, BK, BV and VY. High numbers of wintering birds have been recorded locally in the following counties: PB, PJ, DO, PS, RO, PI, JH, CB, PZ, TU, NA, UO, BO, VS, OL and OP.
Timing: All year round. Breeding extends from early April until early July, peaking during late April and early May, and in mid-June.

Blue Tit *Parus caeruleus*

Sykora modrinka Sykorka belasa Blaumeise

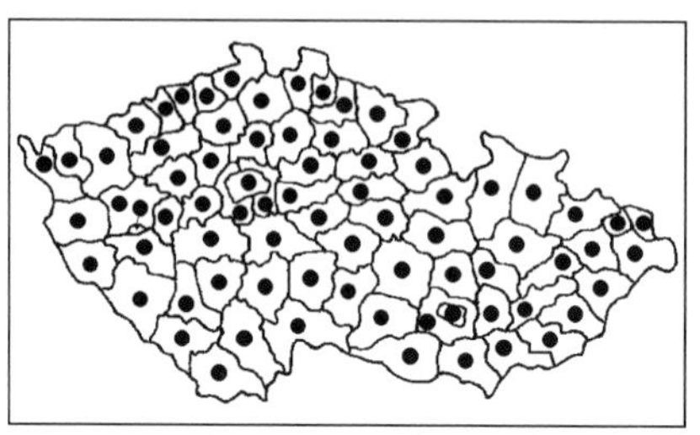

Blue Tit is a common bird throughout the country, with higher densities in lowlands and highlands than in mountains. As a breeder, it has been recorded up to 700 m in the Krusne hory mountains (CV, KV, MO, TP), to about 800 m in the Cesky les (DO, TC), Jeseniky (BR, SU) and Krkonose (SE, TU) mountains, to 950 m in the Orlicke hory mountains (RK), and to 1200 m in the Sumava mountains (CK, PT, KT). Outside the breeding season, it occasionally occurs at higher altitudes. Although this species utilizes a range of woodland habitats, it prefers not too dense deciduous and mixed forest with stands of mature trees. It also occurs in large parks, in hedgerows, orchards, avenues, and mature growths along rivers. Outside the breeding season, it can be found in reedbeds around ponds, in any type of growth in farmland, and in backyards around human settlements. This species rarely occurs in pure conifer plantations. Nests are frequently built in holes in willows or alders, in cracks and crevices in walls, and in stumps, 1–5 m above ground. Breeding density may vary markedly among habitats: it was 25 pairs per km^2 in alder stands, 25 pairs per km^2 in spruce-pine plantations, 7 pairs per km^2 in pine plantations, and 73–100 pairs per km^2 in mature stands of oak around Trebon (JH) at the beginning of the 1970s; at the end of the 1970s, it was 10–20 pairs per km^2 in a mature spruce plantation near Milevsko (TA), and 14–91 pairs per km^2 in avenues of deciduous trees in the Cesky les mountains, and in parks in Praha (AA) it was 11–68 pairs per km^2. During the 1980s, in riverine forest, it was 78 pairs per km^2 in ST county, 120 pairs per km^2 in KM county, and 120–250 individuals per km^2 in OL county, in oaks and growths along a brook in ST county it was 334–356 individuals per km^2, in oak avenues around ponds in CB county it was 100–232 pairs per km^2, in pine stands in TC county it was 4–32 pairs per km^2, in oak forest near Nachod (NA) and Most (MO) it was 6 and 72 pairs per km^2 respectively, and 25 pairs per km^2 in poplar-dominated windbreaks and in hedgerows in farmland in UH county. It was 36–167 pairs per km^2 in parks around several castles in w. Bohemia during the 1980s and beginning of the 1990s. In mature deciduous and mixed forest in NB county it was 17–109 individuals per km^2 at the beginning of the 1990s. Winter density was 150–310 individuals per km^2 in mature stands of oaks, 0–4 individuals per km^2 in spruce plantations, and 19–28 individuals per km^2 in pine plantations around Trebon (JH) at the beginning of the 1970s, 33 individuals per km^2 in pine plantations in TC county in the mid-1970s, 6–130 individuals per km^2 in a beech forest in the Cesky les mountains (TC) in the mid-1970s, 2–3 individuals per km^2 in primeval beech and fir forest at about 900 m in VS county at the end of the 1970s and beginning of the 1980s, and 126 individuals per km^2 in poplar-dominated windbreaks and in hedgerows in farmland in UH county in the mid-1980s. Wintering birds are joined by populations from n. Europe. Factors causing the decline of Blue Tit are unknown.
Status:´ Resident. **Breeding season:** common. **Winter:** common. **Migration:** common. Protected.
Population trends: The breeding population is between 800,000 and 1,600,000 pairs, and has

declined by 20–50% during the past 20 years. The number of wintering birds ranges from 1,000,000 to 2,000,000 individuals.
Distribution: Nationwide. In winter, it may occur locally less commonly in the following counties: LN, PE, JI, TR, ZR, BR and OP. High winter numbers have been reported from the following counties: JH, CB, PJ, PS, CH, CV, MO, TP, UL, CL, LB, JC, SE, MB, NB, PZ, PH, AA, SU, BO, BM, KI, PR and UH.
Timing: All year round. Breeding starts at the beginning of April and continues until mid-July, with peaks at the end of April and in early June.

Azure Tit *Parus cyanus*

Sykora azurova Sykorka lazurova Lasurmeise

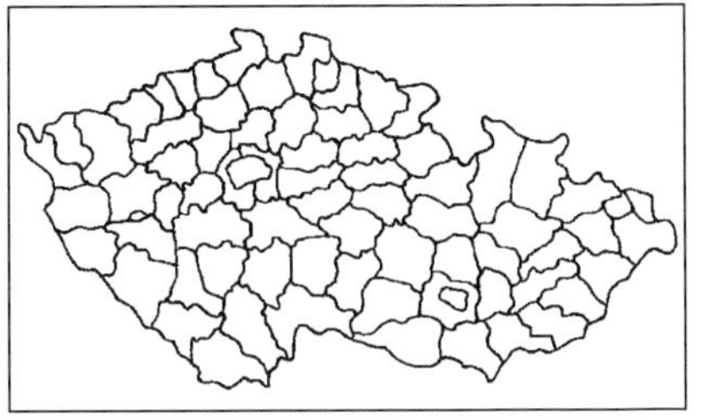

As an occasional autumn and winter visitor, Azure Tit does not occur in the Czech Republic annually. Usually single, 2, or rarely more, join flocks of other *Parus* species. Azure Tit prefers growths along rivers and around other open water, parks, and groups of trees in farmland. There are fewer than 20 records for the Czech Republic since 1800.
Status: Vagrant. **Breeding season:** rare. **Winter:** rare. **Migration:** rare. Protected.
Population trends: No data available.
Distribution: May occur nationwide. No current records.
Timing: It has been recorded from mid-October until early March, with maximum numbers in November.

Great Tit *Parus major*

Sykora konadra Sykorka velka Kohlmeise

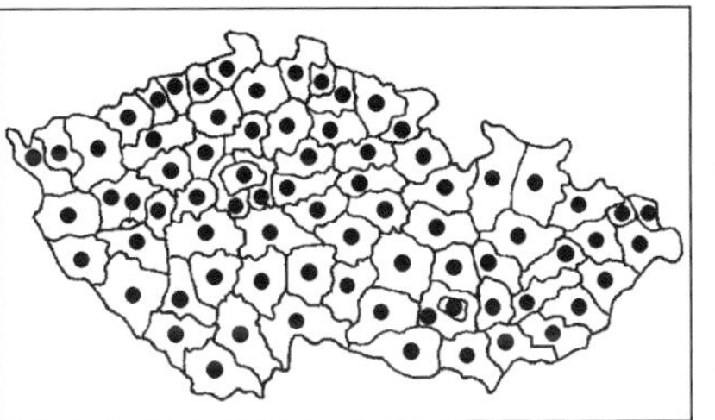

Great Tit is one of the commonest birds in the Czech Republic. As a breeder, it is distributed from lowlands up to about 900 m in the Orlicke hory mountains (RK), to 1000 m in the Jeseniky (BR, SU) and Krkonose (SE, TU) mountains, and to 1200 m in the Krusne hory (CV, KV, MO, TP) and Sumava (CK, PT, KT) mountains. At higher altitudes, from about 850 m, its density usually decreases, and Coal Tit then becomes the most common *Parus* species. All year round, Great Tits use a wide range of habitats, including any type of forest, preferably deciduous with undergrowth, avenues, growths along rivers, hedgerows, windbreaks, woodland in farmland, orchards, gardens, parks and cemeteries. Nests are built in any type of natural, or man-made hole, cavity or crevice. It readily occupies nest boxes. The nest is usually built 1–3 m above ground. Breeding density was 11 pairs per km^2 in alder stands, 2 pairs per km^2 in spruce-pine dominated plantations, 7 pairs per km^2 in pine plantations, and 19–42 pairs per km^2 in mature stands of oak around Trebon (JH) at the beginning of the 1970s, 8–40 pairs per km^2 in a mature spruce plantation near Milevsko (TA), 74–170 pairs per km^2 in deciduous avenues in the Cesky les mountains (DO, TC), and 17–170 pairs per km^2 in parks in Praha (AA) at the end of the 1970s. During the 1980s, it was 3–39 pairs per km^2 and 10–40 pairs per km^2 respectively in pine forest in TC and TA counties, 26 pairs per km^2 and 60 pairs per km^2 respectively in beech forest at the Cesky raj cliff (MB) and Krusne hory mountains, 120–165 pairs per km^2 and 160–235 individuals per km^2 respectively in riverine forest in central and n. Moravia, 1–5 pairs per km^2 in acid-rain-damaged spruce forest in the Krkonose mountains, 9–30 pairs per km^2 in fir-beech mountain forest in the Beskydy mountains (FM, VS), and 35–43 pairs per km^2 in poplar-dominated windbreaks and hedgerows in farmland in UH county. It was 30–170 pairs per km^2 and 10–120 pairs per km^2 respectively in various types of growths in farmland in TC and ST counties, and 46–225 pairs per km² in parkland around castles in w. Bohemia during the 1980s. Winter density was 15–53 individuals per km² in mature stands of oaks, 0–4 individuals per km² in alders, and 4–24 individuals per km² in pine plantations around Trebon (JH) at the beginning of the 1970s, 40 individuals per km² in pine plantations in TC county in the mid-1970s, 43–63 individuals per km² in beech forest in the Cesky les mountains in the mid-1970s, 0–11 individuals per km² in primeval beech and fir forest at about 900 m in VS county, and 77–88 individuals per km² in a mountain village at 730 m in VS county at the end of the 1970s and beginning of the 1980s, and 161 individuals per km² in poplar-dominated windbreaks and hedgerows in farmland in UH county in the mid-1980s.

Status: Resident. **Breeding season:** common. **Winter:** common. **Migration:** common. Protected.

Population trends: The breeding population is between 3,000,000 and 6,000,000 pairs, and has been relatively stable during the past 20 years, although there has been a slight increase since the mid-1980s. The number of wintering birds ranges from 2,000,000 to 4,000,000 individuals.

Distribution: Nationwide. High numbers of wintering birds have been reported from the following counties: JH, CB, CK, TA, PI, BN, PB, PZ, PH, AA, BE, UL, TP, JN, JC, SE, TU, NA, RK, UO, BO, BM, UH, ZL, VS, FM, OV and KI.

Timing: All year round. Breeding starts during early April and continues until mid-July, peaking during late April and early May, and mid- to late June.

European Nuthatch *Sitta europaea*

Nuthatch, Eurasian Nuthatch   Brhlik lesni   Brhlik obycajny   Kleiber

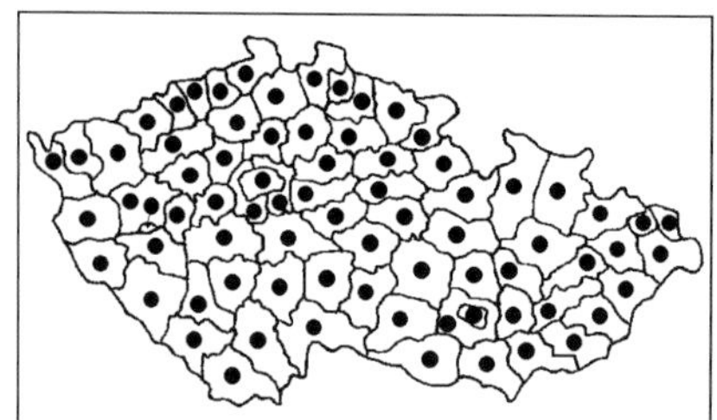

European Nuthatch is a common species throughout the country, except locally in treeless areas. It occurs from lowlands up to 700 m in the Krusne hory mountains (CV, KV, MO, TP), to 800 m in the Cesky les mountains (DO, TC), to 1000 m in the Krkonose (SE, TU) and Orlicke hory (RK) mountains to 1070 in the Jeseniky mountains (BR, SU), to 1150 m in the Beskydy mountains (FM, VS), and to 1200 m in the Sumava mountains (CK, PT, KT). Its density decreases at higher altitudes, where it usually occurs in beech forest. It is typically found in mature deciduous and mixed forest, in large parks and orchards, avenues with old trees, and in mature growths along rivers and around ponds. Breeding in rock crevices at Kokorinsko (ME) has also been recorded. In winter, it occurs more commonly in human habitations such as backyards and gardens. Conifer plantations, or mixed, conifer-dominated forest are less favoured all year round. Nests are frequently built in holes in oak, spruce, pine or alder, 2–4 m above ground. Nuthatches often associate with flocks of Great Tits and Blue Tits at feeders in winter. Breeding density varies between habitats: it was 20–38 pairs per km² in riverine forest in central Moravia, and 102–108 pairs per km² in fragments of forest along the Ohre river (LN) at the beginning of the 1970s, 13–35 pairs per km² in primeval beech and fir forest at about 900 m in VS county, and 10–20 pairs per km² in a mature spruce plantation near Milevsko (TA) at the end of the 1970s. During the 1970s, in city parks with mature trees, breeding density was 28–63 pairs per km² in Vizovice (ZL), 10–38 pairs per km² in Vsetin (VS), and 28 pairs per km² in Lesna (ZL). During the 1980s, it was 80–133 individuals per km² in riverine forest in central Moravia, 18 pairs per km² in an oak forest in MO county, 30 pairs per km² and 52 pairs per km² respectively in beech forest in the Krusne hory mountains and at the Cesky raj cliffs (MB), 50–70 individuals per km² in mixed mountain forest in the Sumava mountains, 29–45 pairs per km² in a variety of mixed woodland in PI county, 66 individuals per km² and 110–118 individuals per km² in mixed mature growths in CK and ST counties, 45–60 pairs per km² in a mature mixed forest in the Bile Karpaty mountains (HO, UH, ZL) at about 600 m, and 25 pairs per km² in poplar-dominated windbreaks and in hedgerows in farmland in UH county. In city parks in Ostrava (OV) and Tachov (TC) it was 4 and 15–72 pairs per km², and in parks around castles in w. and n. Bohemia it was 30–150 pairs per km² during the 1980s and begin-

ning of the 1990s. Winter density was 90–119 individuals per km^2 in mature stands of oak, 21–77 individuals per km^2 in alders, 4–12 individuals per km^2 in spruce plantations, and 19–24 individuals per km^2 in pine plantations around Trebon (JH) at the beginning of the 1970s, 15 individuals per km^2 in pine plantations in TC county in the mid-1970s, 33–91 individuals per km^2 in beech forest in the Cesky les mountains (TC) in the mid-1970s, 34–58 individuals per km^2 in a primeval beech and fir forest at about 900 m in VS county, and 2–3 individuals per km^2 in a mountain village at 730 m in VS county at the end of the 1970s and beginning of the 1980s, 10–15 individuals per km^2 in mixed woods at 280 m in UH county, and 26 individuals per km^2 in poplar-dominated windbreaks and hedgerows in farmland in UH county at the end of the 1980s.
Status: Resident. **Breeding season**: common. **Winter**: common. **Migration**: common. Protected.
Population trends: The breeding population ranges from 600,000 to 1,200,000 pairs, and has been stable during the past 20 years, although year-to-year fluctuations occur. The number of wintering birds is between 400,000 and 800,000 individuals.
Distribution: Nationwide. As a breeder, it may be less common locally in ZN, BE, PB, CL and LN counties. In winter it may occur less frequently locally in KV, LN, RA, ZN, TR, ZR, SY, BK and BR counties. High winter numbers have been reported from the following counties: AA, PZ, PH, BN, PJ, PB, PI, JH, CB, RK, UO, BM, BO, UH, OV, KI and NJ.
Timing: All year round. Breeding starts at the end of March and continues until mid-June, peaking during the last 20 years of April.

Wallcreeper *Tichodroma muraria*

Zednicek skalni Murarik cervenokridly Mauerläufer

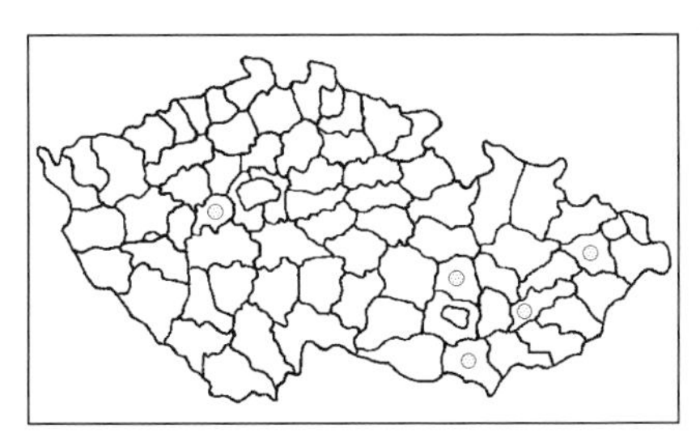

Wallcreeper is a rare species in the Czech Republic. Although birds have been recorded during the breeding season, actual breeding has never been recorded. Typical habitats where Wallcreeper can be found include rocks, walls of castles and ruins, and quarries. It is more likely to be found in the east of the country. One of the regular sites where it can be found is in the Palava hills (BV) with its limestone rocks, where usually solitary birds may occur all year round. Wallcreeper is more common in Slovakia where the breeding population is between 30 and 50 pairs (Murin *et al.* 1994).
Status: Vagrant. **Breeding season**: rare. **Winter**: uncommon/local. **Migration**: uncommon. Protected.
Population trends: No data available. Up to 5 individuals are reported annually.
Distribution: May occur nationwide. Recent winter, and early spring records of solitary birds come from Hostim (BE), Blansko-Moravsky kras (BK), Bystrice pod Hostynem (KM), the Palava hills (BV), Koprivnice (NJ), and Klentnice (BV). Three solitary birds were recorded at Srbsko (BE) in 1997.
Timing: Recorded all year round. However, the majority of recent records are from the beginning of November and early April.

Eurasian Treecreeper *Certhia familiaris*

Treecreeper Soupalek dlouhoprsty Korovnik dlhoprsty Waldbaumläufer

Even though Eurasian Treecreeper occurs across the country from lowlands to the mountains, its strongholds are in the highlands and mountains. As a breeder, it has been recorded up to 1000 m in the Orlicke hory mountains (RK), to 1180 m in the Beskydy mountains (FM, VS), to 1200 m in the Sumava mountains (CK, PT, KT), and to 1300 m in the Jeseniky mountains (BR, SU). Breeding habitat is dense, young coniferous forest. However, breeding in mixed forest, avenues, and in large and mature parks is quite common. In lowlands, this species occurs in mature, broadleaved forest, including riverine forest. During winter, it stays in the same

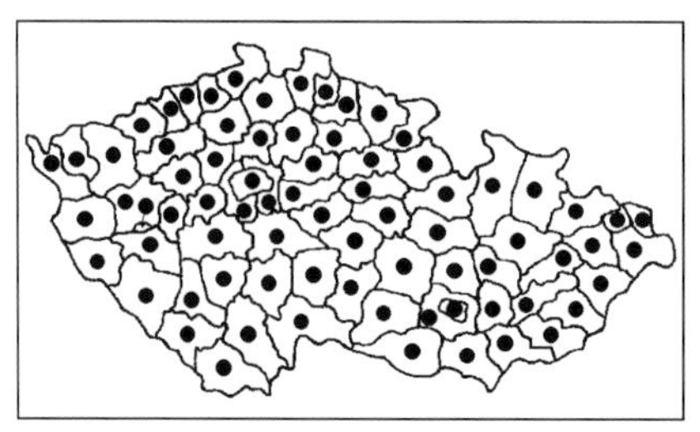

habitats, but also occurs more commonly in mixed and purely deciduous forest. Nests are frequently placed in trees such as spruce, acacia, oak, willow, pine and hornbeam, in piles of logs, and in crevices in cabins and cottages, 0.5–1.5 m above ground. Breeding density varies between counties and habitats: it was 19–58 pairs per km^2 in mature pine and spruce forest around Trebon (JH), and 6–11 pairs per km^2 in riverine forest in KM county at the beginning of the 1970s. During the 1980s, it was 4–65 individuals per km^2 in various types of forest in the Sumava mountains, 0–16 pairs per km^2 in spruce and mixed forest at about 1100 m in the Beskydy mountains, 1–4 pairs per km^2 in acid-rain-damaged spruce and spruce-beech forest in the Krkonose mountains (SE, TU), 26 pairs per km^2 in beech forest at the Cesky raj cliffs (MB), 20–40 pairs per km^2 in pine forest in TA county, 24 pairs per km^2 and 20 pairs per km^2 respectively in oak forest in MO and PI counties, 22 pairs per km^2 in riverine forest in NJ county, and 21–30 pairs per km^2 in a mixed forest in the Bile Karpaty mountains (HO, UH, ZL) at 710 m. It was 9–31 individuals per km^2 in oak and mixed forest near Mlada (NB) at the beginning of the 1990s. Winter density was 0–24 individuals per km^2 in spruce plantations, and 8–15 individuals per km^2 in pine plantations around Trebon (JH) at the beginning of the 1970s, 27 individuals per km^2 in pine plantations in TC county in the mid-1970s, 7–14 individuals per km^2 in primeval beech and fir forest at about 900 m in VS county at the end of the 1970s and beginning of the 1980s, and 3 individuals per km^2 in mixed woods at 280 m in UH county at the end of the 1980s. Wintering birds are joined by individuals from n. Europe. Individuals of the breeding population belong to the *macrodactyla* race.

Status: Resident. **Breeding season:** common. **Winter:** common. **Migration:** common. Protected.

Population trends: The breeding population is between 300,000 and 600,000 pairs, and has declined by 20–50% during the past 20 years. The number of wintering birds ranges from 40,000 to 80,000 individuals.

Distribution: Nationwide. As a breeder, it may be less common locally in the following counties: DC, SO, TC, LB, LN, LT, ZN, TR, BK, CR, VY and BV. Wintering birds may be missing or occur less commonly in the following counties: SO, CV, LN, LT, DC, RA, KL, ZN, TR, CR and BR.

Timing: All year round. Breeding starts during early April, and ends by mid-June. Breeding peaks during late April and late May.

Short-toed Treecreeper *Certhia brachydactyla*

Soupalek kratkoprsty   Korovnik kratkoprsty   Gartenbaumläufer

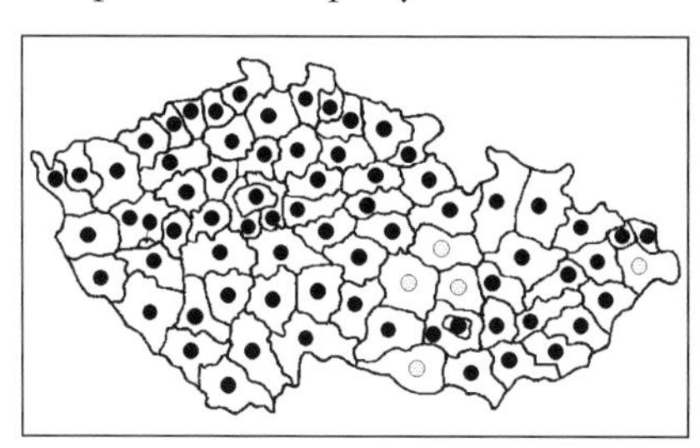

This species is less common than Eurasian Treecreeper in the Czech Republic. In suitable habitats, where their distribution overlaps, the breeding density of both may be approximately the same. Short-toed Treecreeper is distributed across the country, being more abundant in lowlands than at higher altitudes. As a breeder, it has been recorded at up to 450 m in the Ceskomoravska vysocina highlands (HB, JI, PE, ZR), to 500 m in the Cesky les mountains (DO, TC), the foothills of the Jeseniky (BR, SU) and Krkonose (SE, TU) mountains, and to 1000 m in the Sumava mountains (CK, PT, KT). It is found in not too dense deciduous, mixed, oak-dominated forest, riverine forest, larger parks, mature growths around water and in avenues. Occasionally it occurs in pure conifer plantations. Nests are usually placed in trees such as poplar, willow, oak and lime, in holes in cabins, and in piles of logs, 1–2.5 m above ground. Breeding density was 11–13 pairs per km^2 in riverine forest in KM county at the beginning of the 1970s, 2–6 pairs per km^2 in fragments of forest along the Ohre river (LN), and 4 pairs per km^2 in an oak-dom-

inated forest in the Ceske Stredohori highlands (LN, LT) in the mid-1970s. During the 1980s, it was 2 pairs per km² and 59–100 individuals per km² in riverine forest in central and n. Moravia, 15–30 pairs per km² in oak forest around Most (MO), 12–37 pairs per km² in various types of deciduous forest in PI county, 100–120 pairs per km² in growths of mature trees in ST county, and 28–83 pairs per km² in parkland around castles in w. and n. Bohemia. Winter density was 17–20 individuals per km² in mixed woods at 220 m in UH county in the mid-1980s. Individuals occurring in the Czech Republic belong to the *brachydactyla* race.
Status: Resident. **Breeding season:** local/common. **Winter:** common. **Migration:** common. Protected.
Population trends: The breeding population is between 75,000 and 150,000 pairs, and has been stable during the past 20 years. The number of wintering birds ranges from 40,000 to 80,000 individuals.
Distribution: Nationwide. As a breeder, it may be uncommon in the following counties: PT, KT, SO, RA, TP, CL, ME, JN, TU, ZN, TR, ZR, BK, SY, UO, SU, VS, FM and PV. In winter, it may occur less commonly in PT, SO, CV, MO, LT, JN, JC, HB and PV counties.
Timing: All year round. Breeding starts at the beginning of April and continues until the end of May, peaking during mid-April.

Penduline Tit *Remiz pendulinus*

Eurasian Penduline Tit Moudivlacek luzni Kudelnicka luzna Beutelmeise

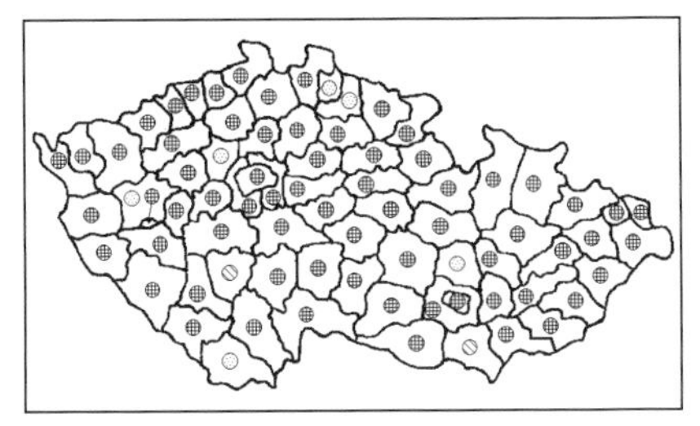

At the beginning of the 20th century, Penduline Tit was rare in the Czech Republic, occasionally breeding at a few places and gradually expanding its range. Major expansion occurred between 1940 and 1960, when breeding was recorded in suitable habitats across the country. It is distributed mainly in lowlands, but is also recorded up to 500 m in CR county and in the foothills of the Krkonose mountains (SE, TU), and to 630 m in ZR county. It is found in mature trees along rivers, at canals, ponds, lakes, and the edges of ponds with reedbeds and stands of trees, in riverine forest, and in poplars. Occasionally it is found in ditches lined with young trees in fields, and even in drier areas away from water. Nests are usually placed in a willow, alder, poplar or birch, 2–6 m

Penduline Tits

above ground. Breeding density was 80 individuals per km^2 in windbreaks in BV county, 10 pairs per km^2 in hedgerows in TC county, 8–130 pairs per km^2 in growths around ponds in CB county, 3–4 pairs per km^{2s} around a pond in DO county during the 1980s and beginning of the 1990s. There were 3 active nests along a 1-km transect of willow-dominated vegetation along a river in UH county in the mid-1980s, and 7 active nests along a 1-km transect of mixed willow and poplar around Nesyt pond (BV) at the end of the 1980s. Areas with high numbers of breeding pairs include ponds around Pardubice (PU), Hradec Kralove (HK), Ceske Budejovice (CB), Lednicke ponds (BV), with dozens of pairs, and the area between Jesenik nad Odrou (NJ) and Ostrava (OV), with up to 100 pairs. After breeding, individuals form flocks of varying size, usually up to 20–25 birds, frequenting edges of ponds with reedbeds.
Status: Migrant and summer visitor. **Breeding season:** local/common. **Winter:** uncommon. **Migration:** local/common. Least concern. Protected.
Population trends: The breeding population is between 2,500 and 5,000 pairs. It has increased by 20–50% during the past 20 years. Occasional wintering of up to 5 individuals may occur.
Distribution: On migration, may occur nationwide. Regular breeding of large numbers is restricted to the following counties: JH, CB, ST, CV, MO, TP, LT, HK, PU, KO, NB, ME, ME, UO, ZN, BV, HO, UH, KM, PR, BO, OL, NJ, OV and KI.
Timing: Spring migration starts during late March, and continues until the end of April, peaking at the end of March and beginning of April. Autumn migration occurs between mid-September and the end of October, peaking during mid-October. Breeding extends from mid-April to the end of June, peaking during early to mid-May.

Golden Oriole *Oriolus oriolus*

Eurasian Golden Oriole   Zluva hajni   Vlha obycajna   Pirol

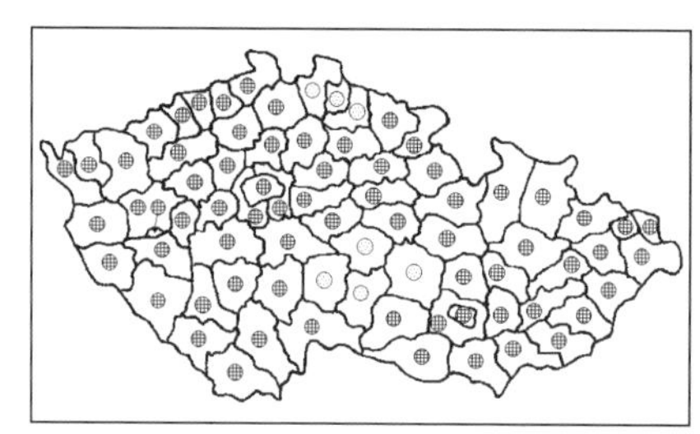

Golden Oriole is a regular but locally rather uncommon breeder in the Czech Republic. It occurs in lowlands and highlands, but has been recorded up to 490 m in the Cesky les mountains (DO, TC), to 500 m in the Krusne hory mountains (CV, KV, MO, TP), to 600 m in the Orlicke hory mountains (RK), to 700 m in the Krkonose mountains (SE, TU), to 800 m in the Sumava mountains (CK, PT, KT), and to 1100 m in beech forest in the Beskydy mountains (FM, VM). It is found in open deciduous, less commonly mixed, forest, mature growths along rivers and around ponds, large mature avenues, parks, orchards and gardens, and windbreaks in farmland. This species avoids large, dense woodland and

Golden Oriole

coniferous forest. Nests are usually placed in oak, acacia, alder or ash, 5–10 m above ground. At the beginning of the 1970s, breeding density was 14–15 individuals per km^2 in abandoned orchards, and 19 individuals per km^2 in growths along rivers in CV county, and 3–50 individuals per km^2 in growths around ponds near Trebon (JH). During the 1980s and beginning of the 1990s, it was 30–60 pairs per km^2 in windbreaks and avenues in ST county, 40 individuals per km^2 in windbreaks in BV county, 10–40 pairs per km^2 and 26 individuals per km^2 in riverine forest in central and n. Moravia, and 5 pairs per km^2 in riverine forest in ST county, 3–25 pairs per km^2 in parkland around castles in w. and n. Bohemia, 18–20 pairs per km^2 in stands of mature poplar and willows along a river near Podoli (UH), 10 pairs per km^2 in poplar-dominated windbreaks and in hedgerows in farmland (UH) at about 180 m, and 23–33 individuals per km^2 in various types of deciduous and mixed forest near Mlada (NB).
Status: Migrant and summer visitor. **Breeding season:** common. **Winter:** does not occur. **Migration:** common. Protected.
Population trends: The breeding population is between 8,000 and 16,000 pairs, and has been stable during the past 20 years.
Distribution: Nationwide. Breeding pairs are rather scarce in the following counties: CK, KT, TC, SO, LB, JN, PB, BN, PE, JI, ZR, HB, BR, VS, FM and BK.
Timing: Spring arrival starts in mid-April, and continues until mid-May, peaking during late April and early May. Autumn departure occurs between early August and mid-September, peaking during late August. Breeding extends from mid-May until early July, peaking during late May and early June.

Red-backed Shrike *Lanius collurio*

Tuhyk obecny Strakos obycajny Neuntöter

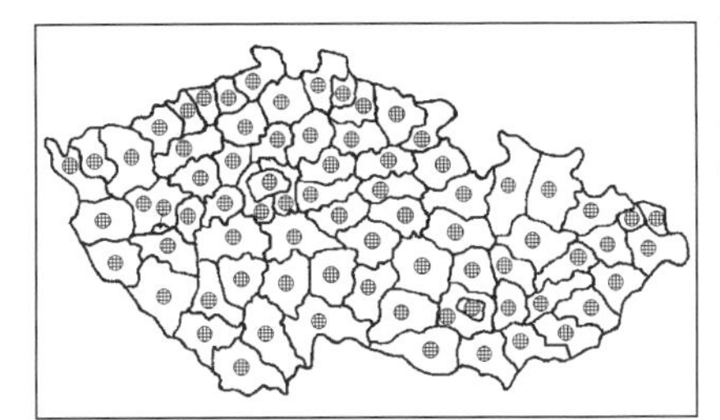

Red-backed Shrike is found throughout the country, but its numbers vary widely from place to place. It occurs from lowlands, which are preferred to higher altitudes, up to 700 m in the Cesky les mountains (DO, TC), to 750 m in the Orlicke hory mountains (RK), to 900 m in Krusne hory mountains (CV, KV, MO, TP), to 1000 m in the Jeseniky (BR, SU) and Krkonose (SE, TU) mountains, and to 1150 m in the Sumava (CK, PT, KT) and Beskydy (FM, VS) mountains. Typical breeding habitats include open terrain, hillsides, pastures with bushes and thorn hedges, hedgerows along county roads, railways, ditches and vineyards, wet meadows with bushes, edges of deciduous or mixed forest and, occasionally, larger orchards, gardens and cemeteries. It generally avoids forest but may be found in clearings or in young spruce. Nests are usually built in blackthorn or rose, 0.5 to 2.5 m above ground. Breeding density was 6 pairs per km^2 in spruce along a brook at 700–790 m in the Krusne hory mountains at the beginning of 1970s. It was 20 pairs per km^2 in bushes on a hillside in the Bile Karpaty mountains (HO, UH, ZL) at about 600 m in the mid-1980s, and 35 pairs per km^2 on a hillside with abandoned orchards near Podoli (UH) at about 210 m at the end of the 1970s; however, 10 years later, the breeding density was only 8 pairs per km^2 (the habitat was relatively unchanged). In the foothills of the Beskydy mountains breeding density was 10–13 pairs per km^2, in pastures in the Krkonose mountains 33 pairs per km^2, in PI county 2–2.5 pairs per km^2, in VS county 2 pairs per km^2, in highlands in KV county 11 pairs per km^2, and in various biotopes around Mlada (NB) 12–33 individuals per km^2 during the 1980s and beginning of the 1990s. Breeding density in 1996 was as follows: 2–2.25 pairs per km^2 in UO county, 1.9 pairs per km^2 in RA county, 1.4–1.6 pairs per km^2 in TU county, 2–2.5 pairs per km^2 in VS county, 0.8–1.0 pairs per km^2 in TP county, 2.5–2.7 pairs per km^2 in TR county, 0.2–0.3 pairs per km^2 in ST county, 4.8 pairs per km^2 in BN county, 2–2.4 pairs per km^2 in NA county, 3.2–3.6 pairs per km^2 in DO county, and 3.8–4.1 pairs per km^2 in ZL county (Holan 1997). These numbers do not reflect overall density in a county, but rather density from certain sites. The breeding population has been declining since the 1970s. The most likely causes of the decrease are habitat destruction and deterioration, increased use of pesticides, and a decline in prey diversity. However, Holan (1997)

suggested the population decline has stopped recently, and numbers of Red-backed Shrikes are increasing in some counties.
Status: Migrant and summer visitor. **Breeding season:** common. **Winter:** does not occur. **Migration:** common. Conservation-dependent. Protected.
Population trends: The breeding population ranges from 25,000 to 50,000 pairs, and has declined by 20–50% during the last 20 years.
Distribution: Nationwide. Counties with high numbers of breeding pairs include UO, TU, VS, FM, PZ, DO, PI, UH, NA, BV and BN. For example, in the Beskydy mountains the population is estimated to be between 400 and 500 pairs.
Timing: Spring migration occurs from late April until mid-May, peaking during early May. Autumn migration starts during mid-August, and continues until early October, and peaks during the first half of September. Birds are rare after early October.

Great Grey Shrike *Lanius excubitor*

Tuhyk sedy Strakos velky Raubwürger

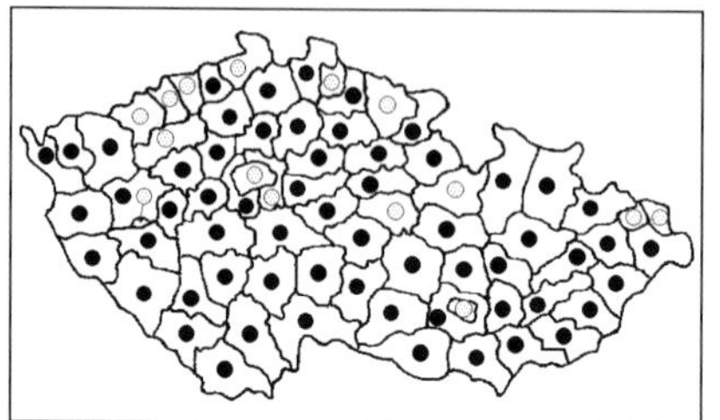

Although Great Grey Shrike has been expanding its range in the Czech Republic since about the mid-1940s, it is an uncommon species with patchy distribution across the country. During the past 50 years or so, it has expanded its range from highlands into lowlands, and into areas in the southeast of the country. Nowadays, it occurs from lowlands up to 570 m in the Jeseniky mountains (BR, SU), to 600 m in the Orlicke hory mountains (RK), to 700 m in the Cesky les mountains (DO, TC), and to 800 m in the Krkonose (SE, TU), Krusne hory (CV, KV, MO, TP) and Sumava (CK, PT, KT) mountains. The majority of the breeding population can be found in highlands, for example in the Ceskomoravska vysocina highlands (HB, JI, PE, ZR), where it regularly breeds between 450 and 650 m. It prefers open country, and is found in wet meadows and pastures with windbreaks, bushes and clusters of trees. It also breeds in not too dense growths along canals and rivers, around ponds, and at the edges of woods in farmland. During winter, it occurs more commonly in lowlands, often along roadsides and railways, than at higher altitudes. Nests are usually placed in spruce, pine or poplar, 2–10 m above ground. Breeding density was 0.1 pairs per km^2 in lowlands in HO county between the mid-1970s and end of the 1980s, 10 pairs per km^2 in hedgerows in TC county at the end of the 1970s and beginning of the 1980s, 1.5 pairs per km^2 in poplar-dominated windbreaks at 260 m in UH county in the mid-1980s, 0.17 pairs per km^2 in the Sumava mountains, and 1.3–1.6 pairs per km^2 in various habitats around Mlada (NB) at the beginning of the 1990s. Winter density was 3–7 individuals per km^2 in farmland at about 420 m in the foothills of the Bile Karpaty mountains (HO, UH, ZL) in the mid-1980s, and 4 individuals per km^2 in poplar-dominated windbreaks and hedgerows in farmland (UH) at the end of the 1980s. The most likely causes of its decline are habitat degradation and reduced food availability caused by agricultural intensification. Most individuals of the breeding population are migratory, and those that remain are presumably joined by birds from ne. Europe. The breeding population belongs to the *excubitor* race. A few individuals of the *homeyeri* race have been collected.
Status: Resident. **Breeding season:** uncommon/local (*excubitor*), rare (*homeyeri*). **Winter:** local/common (*excubitor*), rare (*homeyeri*). **Migration:** local (*excubitor*), rare (*homeyeri*). Vulnerable. Protected.
Population trends: The breeding population is between 1,000 and 2,000 pairs, and has declined by 20–50% during the past 20 years, although at the beginning of the 1970s it had been increasing slowly. The number of wintering birds ranges from 3,000 to 6,000 individuals.
Distribution: Nationwide. As a breeder, it may be rare in the following counties: CV, LN, LT, MO, TP, LB, JN, TU, PH, AA, BM, HK, NA, CR, UO, ZN, BV, BO, BK, VY, PV, SY, UO, SU, BR, PR, VS, ZL, KI, KM, OL and FM. In winter it occurs less commonly in CV, LN, LT, ME, PE, HB, CR, BR, OP, VS and FM counties.

Timing: All year round. Breeding extends from early April until late May, peaking during mid- to late April.

Eurasian Jay *Garrulus glandarius*

Jay   Sojka obecna   Sojka obycajna   Eichelhäher

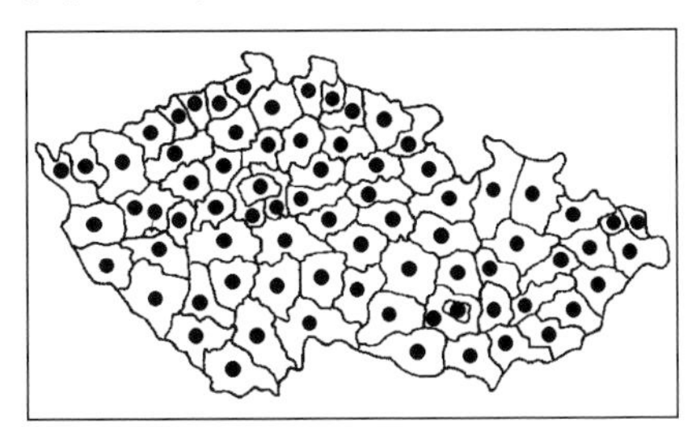

Eurasian Jay is a common, locally abundant permanent resident, distributed throughout the country. As a breeder, it occurs from lowlands up to 500 m in the Krusne hory mountains (CV, KV, MO, TP), to 1000 m in the Jeseniky mountains (BR, SU), to 1100 m in the Orlicke hory mountains (RK), to 1180 m in the Beskydy mountains (FM, VS), to 1200 m in the Sumava mountains (CK, PT, KT), and to 1250 m in the Krkonose mountains (SE, TU). Typical breeding habitats include fairly dense coniferous, mixed and deciduous forest of any age and with undergrowth, where Eurasian Jays frequent edges or clearings. It also breeds in smaller, particularly oak-dominated, forest in farmland, and in parks, gardens and cemeteries in larger towns such as Praha (AA) and Brno (BM). In autumn and winter, solitary birds or small flocks occur in farmland with hedgerows and stands of trees, in rural parkland, larger orchards, and at the edges of towns. Nests are frequently built in spruce, pine, oak, or fir, 3–6 m above ground. Breeding density was 20 pairs per km^2 in riverine forest (KM) at the beginning of the 1970s, 13 pairs per km^2 in mature spruce plantations near Milevsko (TA), 3 pairs per km^2 in oak-dominated forest in NA county, and 14 pairs per km^2 near Frantiskovy Lazne (CH) at the end of the 1970s. During the 1980s, it was 1–2 pairs per km^2 in acid-rain-damaged spruce and spruce-beech forest in the Krkonose mountains, 10–15 pairs per km^2 and 29 individuals per km^2 respectively in pine forest around Tabor (TA) and in TC county, 3 individuals per km^2 in mountain forest in the Sumava mountains, 0–50 individuals per km^2 in riverine, oak-dominated forest in OL county, 5 pairs per km^2 in riverine forest in ST county, 6–8 pairs per km^2 in deciduous forest in PI county, 11 pairs per km^2 in woods in farmland (TC), 10–15 pairs per km^2 in mixed woods at 280 m in UH county, and 18–21 pairs per km^2 in mixed forest in the Bile Karpaty mountains (HO, UH, ZL) at about 600 m. It was 5–44 individuals per km^2 in various types of forest near Mlada (NB) at the beginning of the 1990s. Winter density was 17–34 individuals per km^2 in oak stands surrounding fishponds around Trebon (JH) at the beginning of the 1970s, 23 individuals per km^2 in pine plantations in TC county in the mid-1970s, 0–7 individuals per km^2 in primeval beech-fir forest at about 900 m in VS county at the end of the 1970s and beginning of the 1980s, and 25 individuals per km^2 in mixed woods at 280 m in UH county at the end of the 1980s.

Status: Resident. **Breeding season:** common. **Winter:** common. **Migration:** common. Hunted during fixed season.

Population trends: The breeding population is between 150,000 and 300,000 pairs, and has been stable during the past 20 years. The number of wintering birds ranges from 150,000 to 300,000 individuals. Populations associated with human dwellings have been increasing during the 1990s.

Distribution: Nationwide.

Timing: All year round. Breeding starts at the beginning of April and continues until early June, peaking during late April.

Magpie *Pica pica*

Common Magpie   Straka obecna   Straka obycajna   Elster

Magpie is found throughout the country from lowlands up to 690 m in the Cesky les mountains (DO, TC), to 750 m in the Orlicke hory mountains (RK), to about 900 m in the Krusne hory (CV, KV, MO, TP) and Orlicke hory (RK) mountains, to 1000 m in the Sumava (CK, PT, KT) and Jeseniky (BR, SU) mountains, and to 1200 in the Krkonose mountains (SE, TU). It

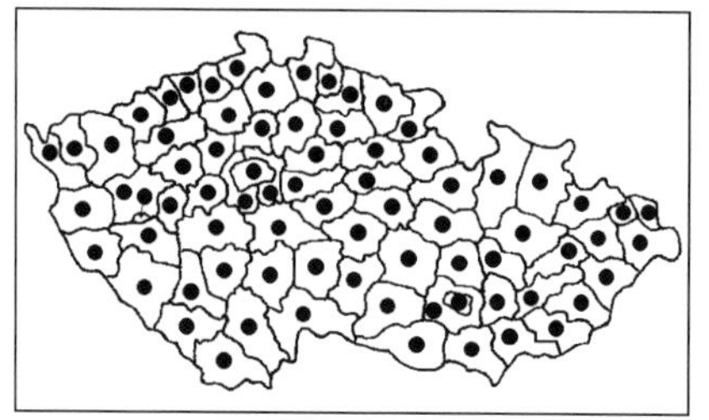

is more common in lowlands than at higher altitudes. Magpie is a typical bird of open country, where hedgerows, windbreaks, woods, tall bushes and stands of trees are available. It often nests in fairly dense growths along rivers, canals and brooks. It occasionally nests in larger town parks, gardens and cemeteries, and permanently inhabits large towns such as Praha (AA), Brno (BM), Ceske Budejovice (CB), Ostrava (OV) and Liberec (LB). It avoids densely forested areas. Nests are usually placed in spruce, blackthorn, willow or alder, 2–8 m above ground. Because of persecution by humans, its density may vary from year to year, and from place to place. During the 1980s, breeding density was 4 pairs per km^2 in a suburb of Ceske Budejovice (CB), 20 pairs per km^2 in woods in farmland in TC county, 2 pairs per km^2 in poplar-dominated windbreaks at 170 m in UH county, and 7 pairs per km^2 in brushy hillsides at about 500 m in the Bile Karpaty mountains (HO, UH, ZL). All year round density in windbreaks in BV county was 9 individuals per km^2 during the 1980s. Winter density was 6 individuals per km^2 in poplar-dominated windbreaks in UH county in the mid-1980s. It was 0.4–1 individuals per km^2 and 0.5–1 individuals per km^2 in farmland in UO county at 350–350 m in 1988/89 and 1991/92 respectively (Vorisek 1993). Winter flocks of up to 40 individuals are quite common.

Status: Resident. **Breeding season:** local/common. **Winter:** local/common. **Migration:** local/common. Hunted all year round.

Population trends: The breeding population is between 40,000 and 80,000 pairs, and has increased by more than 50% during the past 20 years. The number of wintering birds is between 100,000 and 200,000 individuals.

Distribution: Nationwide. The number of wintering birds may be low in the following counties: KV, CV, RA, JI, ZR, TR, BK, BR, VS and FM.

Timing: All year round. Breeding extends from mid-March until early June, peaking in mid-April.

Nutcracker *Nucifraga caryocatactes*

Spotted Nutcracker, Eurasian Nutcracker   Oresnik kropenaty   Oresnica perlava
Tannenhäher

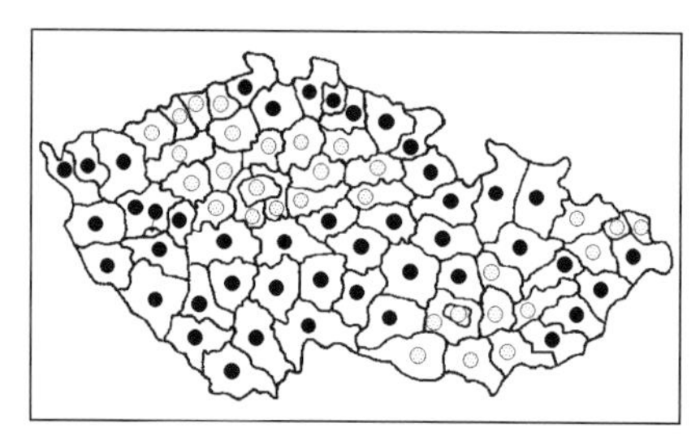

Nutcracker occurs locally in the highlands and mountains of the country. It is found from about 500 m up to 1080 m in Orlicke hory (RK) and Krkonose (SE, TU) mountains, to 1180 m in the Beskydy mountains (FM, VS), to 1200 m in the Krusne hory mountains (CV, KV, MO, TP), and to 1300 m in the Sumava mountains (CK, PT, KT). In the last 30–40 years, it has been expanding its breeding range into lower altitudes in the highlands, particularly in the following counties: CB, JH, TA, ZR and HB. Breeding has also been recorded at about 300 m in central Bohemia. It is found in mountains and highlands in mature spruce forest, and in any conifer plantations at lower altitudes. Nests are mostly placed in spruce, 2–10 m above ground. During the 1980s, breeding density was 5 pairs per km^2 in spruce forest in the Cesky les mountains (DO, TC), 4 individuals per km^2 in spruce forest in the Sumava mountains, and 11 pairs per km^2 in young growths of beech and spruce in s. Bohemia. In late autumn and winter, solitary birds or flocks of varying size (up to 50) can be found in lowlands, where they frequent growths of hazel in larger orchards, gardens and parks. During invasions, local wintering birds are joined by individuals from n. and ne. Europe. Individuals of the breeding population belong to the *caryocatactes* race, while individuals of the *macrorhynchos* race occur during winter invasions.

Status: Resident. **Breeding season:** uncommon/local (*caryocatactes*), rare (*macrorhynchos*). **Winter:** local (*caryocatactes*), uncommon (*macrorhynchos*). **Migration:** local (*caryocatactes*), uncommon (*macrorhynchos*). Least concern. Protected.

Population trends: The breeding population is between 2,500 and 5,000 pairs, and has increased by 20–50% during the past 20 years. The number of wintering birds ranges from 3,000 to 6,000 individuals.
Distribution: Regular breeding of large numbers is restricted to the following counties: JH, CK, PT, KT, KV, PJ, RO, PI, PS, TA, BN, DC, JN, ZR, JI, PE and SU. Winter records come from all but the following counties: AA, RA, LN, LT, KL, UL, DC, MB, HK, PU, ZN, BV and VY. However, birds on passage and wintering birds may occasionally occur elsewhere.
Timing: All year round. Breeding extends from late February until late June, without evident peaks in egg-laying.

Eurasian Jackdaw *Corvus monedula*

Jackdaw Kavka obecna Kavka obycajna Dohle

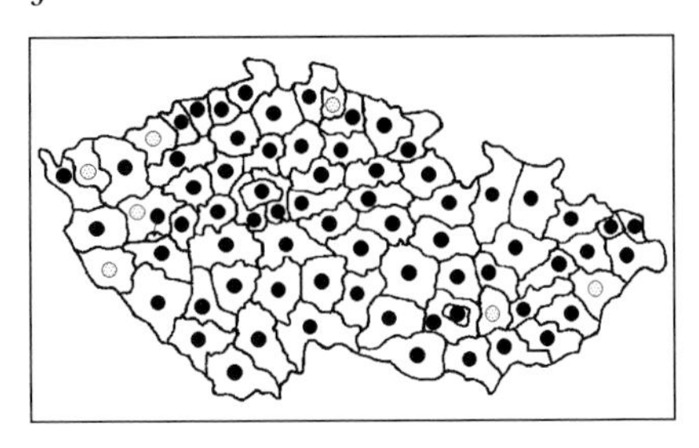

Eurasian Jackdaw is less common in the Czech Republic during the breeding season than outside this period, when flocks of thousands of individuals arrive from ne. Europe. This species has patchy distribution across the country, from lowlands up to 530 m in the Cesky les mountains (DO, TC), to 600 m in the Krusne hory (CV, KV, MO, TP) and the Sumava mountains (CK, PT, KT), to 670 m in the Jeseniky mountains (BR, SU), to 750 m in the Orlicke hory mountains (RK), and to 800 m in the Ceskomoravska vysocina highlands (HB, JI, PE, ZR) and in the Krkonose mountains (SE, TU). Eurasian Jackdaw is more common in lowlands than at higher altitudes. The wide range of breeding habitats includes edges of mature forest, groups of trees in open country, avenues with hollow trees, rock crevices, ruins of castles, church towers and, occasionally, old buildings and artificial nest boxes. However, today most of the nesting colonies are located in urban habitats. Nests are placed in natural cavities in trees such as oak, lime and beech in the same numbers as nests placed in buildings. Nests are usually found from 1 to 10 m above ground in trees, and 5–25 m above ground in buildings. In winter, often in flocks with Rooks, this species frequents farmland in lowlands at dumps, sites around farms, as well as in towns. At the end of the 1970s and beginning of the 1980s, breeding density was 160–190 pairs per km^2 in a city park with mature, hollow oaks and limes in HO county, and 59 pairs per km^2 in a town in TC county; it was 25–28 pairs per km^2 in parkland around castles in w. Bohemia at the end of 1980s and beginning of the 1990s. Winter density was 0.8 individuals per km^2 in Brno (BM) and 7 individuals per km^2 in farmland in BV county at the beginning of the 1970s, and 6–8 individuals per km^2 in farmland around the Morava river in UH county in the mid-1980s. The decline of the breeding population is probably due to the loss of nesting sites such as mature hollow trees, human persecution, and the use of pesticides. The breeding population belongs to the *spermologus* race. Wintering individuals from ne. Europe belong mostly to the former race, and a minority of birds to the *sommeringii* race.
Status: Resident. **Breeding season:** local (*spermologus*), rare (*sommeringii*). **Winter:** common (*spermologus*), local (*sommeringii*). **Migration:** common (*spermologus*), local (*sommeringii*). Endangered. Protected/not hunted all year round.
Population trends: The breeding population is between 10,000 and 20,000 pairs, and has declined by more than 50% during the past 20 years. The number of wintering birds ranges from 200,000 to 400,000 individuals.
Distribution: Nationwide. As a breeder, it may be scarce in the following counties: SO, RA, KT, JN, CK, PZ, KV, PS, LN, LB, BK, VY, PV, FM and ZL. In winter, it occurs less commonly in DO, TC, SO, KV, CV, TP, UL and JN counties. Large numbers of wintering birds have been reported from the following counties: LT, KL, ME, BE, PH, JC, HK, PU, KH, CR, OV, KI, PR, KM, ZL, UH, HO and BV.
Timing: All year round. Autumn arrival of populations from n. and ne. Europe starts at the end of September and continues until the end of October, peaking during mid- to late October. Spring departure occurs in March, peaking during the middle of the month. Breeding extends from the beginning of April until early May, peaking during mid-April.

Rook *Corvus frugilegus*

Havran polni Havran cierny Saatkrähe

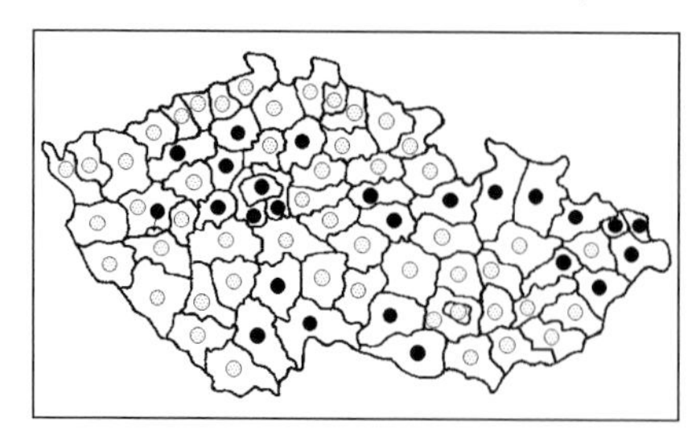

As with Jackdaws, Rooks are numerous outside the breeding season, when large flocks arrive from ne. Europe. As a breeder, Rook is uncommon in the Czech Republic. Colonies of varying size, rarely exceeding several hundred pairs, are scattered in lowlands at 140–300 m. Some of the colonies are traditional nesting sites and have been used for more than 100 years, for example the colonies in Veltrusy (ME) and Lovosice (LT). The following numbers of nests were recorded in some of the well-established colonies: Bozice (ZN) 150–350 between 1968 and 1992, Opava (OP) 250–333 between 1985 and 1991, Veltrusy (ME) 300–817 between 1973 and 1987, Bustehrad (KL) 100 in 1988, various sites in Praha (AA), up to 140 in 1992, Chrudim (CR), 89–524 between 1979 and 1989, Veseli nad Luznici (JH), 15–200 pairs between mid-1975 and the 1990s, and Ceske Budejovice (CB), 44–110 nests between 1989 and 1993. Owing to human persecution, Rooks may change nest sites from year to year in the same area. Breeding habitats are woodland or larger stands of mature tall trees in farmland, along rivers or around ponds, and in larger parks in cities and parkland around castles. Occasional nesting occurs in buildings in towns. In winter, flocks of various size occur only in towns and lowland areas, frequenting farmland, parks in towns, dumps, and gardens and orchards during the day. At night, they roost at the edge of forest, in larger avenues, and in stands of mature trees in farmland. Winter density was 420 individuals per km^2 in Brno (BM), 40 individuals per km^2 in farmland in BV county, and 80–120 individuals per km^2 in farmland around the Morava river (UH) at the end of the 1970s and in the mid-1980s. Flocks of up to 25,000 individuals, with a total number of 100,000–125,000 birds, regularly roost in riverine forest between Uherske Hradiste (UH) and Uhersky Ostroh (UH). The breeding population in Slovakia is estimated to be between 10,000 and 17,000 pairs (Murin *et al.* 1994).

Status: Resident. **Breeding season:** local. **Winter:** common. **Migration:** common. Vulnerable. Hunted during fixed season.

Population trends: The breeding population was 2,000–3,500 pairs in the period 1973–1977, and recently is between 2,600 and 3,600 pairs. The number of wintering birds ranges from 2,000,000 to 4,000,000 individuals.

Distribution: During migration and in winter nationwide, with high numbers in the following counties: LN, LT, CV, MO, TP, KL, ME, AA, PZ, PH, MB, JC, NB, HK, PU, KO, KH, CR, OP, OV, KI, FM, PR, OL, KM, ZL, UH, HO, BV and BO.

Timing: All year round. Autumn arrival of populations from n. and ne. Europe starts at the beginning of October and continues until mid-November, peaking during the second half of October. Spring departure occurs from the beginning of March until mid-April, peaking during the second half of March. Breeding extends from mid-March until mid-April, peaking during early April.

Crow (Carrrion Crow, Hooded Crow) *Corvus corone*

Vrana obecna Vrana obycajna Aaskrähe

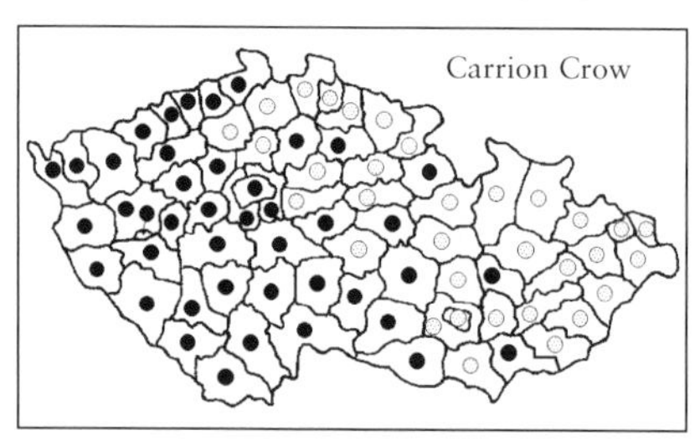

Two races of crow are permanent residents in the Czech Republic. The strongholds of Carrion Crow, *C. c. corone* are in s. Bohemia, w. Bohemia, and n. Bohemia, and it occurs less frequently in the rest of the country. Hooded Crow, *C. c. cornix*, is more widespread, and occupies the whole country. This latter race is more abundant in the east of the country. Both races hybridize. Crows are distributed from lowlands up to 710 m in the Cesky les mountains (DO, TC), to 800 m in the Krusne hory (CV,

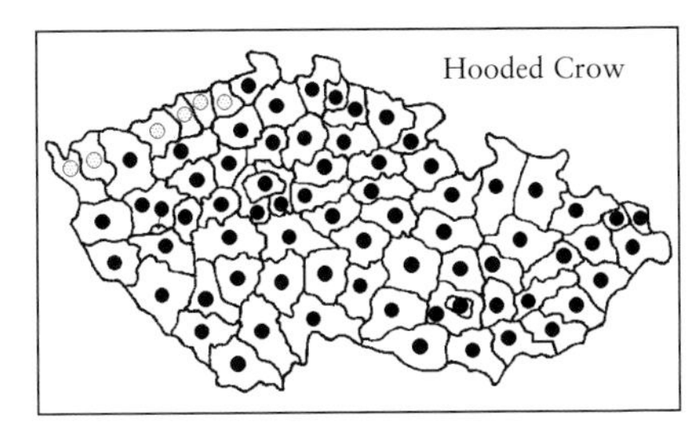

KV, MO, TP), Jeseniky (BR, SU) and Beskydy (FM, VS) mountains, to 1000 m in the Sumava mountains (CK, PT, KT), to 1020 m in the Orlicke hory mountains (RK), and to 1100 m in the Krkonose mountains (SE, TU). Typical breeding habitat is open country with woodland, stands of trees, hedgerows, avenues, and the edges of larger forest complexes extending into meadows, pastures and fields. It occasionally breeds in parks and cemeteries in towns. Nests are usually placed in spruce, pine, alder, oak, willow or larch, 4–20 m above ground. Breeding density of Hooded Crow was 1.5 pairs per km^2 in poplar-dominated windbreaks at 170 m in UH county, 25 individuals per km^2 in deciduous forest in LN county, 0.1–0.4 pairs per km^2 in spruce forest in the Krkonose mountains, and 80 individuals per km^2 in windbreaks in BV county all year round during the 1980s. Breeding density of Carrion Crow was 2 pairs per km^2 in parkland around a castle (LN), and 10 pairs per km^2 in various types of woodland in farmland (TC) during the 1980s. In winter, Crows frequent human settlements and often associate with flocks of Rooks and Eurasian Jackdaws. Winter density of Hooded Crow was 6–14 individuals per km^2 in a mountain village at 730 m in VS county at the end of the 1970s and beginning of the 1980s, and 3 individuals per km^2 in poplar-dominated windbreaks and hedgerows in farmland in UH county at the end of the 1980s.

Status: Resident. **Breeding season**: local/common (both races). **Winter**: local/common (both races). **Migration**: local/common (both races). Hunted all year round (both races).

Population trends: Carrion Crow: the breeding population is between 3,000 and 6,000 pairs, and it has been increasing slightly for the past 20 years. The number of wintering birds ranges from 8,000 to 16,000 individuals. The breeding population of Hooded Crow is between 9,000 and 18,000 pairs, and has been stable for the past 20 years. The number of wintering Hooded Crows is between 15,000 and 30,000 individuals.

Distribution: Carrion Crow: the majority of the breeding population occurs in the following counties: JH, CB, CK, PT, ST, KT, DO, PJ, PM, PS, TC, CH, SO, KV, CV, MO, LN, TP and UL. Winter records come from all but the following counties: ZR, BK, SE, OL and PR. Hooded Crow: found nationwide. As a breeder, it may occur less commonly in the following counties: CK, DO, TC, SO, KV, CV, MO, TP, UL and LB.

Timing: All year round. Breeding of both races starts in mid-March and continues until mid-May (Carrion Crow), and the end of May (Hooded Crow). Breeding peaks during early April (Carrion Crow), and mid-April (Hooded Crow).

Common Raven *Corvus corax*

Raven Krkavec velky Krkavec cierny Kolkrabe

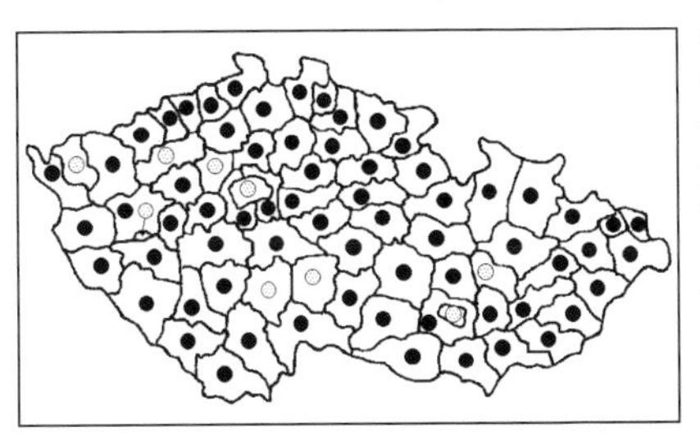

Common Raven was a regular breeding species in the Czech Republic until the middle of the 19th century. Since then, the numbers of breeding pairs has fallen, and during the first 20 years of the 20th century, due to human persecution, it was extirpated as a breeder from the country. At the end of the 1960s, when Common Raven was expanding its range in Europe from the east to the west, breeding was again documented in Moravia, in the east of the Czech Republic, in 1968. In the west of the country, breeding was first recorded in ST and PI counties in 1989. Since the beginning of the 1970s, Common Raven has extended its range into other areas of the country. Nowadays, this species more or less regularly nests in more than half of the countries in the Czech Republic, from lowlands up to the spruce tree-line in mountains. Strongholds, with dozens of pairs, are in the Beskydy mountains (VS, FM), the Jeseniky mountains (BR, SU), the Broumovska vrchovina highlands (NA), and the Krkonose mountains (SE, TU). Typical breeding habitats include larger mountain woodlands with open areas such as meadows and pastures, and holes in rocks.

During Common Raven's expansion in the 1980s, it moved to farmland in the lowlands, and breeding was also documented in woods, windbreaks, hedgerows, and even on pylons. Nests are usually built in beech, pine or oak, and on cliffs, 17–23 m above ground. Breeding density was 0.003 pairs per km^2 in 4 counties in e. Bohemia, 0.2 pairs per km^2 in acid-rain-damaged forest in the Krkonose mountains in the mid-1980s, 9 individuals per km^2 in deciduous forest near Mlada (NB) at the beginning of 1990s, and 4–5 individuals per km^2 in the Bile Karpaty mountains (UH, HO, ZL) in June 1998. Common Raven is more common in Slovakia, where the breeding population is between 1,500 and 2,000 pairs (Murin *et al.* 1994).
Status: Resident. **Breeding season:** uncommon/local. **Winter:** local/common. **Migration:** local/common. Near-threatened. Protected.
Population trends: The breeding population was 5–10 pairs between 1973 and 1977, 30–50 pairs between 1978 and 1985, and recently is 250–400 pairs. The number of wintering birds is estimated to be between 200 and 400 individuals, but may be higher.
Distribution: Because it continues to expand its breeding range, it may occur nationwide. Flocks of up to 90 individuals have recently been recorded at Dolni Ujezd (SY) in October, and Frydlant v Cechach (LB) in January.
Timing: All year round. Breeding extends from mid-February until mid-April, peaking during the first half of March.

Common Starling *Sturnus vulgaris*

Starling, European Starling   Spacek obecny   Skorec obycajny   Star

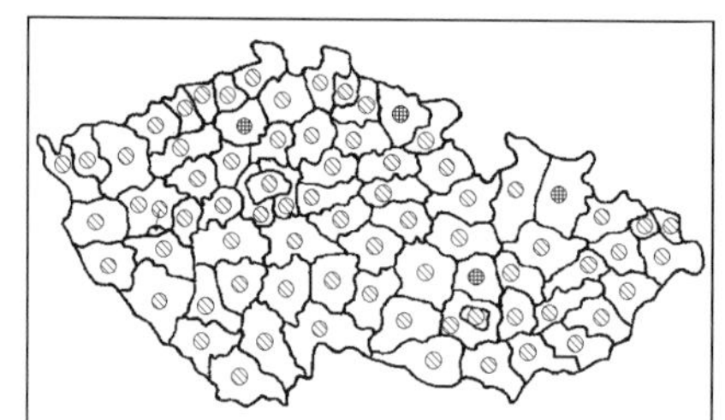

Common Starling is widely distributed across the country. It occurs from lowlands up to 700 m in the Cesky les (DO, TC) and Jeseniky (BR, SU) mountains, to 800 m in the Orlicke hory mountains (RK), to 1000 m in the Krusne hory (CV, KV, MO, TP) and Sumava (CK, PT, KT) mountains, and to about 1100 m in the Krkonose mountains (SE, TU). It is more abundant in lowlands and highlands than at higher altitudes. Common Starling has a wide tolerance to different habitats. It breeds in not too dense deciduous and mixed forest of varying size, in growths along rivers and around ponds, hedgerows, stands of trees in farmland, in avenues, parks, cemeteries, orchards and gardens. Nests are built in holes in trees, and also in crevices in buildings, and under roofs, either in farms, villages or towns, and 4–6 m above ground. It frequently occupies nest boxes. The majority of the breeding population is migratory. However, smaller flocks occur in human settlements during winter. After the breeding season, flocks of hundreds and often thousands of individuals occur around vineyards, and roost in reedbeds around ponds, in hedgerows and in windbreaks. Breeding density was 379–565 individuals per km^2 in mature oak stands between fishponds and meadows, and 45 individuals per km^2 in alders around Trebon (JH) at the beginning of the 1970s, 29 pairs per km^2 in avenues along roads in the Cesky les mountains (DO, TC), and 9–50 pairs per km^2 in parks in Praha (AA) at the end of the 1970s. During the 1980s, it was 20–30 pairs per km^2 and 190–530 pairs per km^2 respectively in growths around Tachov (TC) and Strakonice (ST), 518 individuals per km^2 and 66 individuals per km^2 respectively in growths along brooks in ST and CK counties, 220 pairs per km^2 in beech forest in the Krusne hory mountains, 26 pairs per km^2 in mature poplar-dominated windbreaks at 170 m in UH county, and 22–37 pairs per km^2 in mixed woods opening to pastures at 280 m in UH county. In riverine forest, during the 1980s, it was as follows: near Strakonice (ST) 169 pairs per km^2, in central Moravia 240–310 pairs per km^2 and also 120–300 individuals per km^2, and in n. Moravia 110 pairs per km^2. In parkland around a castle (LN) it was 60 pairs per km^2, in a suburban park in Tachov (TC) it was 44–102 pairs per km^2, and in a park in Ostrava (OV) it was 32–56 pairs per km^2 during the 1980s. Winter density was 0.4 individuals per km^2 in Brno (BM) at the beginning of the 1970s, and 3 individuals per km^2 in meadows with hedgerows at the edge of Uherske Hradiste (UH) in 1988/89. Lack of mature trees with suitable nesting sites in natural habitats and intensive use of pesticides on farms has probably led to a decline in numbers.

Status: Resident. **Breeding season**: common. **Winter**: local. **Migration**: common. Protected.
Population trends: The breeding population is between 800,000 and 1,600,000 pairs, and has fallen by about 20% between the end of the 1970s and end of the 1980s. However, from the beginning of 1990s, numbers have started to increase. The number of wintering birds ranges from 1,500 to 5,000 individuals.
Distribution: Nationwide. High numbers of wintering birds have been reported from the following counties: ST, TC, CH, KV, TP, UL, LB, PB, PU, BO, KI, PV and BV.
Timing: All year round. The migratory part of the population arrives from mid-February until the end of March, peaking during late February and early March. Autumn departure occurs from early October until mid-November, peaking during late October. Breeding extends from early April until mid-June, with peaks during late April and late May.

Rosy Starling *Strunus roseus*

Rose-coloured Starling Spacek ruzovy Skorec ruzovy Rosenstar

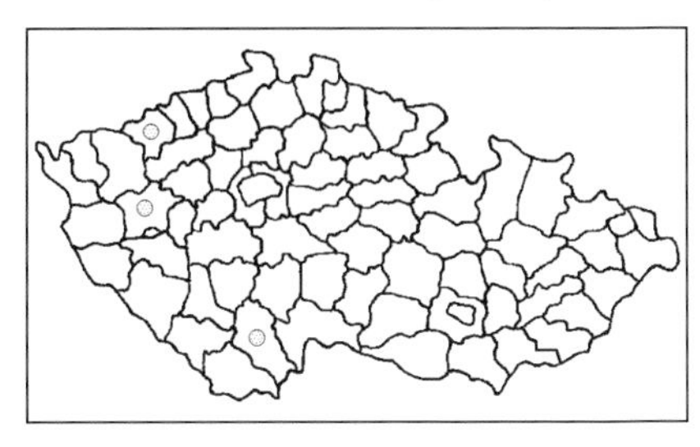

The first records of Rosy Starling in the Czech Republic come from the beginning of the 19th century. Between the 1850s and late 1940s, this species was recorded more commonly than during the past 50 years, when sightings have become irregular. It usually occurs in small flocks, and often associates with Common Starlings. Although possible breeding has been reported, sufficient documentary proof is unavailable. Rosy Starlings occur in open country such as farmland, pastures and meadows in lowlands and highlands.
Status: Vagrant. **Breeding season**: rare. **Winter**: does not occur. **Migration**: rare. Protected.
Population trends: No data available.
Distribution: May occur nationwide. A recent record of a single bird comes from Ceske Budejovice (CB).
Timing: Recorded between March and September, with most observations from late May and early June.

House Sparrow *Passer domesticus*

Vrabec domaci Vrabec domovy Haussperling

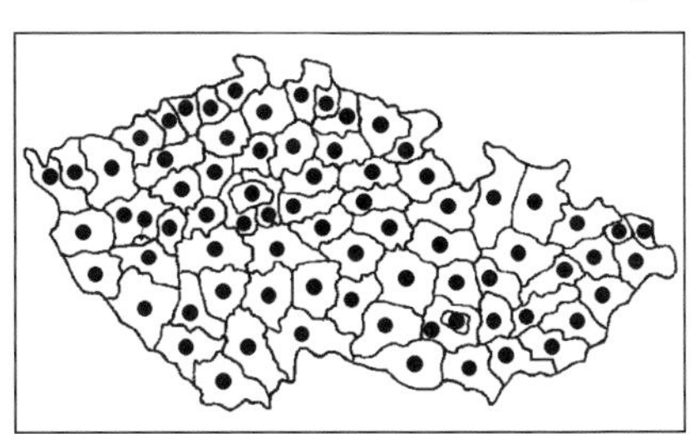

House Sparrow, typical of urban areas, is one of the most abundant birds in the Czech Republic. It is found throughout the country, from lowlands up to the highest human settlements in mountains: up to 750 m in the Orlicke hory mountains (RK), to 800 m in the Jeseniky mountains (BR, SU), to 1000 m in the Sumava mountains (CK, PT, KT), to 1040 in the Krkonose mountains (SE, TU), and to 1200 m in the Krusne hory mountains (CV, KV, MO, TP). It exploits a wide range of man-made and semi-rural habitats. However, in some counties of s. Bohemia and s. Moravia, House Sparrow breeds in rural areas, away from human habitation. Breeding density was 5 individuals per km^2 in growths of mature oak around fishponds (JH), and 835 individuals per km^2 in Brno (BM) at the beginning of the 1970s, 141–165 pairs per km^2 in 2 villages in the Cesky les mountains (DO, TC), and 320–964 pairs per km^2 in various habitats in Praha (AA) in the mid-1970s. During the 1980s, it was 112–613 pairs per km^2 in various parts of Tachov (TC), 760–830 pairs per km^2 on a farm at the edge of a village in UH county, and 150–215 pairs per km^2 around 2 farms in the foothils of the Bile Karpaty mountains (HO, UH, ZL), about 3 km from the closest village. Winter density was 960 individuals per km^2 in Brno (BM) at the beginning of the 1970s, 150 individuals per km^2 in villages at about 600m in the Cesky les mountains in the mid-1970s,

67–112 individuals per km^2 in a mountain village at 730 m in VS county at the end of the 1970s and beginning of the 1980s, and 212–336 individuals per km^2 around a farm at the edge of a village in UH county in the mid-1980s. Local decreases have been reported from many counties across the Czech Republic, while populations have remained stable in others.
Status: Resident. **Breeding season:** common. **Winter:** common. **Migration:** common.
Population trends: The breeding population is between 3,000,000 and 6,000,000 pairs, and has decreased by 20–50% during the past 20 years. The number of wintering birds ranges from 4,000,000 to 8,000,000 individuals.
Distribution: Nationwide.
Timing: All year round. Breeding extends from early April until early August, with peaks during early May, early and late June, and late July.

Tree Sparrow *Passer montanus*

Eurasian Tree Sparrow   Vrabec polni   Vrabec polny   Feldsperling

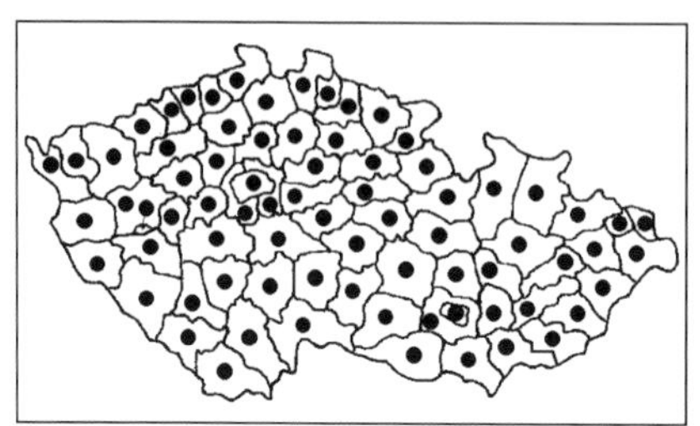

Tree Sparrow occurs in rural areas across the country, but is not so abundant as House Sparrow. It is found in lowlands and highlands, but as a breeder has been recorded up to 600 m in the Cesky les mountains (DO, TC), to 650 m in the Orlicke hory mountains (RK), to 700 m in the Krkonose mountains (SE, TU), to 750 m in the Jeseniky mountains (BR, SU), and to 800 m in the Sumava (CK, PT, KT), Krusne hory (CV, KV, MO, TP) and Jizerske hory (LB, JN) mountains. Typical habitat is open country with windbreaks, hedgerows, avenues, orchards, growths along rivers, edges of deciduous and mixed forest, and parks. It is also found around farms, at the edges of villages, and in cemeteries. Nests are usually built in holes in trees, in artificial nest boxes, and in crevices, 1–5 m above ground, and occasionally in the base of the large nests of White Storks, Grey Herons, and birds of prey. In winter, Tree Sparrows frequently occur in flocks closer to human habitations. Breeding density was 413 individuals per km^2 in growths of mature oak around fishponds (JH) at the beginning of the 1970s, 26–28 pairs per km^2 in villages at about 600 m in the Cesky les mountains (DO, TC), and 189–230 individuals per km^2 in abandoned orchards and growths along brooks in CV county in the mid-1970s, 3 individuals per km^2 in various habitats in Brno (BM), and 13–121 pairs per km^2 in parks in Praha (AA) during the 1970s. During the 1980s, it was 20 pairs per km^2 in pine forest near Tabor (TA), 12 pairs per km^2 in mature oak forest near Most (MO), 90–100 pairs per km^2 in riverine forest in KM county, 50 pairs per km^2 and 150–213 individuals per km^2 respectively in different areas of riverine forest in n. Moravia, 16 individuals per km^2 in growths along brooks in CK county, 50 individuals per km^2 and 236 individuals per km^2 respectively in the same habitat around Trebon (JH) and Strakonice (ST), 413 individuals per km^2 in stands of old oak around Vrbenske ponds (CB), 2,060 individuals per km^2 in windbreaks in BV county, and 130 pairs per km^2 in poplar-dominated windbreaks at 170 m in UH county. It was 64 pairs per km^2 in parkland around a castle (LN), 15–90 pairs per km^2 in growths in Tachov (TC), and 29–42 individuals per km^2 in several towns in NB county during the 1980s and beginning of the 1990s. Winter density was 320 individuals per km^2 in Brno (BM), and 40 individuals per km^2 in mature growths around a fishpond near Trebon (JH) at the beginning of the 1970s, 70 individuals per km^2 in villages at about 600 m in the Cesky les mountains in the mid-1970s, 30–70 individuals per km^2 in a mountain village at 730 m in VS county at the end of the 1970s and beginning of the 1980s, and 39 individuals per km^2 at the edges of mixed woods at 280 m in UH county at the end of the 1980s.
Status: Resident. **Breeding season:** common. **Winter:** common. **Migration:** common.
Population trends: The breeding population is between 500,000 and 1,000,000 pairs. A steady fall in the breeding population was recorded between the mid-1980s and beginning of the 1990s. The number of wintering birds is between 1,000,000 and 2,000,000 individuals.
Distribution: Nationwide.
Timing: All year round. Breeding extends from mid-April to the end of July, with peaks during late April, early May, early June, and early July.

Snowfinch *Montifringilla nivalis*

Snow Finch, White-winged Snowfinch, Eurasian Snowfinch   Penkavak snezni
Sneharka vrchovska   Schneefink

Snowfinch does not occur annually in the Czech Republic. The majority of records are from the 19th and first half of the 20th centuries. Most of the records are of solitary birds, sometimes a few birds or small flocks, found in mountains but also close to large towns. This species has not been seen for 10 years. Individuals occurring in the Czech Republic belong to the *nivalis* race.

Status: Vagrant. **Breeding season:** rare. **Winter:** rare. **Migration:** rare. Protected.

Population trends: No data available.
Distribution: May occur nationwide.
Timing: Recorded from October until March.

Common Chaffinch *Fringilla coelebs*

Chaffinch   Penkava obecna   Pinka obycajna   Buchfink

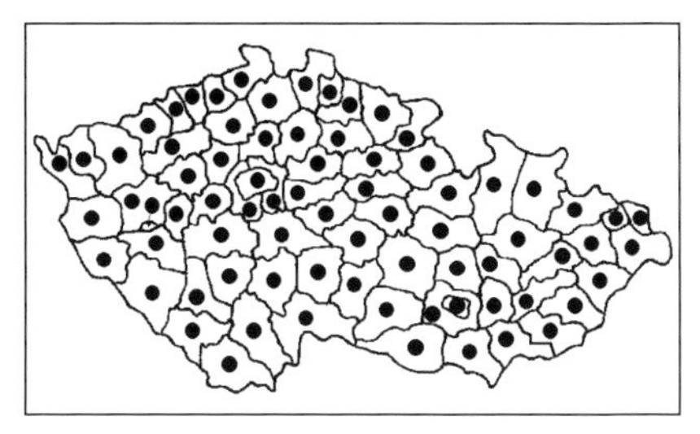

Common Chaffinch is one of the most abundant breeding birds in the Czech Republic. It is distributed from lowlands up to the tree-line in mountains, for example at 950 m in the Bile Karpaty mountains (HO, UH, ZL), to 1100 m in the Orlicke hory mountains (RK), to 1300 m in the Jeseniky (BR, SU) and Sumava mountains (CK, PT, KT), and to 1400 m in the Krkonose mountains (SE, TU). It exploits a wide range of breeding habitats: any type of forest, windbreaks, hedgerows and groups of trees in farmland, bushes and trees along rivers, canals, ditches and ponds, avenues, orchards, gardens, cemeteries and parks. It is often the dominant species in mountain spruce forest, and occasionally occurs in dwarf pines. Nests are placed in trees and bushes, such as spruce, apple, European elder, alder and blackthorn, 1–4 m above ground. The majority of the breeding population is migratory. During migration, flocks of Common Chaffinches are frequently seen in fields, meadows and pastures. In winter it usually occurs around human settlements and farms in lowlands. Breeding density was 18–94 pairs per km^2 in conifer forest, and 96–117 pairs per km^2 in mature growths around ponds near Trebon (JH) at the beginning of the 1970s, 112–212 pairs per km^2 in spruce plantations around Milevsko (TA), 31–40 pairs per km^2 in avenues along roads, and 119–209 pairs per km^2 in villages in the Cesky les mountains (DO, TC), 23 individuals per km^2 in various habitats in Brno (BM), and 63–212 pairs per km^2 in parks in Praha (AA) at the end of the 1970. During the 1980s, it was 99–131 pairs per km^2 in spruce forest around Tachov (TC), 53–188 pairs per km^2 in mixed spruce forest in the Jizerske hory mountains (LB, JN), 70–128 pairs per km^2 in spruce forest in the Krkonose mountains, 174–195 individuals per km^2 in spruce forest in the Sumava mountains, 55–120 pairs per km^2 in pine forest near Tabor (TA), 46–82 pairs per km^2 in pine forest, including dwarf pine, around Tachov (TC), 142 pairs per km^2 in pine forest near Trebon (JH), 110–151 pairs per km^2 in fir-beech forest in the Beskydy mountains (FM, VS), 200 pairs per km^2 and 40 pairs per km^2 respectively in beech forest in the Krusne hory mountains (CV, KV, MO, TP) and Cesky raj cliffs (MB), 120–220 and 156 pairs per km^2 respectively in oak forest near Praha (AA) and Most (MO), 65 pairs per km^2 in oak forest in PI county, 261 pairs per km^2 in poplar-dominated windbreaks and hedgerows at 170 m in UH county, and 137–175 pairs per km^2 in mixed woods at 280 m in UH county; in riverine forest in central and n. Moravia it was 90–100 pairs per km^2 and 187–250 individuals per km^2 respectively, in growths in farmland it was 130–400 pairs per km^2 and 100–470 pairs per km^2 respectively in TC and ST counties, in growths along brooks in CK county it was 182–424 pairs per km^2. Winter density was 4 individuals per km^2

in Brno (BM) at the beginning of the 1970s, 4–20 individuals per km^2 in villages at about 600 m in the Cesky les mountains in the mid-1970s, 3–5 individuals per km^2 in poplar-dominated windbreaks at 170 m in UH county in the mid-1980s, and 22–27 individuals per km^2 in mixed woods at 280 m in UH county at the end of the 1980s.
Status: Resident. **Breeding season**: common. **Winter**: common. **Migration**: common. Protected.
Population trends: The breeding population is between 4,000,000 and 8,000,000 pairs, and has been stable for the past 20 years. The number of wintering birds ranges from 80,000 to 160,000 individuals.
Distribution: Nationwide. Large winter numbers have been reported from the following counties: JH, CK, PJ, UL, LB, AA, PZ, PH, NA, PU, HO, UH, BO, BM and VS.
Timing: All year round. The migratory part of the population arrives from mid-February until the end of March, peaking during late February and early March. Autumn departure starts at the beginning of September and continues until the beginning of November, peaking during late October. Breeding extends from the beginning of April to the beginning of July, with peaks during late April to early May, and early June.

Brambling *Fringilla montifringilla*

Penkava jikavec Pinka severska Bergfink

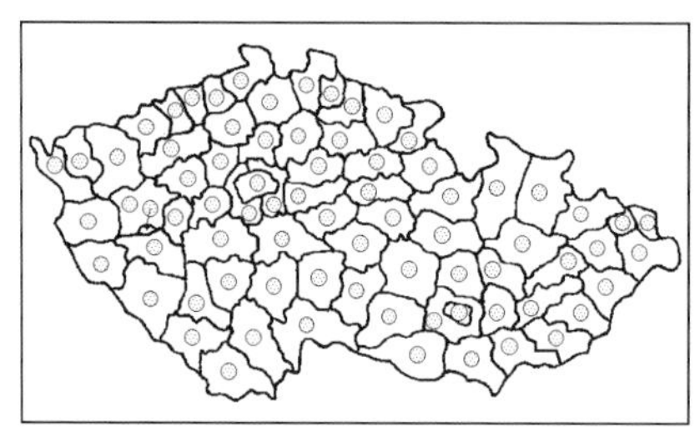

Brambling is an annual winter visitor and rare breeding bird in he Czech Republic; numbers may vary from year to year. It is distributed throughout the country, with varying abundance among the counties. It occurs in lowlands and highlands, where typical habitats include stubble-fields, pastures, meadows, not too dense beech-dominated forest, larger parks, orchards, and wasteland with dense cover. Bramblings often associate with flocks of other species such as Common Chaffinch and Yellowhammer. Accidental breeding was recorded in 1928 and 1980, and might have occurred over the last 20 years. Winter density was 7 individuals per km^2 in a village near Brno (BM) at the beginning of the 1970s, 7 individuals per km^2 in villages at about 600 m in the Cesky les mountains (DO, TC) in the mid-1970s, and 10 individuals per km^2 at the edges of mixed woods and neighboring pastures at 280 m in UH county at the end of the 1980s.
Status: Migrant, rare breeder and winter visitor. **Breeding season**: rare. **Winter**: common. **Migration**: common. Protected.
Population trends: The number of wintering birds is between 200,000 and 400,000 individuals. Changes over the past 20 years have not been recorded.
Distribution: Nationwide. Larger numbers have been recorded in the following counties: JH, PI, PJ, PM, TA, AA, PH, LT, TU, NA, BO, VS and UH. It may occur less commonly in SO, CV, CL, JI, TR, ZR, SY, BR and NJ counties.
Timing: Autumn arrival starts at the end of September and continues until the end of mid-October, peaking during early October. Records from early to mid-September are rare. Larger flocks may not be seen until late November. Spring departure extends from the beginning of March to early April, peaking during late March. Birds on passage can be seen until the end of April. Individual birds are occasionally seen after April.

European Serin *Serinus serinus*

Serin Zvonohlik zahradni Kanarik polny Girlitz

European Serin is a common breeding species throughout the country. As a breeder, it expanded its range in the Czech Republic during the first half of the 19th century. Between 1835 and 1840 it invaded s. Bohemia, during the second half of the 1840s foothills of the Jeseniky mountains (BR, SU), at the end of the 1840s foothills of the Krkonose mountains (SE, TU), and by around 1860 was probably found in all lowlands in the country, and its expansion continued

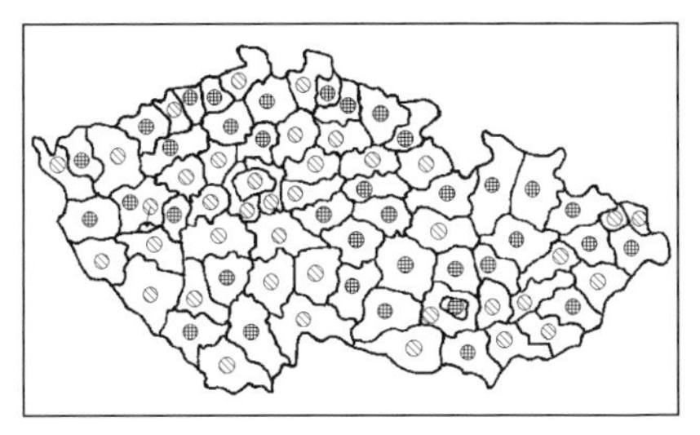

into highlands and mountains (Hudec *et al.* 1983). It occurs from lowlands up to 1010 m in the Jeseniky mountains (BR, SU), to 1020 m in the Krusne hory (CV, KV, MO, TP) and Orlicke hory (RK) mountains, to 1060 m in the Sumava mountains (CK, PT, KT), and to 1250 m in the Krkonose mountains. It frequents open, dry and sunny habitats associated with human settlements, such as gardens, orchards, vineyards, parks and cemeteries. It is also found in avenues, in hedgerows and in woods in farmland, in growths along rivers, canals and around ponds, and at the edges of larger deciduous forest. Nests are usually placed in European elder, spruce, apple or pear, 1–3 m above ground. Although up to 2,000 individuals may winter annually, this is a migratory species. In winter, flocks of varying size, occasionally individual birds, frequent wasteland with dense cover, and sites around farms. Breeding density was 10–29 individuals per km^2 in various habitats in Brno (BM) at the beginning of the 1970s, 280–650 pairs per km^2 in hedgerows around Trebon (JH), and 36–37 pairs per km^2 in villages in the Cesky les mountains (DO, TC) in the mid-1970s, 79–91 pairs per km^2 in parks in Praha (AA), and 116–169 pairs per km^2 in young forest at the edge of Praha (AA) at the end of the 1970s. During the 1980s, it was 9 pairs per km^2 in riverine forest in ST county, 1,240 individuals per km^2 in windbreaks in BV county, 10–40 pairs per km^2 and 40–60 pairs per km^2 respectively in mixed growths in TC and ST counties, 61 pairs per km^2 in poplar-dominated windbreaks at 170 m in UH county, 103–127 pairs per km^2 in a mature lime avenue along the Morava river (UH), and 97–125 pairs per km^2 in an abandoned orchard and in hedgerows around a vineyard at 210 m in UH county, 6–30 pairs per km^2 in parkland around castles in w. and n. Bohemia, and 32 pairs per km^2 in a park in Ostrava (OV). It was 17–18 individuals per km^2 in several towns, and 9 individuals per km^2 in a mixed forest in NB county at the beginning of the 1990s.

Status: Resident. **Breeding season:** common. **Winter:** uncommon. **Migration:** common. Protected.

Population trends: The breeding population is between 450,000 and 900,000 pairs, and has been stable for the past 20 years. The number of wintering birds is estimated to be between 1,000 and 2,000 individuals.

Distribution: Nationwide. High numbers of wintering birds have been reported from the following counties: PH, PZ, DO, KT, CK, BO, UH, AA, NB, MB and TA.

Timing: Spring migration occurs from mid-March until the end of mid-April, peaking during early April. Autumn migration starts during mid-September and continues until early November, peaking during mid- to late October. Breeding extends from mid-April until early July, peaking during early to mid-May and early July.

Greenfinch *Carduelis chloris*

European Greenfinch   Zvonek zeleny   Stehlik zeleny   Grünling

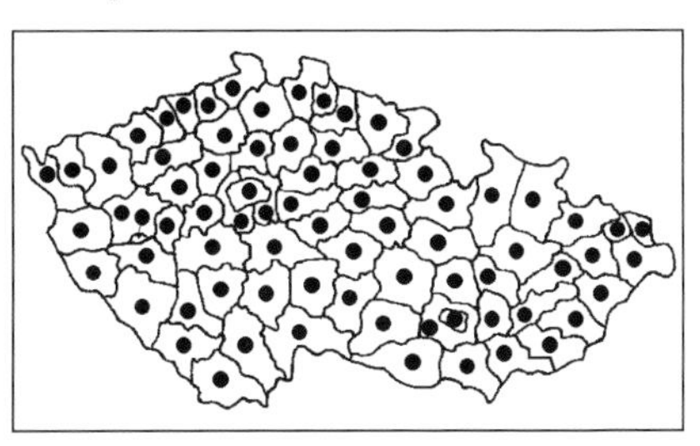

Greenfinch is a common bird distributed widely throughout the country. It occurs in farmland in lowlands and highlands, but breeding birds have been recorded up to 750 m in the Orlicke hory mountains (RK), to 800 m in the Jeseniky mountains (BR, SU), to 990 m in the Krkonose mountains (SE, TU), to about 1000 m in the Krusne hory (CV, KV, MO, TP) and Jizerske hory (LB, JN) mountains, and to 1300 m in the Sumava mountains (CK, PT, KT). It frequents a wide range of rural as well as urban habitats, and occurs at the edges of forest, in young conifer plantations, stands of trees, windbreaks and in hedgerows in farmland, trees and bushes along rivers, canals, ditches and around ponds, avenues, cemeteries, parks, orchards and gardens. Nests are usually built in spruce, cypress, European alder, poplar, juniper, willow or hawthorn, 1–2.5 m above ground. In late autumn and winter, Greenfinch often associates with other finches, and frequents farmland, pastures and wasteland with seed-bearing plants. Breeding density was 15 pairs per km^2 in young spruce forest around a lake at 800 m in TP county at the beginning of the 1970s, 87 individuals per km^2 in growths along a river, and 56–65 pairs per km^2 in hedgerows around Trebon (JH) in the mid-1970s, 10–18 pairs per km^2 in parks in Praha (AA), and 79–110 pairs per km^2 in villages at about 600 m in the Cesky les mountains (DO, TC) at the end of the 1970s. During the 1980s, in mixed growths in farmland, it was 20–120 pairs per km^2 in TC county, 20–180 pairs per km^2 in ST county, 22–75 pairs per km^2 in TA and CB counties, in windbreaks around Breclav (BV) it was 640 individuals per km^2, in young spruce it was 27–173 pairs per km^2 in the Krusne hory mountains, in pines, it was 18–30 pairs per km^2 around Trebon (JH), 13 pairs per km^2 in poplar-dominated windbreaks at 170 m in UH county, 30–50 pairs per km^2 in an abandoned orchard and in hedgerows around a vineyard at 210 m in UH county, and 80–90 pairs per km^2 in a young poplar plantation at the edge of a village (BV); and it was 13–322 pairs per km^2 in various habitats in Tachov (TC), 50–110 pairs per km^2 in mixed growths in Bor u Tachova (TC), and 27–65 pairs per km^2 in gardens and backyards in 2 villages in UH county. Winter density was 10 individuals per km^2 in Brno (BM), and 2 individuals per km^2 in growths around fishponds near Trebon (JH) at the beginning of the 1970s, 43–45 individuals per km^2 in villages at about 600 m in the Cesky les mountains in the mid-1970s, 20 individuals per km^2 in poplar-dominated windbreaks and in hedgerows at 170 m in UH county in the mid-1980s, and 37 individuals per km^2 in pastures with hedgerows and in the remains of an orchard at 210 m in UH county at the end of the 1980s. Part of the breeding population is migratory, and wintering birds are joined by individuals from n. and ne. Europe. The exact causes of Greenfinch's decline are unknown, but are most probably habitat loss due to the removal of hedges in farmland and growths along rivers, and reduced food availability due to loss of fields with seed-bearing plants. The breeding population belongs to the *chloris* race.

Status: Resident. **Breeding season:** common. **Winter:** common. **Migration:** common. Protected.

Population trends: The breeding population is between 500,000 and 1,000,000 pairs, and has declined by 20–50% during the past 20 years. The number of wintering birds ranges from 800,000 to 1,600,000 individuals.

Distribution: Nationwide. Large numbers of wintering birds have been reported from the following counties: JH, TA, PI, ST, PB, PJ, PM, PS, BE, AA, PZ, PH, KH, LB, JN, NA, BO and BM.

Timing: All year round. Breeding occurs from early April until mid-July, with peaks during late April and early June.

Goldfinch *Carduelis carduelis*

European Goldfinch Stehlik obecny Stehlik obycajny Stieglitz

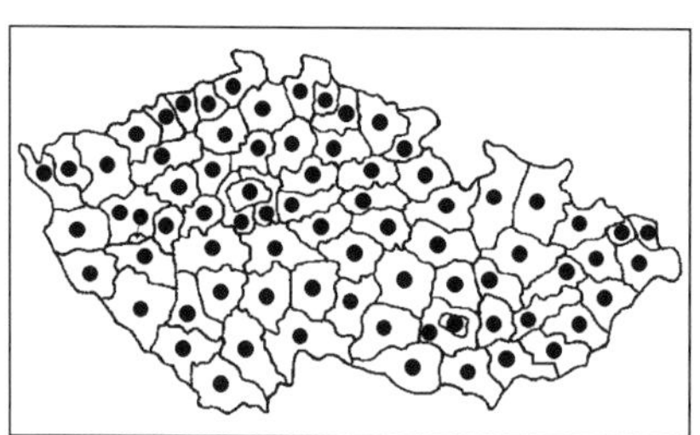

This is a common species throughout the country, but occurs predominantly in lowlands and highlands. As a breeder, it has been found up to 600 m in the Jizerske hory mountains (LB, JN), to 630 m in the Bile Karpaty mountains (HO, UH, ZL), to 750 m in the Orlicke hory mountains (RK), to 800 m in the Jeseniky mountains (BR, SU), to 1000 m in the Sumava mountains (CK, PT, KT), and to 1250 m in the Krkonose mountains (SE, TU). Typical breeding habitat is open country with avenues, tall hedgerows, windbreaks, and small areas of deciduous forest, parkland, orchards, gardens, cemeteries, growths of trees along rivers and canals, and the edges of deciduous forest. After the breeding season, flocks of varying size frequent weedy pastures, dumps and wasteland sites with seed-bearing plants, particularly thistles and ragwort, and also alders along brooks and rivers. Nests are commonly built in apple, pear, chestnut, blackthorn or cherry, 2–5 m above ground. The breeding population is partially migratory, remaining birds are joined by individuals from n. and ne. Europe. Breeding density was 26–37 pairs per km^2 in villages at about 600 m in the Cesky les mountains (DO, TC), and 10–38 pairs per km^2 in parks in Praha

(AA) at the end of the 1970s. During the 1980s, it was 10–60 pairs per km^2 in hedgerows in TC county, 20–100 pairs per km^2 in growths in ST county, 60–140 individuals per km^2 in growths along a brook in CK county, 59 pairs per km^2 in hedgerows and poplar-dominated windbreaks at 170 m in UH county, and 25–42 pairs per km^2 in pastures with hedgerows and in the remains of an orchard at 210 m in UH county; and in various urban habitats in Bor u Tachova (TC) and Tachov (TC) it was 6–102 pairs per km^2, in parkland around a castle in Chodova Plana (TC) it was 10 pairs per km^2, and in a park in Ostrava (OV) it was 21 pairs per km^2. Winter density was 16 individuals per km^2 in Brno (BM) at the beginning of the 1970s, 22 individuals per km^2 in a village at about 600 m in the Cesky les mountains in the mid-1970s, 170 individuals per km^2 near Rozvadov (TC) at about 550 m, 0–2 individuals per km^2 in a mountain village at 730 m in VS county at the end of the 1970s and beginning of the 1980s, 11 individuals per km^2 in hedgerows and poplar-dominated windbreaks at 170 m in UH county in the mid-1980s, and 90–100 individuals per km^2 in pastures with hedgerows and in the remains of an orchard at 210 m in UH county at the end of the 1980s.
Status: Resident. **Breeding season:** common. **Winter:** common. **Migration:** common. Protected.
Population trends: The breeding population is between 200,000 to 400,000 pairs, and has been stable for the past 20 years. The number of wintering birds is between 200,000 and 400,000 individuals.
Distribution: Nationwide. High densities of wintering birds have been recorded in the following counties: KT, PJ, MO, TP, UL, BE, AA, PZ, PH, NB, NA, PU, CR, KI, VS, UH, HO, BV, BM and BO.
Timing: All year round. Breeding starts during late April, rarely earlier, and continues until early August, with peaks at the end of May, end of June, and during mid-July.

Siskin *Carduelis spinus*

Eurasian Siskin   Cizek lesni   Stehlik cizavy   Erlenzeisig

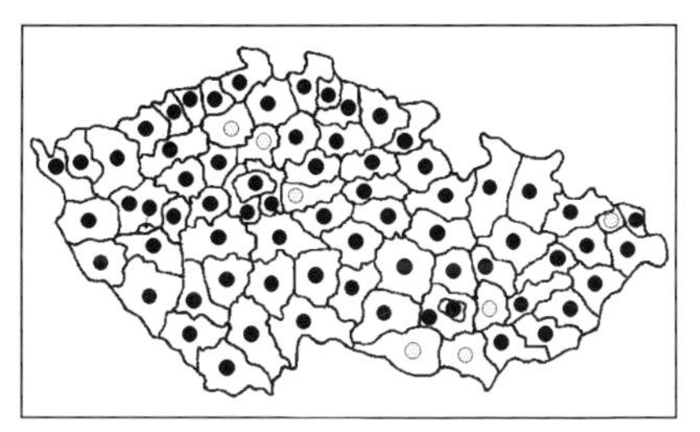

Siskin is a common breeder in highlands and mountains, although the numbers of breeding pairs may fluctuate from year to year. It occurs up to the treeline in mountains, such as 1100 m in the Orlicke hory mountains (RK), at 1300 m in the Jeseniky (BR, SU) and Sumava mountains (CK, PT, KT), and at 1400 m in the Krkonose (SE, TU) mountains. Occasionally, Siskins breed in lowlands, as low as about 180 m. Typical breeding habitat is coniferous forest in highlands and mountains, particularly spruce, with clearings, streams and brooks. However, breeding also occurs in mixed or deciduous, broadleaf-dominated forest with stands of conifers. In winter, flocks of Siskins frequent lowlands and highlands, and are seen in parks, in willows and alders along rivers and around ponds, and in small areas of birch-dominated forest in farmland. Nests are normally placed in spruce, occasionally in larch or pine, about 10 m above ground. Breeding density was 20 pairs per km^2 in spruce plantations in the Jeseniky mountains at the beginning of the 1970s, and 11 pairs per km^2 in spruce plantations at about 550 m around Milevsko (TA) at the end of the 1970s. During the 1980s, it was 10 pairs per km^2 in spruce forest at about 1100 m in the Beskydy mountains (FM, VS), 15 individuals per km^2 and 12 individuals per km^2 in spruce forest and dwarf pines respectively in TC county, 0–14 pairs per km^2 and 2–4 pairs per km^2 respectively in acid-rain-damaged spruce forest in the Jizerske hory (LB, JN) and Krkonose mountains, and 2–3 pairs per km^2 in spruce forest, 23 pairs per km^2 in dwarf pines, and 16 pairs per km^2 in spruce–dwarf-pine forest in the Cesky les mountains (DO, TC). Winter density was 104–111 individuals per km^2 in alders, 118–491 individuals per km^2 in a spruce forest, and 24 individuals per km^2 in growths around a pond at about 450 m around Trebon (JH) at the beginning of the 1970s, 64 individuals per km^2 in pine forest, and 25 individuals per km^2 in beech forest in TC county in the mid-1970s, 5–15 individuals per km^2 in a primeval beech and fir forest at about 900 m in VS county, and 2–3 individuals per km^2 in a mountain village at 730 m in VS county at the end of the 1970s and beginning of the 1980s, 50–65 indi-

viduals per km² in mixed woods at 280 m in UH county, and 49 individuals per km² in poplar-dominated windbreaks and hedgerows in farmland in UH county at the end of the 1980s.
Status: Resident. **Breeding season**: local/common. **Winter**: common. **Migration**: common. Protected.
Population trends: The breeding population is between 90,000 and 180,000 pairs. The minimum and maximum numbers have been relatively stable for the past 20 years, with fluctuations from year to year. The number of wintering birds ranges from 1,200,000 to 2,500,000 individuals.
Distribution: Nationwide. Breeding birds may be scarce in the following counties: ST, AA, MB, PS, CV, UL, UH, OL, RK, VY, KM and NJ. Large winter numbers have been reported from the following counties: JH, CB, PT, PI, PJ, PM, PS, TP, DC, PB, PH, KH, LB, NA, HK, PU, RK, KH, BM, KI, VS, UH, BM and BV.
Timing: All year round. Autumn movements from breeding into non-breeding areas in lowlands occurs between mid-September and the end of October, and return movements to breeding areas from mid-March until early April. Individuals from n. and ne. Europe arrive and depart at the same times. Breeding extends from late March until the end of June.

Linnet *Carduelis cannabina*

Common Linnet, Eurasian Linnet Konopka obecna Stehlik konopiar Bluthänfling

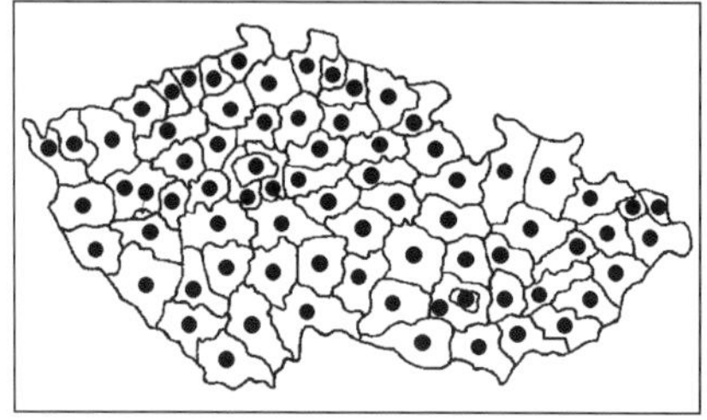

Linnet is distributed widely, being more abundant in lowlands than in highlands. It breeds up to 750 m in the Orlicke hory mountains (RK), to 800 m in the Jeseniky (BR, SU) and the Sumava mountains (CK, PT, KT), to 900 m in the Krusne hory mountains (CV, KV, MO, TP), to about 1100 m in the Beskydy mountains (FM, VS), and to 1400 m in the Krkonose mountains (SE, TU). Non-breeding occurrence has been recorded at even higher altitudes. Typical breeding habitat is farmland with hedges and groups of low trees, gardens, orchards, parks, vineyards, cemeteries, pastures with junipers, the edges of mixed forest, and not too dense growths along rivers (it avoids dense forest). Outside the breeding season, flocks of Linnets usually associate with other finches, and frequent pastures, weedy fields, dumps and wasteland with seed-bearing plants. Nests are usually placed in young trees and bushes such as spruce, vine, juniper, cypress and European elder, 0.5–1.5 m above ground. Average breeding density was 11.5–17 pairs per km² in hedgerows, 2.5–12.5 pairs per km² in growths along rivers and brooks, 5–8 pairs per km² in gardens, orchards and vineyards, and 6–10 pairs per km² in villages across the country during the 1970s. During the 1980s, it was 10–20 pairs per km² in woods in farmland (TC), 100 individuals per km² in windbreaks in BV county, 16 pairs per km² in parkland around a castle (LN), 0–14 pairs per km² at peatbogs in the Krkonose mountains, 6–11 pairs per km² in poplar-dominated windbreaks and hedgerows at 170 m in farmland in UH county, and 7–9 pairs per km² in pastures with hedgerows and in the remains of an orchard at 210 m in UH county. Although Linnet is predominantly a migratory species, flocks of dozens, rarely hundreds, of individuals can be found in winter, mostly in lowlands. Winter density was 5 individuals per km² in Brno (BM) at the beginning of the 1970s, and 9–12 individuals per km² in hedgerows and in poplar-dominated windbreaks at 170 m in UH county in the mid-1980s.
Status: Resident. **Breeding season**: common. **Winter**: common. **Migration**: common. Protected.
Population trends: The breeding population is between 60,000 and 120,000 pairs, and has declined by 20–50% during the past 20 years. The number of wintering birds ranges from 30,000 to 60,000 individuals.
Distribution: Nationwide. As a breeder, it may be locally scarce in SO, CL, PB, ZR, BR and HK counties. High winter numbers have been reported from the following counties: TA, PB, AA, PH, PU, RK, OL and PR.
Timing: All year round. The migratory part of the population arrives from mid-March until early April, peaking during late March. Autumn departure occurs between the beginning of

October and mid-November, peaking during late October. Breeding extends from the beginning of April to mid-August, with peaks during early May and early June.

Twite *Carduelis flavirostris*

Konopka zlutozoba Stehlik horsky Berghänfling

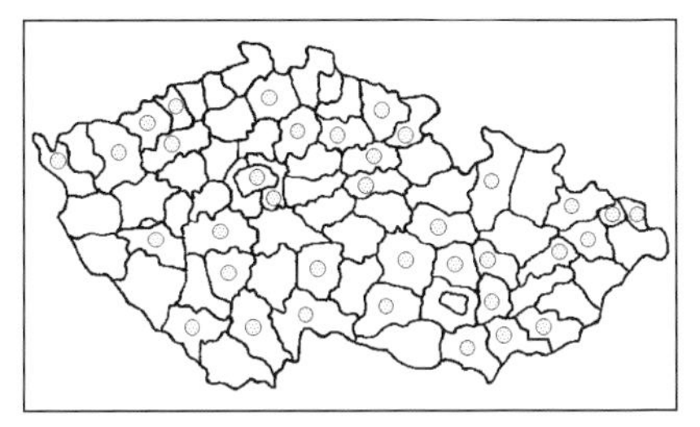

Twite was a rare visitor to the Czech Republic until the end of the 1950s, and was not recorded annually. Since the beginning of the 1960s, the number of birds reported annually has been increasing. Individual birds or, more commonly, flocks of up to 100 individuals, occur in lowlands and highlands, where they often associate with Linnets and Goldfinches. Typical habitats include weedy fields and pastures, and stubble-fields, often close to water. Birds occurring in the Czech Republic belong to the *flavirostris* race.

Status: Winter visitor. **Breeding season:** rare. **Winter:** uncommon. **Migration:** uncommon. Protected.

Population trends: The number of wintering birds is estimated to be between 200 and 500 individuals. The numbers have been increasing over the past 10–15 years.

Distribution: May occur nationwide. Recent records are from Tovacov (PR), Praha (AA), Hury (CB), Dehtar pond (CB), Lansky pond (SY), Svitavy (SY), Mnichovo Hradiste (MB), Troubky (PR), Nove Mlyny (BV), Chlumcany (PJ), Svitavy (SY), Podoli (BO), Domazelice (PR), Svatoborice (HO), Mistrin (HO), and Jarohnevicky pond (HO), Vlcnov (UH).

Timing: It occurs from mid-September until early April, with peak numbers in November, December and January.

Common Redpoll *Carduelis flammea*

Redpoll Cecetka zimni Stehlik cecetavy Birkenzeisig

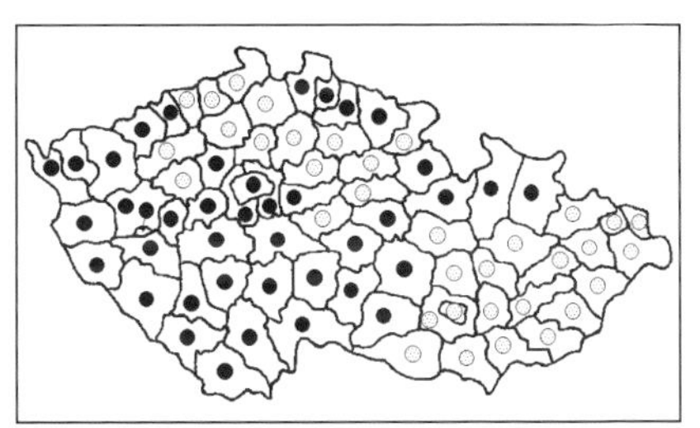

Common Redpoll has been known as a breeding bird in the Czech Republic for less than 150 years. Breeding in the country was first documented in the Krkonose mountains (SE, TU), although breeding probably occurred in the Kralicky Sneznik mountains (UO) in 1854. However, for 100 years after this, breeding was only accidental, and not sufficiently documented. The nesting of larger numbers was recorded in the Sumava mountains (CK, PT, KT) in 1952 and, since then, Common Redpoll has expanded its range: into the Krkonose mountains (SE, TU) in 1953, to the Jeseniky mountains (BR, SU) in 1967, to the Ceskomoravska vysocina highlands (HB, JI, PE, ZR) in 1968, to the Krusne hory mountains (CV, KV, MO, TP) in 1969, to the Jizerske hory (LB, JN) and Novohradske hory (CK, CB) mountains in 1971, and to the Orlicke hory mountains (RK) in 1979 (Hudec *et al.* 1983). From the end of the 1960s and beginning of the 1970s, Common Redpoll expanded its range into lowlands, and breeding was also recorded in larger towns. Breeding pairs are scattered across the country, usually in highlands and mountains. However, breeding occurs from about 200 m up to the dwarf-pine zone in mountains. Typical habitats are dwarf pine, and the edges of spruce forest in mountains, pine forest, growths of alder, birch and willow along rivers and around ponds, parkland at lower altitudes, and parks and gardens in larger towns. In winter, flocks of Common Redpolls occur in woodland with stands of birch, in alder growths along rivers, on wasteland with seed-bearing plants, and in farmland and in city parks. Nests are placed in birch, spruce, European elder, willow or dwarf pine, 1–4 m above ground. Breeding density was 73 pairs per km^2 at a peatbog covered with pine at about 450 m near Trebon (JH) in the mid-1970s. During the 1980s, it was 15 individuals

per km^2 in TC county, 55 pairs per km^2 in young spruce growths in the Jizerske hory mountains, 2–32 pairs per km^2 in the Krkonose mountains, and 18–66 pairs per km^2 in different-aged spruce forest in the Krusne hory mountains. Winter density was 2 individuals per km^2 in Brno (BM) at the beginning of the 1970s. During invasions, flocks of hundreds and thousands of individuals arrive from n. Europe. The breeding population belongs to the *cabaret* race, and is joined by individuals of the *flammea* race in winter.
Status: Resident. **Breeding season:** uncommon/local (*cabaret*), rare (*flammea*). **Winter:** local (both races). **Migration:** local (both races). Least concern. Protected.
Population trends: The breeding population is between 6,000 and 12,000 pairs, and has increased by 20–50% over the past 20 years, although local decreases have been reported. The number of wintering birds ranges from 10,000 to 20,000 individuals.
Distribution: Breeding of high numbers is restricted to the following counties: JH, CK, PT, KT, CH, RO, PJ, SE, TU and JI. Wintering birds have been recorded nationwide, with high densities in the following counties: CK, PT, ST, CH, PJ, PM, TC, BN, LB, JN, BE, PZ and TU.
Timing: All year round. Breeding extends from late April until late July, with peaks during mid-May and late June. Breeding occasionally starts during early to mid-April.

Arctic Redpoll *Carduelis hornemanni*

Cecetka belava Stehlik polarny Polarbirkenzeisig

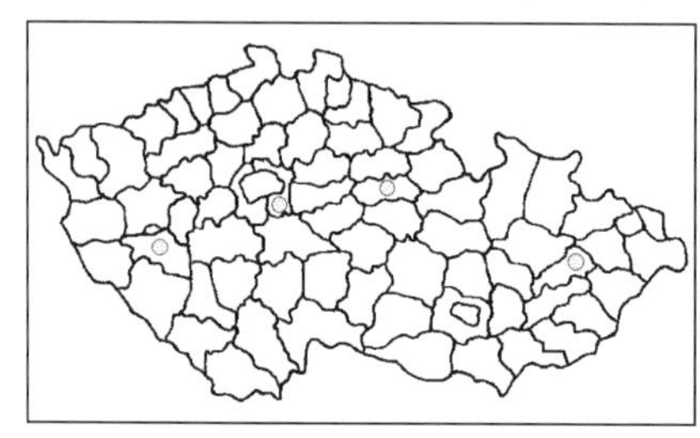

This species occurs in small numbers in the Czech Republic. Usually solitary birds or occasionally small flocks of up to 15 individuals are recorded. Arctic Redpolls can be found in the same habitats as Common Redpolls. Most of the records are from e. Bohemia and n. Moravia. Birds visiting the Czech Republic belong to the *exilipes* race.
Status: Vagrant. **Breeding season:** rare. **Winter:** uncommon. **Migration:** uncommon. Protected.
Population trends: Up to 50 individuals may be observed during winter. No data available to estimate population trends.
Distribution: May occur nationwide. The most recent records come from Prerov (PR) and Chlumcany (PJ).
Timing: It has been recorded from late November until early March, with most records in December and January.

Two-barred Crossbill *Loxia leucoptera*

Krivka belokridla Krivonos bielokridly Bindenkreuzschnabel

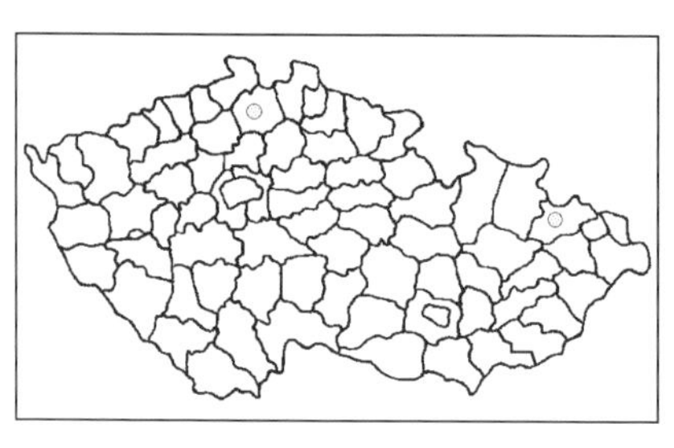

Two-barred Crossbill does not occur in the Czech Republic annually. During invasions, which are usually local, solitary birds or small flocks can be found. The largest documented invasion was recorded in 1889, when flocks of hundreds of birds were seen, and the last large invasion occurred in 1929/30 (Hudec *et al.* 1983). Typical habitats are conifer forest, preferably stands of larch, or mixed forest with mature conifers in highlands and mountains.
Status: Vagrant. **Breeding season:** rare. **Winter:** rare. **Migration:** rare. Protected.
Population trends: Up to 7 individuals have been recorded during a winter. No data available for an estimate of population trends.
Distribution: May occur nationwide, usually in mountains. One recent record is from Prachen (CL).
Timing: It has been recorded all year round except in April. The most records are from September and October.

Common Crossbill *Loxia curvirostra*

Crossbill Krivka obecna Krivonos obycajny Fichtenkreuzschnabel

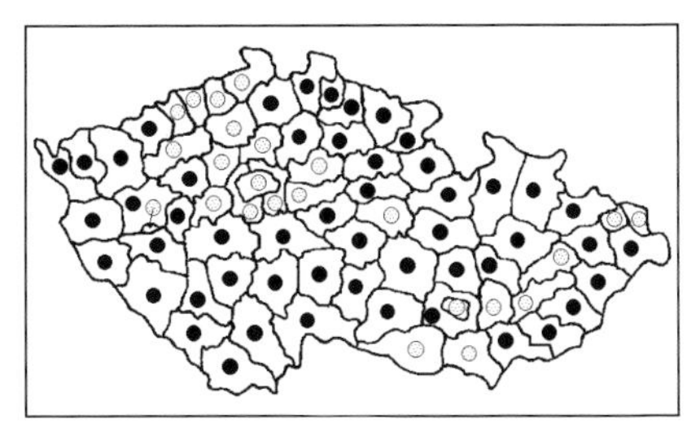

Common Crossbill is a locally common but irregular breeding species in the Czech Republic. Breeding is restricted to spruce and pine forest in highlands and mountains and, occasionally during invasions, in lowlands at about 200 m. Outside the breeding season, and in years with poor conifer cones, Common Crossbills occur at lower altitudes, in mixed forest and in larger city parks with conifers. Regular breeding of large numbers occurs in mountain spruce forest at about 1000 m, for example in the Krusne hory mountains (CV, KV, MO, TP), the Krkonose mountains (SE, TU), the Orlicke hory mountains (RK), the Kralicky sneznik mountains (UO), the Jeseniky mountains (BR, SU), the Beskydy mountains (VS, FM), the Ceskomoravska vysocina highlands (HB, JI, PE, ZR), the Novohradske hory mountains (CK, CB), and the Sumava mountains (CK, PT, KT). Nests are placed in a spruce or pine, 10–30 m above ground. The annual numbers of Common Crossbill may vary from year to year, being influenced by invasions from n. Europe. Breeding density was 28–68 individuals per km^2 in pine-spruce forest near Trebon (JH) at the beginning of the 1970s. During the 1980s, it was 4–24 individuals per km^2 in spruce forest in the Sumava mountains, 13 individuals per km^2 and 19 individuals per km^2 respectively in spruce and pine forest in TC county, and 1–3 pairs per km^2 in acid-rain-damaged spruce and spruce-beech forest in the Krkonose mountains.Winter density (December–February) was 0–28 individuals per km^2 in a spruce forest near Trebon (JH) at the beginning of the 1970s, 30 individuals per km^2 in a pine forest in TC county in the mid-1970s, 0–10 individuals per km^2 in primeval beech and fir forest at about 900 m in VS county, 0–1 individuals per km^2 in a mountain village at 730 m in VS county at the end of the 1970s and beginning of the 1980s, and 10–14 individuals per km^2 in spruce forest at 690 m in the Bile Karpaty mountains (HO, UH, ZL) at the end of the 1980s. The Czech population belongs to the *curvirostra* race. In 1976, *Loxia c. curvirostra* var. *rubrifasciata* was documented in the Krkonose mountains (Weber 1976).

Status: Resident. **Breeding season:** local/common. **Winter:** local/common. **Migration:** local/common. Protected.

Population trends: The breeding population is between 30,000 and 100,000 pairs. Population trends for the past 20 years are largely unknown. However, since 1987 the population has apparently been increasing. The number of wintering birds ranges from 60,000 to 120,000 individuals.

Distribution: Breeding may be scarce in the following counties: BO, VY, TR, JI, ZR, PI, PB, CV, PU, KH, ST, OL and SU. Non-breeding birds may be rather rare in CV, MO, TP, UL, LN, LT, CL, ME, NB, KO, HK, PU, BR, OP, KI, HO, BV and ZN counties. High winter numbers have been observed in the following counties: JH, CK, PT, BE, CB and PB.

Timing: All year round. The main occurrence outside the regular breeding areas is recorded in June and July, and October and December. Breeding extends from late January until the end of April, with the peak in February.

Parrot Crossbill *Loxia pytyopsittacus*

Krivka velka Krivonos sosnovy Kiefernkreuzschnabel

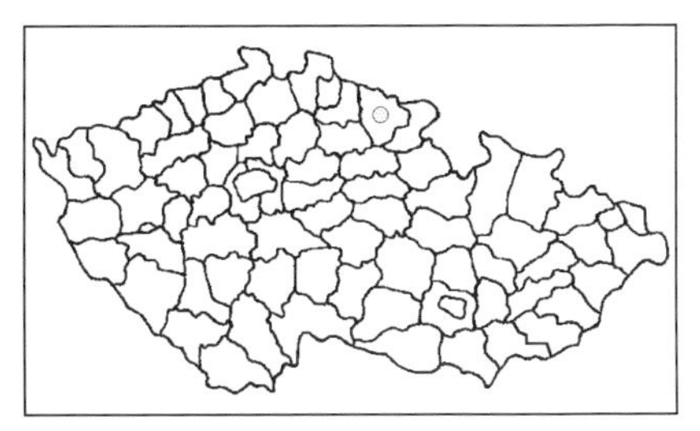

Parrot Crossbill is a rare and irregularly occurring species in the Czech Republic. Usually solitary birds, or occasionally small flocks, may be found across the country, from lowlands up to the limit of montane coniferous forest. This species usually occurs in pine and mixed, pine-dominated, forest. Parrot Crossbills often associate with flocks of Common Crossbills.

Status: Vagrant. **Breeding season:** rare. **Winter:** rare. **Migration:** rare. Protected.

Population trends: No data available for estimate of population trends.
Distribution: May occur nationwide.
Timing: It has been recorded all year round, with most records in October.

Common Rosefinch *Carpodacus erythrinus*

Scarlet Rosefinch, Scarlet Grosbeak Hyl rudy Cervenak karminovy Karmingimpel

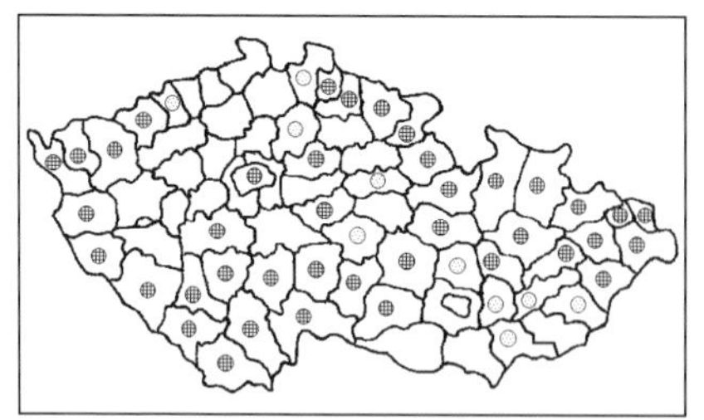

Common Rosefinch is a relatively new species to the Czech Republic. The first documented records from the country are from 1889, when 7 birds were observed near Zbraslav nad Vltavou (PZ), and from 1891 when a male was collected in the Jeseniky mountains (BR, SU). Breeding in Moravia was first recorded in 1962 near Tovacov (PR), and the first breeding record in Bohemia was from the Krkonose mountains (SE, TU) in 1968. Since then, this species has been expanding its range in the Czech Republic. Breeding in the Jeseniky mountains (BR, SU) was recorded in 1970, in the Sumava mountains (CK, PT, KT) in 1973, in the Orlicke hory mountains (RK) in 1978, in the Beskydy mountains (FM, VS) in 1979, in the Krusne hory mountains (CV, KV, MO, TP) in 1984, in the Ceskomoravska vysocina highlands (HB, JI, PE, ZR) in 1986, and in the Jizerske hory mountains (LB, JN) in 1989. Strongholds of the breeding population are the Krkonose mountains, with 80–100 pairs, the Sumava mountains, with about 100 pairs, the Jeseniky mountains, with 40–60 pairs, the Beskydy mountains, with 30–40 pairs, and OV county, with several dozen pairs. It breeds from lowlands at about 200 m, up to about 900 m in the Orlicke hory mountains, to 1100 m in the Sumava mountains, and to 1300 m in the Krkonose mountains. Typical breeding habitats include meadows with scattered scrub, willow thickets along rivers and brooks, mountain meadows with bushes and thickets near forest edges, dumps, and gardens with dense scrub cover at the edges of villages. Nests are built in raspberry bushes, willow thickets, blackberry bushes, rose, spruce, apple trees, and currant bushes, 0.5–3.5 m above ground. Breeding density was 50 pairs per km^2 in growths along a brook in CK county in the mid-1980s, and 15 pairs per km^2 in the Jizerske hory mountains in 1994. A 5-km transect along a river in CK county held 60 singing males in the mid-1980s. This species is more common in Slovakia, where the breeding population is between 500 and 1,000 pairs (Murin *et al.* 1994).
Status: Summer visitor. **Breeding season:** uncommon/local. **Winter:** does not occur. **Migration:** local. Endangered. Protected.
Population trends: Between 1973 and 1977 the breeding population was 30–50 pairs; recently it is 350–450 pairs. The population continues to increase.
Distribution: Between 1962 and 1972, breeding was documented in PR, OV, BR and SU counties. Between 1973 and 1977, it expanded its range into CK, PT, KT, TR, ZR, VS, SE and TU counties. After 1977, it expanded into the following counties (where regular or occasional breeding occurs): NJ, KH, ST, DO, SY, PI, PB, CB, TA, NB, JH, AA, BV, JI, JN, RK, TR, KM, OL, OP, VY, HO, UO, PV and FM.
Timing: Spring migration starts mid-May and continues until early to mid-June, peaking at the end of May and beginning of June. It rarely arrives before mid-May. Autumn migration occurs from late July until the end of August. Breeding extends from late May until early July, peaking during late June.

Pine Grosbeak *Pinicola enucleator*

Hyl krivci Smreciar krivonosy Hakengimpel

Pine Grosbeak does not occur annually, although during the 19th century it was considered a regular winter visitor to the Czech Republic. Usually solitary birds and, less commonly, a flock of a few individuals, are recorded from lowlands up to the mountains across the country. It occurs in spruce, mixed and, rarely, deciduous forest with an undergrowth of berry-bearing

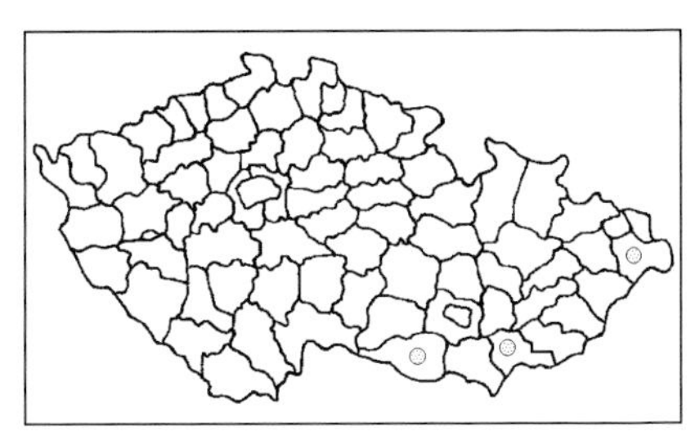

scrub, in avenues, and in mountain-ash.
Status: Vagrant. **Breeding season:** rare. **Winter:** rare. **Migration:** rare. Protected.
Population trends: No data available for an estimate of population trends. The number of birds recorded in winter does not usually exceed 10 individuals.
Distribution: May occur nationwide. A recent record is from Velka nad Velickou (HO).
Timing: Mostly recorded from September to December, less commonly from February to March. Unusual records come from April, July and August.

Common Bullfinch *Pyrrhula pyrrhula*

Bullfinch, Eurasian Bullfinch   Hyl obecny   Hyl obycajny   Gimpel

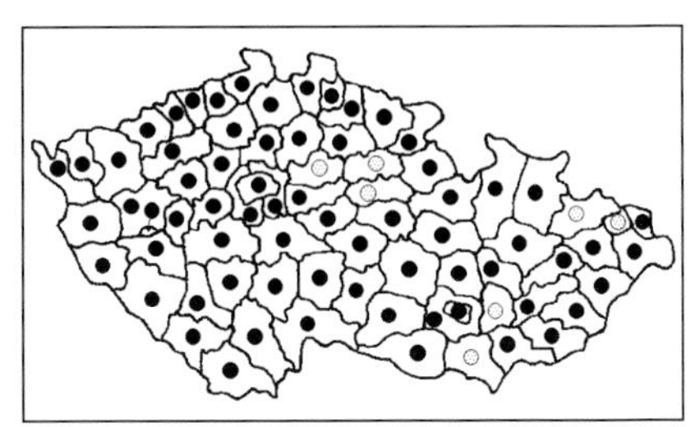

Common Bullfinch is a regular breeder in the Czech Republic, being more common in highlands and mountains than in lowlands. It breeds across the country, from about 350 m up to 1200 m in the Beskydy (FM, VS) and Sumava (CK, PT, KT) mountains, to 1300 m in the Jeseniky mountains (BR, SU), and to 1400 m in the Krkonose mountains (SE, TU). Breeding habitat is coniferous forest in highlands or mountains and, less commonly, mixed mountain forest. Occasional breeding occurs in riverine and mixed forest in lowlands, and in larger city parks and gardens with conifers and thick undergrowth. Outside the breeding season, Common Bullfinch also frequents lowlands, where it is found in any type of forest, larger gardens, orchards and parks with scrub undergrowth and, less frequently, open country with hedgerows, groups of berry-bearing shrubs and trees, and growths along rivers and brooks. Nests are placed in spruce, cypress, pine, juniper or oak, 1–3 m above ground. During the 1970s, breeding density was 4 pairs per km^2 in primeval beech and fir forest at about 900 m in VS county, and 8–11 pairs per km^2 in a mature spruce plantation near Milevsko (TA) at 430–630 m, 14 individuals per km^2 in various habitats in Brno (BM), and 5 pairs per km^2 in a large park in Praha (AA). During the 1980s it was 1–4 pairs per km^2 in acid-rain-damaged spruce and spruce-beech forest in the Krkonose mountains, 4–9 pairs per km^2 in the Beskydy mountains, 5–7 individuals per km^2 in spruce forest in the Sumava mountains, 50 pairs per km^2 in growths along a brook in CK county, 13 pairs per km^2 in mature beech forest at the Cesky raj cliffs (MB), 10–20 pairs per km^2 in spruce and spruce-dwarf-pine in the Cesky les mountains (DO, TC), and 3–5 pairs per km^2 in mature mixed forest in the Bile Karpaty mountains (HO, UH, ZL) at about 600 m. During the 1990s, in spruce and spruce-beech forest in the Beskydy mountains, above 1000 m, it was 3–20 pairs per km^2, in mature mixed forest (NB) it was 9 individuals per km^2, and in spruce around Zabreh na Morave (SU) it was 75 pairs per km^2. Winter density was 1 individual per km^2 in a spruce and pine forest around Trebon (JH) at the beginning of the 1970s, 31 individuals per km^2 in pine plantations in TC county in the mid-1970s, 12 individuals per km^2 in Brno (BM) at the beginning of the 1970s, 2–3 individuals per km^2 in a mountain village at 730 m in VS county at the end of the 1970s and beginning of the 1980s, 9–12 individuals per km^2 in mixed woods at 280 m in UH county, and 5 individuals per km^2 in poplar-dominated windbreaks and hedgerows in farmland in UH county at the end of the 1980s. The breeding population belongs to the *pyrrhula* race.
Status: Resident. **Breeding season:** local/common. **Winter:** common. **Migration:** common. Protected.
Population trends: The breeding population is between 100,000 and 200,000 pairs, and has been stable for the past 20 years. The number of wintering birds ranges from 100,000 to 200,000 individuals.
Distribution: Nationwide. As a breeder, it may be scarce in the following counties: LT, ME, KL, NB, JC, LN, TR, PI, ST, DO, HK, PU, HO, BV, VY, PV, OP and PR. Large numbers of

wintering birds have been reported from the following counties: TA, CV, LT, DC, NA and JN. **Timing:** All year round. Breeding extends from mid-April until mid-July, with peaks during the first half of May and late June.

Hawfinch *Coccothraustes coccothraustes*

Dlask tlustozoby Glezg obycajny Kernbeißer

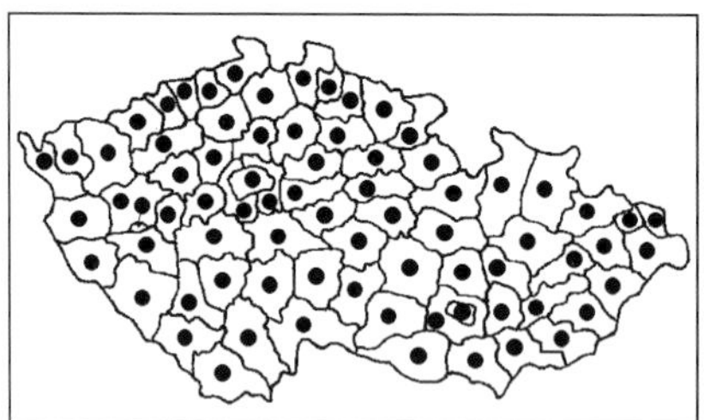

Hawfinch is a regular, locally fairly common breeder in the Czech Republic. It occurs more in lowlands and highlands than in mountains. Breeding has been recorded up to 580 m in the Ceskomoravska vysocina highlands (HB, JI, PE, ZR) and in the Bile Karpaty mountains (HO, UH, ZL), to 600 m in the Orlicke hory mountains (RK), to 700 m in the Cesky les mountains (DO, TC), to 800 m in the Krusne hory (CV, KV, MO, TP) and Jeseniky (BR, SU) mountains, to 1100 m in the Krkonose mountains (SE, TU), and to 1200 m in the Sumava mountains (CK, PT, KT). Breeding habitats include not too dense deciduous oak- or beech-dominated forest, mixed forest, tall hedgerows, windbreaks, and woodland in open country, mature growths along rivers and around ponds, avenues, larger gardens, orchards, cemeteries and parks. Nests are built in oak, apple, pear, spruce, ash, or European elder, 1–7 m above ground. The breeding population is partially migratory. Wintering birds, which are joined by individuals from n. Europe, often stay in flocks of varying size and frequent hornbeams. During the 1970s, breeding density was 34–38 pairs per km^2 and 60 pairs per km^2 respectively in riverine forest near Zahlinice (KM) and Prerov (PR), 2 pairs per km^2 in parks in Brno (BM), 22 pairs per km^2 in oak- and elm-dominated riverine forest near the Odra river (NJ), and 6 pairs per km^2 in oak-hornbeam forest in NA county. During the 1980s, it was 25 pairs per km^2 in oak-hornbeam forest around Pisek (PI), 34 individuals per km^2 and 20 pairs per km^2 in riverine forest in n. Moravia, 7 pairs per km^2 in mature oak forest at the Cesky raj cliffs (MB), 19 pairs per km^2 in beech-lime forest in PI county, 72 individuals per km^2 in growths along a brook in CK county, 3–25 individuals per km^2 in forest in the Sumava mountains, 10 pairs per km^2 in poplar-dominated windbreaks at 170 m in UH county, 27–32 pairs per km^2 in an abandoned orchard around a vineyard at 210 m in UH county, 4–7 pairs per km^2 in a park in Ostrava (OV), and 10 pairs per km^2 in parkland around a castle (LN). In oak and mixed forest near Mlada (NB) it was 10–26 individuals per km^2 at the beginning of the 1990s. Winter density was 6 individuals per km^2 in Brno (BM) at the beginning of the 1970s, 0–1 individuals per km^2 in a mountain village at 730 m in VS county at the end of the 1970s and beginning of the 1980s, and 5–8 individuals per km^2 in mixed woods at 280 m in UH county at the end of the 1980s.

Status: Resident. **Breeding season**: common. **Winter**: common. **Migration**: common. Protected.

Population trends: The breeding population is between 150,000 and 300,000 pairs, and has been stable for the past 20 years. The number of wintering birds ranges from 20,000 to 40,000 individuals.

Distribution: Nationwide. As a breeder it occurs less commonly in ST, KT, DO, SO, LB, JN, SE, PI, PE, ZR, SY and SU counties. Wintering birds may be rather scarce in the following counties: PT, CV, DC, KL, JN, ZR, PE and LB.

Timing: All year round. Breeding extends from mid-April until early June, peaking during early to mid-May.

Lapland Longspur *Calcarius lapponicus*

Lapland Bunting Strnad laponsky Ostroharka severska Spornammer

There are several records of Lapland Longspurs from the Czech Republic collected in the 19th century, and the first 60 years of the 20th century. Even though the number of records has been increasing since 1960, Lapland Longspur has not been recorded annually. Usually soli-

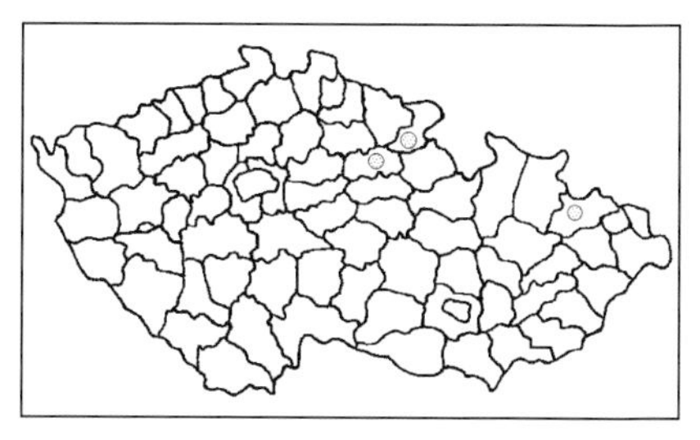

tary birds or, rarely, a flock of a few individuals, occur more commonly in the west of the country. Typical habitats are open weedy pastures, grassy areas and stubble-fields.

Status: Vagrant. **Breeding season:** rare. **Winter:** uncommon. **Migration:** uncommon. Protected.

Population trends: Up to 7 individuals are recorded per winter. No data available for estimation of population trends.

Distribution: May occur nationwide. A recent record of 1 individual comes from Rozkos dam (NA).

Timing: It has been recorded from September until April.

Snow Bunting *Plectrophenax nivalis*

Snehule severni Snehulka severska Schneeammer

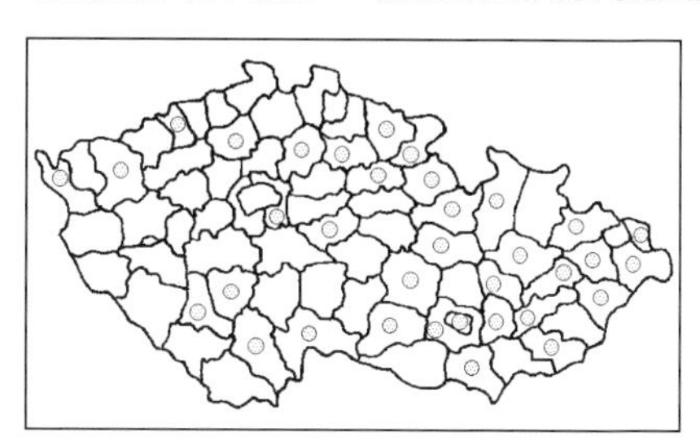

Snow Bunting occurs annually as a spring and autumn migrant, and as a winter visitor, in the Czech Republic. Individual birds, less commonly flocks of a few, are scattered across the country, with more records from the east. Occasionally, larger flocks of up to a few hundred can be seen. This species occurs in open farmland, usually in lowlands. Typically found in pastures, cultivated fields and stubble-fields.

Status: Migrant and winter visitor. **Breeding season:** rare. **Winter:** uncommon. **Migration:** uncommon. Protected.

Population trends: The number of wintering birds is estimated to be between 300 and 700 individuals. No data available for estimating population trends.

Distribution: May occur nationwide. Recent records of up to 50 individuals come from Grygov (OL), Smetana (UO), Tovacov (PR), Spindleruv Mlyn (TU), Nove Mlyny (BV), Mnichovo Hradiste (MB), Bartosovice v Orlickych horach (RK), Mohelno (TR), Tovacov (PR), Holice (OL), Troubky (PR), Prerov (PR), Zahlinice (KM) and Hulin (KM). Regular records have come from various places in PR county.

Timing: Occurs from September until May, with the majority of records between November and March.

Yellowhammer *Emberiza citrinella*

Yellow Bunting Strnad obecny Strnadka obycajna Goldammer

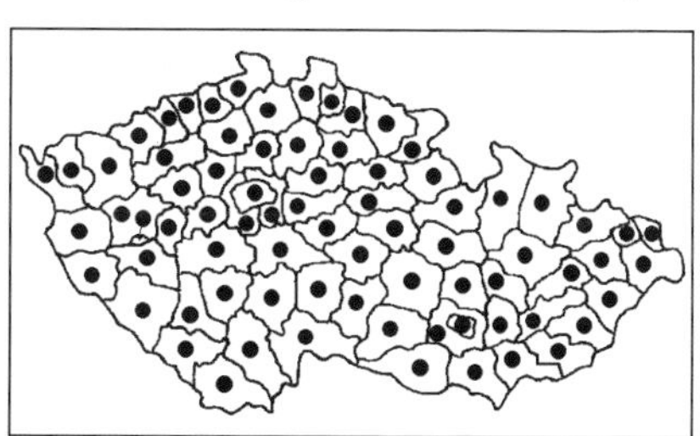

Yellowhammer is one of the commonest birds in the Czech Republic. Distributed across the country, it occurs from lowlands up to 800 m in the Jeseniky mountains (BR, SU), to 900 m in the Sumava mountains (CK, PT, KT), to 1025 m in the Orlicke hory (RK) and Krusne hory (CV, KV, MO, TP) mountains, to about 1100 m in the Beskydy mountains (FM, VS), and to 1350 m in the Krkonose mountains (SE, TU). It is typically found in cultivated land with hedgerows, groups of trees and bushes, plantations, and woodland, where it prefers dry and sunny places such as hillsides with overgrown scrub, and the edges of villages. It also breeds at the edges of clearings in large areas of deciduous or mixed forest. It usually avoids dense forest and wetland. In winter, it is often found in flocks with Common Chaffinch, Greenfich, Brambling or Linnet, and frequents weedy, stubble- and turnip fields, farmland and villages. Nests are placed on the ground, in grass or other vegetation, and in bushes or trees such as spruce, rose, blackberry, blackthorn and hawthorn, 0.2–1.5

m above ground. Breeding density varies among habitats: it was 52–65 pairs per km^2 in abandoned orchards in CV county at the beginning of the 1970s, 22–83 pairs per km^2 in hedgerows and along a river, 19–21 pairs per km^2 in pine forest around Trebon (JH), 37 pairs per km^2 in an avenue along a road and 5 pairs per km^2 in an avenue near forest in TC county in the mid-1970s, and 34–48 pairs per km^2 in young forest at the edge of Praha (AA) at the end of the 1970s. During the 1980s, in mixed growths in farmland, it was 83–284 pairs per km^2 in TA and CB counties, 50–480 pairs per km^2 in ST county, and 40–250 pairs per km^2 in TC county, it was 1–4 pairs per km^2 in acid-rain-damaged spruce and spruce-beech forest in the Krkonose mountains, 14–27 pairs per km^2 in mixed woods in CH county, 60 pairs per km^2 in pine forest in TA county, 9–73 pairs per km^2 in spruce forest in the Krusne hory mountains, 17–21 pairs per km^2 in poplar-dominated windbreaks and hedgerows at 170 m in farmland (UH), and 35–42 pairs per km^2 in pastures with hedgerows and in the remains of an orchard at 210 m in UH county. It was 10–14 pairs per km^2 in parkland around castles in w. Bohemia, 13 pairs per km^2 in a park in Ostrava (OV), and 17–75 pairs per km^2 in gardens around Tachov (TC) during the 1980s and beginning of the 1990s. Winter density was 2–35 individuals per km^2 in growths around a pond at about 450 m around Trebon (JH), and 0.4 individuals per km^2 in Brno (BM) at the beginning of the 1970s; 18 individuals per km^2 in a pine forest in TC county, 13–96 individuals per km^2 in villages at about 600 m in the Cesky les mountains (DO, TC), and 12 individuals per km^2 near Rozvadov (TC) at about 550 m in the mid-1970s; 12–34 individuals per km^2 in a mountain village at 730 m in VS county at the end of the 1970s and beginning of the 1980s; 95–112 individuals per km^2 at the edges of mixed woods at 280 m in UH county, and 106 individuals per km^2 in poplar-dominated windbreaks and in hedgerows in farmland in UH county in the mid-1980s. Wintering birds are joined by individuals from ne. Europe. The breeding population belongs to the *citrinella* race.

Status: Resident. **Breeding season**: common. **Winter**: common. **Migration**: common. Protected.

Population trends: The breeding population is between 2,000,000 and 4,000,000 pairs, and has been stable for the past 20 years. The number of wintering birds ranges from 1,500,000 to 3,000,000 individuals.

Distribution: Nationwide. Large numbers of wintering birds have been reported from the following counties: BN, TA, PI, PM, PS, PJ, PZ, PH, LT, LB, HK, NA, OP, OL and UH.

Timing: All year round. Breeding occurs from early April until the end of August, with peaks during late April and late June.

Ortolan Bunting *Emberiza hortulana*

Strnad zahradni   Strnadka zahradna   Ortolan

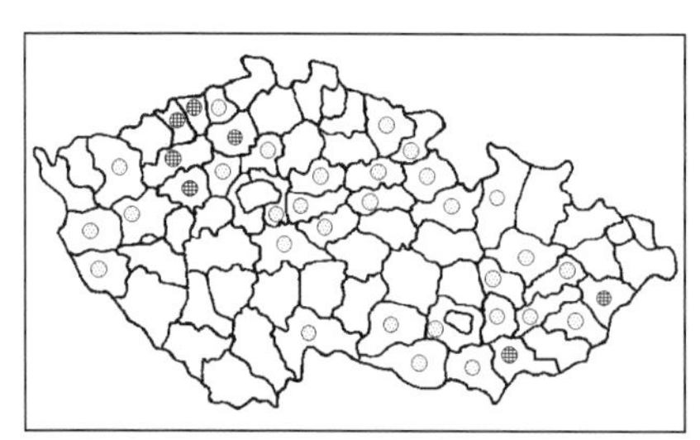

Ortolan Bunting is a rare breeder in the Czech Republic. Its numbers and distribution have been changing over the past 150 years. In the first half of the 19th century, it was a rare migrant and there were only a few records from the country. Breeding was first documented around 1860 in n. Bohemia, and in 1886 in s. Moravia. Since then, Ortolan Bunting has been expanding its range. Between 1860 and 1880, it was a regular breeder in n. Bohemia; at the end of the 19th century it was distributed across s. Moravia and central Moravia, with local populations in w. Bohemia and s. Bohemia; and during the first half of the 20th century its expansion continued: in the 1950s it reached its maximum distribution in the Czech Republic (Hudec *et al.* 1983), being recorded up to 500 m in the Ceskomoravska vysocina highlands (HB, JI, PE, ZR), to 610 m in PS county, and to 700 m in the Krkonose mountains (SE, TU). During the 1960s, the number of breeding pairs declined drastically, and Ortolan Bunting disappeared from many previously occupied areas. The exact reasons for the decrease are unknown, but are most likely related to changes in agriculture including the loss of suitable habitats. Ortolan Bunting is found in lowlands and highlands up to 500 m. It is typically found on dry and warm hillsides with scattered scrub, in abandoned orchards, vineyards, avenues along county roads, fields of various crops and cereals, and

at the edges of not too dense deciduous and mixed woods. Data on breeding density are scarce: 4 males were singing 0.8 km from Most (MO) in 1970, and 5–6 pairs were recorded on a 5-km transect near Drinov (MO) in 1977. Records since the beginning of the 1990s indicate that numbers of Ortolan Buntings are increasing, and new sites are are being occupied.
Status: Migrant and summer visitor. **Breeding season**: uncommon. **Winter**: does not occur. **Migration**: uncommon/local. Endangered. Protected.
Population trends: The breeding population is between 200 and 300 pairs.
Distribution: On migration, it may occur nationwide. Regular breeding distribution is more or less restricted to a few areas in n. Bohemia, central Bohemia and s. and n. Moravia. Recent records come from Lobec (ME), Velky Tisy pond (JH), Zizelice (KO), Rana (LN), Lisky u Postupic (BN), Zehunsky pond (NB), Hradcany (NB), Msecke Zehrovice (RA), Radejov (HO), Lednice (BV), Bulanka (KO), Chvalcov (KM), Nove Dvory (PR), Ceske Budejovice (CB), Studenec (TR), Cejc (HO), Hovorany (HO), and Uherce (PS).
Timing: Spring arrival starts during mid-April, peaking during late April, and continues until the end of May. Autumn departure occurs from late August until the end of September, peaking during late September. Birds are occasionally seen during early October. Breeding extends from late April until the end of June, peaking during mid-May.

Reed Bunting *Emberiza schoeniclus*

Common Reed Bunting Strnad rakosni Strnadka trstinova Rohrammer

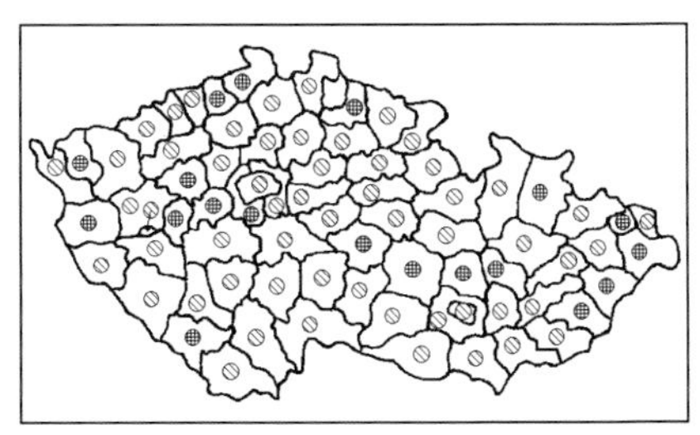

Reed Bunting is associated with fishpond areas, wetlands and other 'wet' sites in the Czech Republic. It is distributed throughout the country, mainly in lowlands, where locally it may be a fairly common species. As a breeder, it has been recorded up to 350 m in the foothills of the Jeseniky mountains (BR, SU), to 480 m in the foothills of the Krkonose mountains (SE, TU), to 600 m in the Ceskomoravska vysocina highlands (HB, JI, PE, ZR), and to 730 m in the Sumava mountains (CK, KT, PT). It occupies tall vegetation, reedmace, reedbeds, and willow thickets in marshes, the edges of ponds, wet meadows, habitat along canals, ditches and oxbows, and occasionally along rivers. It usually avoids extensive flooded reedbeds. Wintering birds frequent reedbeds, but also associate with flocks of Yellowhammers and occur in farmland close to water, main-

Reed Bunting

ly in lowlands. Nests are built in sedge or grass, in reedbeds, in tangles of vegetation on the ground, and in nettles, 0.1–0.3 m above the water or the ground. Breeding density was 70 pairs per km^2 at ponds at about 320–350 m around Sedlcany (BN), and 2 pairs per km^2 at wet meadows around Trebon (JH) in the mid-1970s; 5–570 pairs per km^2 at various ponds in BV county, 25–43 pairs per km^2 at peatbogs in CH county, and 130–300 pairs per km^2 at ponds in CB and JH counties in s. Bohemia during the 1970s. During the 1980s, it was 3 pairs per km^2 at marshes with scattered trees in TC county, 190–500 pairs per km^2 in reedbeds at several ponds in JH county, 60–160 individuals per km^2 around Vrbenske ponds (CB), 7–19 pairs per km^2 at oxbows near Hustenovice (UH), and 54–110 pairs per km^2 in reedbeds around gravel pits at about 170 m in Ostrozska Nova Ves (UH). The breeding population is migratory, and the origin of wintering birds is unknown. Breeding birds belong to the *ukrainae* race. Individuals of the *schoeniclus* race have been recorded in spring and autumn migration, and during winter.

Status: Migrant and summer visitor. **Breeding season:** local (*ukrainae*), rare (*schoeniclus*). **Winter:** local (both races). **Migration:** local (both races). Protected.

Population trends: The breeding population is between 40,000 and 80,000 pairs, and has decreased slightly since the mid-1980s. The number of wintering birds range from 800 to 1,600 individuals.

Distribution: Nationwide. As a breeder, it may occur less commonly in the following counties: CK, SO, CV, UL, LB, SE, TU, NA, KL, CR, SY, BR, VS and ZL. Large numbers of wintering birds have been reported from the following counties: JH, CB, AA, NB, PH, BV, HO, KO, PV, PU and KI.

Timing: Spring migration occurs from the last decade of February until the end of April, peaking during the first half of March. Autumn migration occurs between the beginning of September and the end of October, peaking during late October. Breeding starts in mid-April and continues until mid-July, with peaks during late April and late May.

Corn Bunting *Emberiza calandra*

Strnad lucni Strnadka lucna Grauammer

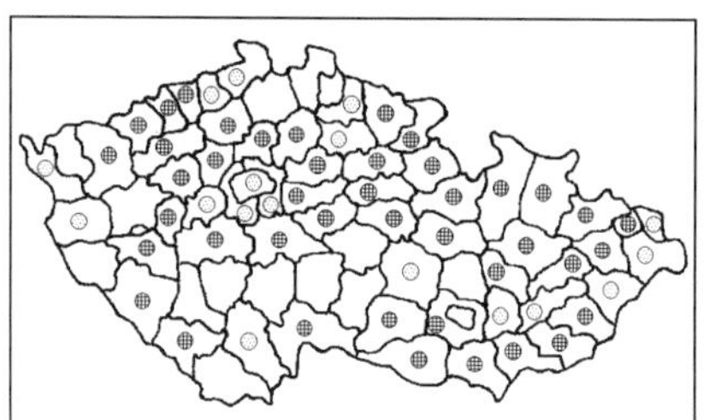

Corn Bunting is a regular breeding species, scattered throughout the Czech Republic. From about the 1850s until the early 1960s, it expanded its range across the country. Its numbers have fluctuated during the past 150 years. During the 19th, and first 20 years of the 20th century, it was considered a common species in lowlands. In the 1920s, it became locally rare as a result of agricultural intensification, and its disappearance from various parts of the country continued. At the end of the 1960s, Corn Bunting was a rare breeder, and its numbers were still decreasing at the end of the 1980s. It prefers farmland in lowlands and highlands up to about 500–550 m, as in the Orlicke hory mountains (RK), and Oderske vrchy hills (OL, PR), and to about 600 m in the Bile Karpaty mountains (HO, UH, ZL). It is typically found in meadows and pastures with scattered trees and bushes, cultivated fields, fields surrounding railways, along country roads, avenues in hedgerows, and around brooks, canals and ponds. It avoids forest and wetland. After the breeding season, it is often found in small flocks, frequenting weedy pastures, meadows, stubble-fields, and reedbeds around ponds. Nests are placed on the ground, in grass in meadows, in grass and brush at the edge of forest, and in plants along country roads. High numbers of breeding pairs have recently been reported from Javornik nad Velickou (HO), and the Bile Karpaty mountains (HO, UH, ZL), with up to 250 pairs, from areas around Znojmo (ZN), with 50–60 pairs, and from Lednicke ponds (BV), where the breeding population is 100–150 pairs. Breeding density was 25–40 pairs per km^2 in abandoned orchards in CV county, and 15 individuals per km^2 in steppe-like habitat in the Ceske Stredohori highlands (LN, LT) at the beginning of the 1970s; and 19 pairs per km^2 near Cesky Brod (KO) in the mid-1970s. It was 7–15 pairs per km^2 along a railway and in surrounding hillsides at about 530 m in the Bile Karpaty mountains (HO, UH, ZL) in the mid-1980s, and 23–114 individuals per km^2 in

various habitats around Mlada (NB) at the beginning of the 1990s.
Status: Resident. **Breeding season:** uncommon/local. **Winter:** local. **Migration:** local. Endangered. Protected.
Population trends: Between 1973 and the end of 1980s, the breeding population was 700–1,400 pairs; in 1994 it was 1,400–2,800 pairs. The breeding population has been increasing since the early 1990s. The number of wintering birds is estimated to be between 150 and 400 individuals, but has probably been higher in recent years.
Distribution: On migration it may occur nationwide. Strongholds of the breeding population are in the following counties: CV, MO, LN, ME, MB, HK, PU, CR, BV and HO. Solitary wintering birds, flocks of up to 100, occasionally more, have been reported from the following counties: LN, TP, SE, JC, PU, CR, KO, PB, PH, BK, VY, BV, HO, KM, NJ, KI, NB, BO and PU.
Timing: Spring arrival starts in mid-February, and continues until early April. Autumn departure occurs between the end of September and the end of November. Breeding extends from late April until early July, peaking at the beginning of May.

ACCIDENTALS

Brief information on families in each order is provided in the species accounts. Because all species of Procellariiformes are 'accidental' in the Czech Republic, some information on the families is provided here. **Procellariiformes** include 3 families with 39 species in the w. Palearctic. Three species of the **Procellariidae** and **Hydrobatidae** families have been recorded in the Czech Republic.

White-billed Diver *Gavia adamsi*

Yellow-billed Loon, Yellow-billed Diver Potaplice zlutozoba Potaplica bielozoba Gelbschnable-Eistaucher

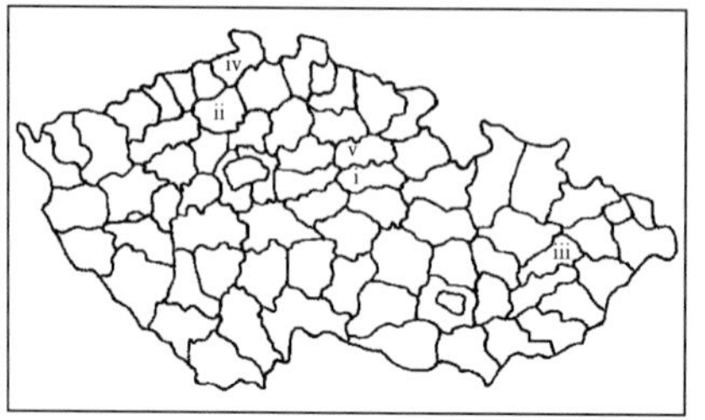

Five White-billed Divers have been recorded. One of them was observed at a pond (i), the remaining birds were seen at larger rivers. These records were verified by the CFC. Another record from the 19th century was not accepted.
Status: Accidental. Protected.
Population trends: No data available.
Distribution: i/ Bukovka (PU), ii/ Roudnice nad Labem (LT), iii/ Lobodice (PR), iv/ Decin (DC), v/ Skochovice (HK).
Timing: i/ 8 January 1935, ii/ 28 January 1942, iii/ 25 December 1942, iv/ 10–17 February 1976, v/ 21 November 1996.

Fulmar *Fulmarus glacialis*

Northern Fulmar Burnak ledni Fulmar ladovy Eissturmvogel

Five records of this species have been accepted by the CFC. Two other records were rejected. Four of the birds were collected as specimens (i–iv); these individuals belonged to the *auduboni* race.
Status: Accidental. Protected.
Population trends: No data available.
Distribution: i/ Frymburk (CK), ii/ Dlouha Ves (HB), iii/ Marianske Lazne (CH), iv/ Kytin (PB), v/ Houston (KL).
Timing: i/ winter 1903–06, ii/ 1927–30, iii/ 24 January 1955, iv/ 18 February 1962, v/ end of February 1962.

Cory's Shearwater *Calonectris diomedea*

Burnak sedy Vichrovnik plavy Gelbschnabel-Sturmtaucher

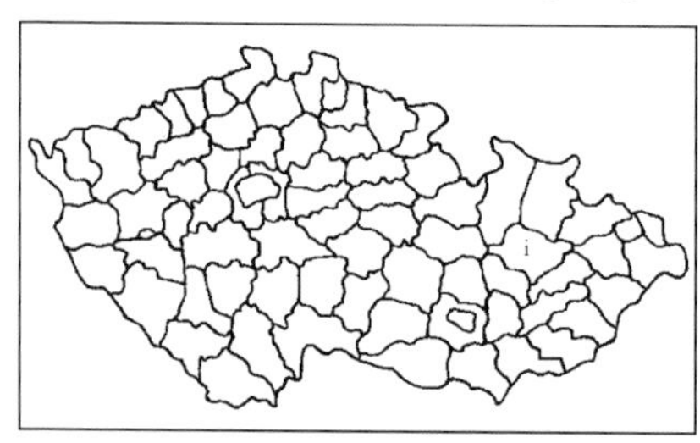

The only record is an individual collected in central Moravia. It has been accepted by the CFC.
Status: Accidental. Protected.
Population trends: No data available.
Distribution: i/ Olomouc (OL).
Timing: i/ mid-May 1936.

European Storm-petrel *Hydrobates pelagicus*

Storm Petrel Burnacek maly Vichrovnicek morsky Sturmschwalbe

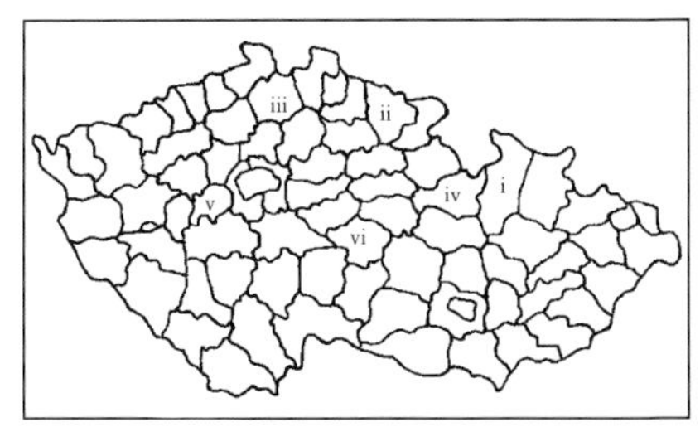

There are 6 records of Storm Petrels, with a total number of 6 individuals. All of them were collected. These records have been accepted by the CFC.
Status: Accidental. Protected.
Population trends: No data available.
Distribution: i/ Bohdikov (SU), ii/ Zacler (TU), iii/ Zakupy (CL), iv/ Rybnik (UO), v/ Beroun (BE), vi/ Podebady (HB).
Timing: i/ 5 December 1863, ii/ 1879, iii/ October 1912, iv/ 20 December 1929, v/ 10 October 1952, vi/ February 1953.

Northern Gannet *Morus bassanus*

Gannet Terej bily Sula biela Baßtölpel

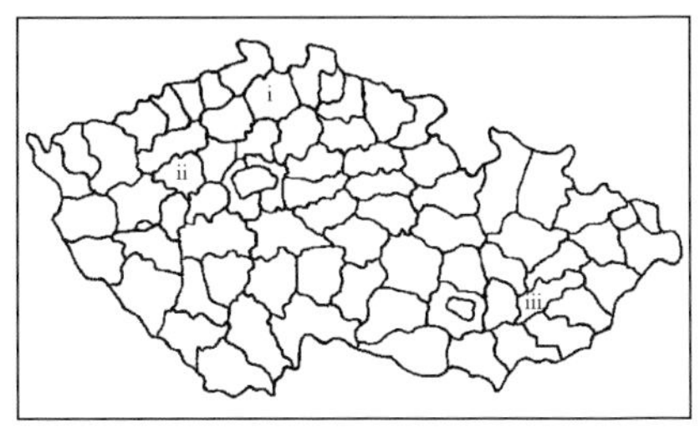

Three records of solitary birds have been accepted by the CFC. Two of them were collected (i and ii), and 1 was a sight record. Two additional records have not been accepted because of insufficient data.
Status: Accidental. Protected.
Population trends: No data available.
Distribution: i/ Litice (CL), ii/ Zdeslav (RA), iii/ Zahlinice (KM).
Timing: i/ 23 November 1903, ii/ beginning of November 1928, iii/ 9 September 1962.

Shag *Phalacrocorax aristotelis*

European Shag Kormoran chocholaty Kormoran chochlaty Krähenscharbe

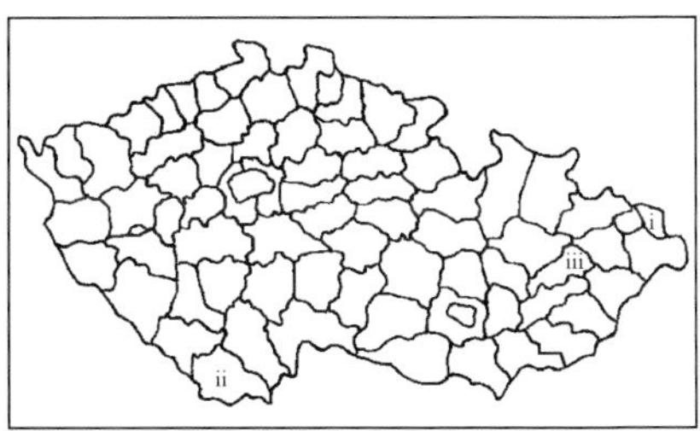

Three records. An adult (i) bird was seen at ponds, 2 adults at a large dam (ii), and a solitary bird at a pond (iii). All records have been accepted by the CFC.
Status: Accidental. Protected.
Population trends: No data available.
Distribution: i/ Karvina (KI), ii/ Lipno dam (CK), iii/ Tovacovske ponds (PR) .
Timing: i/ 3 April 1977, ii/ 1–2 December 1979, iii/ 11 March 1999.

Pygmy Cormorant *Phalacrocorax pygmeus*

Kormoran maly Kormoran maly Zwergscharbe

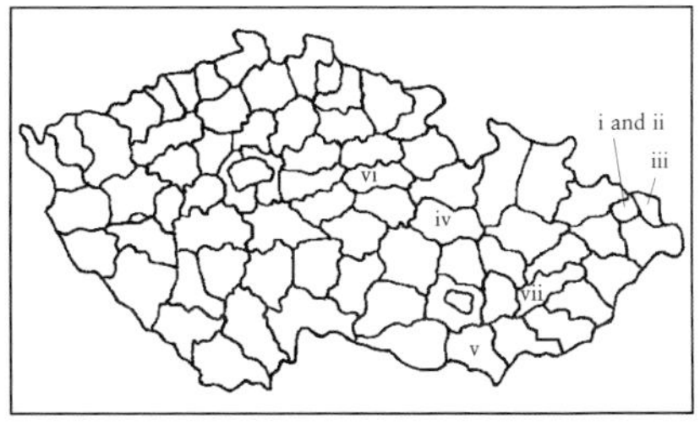

Seven records with a total number of 9 birds. In one case (ii), 3 birds were seen together. Four records come from Moravia, 2 from e. Bohemia. All of them have been accepted by the CFC.
Status: Accidental. Protected.
Population trends: No data available.
Distribution: i/ ponds near Ostrava (OV), ii/ ponds near Ostrava (OV), iii/ the river Olse in Tesin (KI), iv/ ponds near Svitavy (SY), v/ Lednicke ponds (BV),

vi/ Soprec pond (PU), vii/ Zahlinicke ponds (KM).
Timing: i/ 10 October 1856, ii/ October 1864, iii/ November 1864, iv/ 30 September 1951, v/ 27 May 1959, vi/ 17 July 1981, vii/ 16 October 1998.

Cattle Egret *Bubulcus ibis*

Volavka rusohlava Hltavka chochlata Kuhreiher

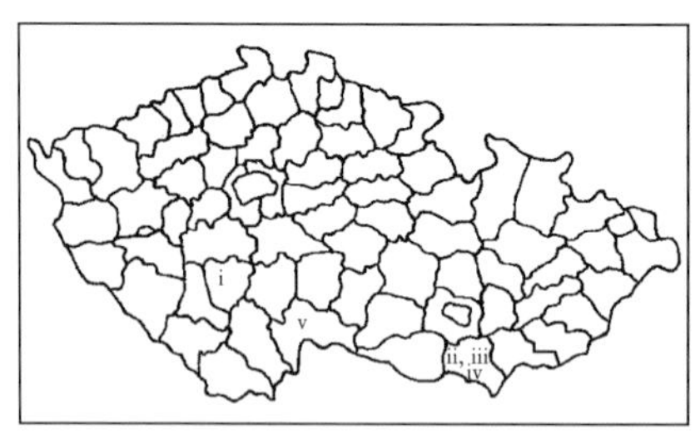

Five records of solitary birds. The first record for the Czech Republic was of a trapped captive (i), probably the second bird as well (ii). All records have been accepted by the CFC.
Status: Accidental. Protected.
Population trends: No data available.
Distribution: i/ Radobytce (PI), ii/ Lednicke ponds (BV), iii/ Nesyt pond (BV), iv/ Nove Mlyny (BV), v/ Stara Hlina (JH).
Timing: i/ 10 October 1966, ii/ 20–28 October 1972, iii/ 3 June 1974, iv/ 30 October 1983, v/ 6–7 May 1998.

Snow Goose *Anser caerulescens*

Husa snezni Hus snezna Schneegans

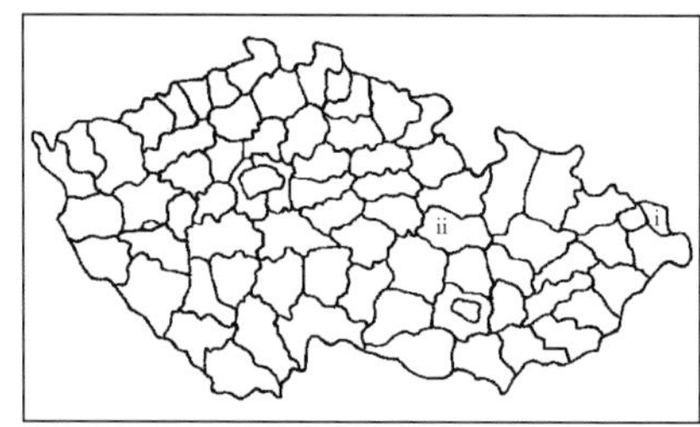

Two records of Snow Goose have been accepted by the CFC. One of these is of a solitary bird (i), the other is a record of 2 birds. Other unaccepted records come from 1980–1981 and include individuals which had escaped from captivity.
Status: Accidental. Hunted during fixed season.
Population trends: No data available.
Distribution: i/ the river Olse in Karvina (KI), ii/ Horky (SY).
Timing: i/ 24 February and 7 March 1929, ii/ 7 March 1947.

American Wigeon *Anas americana*

Hvizdak americky Kacica bielohlava Nordenamerikanische Pfeifente

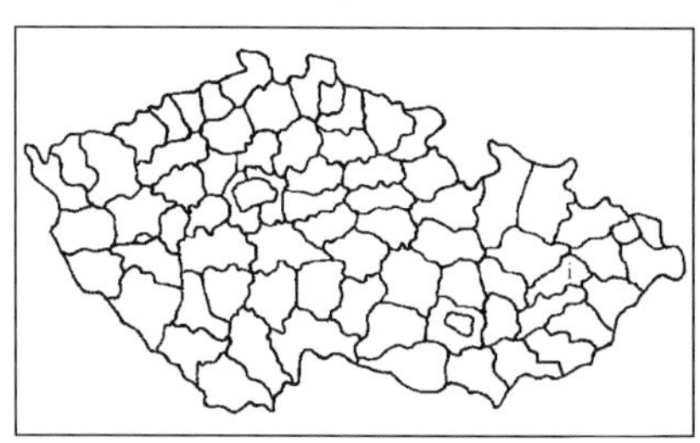

The only record was of a male in a breeding plumage. However, the possibility of it being an escape was not rejected (Doupal 1991). The record was accepted by the CFC.
Status: Accidental. Protected/not hunted all year round.
Population trends: No data available.
Distribution: i/ Tovacov gravel pit (PR).
Timing: i/ 10 February 1990.

Blue-winged Teal *Anas discors*

Cirka modrokridla Kacica modrokridla Blauflügelente

An adult male was recorded at one of the best sites for waterfowl in Moravia. It was suggested by the observer that the bird might have been an escape. However, because of its behaviour the CFC believed it was a wild bird and the record was accepted.

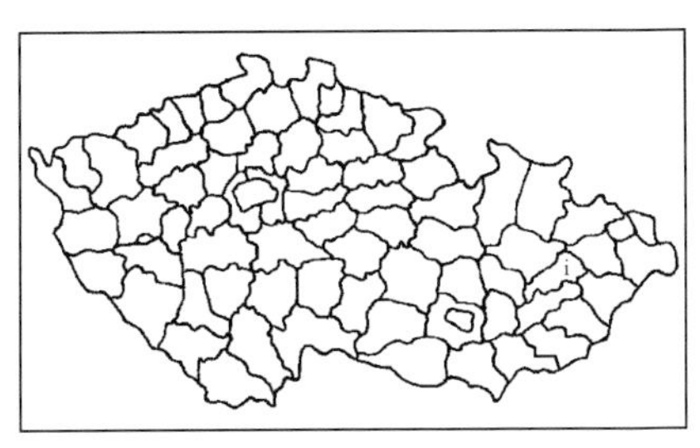

Status: Accidental. Protected.
Population trends: No data available.
Distribution: i/ Tovacovske ponds (PR).
Timing: i/ 24 April 1996.

Marbled Duck *Marmaronetta angustirostris*

Marbled Teal   Cirka uzkozoba   Kacica uzkozoba   Marmelente

The only record verified by the CFC is of 3 males and 1 female (all collected). Another record of a single bird from 1896 was not accepted.
Status: Accidental. Protected/not hunted all year round.
Population trends: No data available.
Distribution: i/ ponds around Hluboka nad Vltavou (CB).
Timing: i/ 25–26 July 1892.

King Eider *Somateria spectabilis*

Kajka kralovska   Kajka kralovska   Prachteiderente

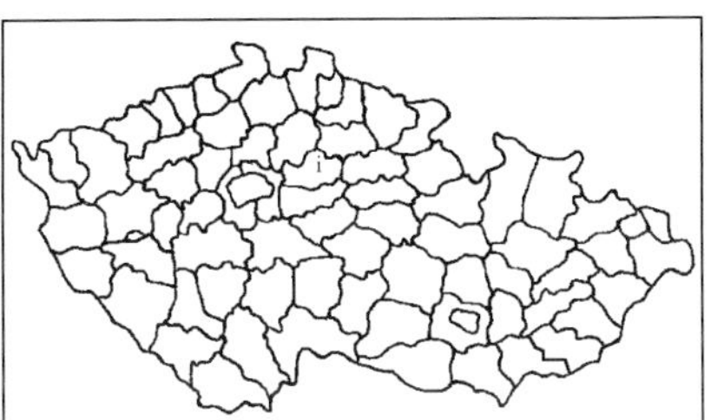

A male in an immature plumage was recorded in central Bohemia. This record was accepted by the CFC.
Status: Accidental. Protected.
Population trends: No data available.
Distribution: i/ the Labe river in Nymburk (NB).
Timing: i/ 19 February 1996.

Surf Scoter *Melanitta perspicillata*

Turpan pestrozoby   Turpan okuliarnaty   Brillenente

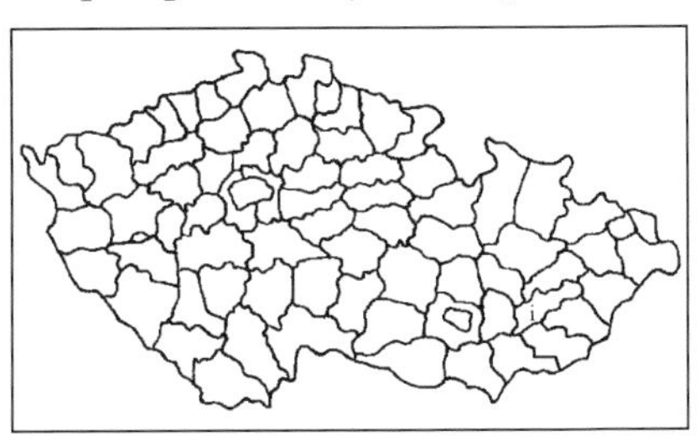

A solitary bird in immature plumage was seen at ponds in central Moravia. The record was accepted by the CFC.
Status: Accidental. Protected/not hunted all year round.
Population trends: No data available.
Distribution: i/ Zahlinicke ponds (KM).
Timing: i/ 20 July 1967.

Barrow's Goldeneye *Bucephala islandica*

Hohol islandsky   Hlaholka velka   Spatelente

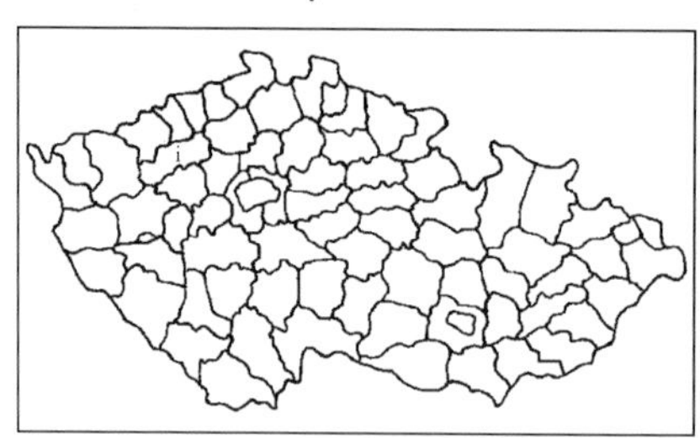

A solitary male Barrow's Goldeneye was seen together with a pair of Common Goldeneye at the Ohre river in n. Bohemia, and was present at the same place for several days. The record was accepted by the CFC.
Status: Accidental. Protected/not hunted all year round.
Population trends: No data available.
Distribution: i/ Kadan (LN).
Timing: i/ 21 November 1987.

Black-shouldered Kite *Elanus caeruleus*

Black-winged Kite   Lunec sedy   Luniak sivy   Gleitaar

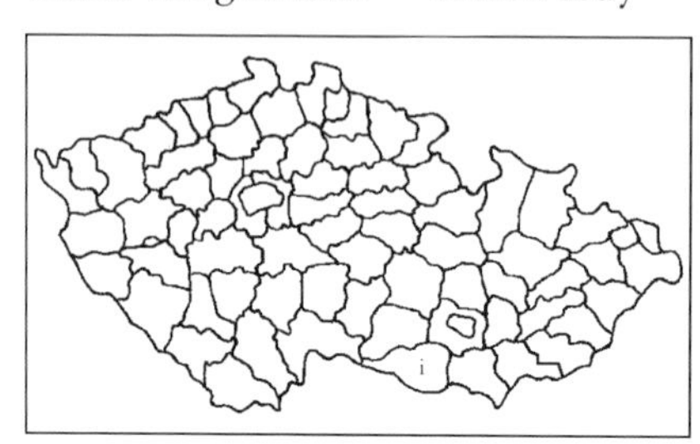

The only record verified by the CFC was of an injured female captured in s. Moravia. Three additonal observations of this species from w. Bohemia have not been accepted.
Status: Accidental. Protected.
Population trends: No data available.
Distribution: i/ Olbramovice (ZN).
Timing: i/ 31 March 1938.

Egyptian Vulture *Neophron percnopterus*

Sup mrchozravy   Zdochlinar biely   Schmutzgeier

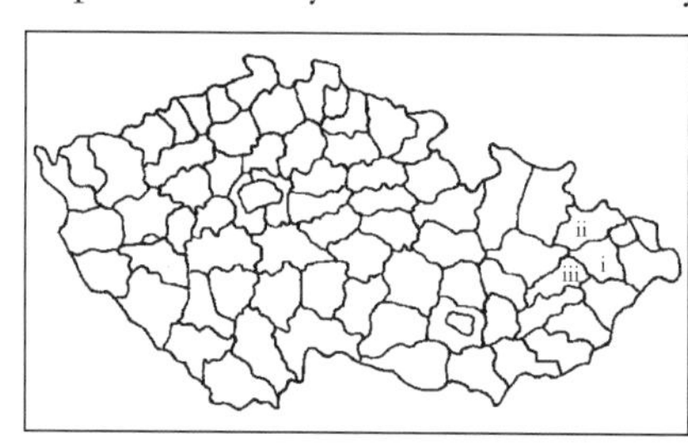

Three records of solitary birds (2 adults, 1 juvenile) come from the eastern part of the country during the past decade. The records have been accepted by the CFC.
Status: Accidental. Protected.
Population trends: No data available.
Distribution: i/ Hermanice (NJ), ii/ Stepankovice (OP), iii/ Prerov (PR).
Timing: i/ 26 June 1988, ii/ 12 May 1991, iii/ 26 May 1994.

Levant Sparrowhawk *Accipiter brevipes*

Krahujec kratkoprsty   Jastrab kratkoprsty   Kurzfangsperber

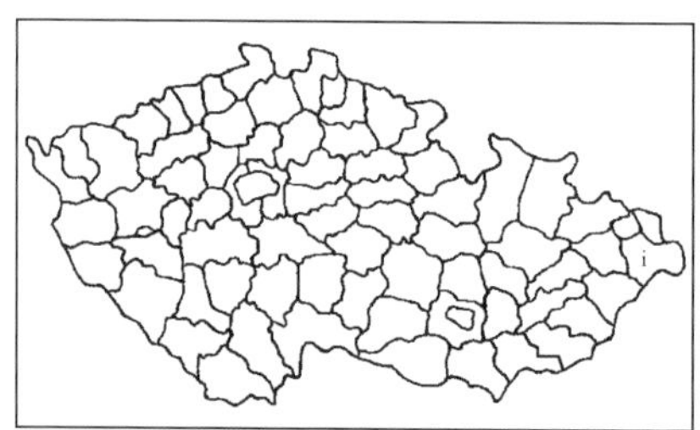

The only record is of a juvenile female which was collected in the northeastern part of the country. This record was accepted by the CFC.
Status: Accidental. Protected.
Population trends: No data available.
Distribution: i/ Mitrovice near Nova Bela (FM).
Timing: i/ 9 September 1958.

Steppe Eagle *Aquila nipalensis*

Orel stepni Orol stepny Steppenadler

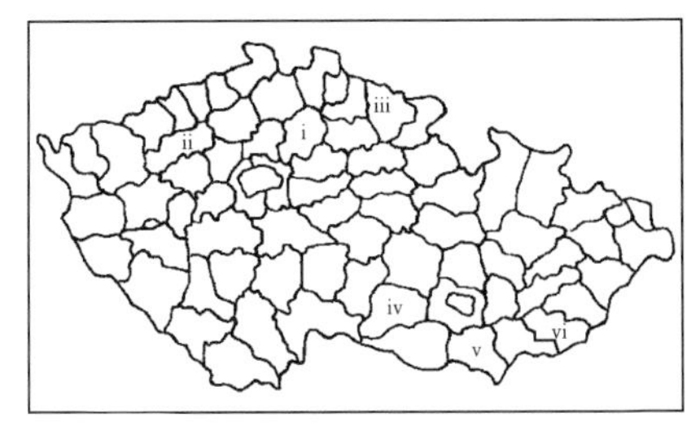

Six records of solitary birds have been verified by the CFC. Three birds were collected (i–iii), 2 captured and kept in captivity, and 1 individual was seen (vi). Three additional records of Steppe Eagles from this century have not been accepted. The birds were identified as the *orientalis* race.

Status: Accidental. Protected/not hunted all year round.

Population trends: No data available.

Distribution: i/ Koprnik (MB), ii/ Louny (LN), iii/ Mlade Buky (TU), iv/ Zahradka (TR), v/ Hustopece (BV), vi/ Moravsky Pisek (HO).

Timing: i/ July 1914, ii/ June 1932, iii/ 28 August 1943, iv/ 15 May 1967, v/ 27 January 1985, vi/ 15 October 1997.

Bonnelli's Eagle *Hieraaetus fasciatus*

Orel jestrabi Orol jastrabovity Habichtsadler

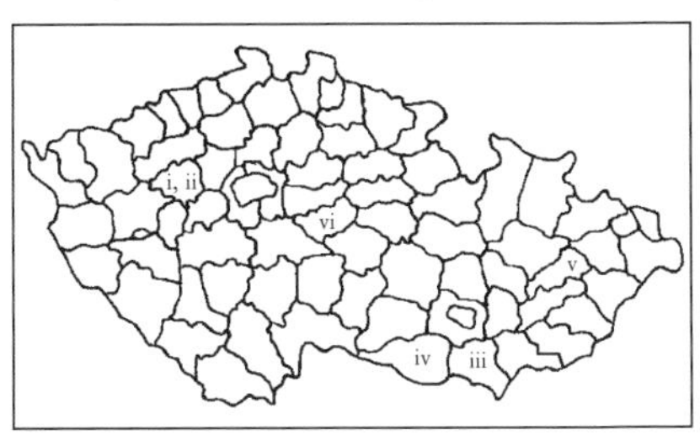

Six records of solitary Bonnelli's Eagles have been accepted by the CFC; 1 additional record from the early 1980s was rejected. Four birds were collected (i–iv), and 1 (v) was killed by power lines.

Status: Accidental. Protected.

Population trends: No data available.

Distribution: i/ Doupno near Krivoklat (RA), ii/ Nove Straseci (RA), iii/ Ivan (BV), iv/ Olbramovice (ZN), v/ Tovacov (PR), vi/ Zbysov (KH).

Timing: i/ April 1862, ii/ the end of July 1866, iii/ autumn 1927, iv/ 28 July 1945, v/ 28 September 1958, vi/ 5 May 1978.

Lanner Falcon *Falco biarmicus*

Lanner Raroh jizni Sokol tmavy Lanner

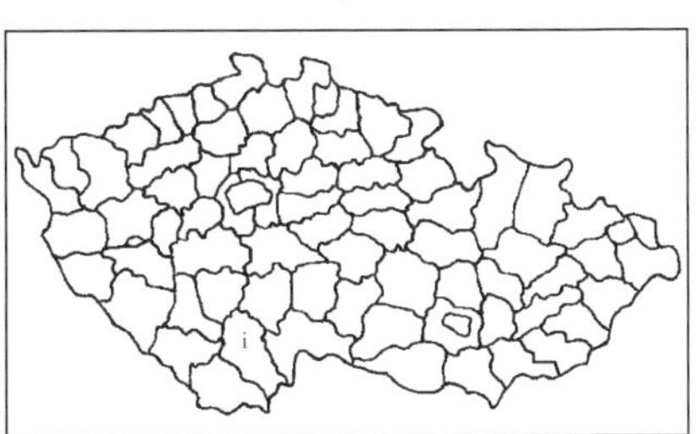

There are at least 3 records of Lanner Falcon. However, only 1 has been accepted by the CFC: an adult female of the *feldeggii* race was collected in s. Bohemia.

Status: Accidental. Protected.

Population trends: No data available.

Distribution: i/ Haklovy Dvory (CB).

Timing: i/ September 1906.

Gyr Falcon *Falco rusticolus*

Gyrfalcon Raroh lovecky Sokol polovnicky Gerfalke

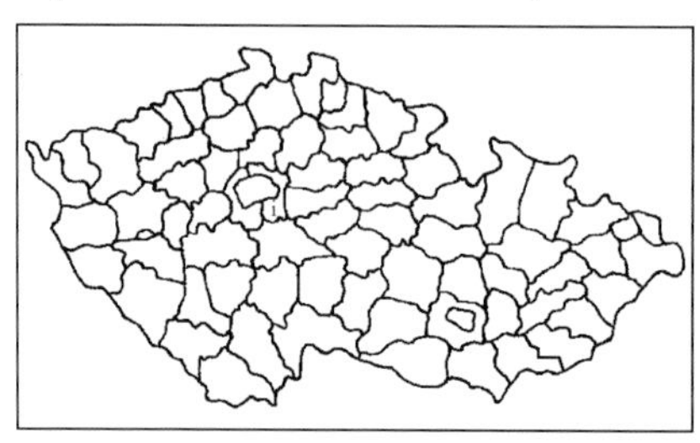

At least 2 records of Gyr Falcon exist, but only 1 was accepted by the CFC. An immature female belonging to *islandicus* race was collected in c. Bohemia.
Status: Accidental. Protected.
Population trends: No data available.
Distribution: i/ Vetrusice (PH).
Timing: i/ spring 1926.

Baillon's Crake *Porzana pusilla*

Chrastal nejmensi Chriastel najmensi Zwergsumpfhuhn

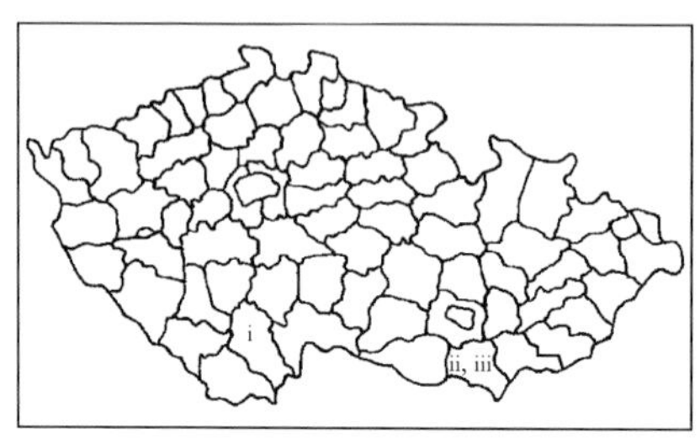

Two specimens have been collected (i–ii), and a nest (iii) has been found. There are additional reports of this species during migration, and from the breeding season. However, the reports are not reliable. The 3 records listed below have been accepted by the CFC.
Status: Accidental. Protected.
Population trends: No data available.
Distribution: i/ Ceske Budejovice (CB), ii/ Podivin (BV), iii/ Sakvice (BV).
Timing: i/ 24 May 1881, ii/ 2 June 1941, iii/ 8 June 1946.

Purple Swamp-hen *Porphyrio porphyrio*

Purple Gallinule Slipka modra Sliepocka modra Purpurhuhn

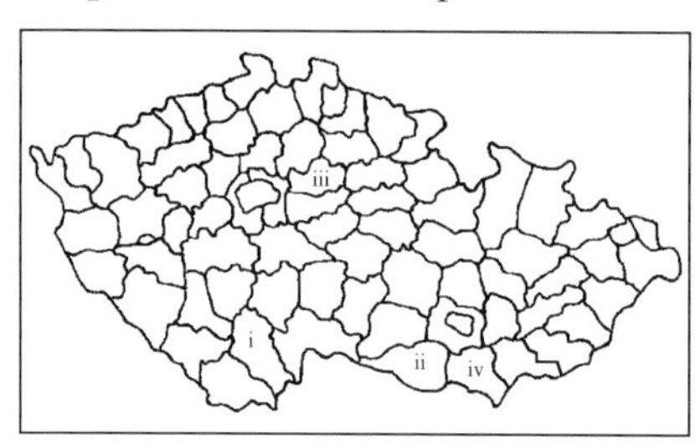

This species has been recorded 4 times. Two specimen belong to the *porphyrio* race (i and ii), and 2 to the *aegyptiacus* race (iii and iv). Three of these were adult birds (i–iii), and 1 a juvenile. All records have been verified by the CFC.
Status: Accidental. Protected.
Population trends: No data available.
Distribution: i/ Nove Hrady (CB), ii/ Jaroslavice (ZN), iii/ Zehunsky pond (NB), iv/ Lednicke ponds (BV).
Timing: i/ autumn 1884, ii/ 21 August 1957, iii/ 16 July 1905, iv/ 12 September 1910.

Houbara Bustard *Chlamydotis undulata*

Houbara Drop obojkovy Drop hrivnaty Kragentrappe

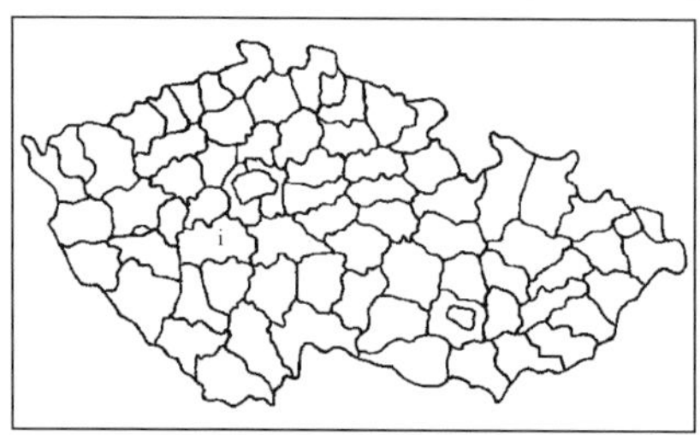

The only record is of a female of the *macqueenii* race, that was found dead in c. Bohemia. The record was verified by the CFC.
Status: Accidental. Protected.
Population trends: No data available.
Distribution: i/ Myslovice (PB).
Timing: i/ 6 September 1889.

Cream-coloured Courser *Cursorius cursor*

Behulik plavy Behavec plavy Rennvogel

There are 5 records, but only 3 have been accepted by the CFC. All of the accepted records are of solitary birds from the end of the 19th, and beginning of the 20th centuries.
Status: Accidental. Protected.
Population trends: No data available.
Distribution: i/ Hodkovice nad Mohelkou (LB), ii/ Bezdekov (LN), iii/ Strasnov (MB).
Timing: i/ 2 May 1891, ii/ 29 August 1893, iii/ 6 August 1929.

Collared Pratincole *Glareola pratincola*

Ouhorlik stepni Prieloznik obycajny Rotflügel-Brachschwalbe

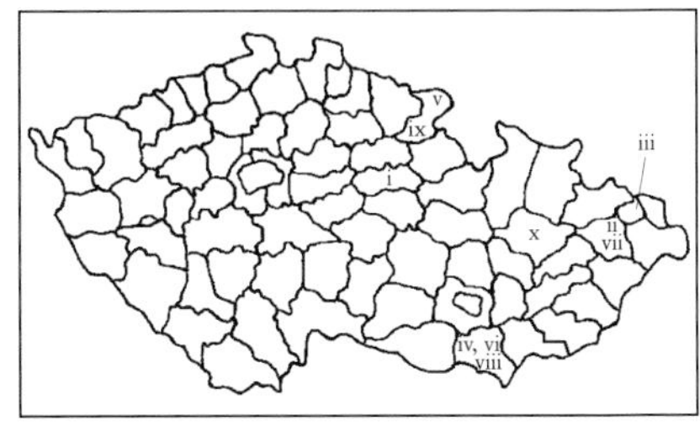

There are 10 records of solitary Collared Pratincoles including both adult and juvenile birds. Two additional individuals (ii and vii) were identified as *Glareola* sp. only, and the records were credited to this species. The CFC accepted all of the reports.
Status: Accidental. Protected.
Population trends: No data available.
Distribution: i/ Oplatil pond near Pardubice (PU), ii/ Novy Jicin (NJ), iii/ Ostrava–Zabreh (OV), iv/ Lednicke ponds (BV), v/ Rozkos dam (NA), vi/ Lednicke ponds (BV), vii/ Jistebnik nad Odrou (NJ), viii/ Lednicke ponds (BV), ix/ Rozkos dam (NA), x/ Chomoutov (OL).
Timing: i/ 16 May 1862, ii/ 10 August 1904, iii/ May–June 1924, iv/ summer 1959–60, v/ 17–18 June 1972, vi/ 7 April 1974, vii/ 31 August 1977, viii/ 12–13 September 1981, ix/ 23 April 1995, x/ 13 May 1996.

Collared Pratincole

Black-winged Pratincole *Glareola nordmanni*

Ouhorlik cernokridly Prieloznik ciernokridly Schwarzflügel-Brachschwalbe

Two birds have been seen, and the records have been accepted by the CFC.
Status: Accidental. Protected.
Population trends: No data available.
Distribution: i/ Ostrava–Hermanice (OV), ii/ Lednicke ponds (BV).
Timing: i/ 15 September 1951, ii/ 12 November 1970.

American Golden Plover *Pluvialis dominica*

Lesser Golden Plover Kulik hnedokridly Kulik brnavokridly
Amerikanischer Goldregenpfeifer

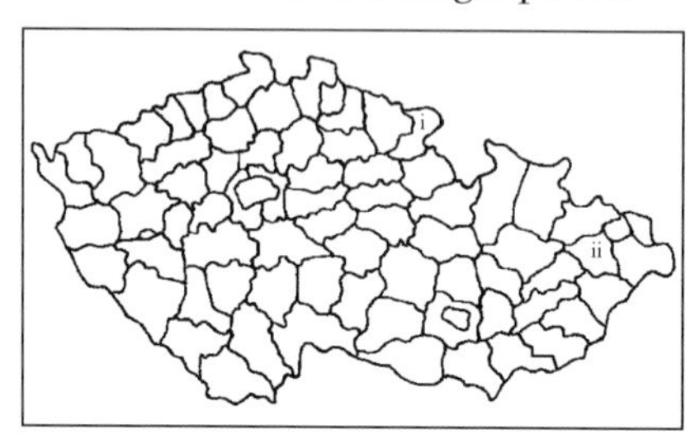

There are only 2 records of solitary birds; both of these from the past 20 years. One of the birds was identified as of the *dominica* race (i), and the other, perhaps as race *fulva*. Both records were accepted by the CFC.
Status: Accidental. Protected.
Population trends: No data available.
Distribution: i/ Rozkos dam (NA), ii/ Bartosovice (NJ).
Timing: i/ 18 September–4 October 1981, ii/ 21 October 1989.

Spur-winged Lapwing *Hoplopterus spinosus*

Spur-winged Plover Cejka trnita Cibik trnokridly Spornkiebitz

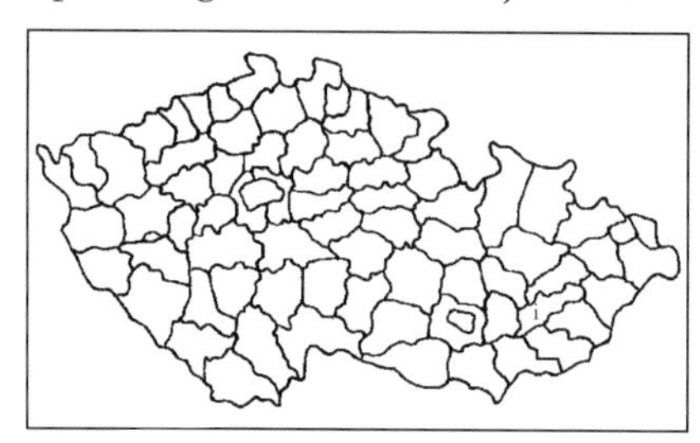

The only Spur-winged Plover recorded was a solitary bird in a flock of Northern Lapwings at ponds in c. Moravia (Salek 1995). The record was accepted by the CFC.
Status: Accidental. Protected.
Population trends: No data available.
Distribution: i/ Zahlinicke ponds (KM).
Timing: i/ 21 September 1989.

Sociable Lapwing *Vanellus gregarius*

Sociable Plover Keptuska stepni Cibik stepny Steppenkiebitz

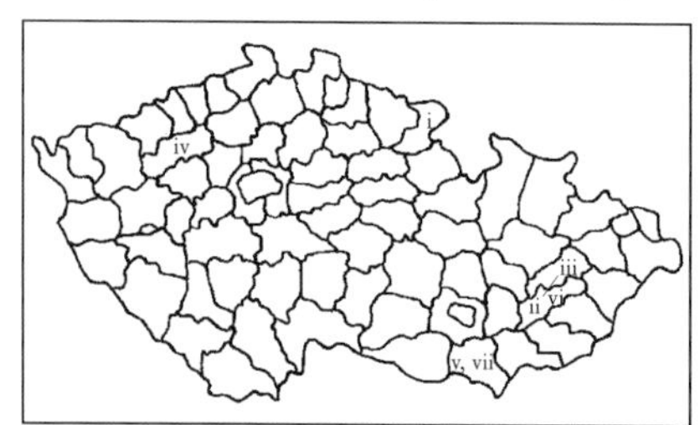

This species has been recorded 7 times, with a total of 9 birds. In 1 case (iii) 3 individuals were seen together. All reports were accepted by the CFC.
Status: Accidental. Protected.
Population trends: No data available.
Distribution: i/ Rozkos dam (NA), ii/ Zahlinicke ponds (KM), iii/ Chropynsky pond (KM), iv/ Necichy (LN), v/ Lednicke ponds (BV),

vi/ Zahlinicke ponds (KM), vii/ Soutok (BV).
Timing: i/ 2 October 1971, ii/ 28 March 1981, iii/ 2 April 1985, iv/ 12 April 1985, v/ 27 September–11 October 1986, vi/ 19–23 October 1996, vii/ 25 April 1997.

White-rumped Sandpiper *Calidris fuscicollis*

Jespak tundrovy Pobreznik tundrovy Weißbrüzel-Strandläufer

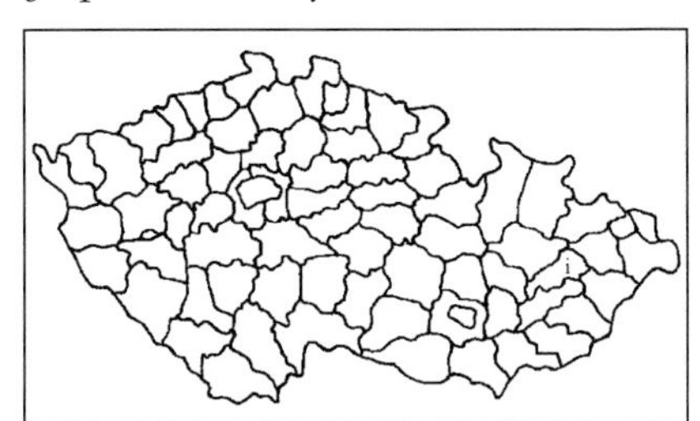

A single bird was seen in c. Moravia. The record was accepted by the CFC.
Status: Accidental. Protected.
Population trends: No data available.
Distribution: i/ Tovacovske ponds (PR).
Timing: i/ 23 September 1997.

Baird's Sandpiper *Calidris bairdii*

Jespak dlouhokridly Pobreznik plavy Baird-Strandläufer

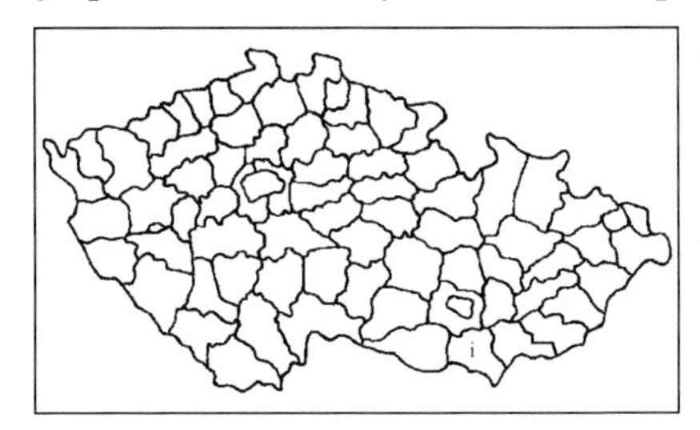

A juvenile female was trapped and banded at Nesyt pond (BV). The record was accepted by the CFC.
Status: Accidental. Protected.
Population trends: No data available.
Distribution: i/ Lednicke ponds (BV).
Timing: i/ 2 September 1981.

Pectoral Sandpiper *Calidris melanotos*

Jespak skvrnity Pobreznik skvrnity Graubrust-Strandläufer

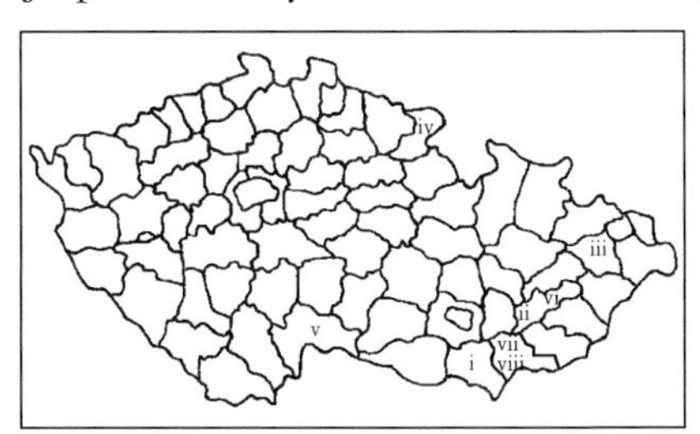

There are 8 records of solitary birds. Two birds were trapped and banded (ii, vii), the remaining birds were adults and juveniles. In the case of the last 2 records, 2 different birds were recorded: the first one on 11 October was banded, the second one on 12 October was an unbanded individual. All records were accepted by the CFC.
Status: Accidental. Protected.
Population trends: No data available.
Distribution: i/ Lednicke ponds (BV), ii/ Zahlinicke ponds (KM), iii/ Stary pond near Jistebnik nad Odrou (NJ), iv/ Rozkos dam (NA), v/Sluzebny pond (JH), vi/ Zahlinicke ponds (KM), vii/ Bzenec (HO), viii/ Bzenec (HO).
Timing: i/ 12 September 1973, ii/ 25 September 1976, iii/ 28–29 September 1980, iv/ 17–27 September 1989, v/ 28 August 1993, vi/ 27–29 April 1997, vii/ 11 October 1997, viii/ 12 October 1997.

Purple Sandpiper *Calidris maritima*

Jespak morsky Pobreznik morsky Meerstrandläufer

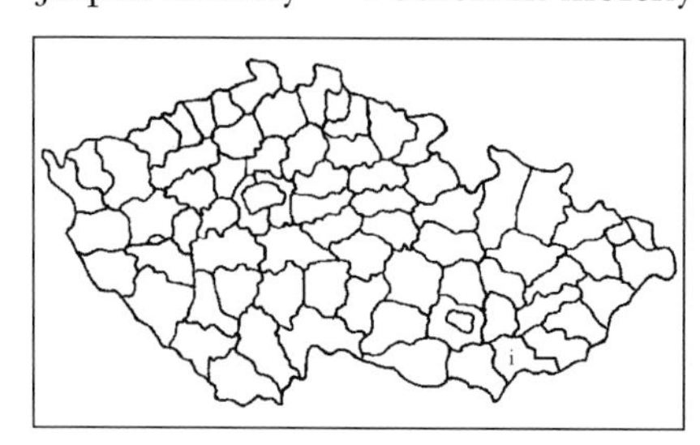

A single bird recorded in flooded fields is the only record. The record was accepted by the CFC.
Status: Accidental. Protected.
Population trends: No data available.
Distribution: i/ Bzenec (HO)
Timing: i/ 4 October 1997.

Buff-breasted Sandpiper *Tryngites subruficollis*

Jespak plavy Pobreznik travovy Graslaufer

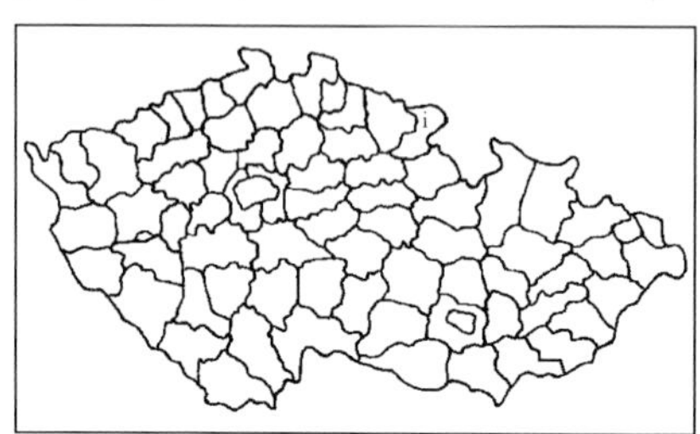

A single bird observed in e. Bohemia is the only known record, and was accepted by the CFC.
Status: Accidental. Protected.
Population trends: No data available.
Distribution: i/ Rozkos dam (NA).
Timing: i/ 15 October 1983.

Slender-billed Curlew *Numenius tenuirostris*

Koliha tenkozoba Hvizdak tenkozoby Dünnschnabel-Brachvogel

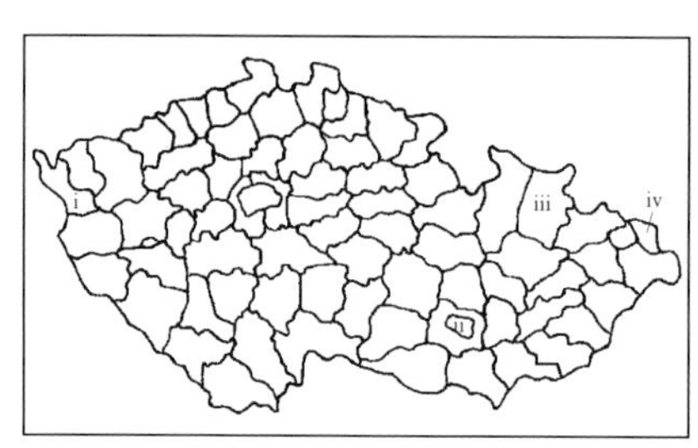

Four records, with a total number of 7 birds. Three times a solitary bird was seen, and in 1 case (iii) 4 birds were recorded. These records were verified by the CFC. Two additional records from the beginning of the 20th century were not accepted because of unsufficient data.
Status: Accidental. Protected.
Population trends: No data available.
Distribution: i/ Cheb county (CH), ii/ near Brno (BM), iii/ Svobodne Hermanice (BR), iv/ Melcina pond near Karvina (KI).
Timing: i/ March 1885, ii/ September 1899, iii/ autumn 1934, iv/ 7 April 1974.

Greater Yellowlegs *Tringa melanoleuca*

Vodous velky Kaluziak jaraby Grösser Gelbschenkel

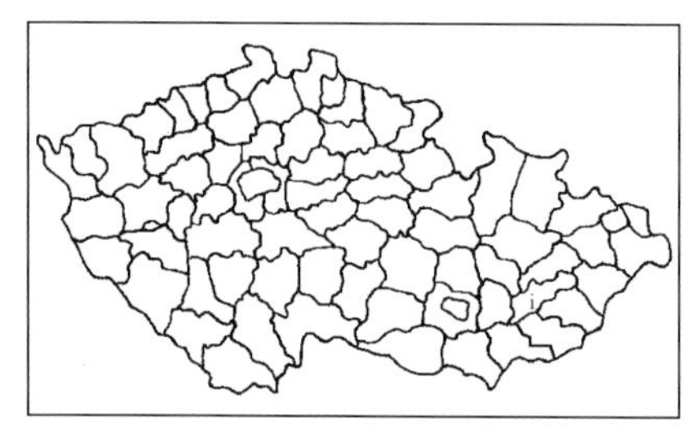

The only record is of an immature male collected in c. Moravia. The record was verified by the CFC.
Status: Accidental. Protected.
Population trends: No data available.
Distribution: i/ Zahlinicke ponds (KM).
Timing: i/ 26 August 1964.

Terek Sandpiper *Xenus cinereus*

Vodous maly Brdonik sivy Terekwasserläufer

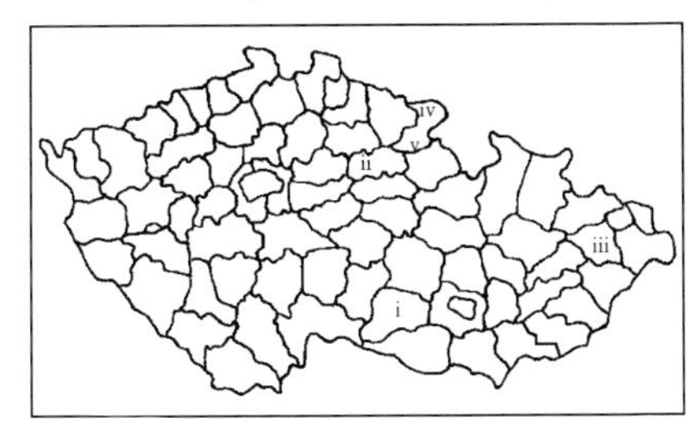

Recorded 5 times: always as solitary birds. All of the records were accepted by the CFC.
Status: Accidental. Protected.
Population trends: No data available.
Distribution: i/ Mysnik pond near Namest nad Oslavou (TR), ii/ Smirice (HK), iii/ Horni pond near Bartosovice (NJ), iv–v/ Rozkos dam (NA).
Timing: i/ 3–4 June 1962, ii/ 19–20 May 1979, iii/ 5–10 September 1981, iv/ 24 June 1983, v/ 29 July 1989.

Great Black-headed Gull *Larus ichthyaetus*

Pallas's Gull Racek velky Cajka orlia Fischmöwe

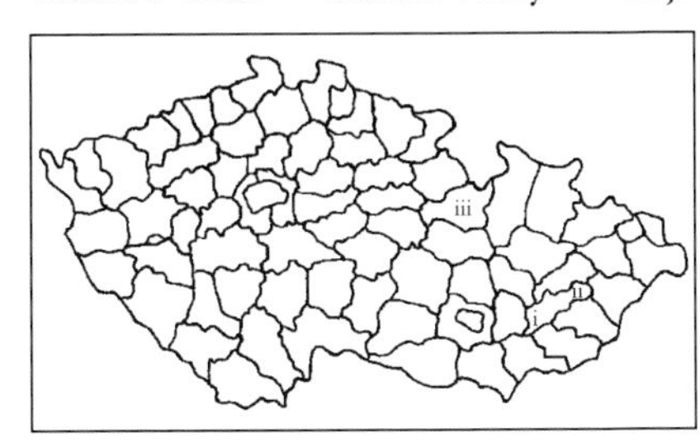

Four Great Black-headed Gulls have been recorded 3 times: a juvenile bird (i), an immature bird (ii), and 2 adults (iii). The records were verified by the CFC.
Status: Accidental. Protected.
Population trends: No data available.
Distribution: i–ii/ Zahlinice (KM), iii/ Ceske Hermanice (UO).
Timing: i/ 27 November, 1992, ii/ 16 November 1995, iii/ 13 April 1996.

Sabine's Gull *Larus sabini*

Racek Sabinuv Cajka vidlochvosta Schwalbenmöwe

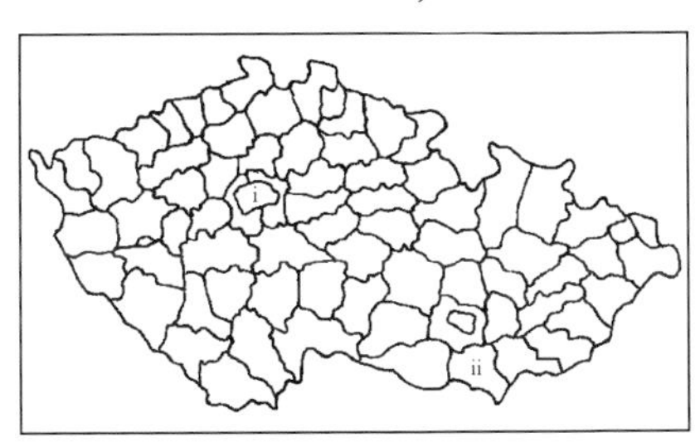

There are 2 records of juvenile Sabine's Gulls. Both of these come from traditional waterfowl wintering sites. The records were verified by the CFC.
Status: Accidental. Protected.
Population trends: No data available.
Distribution: i/ River Vltava in Praha (AA), ii/ Nove Mlyny (BV).
Timing: i/ 8–19 December, 1985, ii/ 16 February, 1990.

Bonaparte's Gull *Larus philadelphia*

Racek Bonapartuv Cajka ciernozoba Bonaparte-Möwe

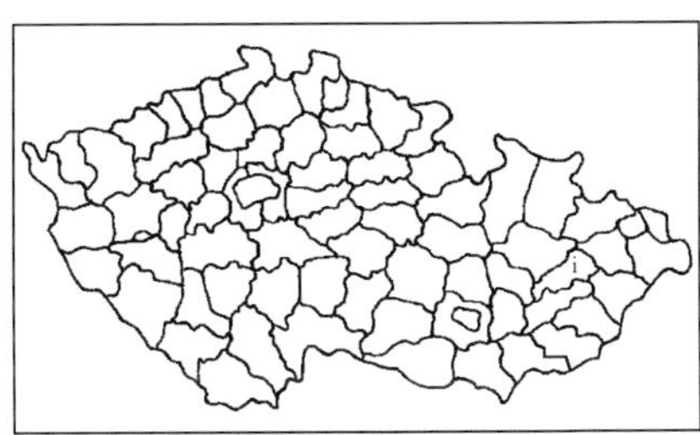

There is only 1 record of Bonaparte's Gull, and this was verified by the CFC. An adult bird was seen at one of the best places in the country for Lariidae species.
Status: Accidental. Protected.
Population trends: No data available.
Distribution: i/ Hradecky pond near Tovacov (PR).
Timing: i/ 24 April 1988.

Audouin's Gull *Larus audouinii*

Racek Audouinuv Cajka ostrovna Korallenmöwe

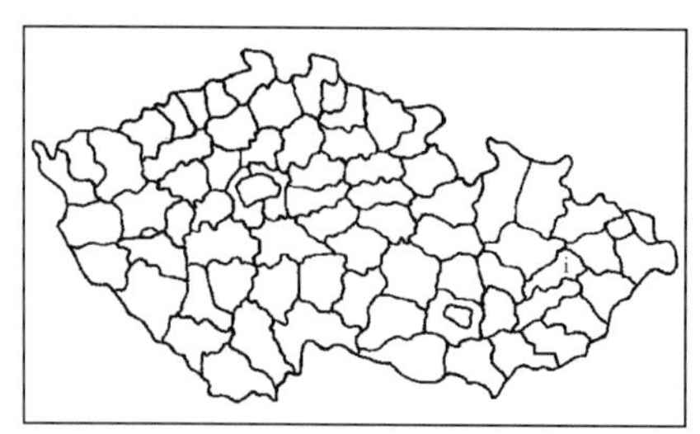

An adult Audouin's Gull was seen in a flock of Black-headed Gulls, Common Gulls, Herring Gulls, and Yellow-legged Gulls at a drained fishpond. Five days later, the same bird was seen again (Sirek and Pohanka 1994). This is the most northerly record of this species in Europe. The record was verified by the CFC.
Status: Accidental. Protected.
Population trends: No data available.
Distribution: i/ Hradecky pond near Tovacov (PR).
Timing: i/ 4 November and 9 November 1993.

Ring-billed Gull *Larus delawarensis*

Racek delawarsky Cajka obruckozoba Ringschnabelmöwe

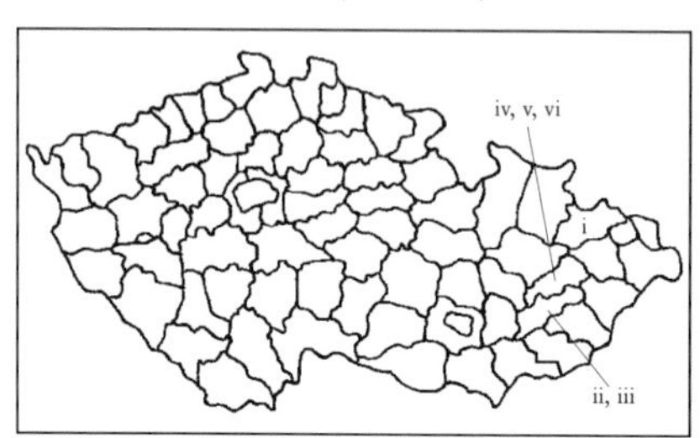

Before 1995, there had been only 1 record of this species. In 1995, 5 new records were verified by the CFC. However, (ii and iii) and (iv, v, and vi) might have been the same bird. Four birds were immatures (i–iv), and there was only 1 adult? (v).
Status: Accidental. Protected.
Population trends: No data available.
Distribution: i/ Dolni Benesov (OP), ii–iii/ Zahlinicke ponds (KM), iv–vi/ Tovacovske ponds (PR).
Timing: i/ 16 July 1994, ii/ 13 October 1995, iii/ 28 October 1995, iv/ 31 October 1995, v/ 7 November 1995, vi/ 7–8 November 1995.

Ring-billed Gull

Iceland Gull *Larus glaucoides*

Racek polarni Cajka bielokridla Polarmöwe

The first Iceland Gull for the country was collected at Zofinka pond near Lutova in s. Bohemia. The record was verified by the CFC.
Status: Accidental. Protected.
Population trends: No data available.

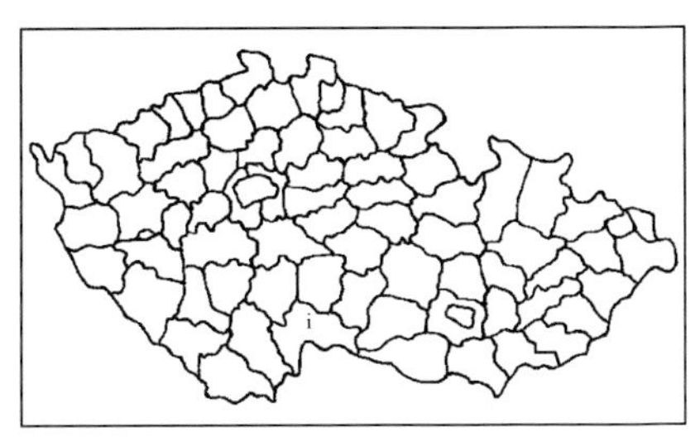

Distribution: i/ Zofinka pond (JH).
Timing: i/ 7 July 1990.

Glaucous Gull *Larus hyperboreus*

Racek sedy   Cajka bleda   Eismöwe

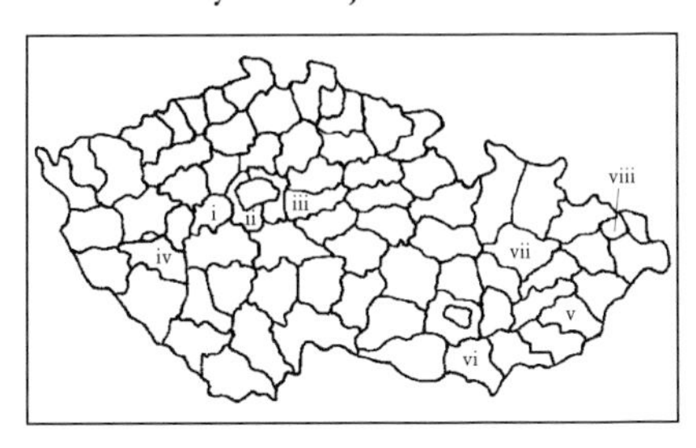

There are 8 records of solitary Glaucous Gulls which have been accepted by the CFC. An additional 5 records have been rejected. Six of the records involved immatures (ii, iii, v, vi, vii, viii), 1 adult bird (i), and 1 bird was not aged (iv).
Status: Accidental. Protected.
Population trends: No data available.
Distribution: i/ Beroun (BE), ii/ Dolany nad Vltavou (PZ), iii/ Mlekovice (KO), iv/ Spalene Porici (PJ), v/ Napajedla (ZL), vi/ Ivan (BV), vii/ Sumvald (OL), viii/ Bohumin (OV).
Timing: i/ 1866, ii/ 1885, iii/ 1921, iv/ 1935, v/ 19 November 1943, vi/ 17 November 1993, vii/ 13–18 April 1995, viii/ 23 December 1995.

Sandwich Tern *Sterna sandvicensis*

Rybak severni   Rybar sivy   Brandseeschwalbe

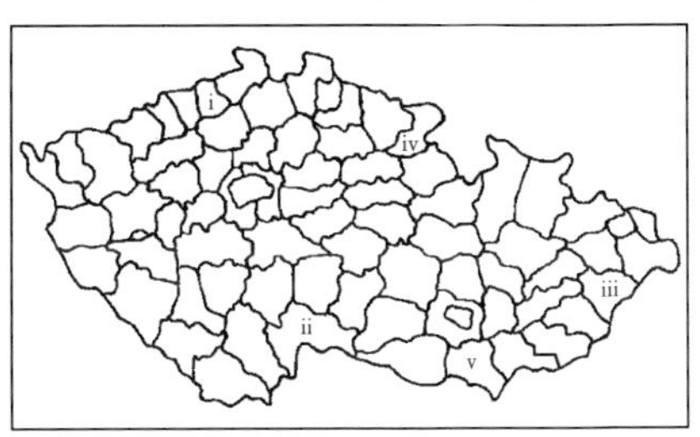

There are 5 records, wih a total of 10 birds, that have been accepted by the CFC. In 1 case (i), 6 individuals were seen at the Labe river. Some of the birds were adults (ii, iv, v), the others (i and iii) were recorded without age being specified.
Status: Accidental. Protected.
Population trends: No data available.
Distribution: i/ River Labe near Nestedice (UL), ii/ Jindrichuv Hradec (JH), iii/ Chorynske ponds (VS), iv/ Rozkos dam (NA), v/ Nove Mlyny (BV).
Timing: i/ 11–16 November 1887, ii/ November 1910, iii/ 6 August 1980, iv/ 14 May 1983, v/ 9 September 1984.

Common Guillemot *Uria aalge*

Guillemot   Alkoun uzkozoby   Norec tenkozoby   Trottellumme

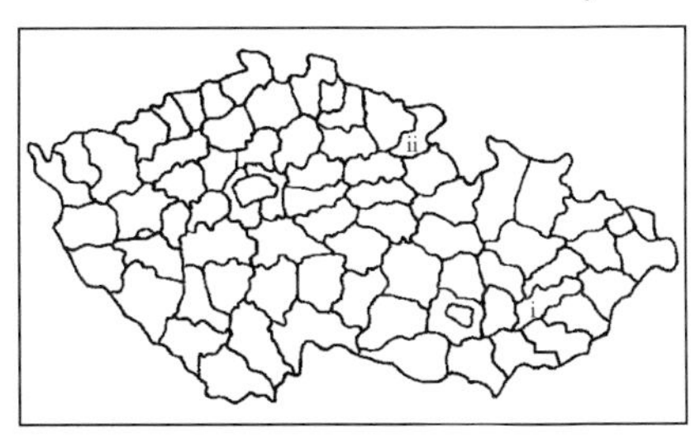

There are 2 records: a flock of 4 birds (i) was seen at the Morava river, and a flock of 4 immatures and 1 adult in non-breeding plumage was seen at a dam in e. Bohemia (ii). Both records were accepted by the CFC.
Status: Accidental. Protected.
Population trends: No data available.
Distribution: i/ Kromeriz (KM), ii/ Rozkos dam (NA).

Timing: i/ 15 November 1971, ii/ 23 December 1979.

Razorbill *Alca torda*

Alka mala Alka mala Tordalk

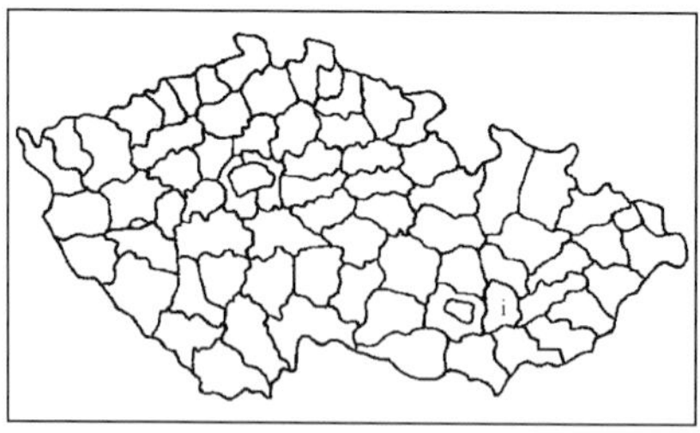

The only record of Razorbill is from the 19th century. Four individuals were collected at the Litava river. The record was verified by the CFC.
Status: Accidental. Protected.
Population trends: No data available.
Distribution: i/ River Litava near Hrusky (VY).
Timing: i/ February 1890.

Black Guillemot *Cepphus grylle*

Alkoun obecny Svistun zrkadlovy Gryllteiste

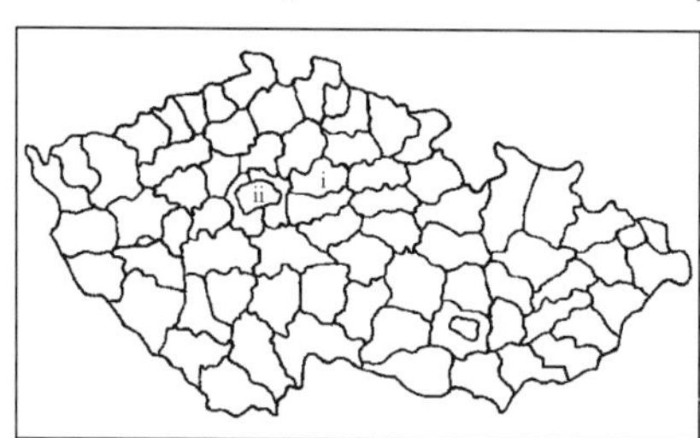

Two records, with a total number of 7 birds. In one case (i), an adult individual in non-breeding plumage was seen. The remaining 6 birds (ii), were recorded without age or plumage status being specified. Both records were accepted by the CFC.
Status: Accidental. Protected.
Population trends: No data available.
Distribution: i/ Podebrady (NB), ii/ Praha (AA).
Timing: i/ 7 February 1979, ii/ 15 January, 1986.

Little Auk *Alle alle*

Alkoun maly Alkovec drobny Krabbentaucher

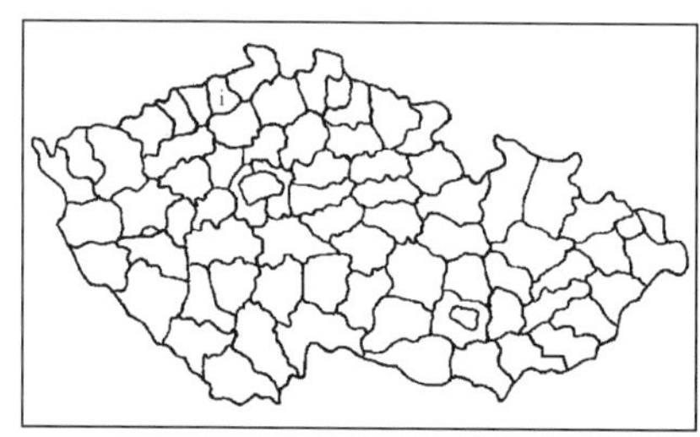

The only record is of an individual found exhausted in n. Bohemia. The specimen is in a collection, and this record was verified by the CFC.
Status: Accidental. Protected.
Population trends: No data available.
Distribution: i/ Usti nad Labem (UL).
Timing: i/ 14 June 1976.

Alpine Swift *Tachymarptis melba*

Rorys velky Dazdovnik skalny Alpensegler

This species has been recorded 11 times with a total of 18–20 birds, presumably belonging to the *melba* race. More than 1 bird was recorded 3 times; 3 individuals (i), 3–5 individuals (vi), and 5 individuals (viii). All records were accepted by the CFC.
Status: Accidental. Protected.
Population trends: No data available.
Distribution: i/ Krkonose mountains (TU), ii/ Valasske Mezirici (VS), iii–iv/ Praha (AA), v/ Liba (CH), vi/ Usti nad Labem (UL), vii/ Palava hills (BV), viii/ Hovezi (VS), ix/ Hrachovec

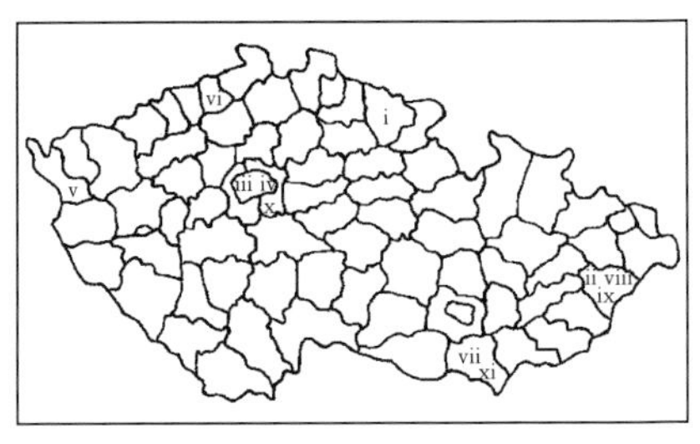

(VS), x/ Mesice (PH), xi/ Breclav (BV).
Timing: i/ 12 July 1826, ii/ 21 May 1899, iii/ 3 May 1944, iv/ 15 May 1957, v/ 23 August 1963, vi/ 10 April 1964, vii/ 7 June 1974, viii/ 18 July 1978, ix/ 4 September 1978, x/ 23 April 1988, xi/ 11–12 July 1996.

Calandra Lark *Melanocorypha calandra*

Kalandra zpevna   Skovran stepny   Kalanderlerche

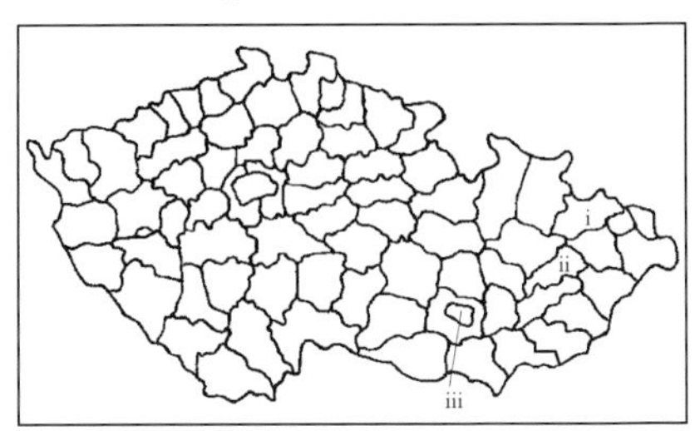

Four specimens have been collected. One of them, however, lacked specific documentation, and the record was not verified by the CFC.
Status: Accidental. Protected.
Population trends: No data available.
Distribution: i/ Lodenice (OP), ii/ Tucin (PR), iii/ Brno (BM).
Timing: i/ 1980–94, ii/ 1911, iii/ 1929.

Black Lark *Melanocorypha yeltoniensis*

Kalandra cerna   Skovran cierny   Mohrenlerche

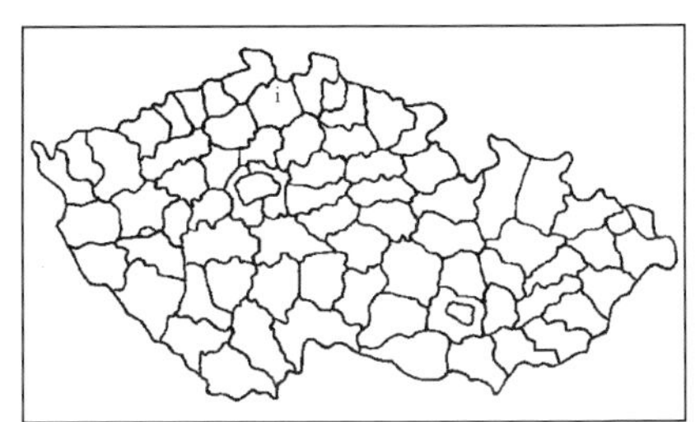

The only record verified by the CFC was of an adult male (collected). There are 2 other records from the 19th century and 2 from the 20th century, but these have not been accepted owing to lack of evidence.
Status: Accidental. Protected.
Population trends: No data available.
Distribution: i/ Zakupy (CL).
Timing: i/ 28 November 1981.

Black Lark

Richard´s Pipit *Anthus novaeseelandiae*

Linduska velka Labtuska velka Spornpieper

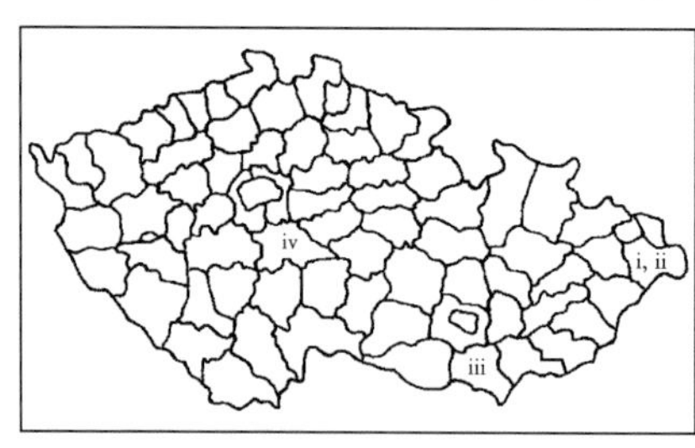

Four records, with a total of 5 birds, have been accepted by the CFC. Two other records lack sufficient evidence, and have not been accepted. In 1 case (iii), 2 individuals were seen together.
Status: Accidental. Protected.
Population trends: No data available.
Distribution: i–ii/ Mistek (FM), iii/ Brezi (BV), iv/ Postupice (BN).
Timing: i/ September 1852, ii/ September 1856–1868, iii/ 20 September 1925, iv/ 17 July 1963.

Siberian Accentor *Prunella montanella*

Pevuska horska Vrcharka okrova Bergbraunelle

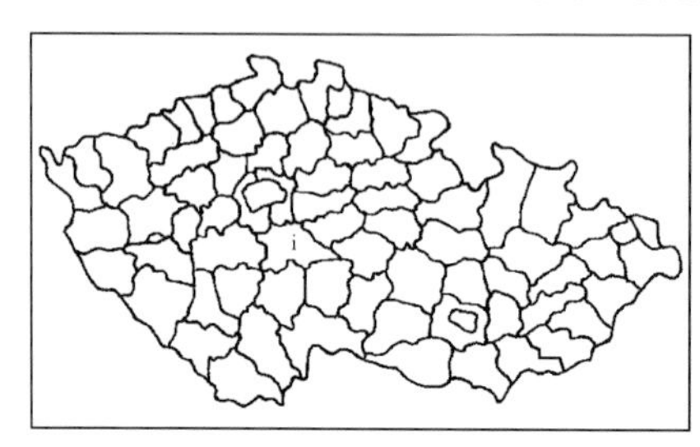

The only record accepted is for a trapped juvenile female. A published record from 1894 was not verified by the CFC (lack of evidence).
Status: Accidental. Protected.
Population trends: No data available.
Distribution: i/ Postupice (BN).
Timing: i/ 29 December 1943.

Black-eared Wheatear *Oenanthe hispanica*

Belorit okrovy Skaliar okrovy Mittelmeer-Steinschmätzer

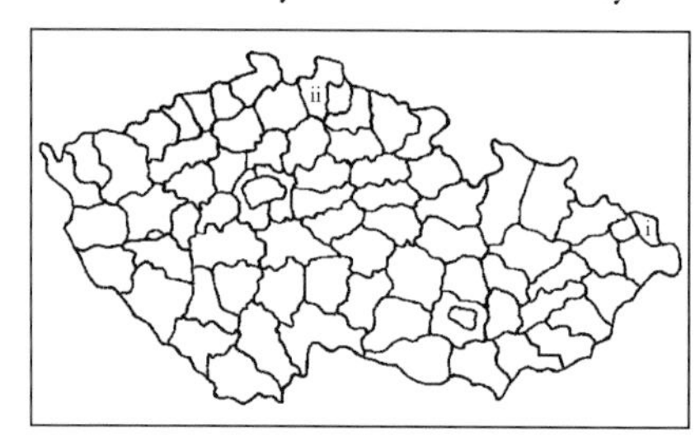

Two records of solitary males have been accepted by the CFC. A third record from 1960 was not verified (lack of evidence).
Status: Accidental. Protected.
Population trends: No data available.
Distribution: i/ Karvina-Stare Mesto (KI), ii/ Smrk in the Jizerske hory mountains (LB).
Timing: i/ 21 May 1978, ii/ 29 August 1985.

Rock Thrush *Monticola saxatilis*

Rufous-tailed Rock Thrush Skalnik zpevny Skaliar pestry Steinrötel

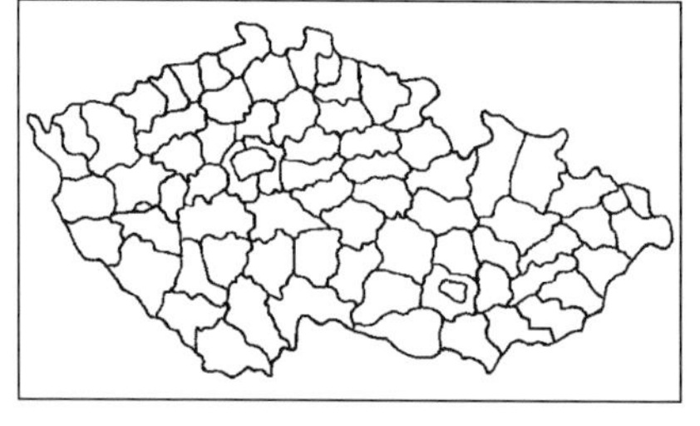

Rock Thrush was a regular breeder in the Czech Republic during the 19th century, with breeding sites scattered across the country. In the 20th century, breeding was recorded in the Krkonose mountains (SE, TU), in the Palava hills (BV), at Hady near Brno (BM), in the Bile Karpaty (HO, UH, ZL), Jeseniky (BR, SU) and Beskydy (FM, VS) mountains. Breeding probably last occurred in the Czech Republic in the Palava hills in 1979. Its extirpation as a breeder is probably due to a reduction in avail-

able food, breeding sites alongside an overall decline in Europe. Between 1985 and 1997, it was not recorded in the Czech Republic at all. The breeding population in neighbouring Slovakia is between 15 and 30 pairs, and has declined by at least 50% over the past 20 years (Murin *et al.* 1994). Because the nearest breeding population is in Slovakia, Rock Thrushes are most likely to be seen in the east of the country.
Status: Extinct in the wild.
Population trends: No data available.
Distribution: See above. Between the 1950s and 1970s, most of the traditional breeding sites were unoccupied.
Timing: This species occured between late March and the end of September.

Eyebrowed Thrush *Turdus obscurus*

Drozd plavy Drozd olivkasty Weissbrauendrossel

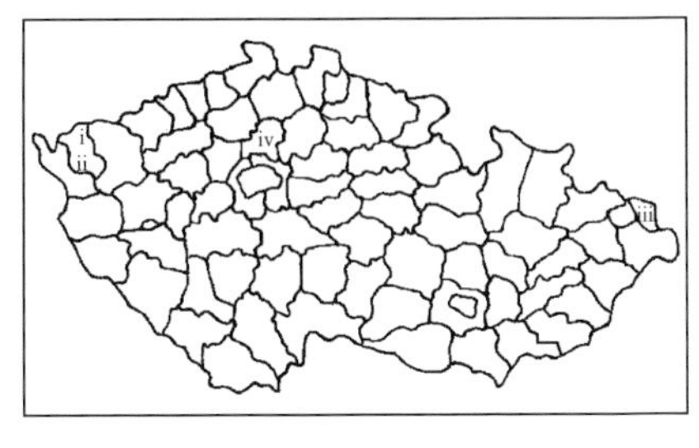

This species was recorded twice in the 19th and twice in the 20th centuries. The first 2 birds were collected (i and ii), the others were seen but not collected. All records were verified by the CFC. An additional 2 records from the end of the 19th century have not been accepted.
Status: Accidental. Protected.
Population trends: No data available.
Distribution: i–ii/ Luby-Olovi (SO), iii/ Vernovice (KI), iv/ Luzec (ME).
Timing: i–ii/ before 1852, iii/ 1 December 1979, iv/ 15 March 1980.

Dusky Thrush *Turdus naumanni*

Naumann's Thrush Drozd rezavy Drozd hrdzavy Naumannsdrossel

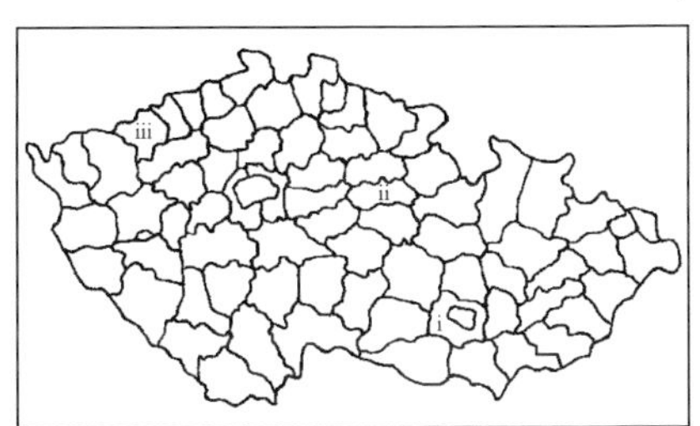

Three Dusky Thrushes have been recorded in the Czech Republic. Two of these (i and iii) were collected. All records have been accepted by the CFC. The specimens belong to the *naumanni* race.
Status: Accidental. Protected.
Population trends: No data available.
Distribution: i/ Brno-Sobesice (BO), ii/ Bukovka (PU), iii/ Liba (CV).
Timing: i/ winter 1836–37, ii/ 24 March 1963, iii/ 3 November 1964.

Dark-throated Thrush *Turdus ruficollis*

Red-throated Thrush Drozd tmavohrdly Drozd hnedosivy Bechsteindrossel

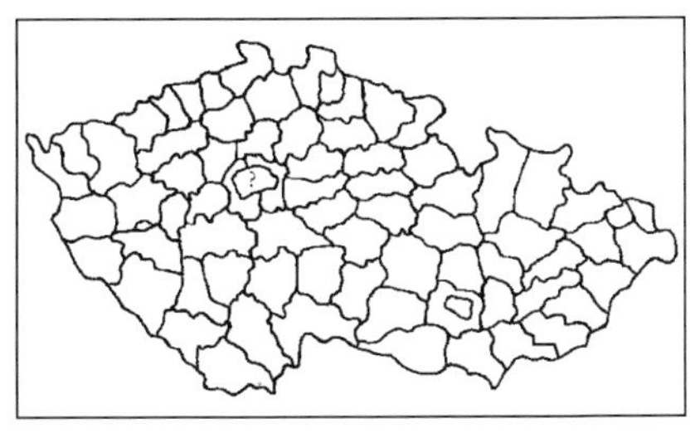

A juvenile bird was found in a market in Praha (AA) sometime between 1854 and 1870, and prepared as a specimen. However, the exact place where the individual was collected is unknown. This specimen was used as a model for a picture in Fric's (1870) book on European birds. This record of the *atrogularis* race was accepted by the CFC. Two other records from the 19th century were not accepted (lack of evidence).
Status: Accidental. Protected.
Population trends: No data available.
Distribution: See above
Timing: See above.

American Robin *Turdus migratorius*

Drozd stehovavy   Drozd stahovavy   Wanderdrossel

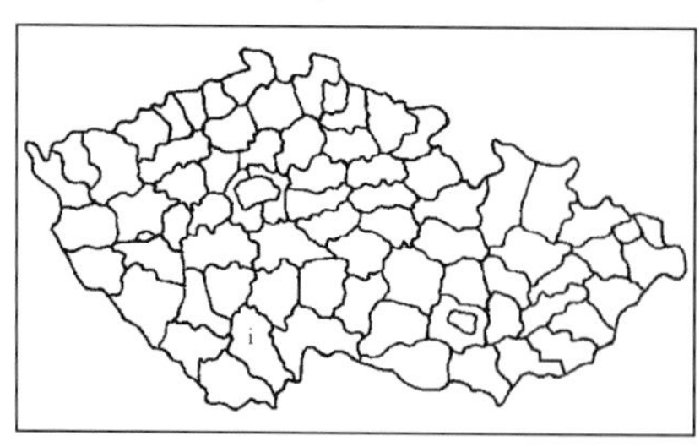

The only record accepted by the CFC is of an individual collected in the middle of the 19th century. Two other records from the end of the 19th century have not been accepted.
Status: Accidental. Protected.
Population trends: No data available.
Distribution: i/ Hluboka nad Vltavou (CB).
Timing: i/ around 1860.

Olivaceous Warbler *Hippolais pallida*

Sedmihlasek sedy   Sedmohlasok bledy   Blaßspötter

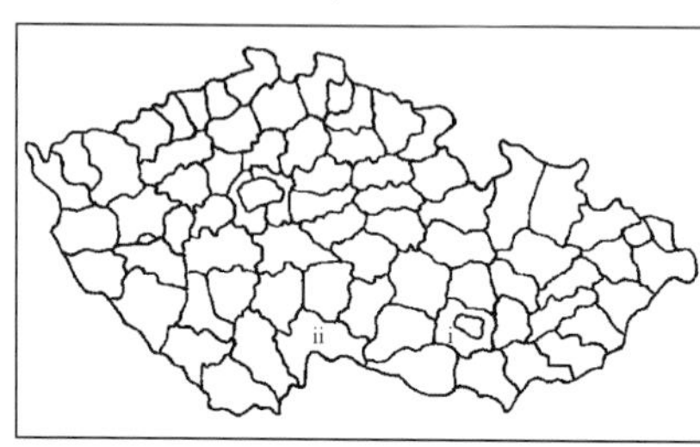

Two records of single singing males belonging to the *elaeica* race have been accepted by the CFC. Two other records, 1 of them including an adult bird feeding a nestling in c. Moravia (ZL) were not accepted.
Status: Accidental. Protected.
Population trends: No data available.
Distribution: i/ Brno-Novy Liskovec (BO), ii/ Chlum u Trebone (JH).
Timing: i/ 6 June 1972, ii/ 23 May 1990.

Melodious Warbler *Hippolais polyglotta*

Sedmihlasek svitorivy   Sedmohlasok stebotavy   Orpheusspötter

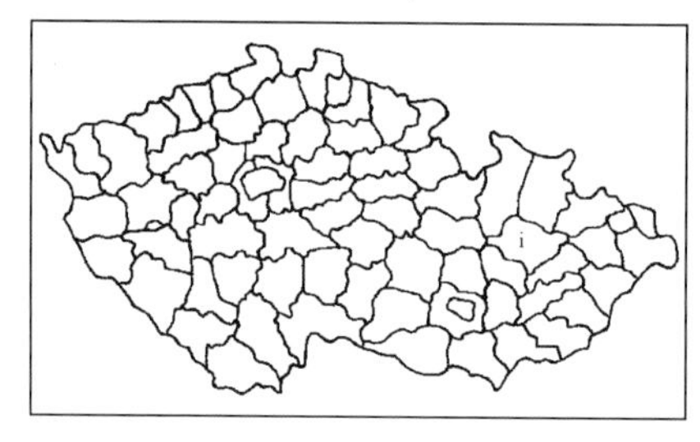

The only record is of an individual found dead, then collected for the Natural History Museum in Vienna. The record was accepted by the CFC.
Status: Accidental. Protected.
Population trends: No data available.
Distribution: i/ Olomouc (OL).
Timing: i/ 3 July 1864.

Dartford Warbler *Sylvia undata*

Penice kastanova   Penica hneda   Provence-Grasmucke

An adult male belonging to the *undata* race was found dead under power lines. The record was accepted by the CFC. One other record, of a singing male in Breclav (BV) county, was not verified.
Status: Accidental. Protected.
Population trends: No data available.
Distribution: i/ Polna (JI).
Timing: i/ 12 June 1969.

Dartford Warbler

Sardinian Warbler *Sylvia melanocephala*

Penice belohrdla   Penica siva   Samtkopfgrasmücke

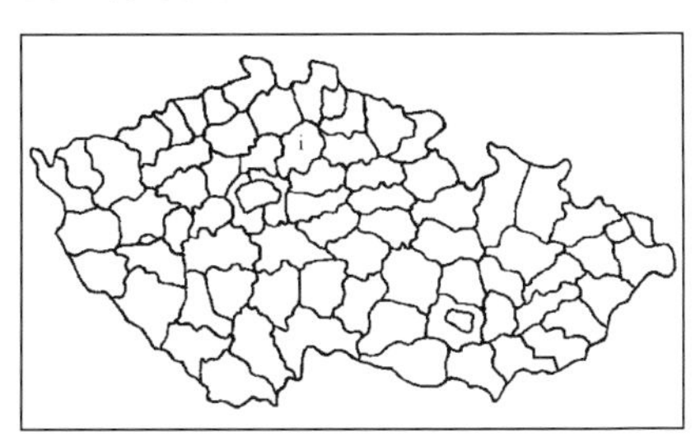

A singing male belonging to the *melanocephala* race was recorded in oak forest, at 260 m. The record was verified by the CFC.
Status: Accidental. Protected.
Population trends: No data available.
Distribution: i/ Mnichovo Hradiste (MB).
Timing: i/ 17 May 1985.

Orphean Warbler *Sylvia hortensis*

Penice mistrovska   Penica mistrovska   Orpheusgrasmus

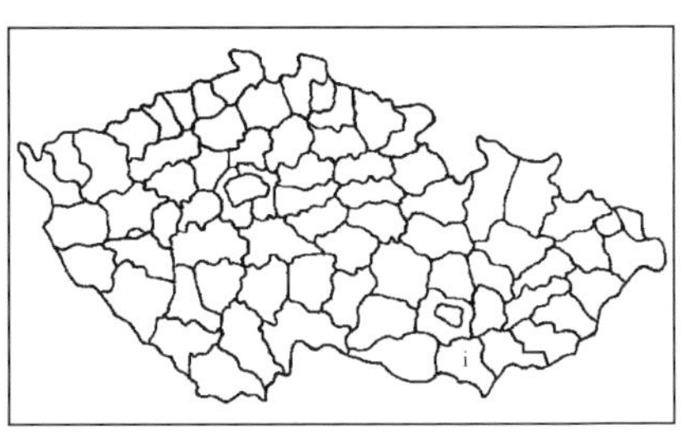

There were reports of singing males and trapped birds from s. Moravia from the second half of the 19th and beginning of the 20th centuries. These reports, according to the CFC, were undocumented and dubious. A singing male was recorded near Nesyt pond (BV). The latter record was verified by the CFC.
Status: Accidental. Protected.
Population trends: No data available.
Distribution: i/ Sedlec u Mikulova (BV).
Timing: i/ 7 May 1978.

Pallas's Leaf Warbler *Phylloscopus proregulus*

Pallas's Warbler Budnicek zlatohlavy Kolibkarik kralikovity Goldhahnchen-Laubsänger

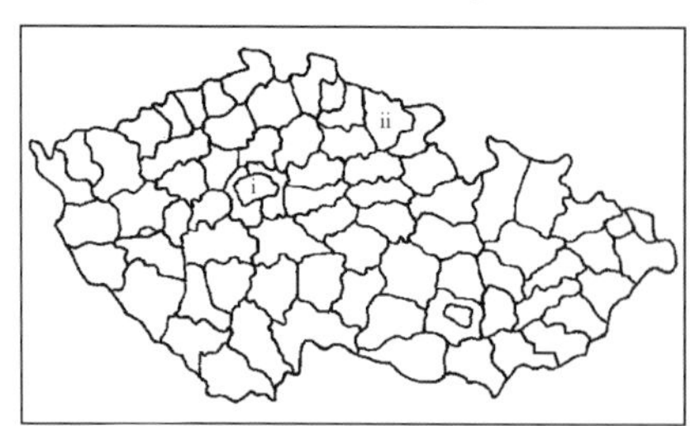

There are 2 records of individuals of the *proregulus* race, both being trapped and banded during autumn passage. Both records were accepted by the CFC.
Status: Accidental. Protected.
Population trends: No data available.
Distribution: i/ Praha (AA), ii/ Horni Marsov (TU).
Timing: i/ 18 October 1987, ii/ 31 October 1996.

Yellow-browed Warbler *Phylloscopus inornatus*

Inornate Warbler Budnicek pruhohlavy Kolibkarik zltkastotemenny Gelbbrauen-Laubsänger

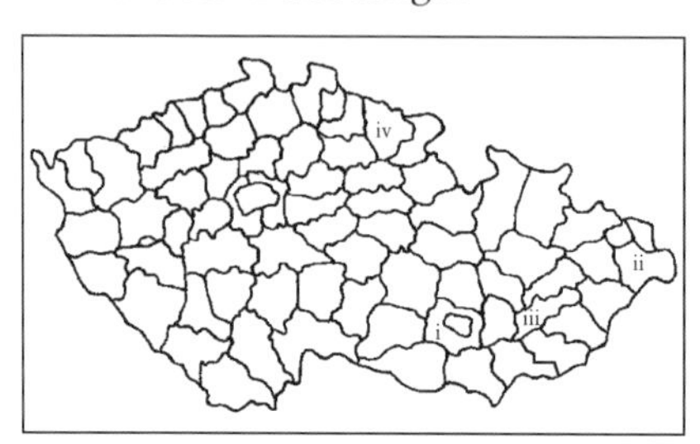

Three solitary birds have been recorded in Moravia, and 1 individual was banded in the Krkonose mountains (SE, TU). All 3 records were accepted by the CFC. Yellow-browed Warblers recorded in the Czech Republic belong to the *inornatus* race. A record from the end of the 19th century was not verified (lack of evidence).
Status: Accidental. Protected.
Population trends: No data available.
Distribution: i/ Dolni Kounice (BO), ii/ Dolni Frycovice (FM), iii/ Zahlinice (KM), iv/ Horni Marsov (TU).
Timing: i/ 30 March 1956, ii/ 24 August 1969, iii/ 19 March 1983, iv/ 14 October 1996.

Radde's Warbler *Phylloscopus schwarzi*

Budnicek tlustozoby Kolibkarik dlhochvosty Bartlaubsänger

The only record is of an individual trapped and banded during autumn migration. The record was verified by the CFC.
Status: Accidental. Protected.
Population trends: No data available.
Distribution: i/ Mt Serlich in the Orlicke hory mountains (RK).
Timing: i/ 12 October 1991.

Iberian Chiffchaff *Phylloscopus brehmii*

Budnicek ibersky

The only record was of a singing male seen at 1000 m in Velka Upa. The bird occurred at the edge of 30–40 year-old pine forest, where its song was recorded, and then analyzed by experts. The record was accepted by the CFC.
Status: Accidental. Protected.
Population trends: No data available.
Distribution: i/ Velka Upa in the Krkonose mountains (TU).

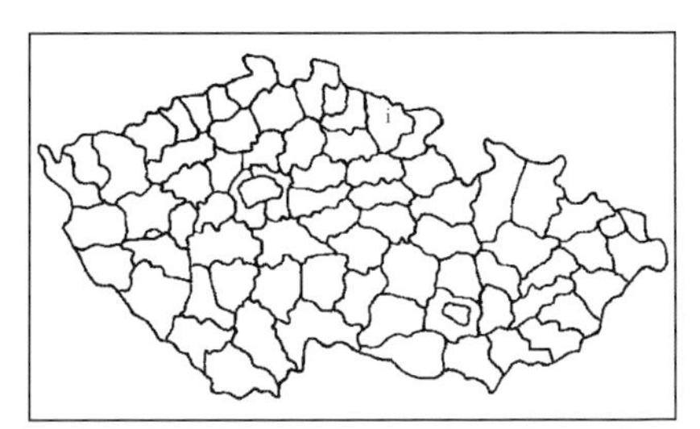

Timing: i/ 1–2 July 1992.

Lesser Grey Shrike *Lanius minor*

Tuhyk mensi Strakos kolesar Schwarzstirnwürger

Lesser Grey Shrike was a relatively common breeder, widely distributed across the country during the 19th century. However, at the beginning of the 20th century, it disappeared from some areas, and this trend continued until the middle of the century. From the 1970s onwards, breeding was irregular. Between 1985 and 1995, Lesser Grey Shrike probably became extinct as a breeder in the Czech Republic, no nesting being recorded. The breeding population in neighbouring Slovakia is between 400 and 600 pairs (Murin *et al.* 1994). Several possible causes for Lesser Grey Shrike's decline, and which apply to the situation in the Czech Republic, are given by Tucker and Heath (1994).
Status: Because of the nature of its occurrence in the Czech Republic, this species is considered to be extinct in the wild.
Population trends: Between 1973 and 1977 the breeding population was 10–30 pairs, and declined until the early 1990s.
Distribution: Between 1973 and 1977, breeding was recorded in the following counties: DO, PS, CB, HK, ZN, TR, SU, BV, HO, UH, KM, OL and VS. At the end of the 1970s, breeding was recorded in VS county in c. Moravia, and BV county in s. Moravia. Three recent records from 1994 come from Soutok (BV), where a pair was seen for about 2 weeks (May), Lednice (BV), where 3 individuals were seen (July), and Novosedly u Mikulova (BV), where 1 bird (August) was recorded. In May 1998, a single bird was seen in SY county.
Timing: It has occurred from mid-April until mid-October.

Woodchat Shrike *Lanius senator*

Tuhyk rudohlavy Strakos cervenohlavy Rotkopfwürger

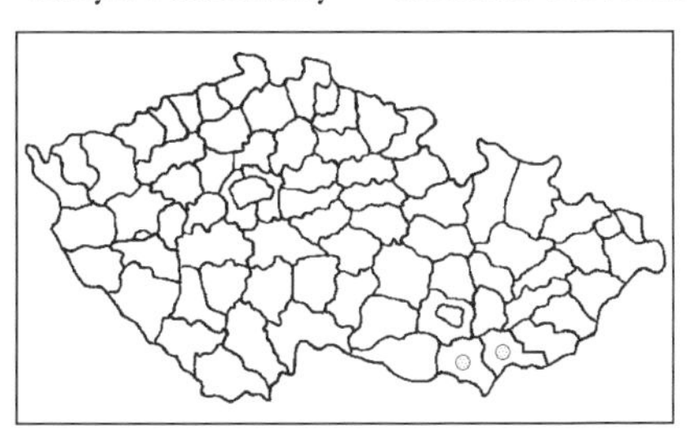

During the 19th century, Woodchat Shrike was a regular breeder in the Czech Republic, but since the end of that century its numbers have fallen (Knezourek 1910–12). However, regular breeding was still documented in several counties of n. Bohemia and c. Bohemia until the end of the 1950s. As a breeder, Woodchat Shrike occurred quite often in OL and PR counties in n. Moravia, and particularly in ZN, TR, BO, BV, HO, UH, VY, ZL and KM counties in s. Moravia, where locally it was a common breeder until 1960. Since the 1960s, the population has declined drastically, and Woodchat Shrike has become a rare species. In 1988, fledged Woodchat Shrikes were found in HO county, and this can be considered a breeding record. The probable causes of its extirpation are habitat degradation and the loss of food resources. The breeding population in neighboring Slovakia is 1–25 pairs (Murin *et al.* 1994).

Woodchat Shrike

Status: Critically endangered. Protected.
Population trends: Between 1973 and 1977 the breeding population was 10–30 pairs, between 1985 and 1989 it was estimated to be between 0–3 pairs.
Distribution: Between 1973 and 1977 breeding was recorded in the following counties: CV, LN, LT, TU, ZN, BV, VY, HO and UH. Between 1977 and 1987, breeding might have occurred in s. Moravia. A male was recored from June–July 1995 around Mistrin (HO). In July 1996, a juvenile was seen in Breclav-Lany (BV) but breeding was not recorded.
Timing: This species is recorded from mid-April until mid-September.

Yellow-billed Chough *Pyrrhocorax graculus*

Alpine Chough, Chough Kavce zlutozobe Cavka zltozoba Alpendohle

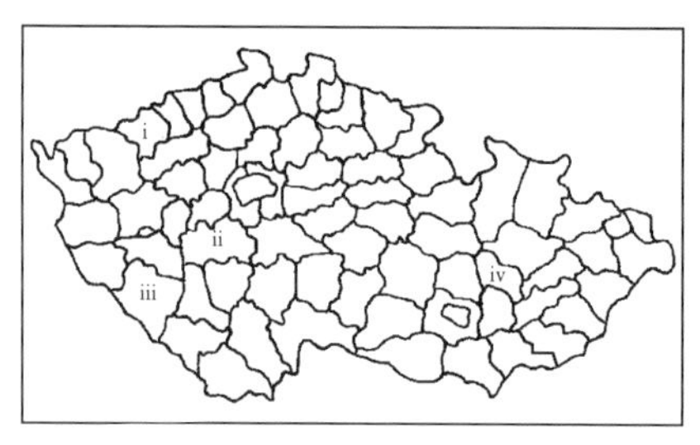

Four single Alpine Choughs have been recorded. Three of them were collected (i–iii), and 1 was seen for almost 1 week at the same place. All records were accepted by the CFC.
Status: Accidental. Protected.
Population trends: No data available.
Distribution: i/ Vysluni (CV), ii/ Strasice (PB), iii/ Alzbetin u Zelezne Rudy (PT), iv/ Ochoz u Konice (PV).
Timing: i/ June 1904, ii/ 10 April 1944, iii/ 2 December 1972, iv/ 3–8 August 1985.

Citril Finch *Serinus citrinella*

Zvonohlik citronovy Kanarik zlutozeleny Zitronengirlitz

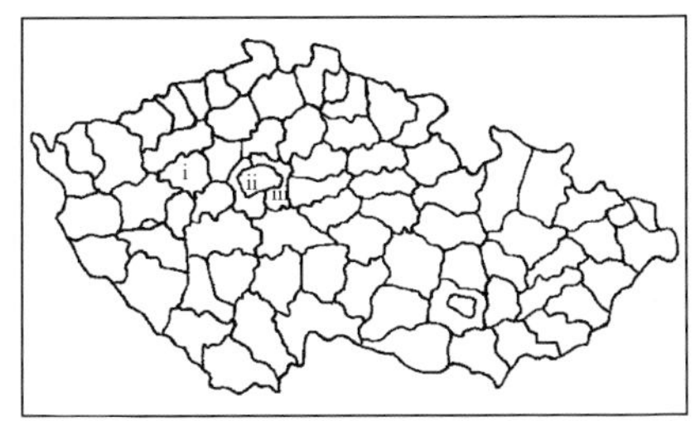

Two individuals (i and ii) have been collected, and the third bird was a female that was trapped and banded. All records were verified by the CFC. Other unaccepted records include a sighting of 3 birds during the second half of the 19th century.
Status: Accidental. Protected.
Population trends: No data available.
Distribution: i/ Krivoklat (RA), ii/ Praha (AA), iii/ Uvaly (PH).
Timing: i/ 1880, ii/ March 1890, iii/ 30 October 1972.

Pine Bunting *Emberiza leucocephalos*

Strnad belohlavy Strnadka bielohlava Fichtenammer

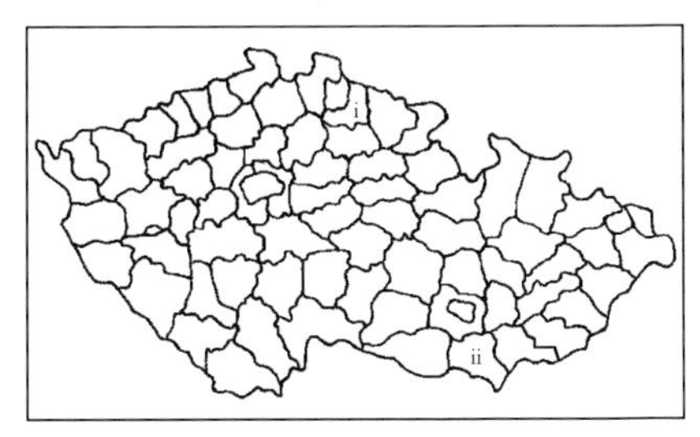

Records accepted by the CFC include a single male (i) that was collected, and sightings of 2 males and 1 female (ii). Three other records were not accepted (lack of evidence).
Status: Accidental. Protected.
Population trends: No data available.
Distribution: i/ Horni Polubny (SE), ii/ Novy Dvur u Lednice (BV).
Timing: i/ October 1889, ii/ 23 October 1962.

Cirl Bunting *Emberiza cirlus*

Strnad cvrcivy Strnadka svrciva Zaunammer

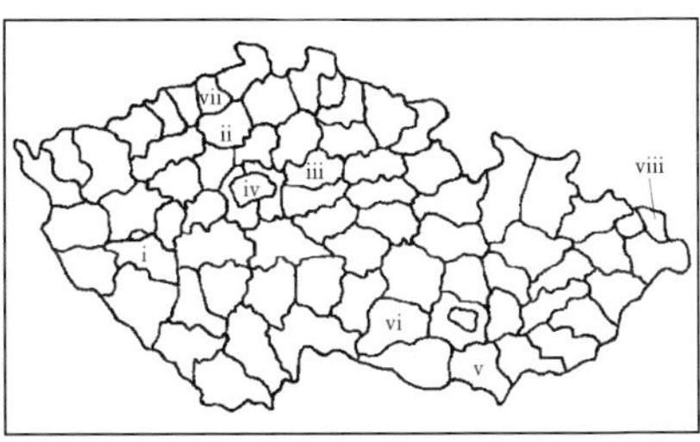

There are 8 records, with a total of 21 individuals, accepted by the CFC. Most single birds have been seen or collected, except 1 record that included 2 collected birds (iii), and a sight record of 12 individuals (vii). Other records from the 19th century and beginning of the 20th century were not accepted (lack of evidence).
Status: Accidental. Protected.
Population trends: No data available.
Distribution: i/ Klecany (PJ), ii/ Trebenice (LT), iii/ Podebrady (NB), iv/ Praha (AA), v/ Valtice (BV), vi/ Breznik (TR), vii/ Cermna (UL), viii/ Detmarovice (KI).
Timing: i/ around 1850, ii/ June 1897, iii/ 1914, iv/ probably April 1921, v/ 31 March 1953, vi/ 2–3 November 1954, vii/ 7 February 1960, viii/ 7 March 1990.

Rock Bunting *Emberiza cia*

Strnad vinicny Strnadka cia Zippammer

There are 9 records, with a total of 35–37 birds, that have been accepted by the CFC. Four of these include sightings of or collection of single birds, another 5 involve from 2 to about 20 individuals. It was suggested in the 19th century that Rock Bunting bred in the Czech Republic. However, there was no evidence to support this claim. There are also other reports from the 19th century, but these were not accepted by the CFC. The breeding population in Slovakia is 150–250 pairs (Murin *et al.* 1994).

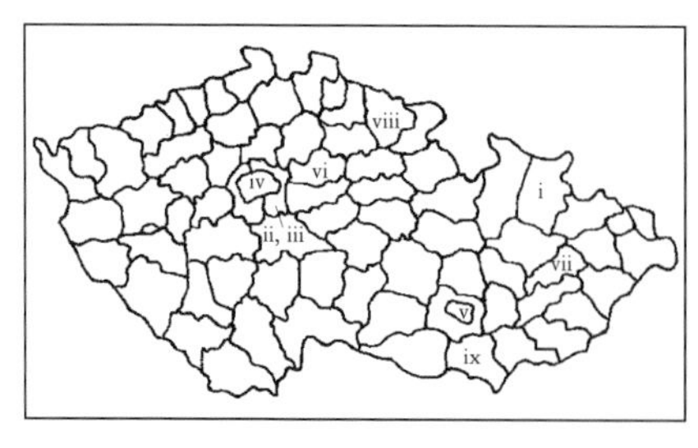

Status: Accidental. Protected.
Population trends: No data available.
Distribution: i/ Krnov (BR), ii/ Struharov (PH), iii/ Nepomuk (PH), iv/ Praha-Stromovka (AA), v/ Brno (BM), vi/ Dymokury (NB), vii/ Hranice (PR), viii/ Krkonose mountains (TU), ix/ Mikulov (BV).
Timing: i/ summer 1818, ii/ September 1871, iii/ 12 December 1885, iv/ 2 December 1905, v/ autumn 1907, vi/ around 1914, vii/ 1949, viii/ April 1966, ix/ 26 May 1985.

Rustic Bunting *Emberiza rustica*

Strnad rolni Strnadka rolna Waldammer

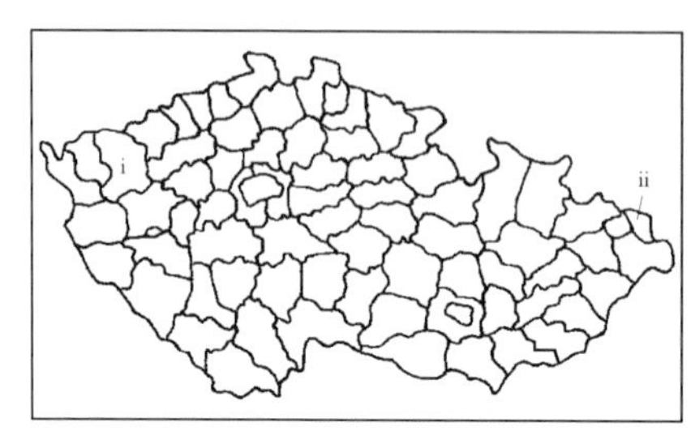

Two records involve singing males. Both records were verified by the CFC. Two other unaccepted records were of a male, from 1930, and a flock of 25–30 individuals, from 1983.
Status: Accidental. Protected.
Population trends: No data available.
Distribution: i/ Hroznetin (KV), ii/ Dolni Lutyne (KI).
Timing: i/ 23 April 1982, ii/ 31 March 1986.

Little Bunting *Emberiza pusilla*

Strnad malinky Strnadka mala Zwergammer

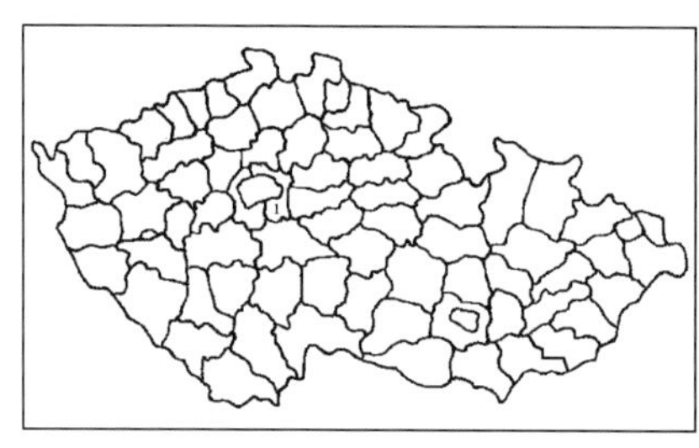

The only record is of an individual that was trapped and banded. The record was verified by the CFC.
Status: Accidental. Protected.
Population trends: No data available.
Distribution: i/ Lipence u Prahy (PH).
Timing: i/ 31 January 1981.

Yellow-breasted Bunting *Emberiza aureola*

Strnad obojkovy Strnadka obojkova Weidenammer

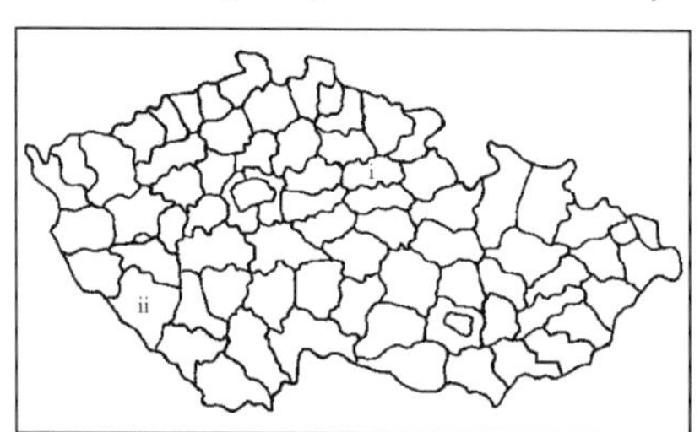

Two individuals have been recorded; both records were verified by the CFC. One other record from the end of the 19th century was not accepted.
Status: Accidental. Protected.
Population trends: No data available.
Distribution: i/ Chotelice (HK), ii/ Klatovy (KT).
Timing: i/ 29 July 1931, ii/ 10 July 1984.

Red-headed Bunting *Emberiza brunniceps*

Strnad hnedohlavy Strnadka rysavohlava Braunkopfammer

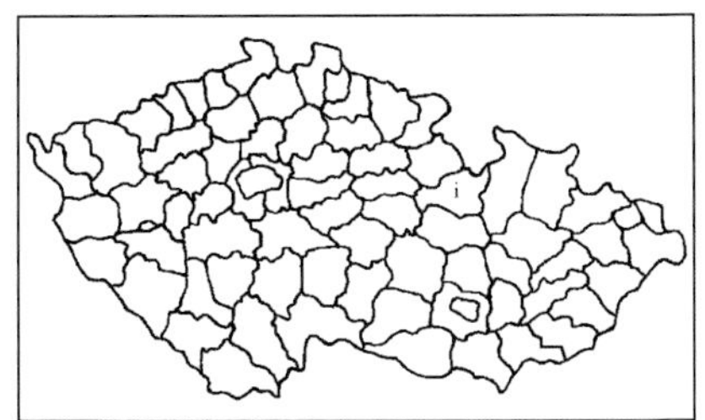

The only record is of an adult male that was trapped and held in captivity before being taken as a specimen for the Moravian Museum in Brno. The record was accepted by the CFC.
Status: Accidental. Protected.
Population trends: No data available.
Distribution: i/ Lanskroun (UO).
Timing: i/ 29 December 1961.

Black-headed Bunting *Emberiza melanocephala*

Strnad cernohlavy Strnadka ciernohlava Kappenammer

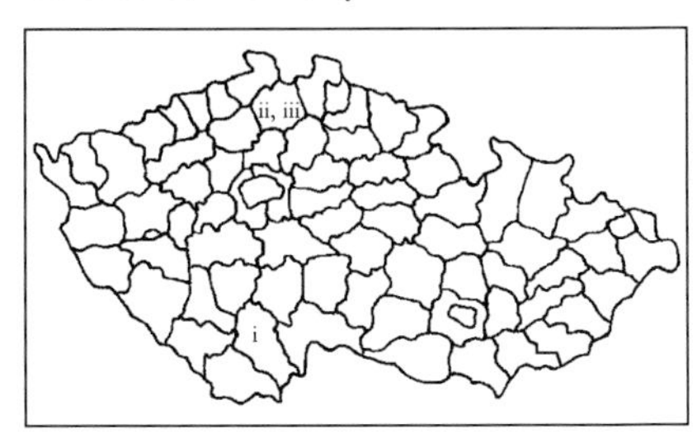

There are 3 records, with a total of 3 individuals. The first bird was collected, and the 2 others were trapped and banded. All records were verified by the CFC.
Status: Accidental. Protected.
Population trends: No data available.
Distribution: i/ around Ceske Budejovice (CB), ii/ Struznice (CL), iii/ Jestrebi (CL).
Timing: i/ between 1832 and 1871, ii/ 27 May 1979, iii/ 18 June 1994.

WHERE TO WATCH BIRDS

The Czech Republic offers wonderful birdwatching opportunities in a wide variety of habitats. Most of the sites are on public land, and no special permission to enter is required. Since many of these sites are conservation areas (ponds, marshes, riverine forest, nature reserves in mountains), one must obey the rules for visitors.

This section lists several birdwatching sites for each region of the country. The selection of sites is subjective, based on my own experience. However, these sites are frequently visited by numerous ornithologists and birdwatchers, and they are often mentioned in the species acounts because they hold many birds.

The selection of species in this section represents typical as well as 'possible' species for each site. Although a map is provided, and access is described for each site, one may want to use a road atlas of the Czech Republic to find these sites.

The scale of the maps in this section is 1:200,000, except for the map of the Bile Karpaty mountains, where it is 1:400,000.

CENTRAL BOHEMIA

Parkland in Pruhonice (PH)

General characteristics

50°02'N 14°29'E

This is an area of parkland in a small village, and easily accessible from Praha. Although the whole area is a wonderful place for birdwatching, sites with mature conifers and deciduous trees offer the best opportunity to see rare species, particularly during migration. Several brooks run across the park, and small lakes are situated here and there. The altitude of the park is about 250–340 m.

Species

Among breeding species are Wood Pigeon, Turtle Dove, Tawny Owl, Long-eared Owl, Grey-headed Woodpecker, Green Woodpecker, Lesser Spotted Woodpecker, Rufous Nightingale, Common Redstart, Grasshopper Warbler, River Warbler and Golden Oriole.

Access

From Praha take highway E50 or E55 (to Brno). Pruhonice lies 8 km southeast of Praha. For details of access see a detailed map of Praha.

Ponds around Sedlcany (BN)

General characteristics

49°41'N 14°11'E

This is a system of several small ponds with a larger pond, called Musik, surrounded by farmland at 320–400 m. Although relatively small, the ponds provide suitable breeding habitat for waterfowl as well as passerines and are used as a stopover by birds on passage. Some of the ponds extend into wet meadows, and most have littoral vegetation and reeds.

Species

Breeding species include Little Grebe, Great Crested Grebe, Black-necked Grebe, Gadwall, Common Teal, Garganey, Northern Shoveler, Common Pochard, Tufted Duck, Water Rail, Yellow Wagtail, *Locustella* spp., *Acrocephalus* spp., Penduline Tit and Reed Bunting. Among non-breeding summer residents or birds on passage are Montagu's Harrier, Osprey, Common Crane, various waterfowl, shorebirds, and gulls.

Access

The ponds lie between the villages of Sedlcany, Solopysky and Dublovice and are accessible by county roads. From Praha take highway E55 to Benesov (42 km) and from here to the intersection with highway 18 (15 km). From the intersection travel to Sedlcany on highway 18 (13.5 km).

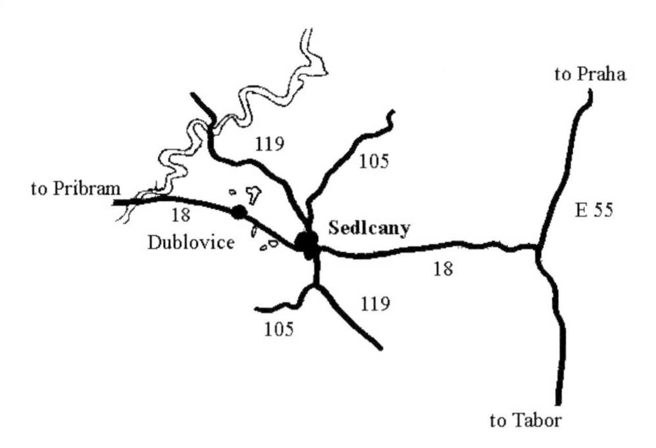

Praha – Stromovka (AA)

General characteristics

50°05'N 14°24'E

Although there are many parks suitable for birdwatching in Praha, Stromovka is one of the largest, and a good range of species can be seen. Mature deciduous and coniferous trees dominate the park, but there are areas with bushes as well. There are marked pathways which are easy to follow. Some areas of the park are busier than others.

Species

Among breeding species are Eurasian Sparrowhawk, Common Kestrel, Turtle Dove, Tawny Owl, Long-eared Owl, Green Woodpecker, Rufous Nightingale, River Warbler, Marsh Warbler and Spotted Flycatcher, although many 'surprises' are possible. On migration, numerous species of raptor and warbler can be seen as well.

Access

For details of public transport and access to the parts of the river outside the inner city, see a detailed map of Praha.

Praha – Sarka (AA)

General characteristics

50°05'N 14°24'E

This is a scenic valley at the west edge of Praha with a parkland landscape. Natural habitats blend with developed sites and offer attractive birdwatching. The habitats range from rocky slopes to deciduous and mixed forest, orchards, brooks, and farmland.

Species

Breeding species include Common Buzzard, Common Kestrel, Common Quail, Wood Pigeon, Tawny Owl, Long-eared Owl, Common Kingfisher, Grey-headed Woodpecker, Black Woodpecker, Grey Wagtail, Rufous Nightingale, Grasshopper Warbler, River Warbler, Marsh Warbler, Reed Warbler, Icterine Warbler, Short-toed Treecreeper and Golden Oriole.

Access

For details of public transport and access to Sarka, see a detailed map of Praha.

Praha – Trojska kotlina (AA)

General characteristics

50°05'N 14°24'E

This is a valley in the northern part of Praha with dry steppe-like habitats, deciduous and mixed woods, slopes, as well as open water, including the river Vltava. The altitude is 180–240 m. The diversity of habitats provides suitable breeding conditions for several passerines as well as non-passerines. Sites particularly favoured by birds are located along the river, as well as within the zoological garden.

Species

Among breeding species are Eurasian Sparrowhawk, Common Buzzard, Common Kestrel, Grey Partridge, Common Quail, Moorhen, Tawny Owl, Long-eared Owl, Common Kingfisher, Grey-headed Woodpecker, Green Woodpecker, Black Woodpecker, Lesser Spotted Woodpecker, Rufous Nightingale, Short-toed Treecreeper, Penduline Tit and Golden Oriole.

Access

For details of public transport and access to Trojska kotlina, see a detailed map of Praha.

The Vltava river in Praha (AA)

General characteristics

50°05'N 14°24'E

Although it runs through a large city with heavy traffic along the banks, the Vltava river is one of the most important wintering areas for waterfowl in the Czech Republic. On a stretch of about 25 km, including the section of river in the inner city, thousands of waterfowl can be recorded during a single day between the end of October and mid-March. Two sites with high numbers as well as good species diversity are: the area between Karluv most bridge and Strelecky ostrov island in the centre of the town; and at the northern edge of Praha, close to the zoological garden in Praha-Troja. All sites suitable for birdwatching are accessible by public transport or on foot.

Species

Among wintering species are Black-throated Diver, Little Grebe, Great Crested Grebe, Red-necked Grebe, Great Cormorant, Grey Heron, Mute Swan, Common Shelduck, Eurasian Wigeon, Gadwall, Pintail, Red-crested Pochard, Ferruginous Duck, Tufted Duck, Greater Scaup, Common Eider, Long-tailed Duck, Common Scoter, Velvet Scoter, Common Goldeneye, Smew, Goosander, Common Coot, Little Gull, Black-headed Gull, Common Gull, Herring Gull, and Common Kingfisher. Some of the ducks and gulls can be seen all year round.

Access

For details on public transport and access to sections of the river outside the inner city, see a detailed map of Praha.

EAST BOHEMIA

Ponds around Bohdanec (PU)

General characteristics

50°03'N 15°40'E

This area includes about 10 ponds of varying size, ranging from 0.04 km^2 to 0.85 km^2 at 215–235 m. These ponds have rich littoral vegetation and are surrounded by reeds. The ponds located on farmland and in woodland are important for breeding as well as migrating birds. More than 190 species have been recorded in the area, including about 80 regularly breeding species.

Species

Breeding species include Little Grebe, Great Crested Grebe, Little Bittern, Northern Shoveler, Common Pochard, Tufted Duck, Marsh Harrier, Water Rail, *Locustella* spp., *Acrocephalus* spp. and Penduline Tit. Among migrating and non-breeding species are Red-necked Grebe, Great Cormorant, Great Bittern, Night Heron, Eurasian Wigeon, Greater Scaup, Common Goldeneye, Red-breasted Merganser, Goosander, Osprey, European Golden Plover, Grey Plover, numerous *Calidris* spp., and *Tringa* spp., Common Gull, Little Gull, Common Tern, and Black Tern.

Access

From Pardubice, take highway 36 to Lazne Bohdanec (12 km). From here, travel on highway 33 to Stare Zdanice (access to Oplatil pond, which lies on the east side of the road). All the ponds can be accessed by county roads from Lazne Bohdanec. From Praha, take highway D11 to Podebrady (41 km), from Podebrady highway 11 to Chlumec nad Cidlinou (23 km), and from here highway 36 to Lazne Bohdanec (18 km).

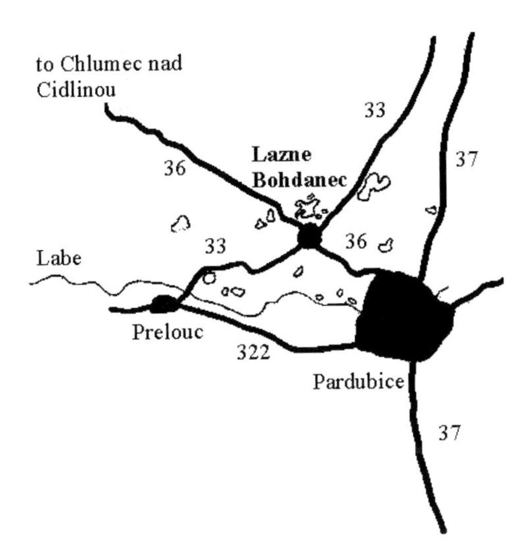

Hvezda and Novy ponds near Svitavy (SY)

General characteristics

49°53'N 16°25'E

These are the 2 largest ponds (no more than 2 km^2 each) in a system of ponds between Svitavy and Opatov. Several other smaller ponds are located here as well. They lie at 400–460 m and are mostly surrounded by farmland and woodland. Although they provide nesting sites for several species of waterfowl, they are more important for migrants.

Species

Among birds on passage are Red-throated Diver, Black-throated Diver, Red-necked Grebe, Great Cormorant, Great White Egret, Eurasian Wigeon, Pintail, Red-breasted Merganser, Osprey, Jack Snipe, Little Gull, Caspian Tern, Whiskered Tern, White-Winged Black Tern and Bearded Tit.

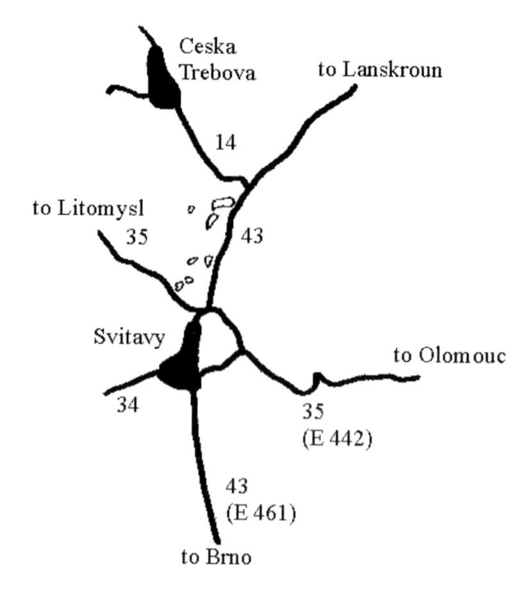

Access

From Svitavy, take highway 43 to Lanskroun. The ponds are found at about 14 km between Svitavy and Opatov, to the west of the road. From Brno, take highway 43 to Svitavy (66 km).

Kralicky Sneznik mountains (UO, SU)

General characteristics

50°03'–50°04'N 14°44'–14°46'E

These, the smallest mountains in the Czech Republic, are found on the Czech Republic-Poland border, partly in eastern Bohemia and partly in northern Moravia. The highest peak in this 76-km^2 area of mountains is Mt Kralicky Sneznik (1200 m). Spruce-dominated forest covers the majority of the mountains, with remnant fir-beech woodland. Dwarf pines dominate at the peaks. Small patches of peatbogs can be found in the alpine zone. These mountains are an important area for several breeding species. About 120 species have been recorded so far, and 110 of these are breeding.

Species

Among breeding species are Black Stork, Hobby, Corn Crake, Stock Dove, Eagle Owl, Tengmalm's Owl, Common Kingfisher, Meadow Pipit, Water Pipit (about 20 pairs), Northern Wheatear, Red-breasted Flycatcher, Common Redpoll and Common Rosefinch.

Access

From Brno, take highway E461 to Svitavy (66 km), from here travel on highway 43 to the village of Bukovice (43 km). From Bukovice, take highway 11 to Cervena Voda (8 km), and from Cervena Voda highway 43 to Kraliky (9 km). From here, county roads run across the mountains.

Rozkos reservoir (NA)

General characteristics

50°24'N 16°05'E

This is a reservoir of about 10 km^2 near Ceska Skalice at 284 m. Although it is used for water sports and other activities, several shallow bays and a peninsula on the east side provide favourable sites for numerous waterfowl and shorebirds. Reeds are rather scarce, and bushes and stands of trees, mostly willows, are scattered along the banks. Although 270 species have been recorded at Rozkos reservoir, most of these are migrants. The best time to visit, therefore, is during spring (mid-March and the beginning of May) and autumn (mid-July and mid-October) migration.

Species

Only a few common species nest at the reservoir, including a colony of Black-headed Gulls. However, a mature mixed forest attracts breeding European Honey Buzzard, Green Woodpeckers, Great Spotted Woodpeckers, and various passerines such as Spotted Flycatchers, Pied Flycatchers, Short-toed Treecreepers, Golden Orioles, *Sylvia* spp., *Phylloscopus* spp, and *Parus* spp. Among migrating species are Red-throated Diver, Black-throated Diver, Great Crested Grebe, Red-necked Grebe, Slavonian Grebe, Great Cormorant, Great White Egret, Night Heron, Grey Heron, Greylag Goose, Greater Scaup, Common Eider, Common Scoter, Common Goldeneye, Red-breasted Merganser, Goosander, White-tailed Eagle, Marsh Harrier, Osprey, Black-tailed Godwit, Grey Plover, Whimbrel, Turnstone, numerous *Charadrius* spp., *Calidris* spp., *Tringa* spp., Common Gull, Herring Gull, Common Tern and Black Tern. Flocks of waterfowl may number hundreds, and flocks of shorebirds dozens of individuals.

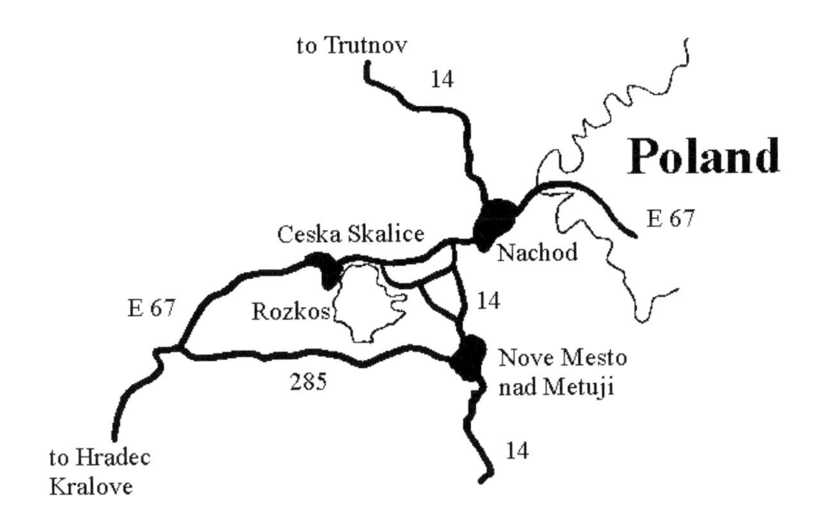

Access

The reservoir lies east of Ceska Skalice (NA) along highway E67, about 30 km northeast of Hradec Kralove. The reservoir is accessible from several roads from Ceska Skalice, although some parts are accessible on foot only.

NORTH BOHEMIA

The Labe river between Horni Pocaply and Roudnice nad Labem (ME, LT)

General characteristics

50°26'–50°27''N 14°17'–14°21'E

This is a 15-km stretch of the largest river in the Czech Republic, the Labe. This is one of the best wintering sites for waterfowl in the country. The numbers of most waterfowl species exceed dozens, hundreds and, occasionally, thousands of individuals. Rare visitors from northern Europe are often recorded too. The altitude of the area is 190–215 m.

Species

High numbers of the following species are recorded annually: Mute Swan, Mallard, Common Pochard, Tufted Duck, Goosander, Common Goldeneye and Common Coot. Among other species are Little Grebe, Great Crested Grebe, Slavonian Grebe, Greater Cormorant, Grey Heron, Greater Scaup, Long-tailed Duck, Common Scoter, Smew, White-tailed Eagle, Moorhen and Black-headed Gull.

Access

From Roudnice nad Labem walk on the bank along the river. From Praha take highway E55 to the village of Nova Ves and stay on this until the intersection with highway 240 (about 40 km from Praha). From this intersection, continue on highway 240 to Roudnice nad Labem (4 km).

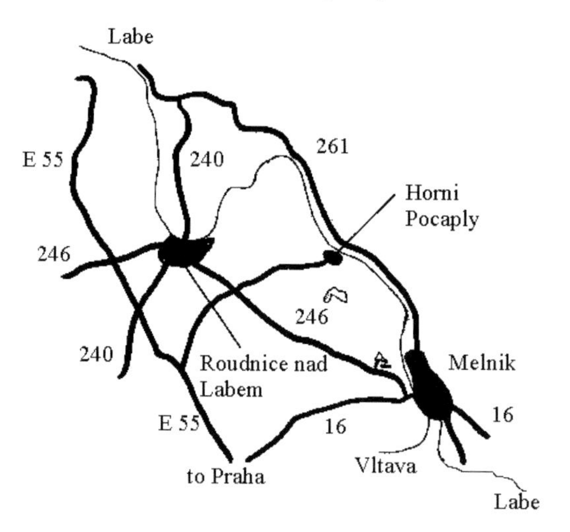

Lenesicky pond (LN)

General characteristics

50°22'N 13°42'E

Lenesicky pond is a system of 1 large (0.8 km^2) and 5 small (0.3 km^2) fishponds, about 4 km northwest of the village of Lenesice at 185 m. The average annual temperature is 8.6°C. The ponds have littoral vegetation and growths of bushes and trees around their banks. They are used for fish-farming. By the beginning of the 1990s, 180 migrating and breeding species had been recorded at the ponds and in their environs.

Species

Breeding species include Little Grebe, Great Crested Grebe, Black-necked Grebe, Mute Swan, Gadwall, Common Pochard, Tufted Duck and Rufous Nightingale. Among migrating and non-breeding species are Red-necked Grebe, Great Cormorant, Great White Egret, Grey Heron, Long-tailed Duck, Velvet Scoter, Common Goldeneye, Goosander, White-headed Duck, Osprey, Black Tern, and about 2 dozen species of shorebird.

Access

From Louny, take highway 28, and after 1.5 km turn left and take the county road running around the pond. From Praha, take highway E55 to the village of Dusniky (about 43 km), and from Dusniky, travel on highway 246 to Louny (34 km).

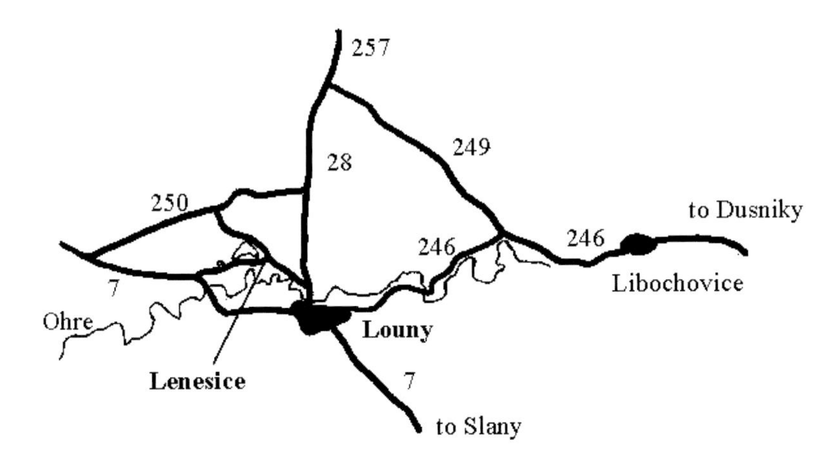

The Jizerske hory mountains (LB, JN)

General characteristics

50°46'–50°48'N 15°03'–15°12'E

The Jizerske hory mountains, with an area of about 160 km^2, run along the border between the Czech Republic and Poland. Much of the area is covered by spruce plantations, and most of these have been damaged by acid-rain. Remnant beech forest is found on the northern slopes of the mountains. The altitude ranges from about 500 m up to peaks such as Smrk (1124 m) and Jizera (1122 m). Valuable habitats include peatbogs, pastures and meadows. This area is important for several endangered breeding species.

Species

Among breeding species are Black Stork, Eurasian Sparrowhawk, Black Grouse, Common Snipe, Stock Dove, Tengmalm's Owl, Northern Wheatear, Red-breasted Flycatcher, Pied Flycatcher, Nutcracker and Common Rosefinch.

Access

(See page 294 for map.) From Praha, take highway E65 to Turnov (about 81 km), from here highways 35 and 278 to Jablonec (17 km) or highway 35 and the E442 to Liberec (21 km). The mountains are accessible from either town using highways and county roads that criss-cross the area. Trails in the mountains are well marked.

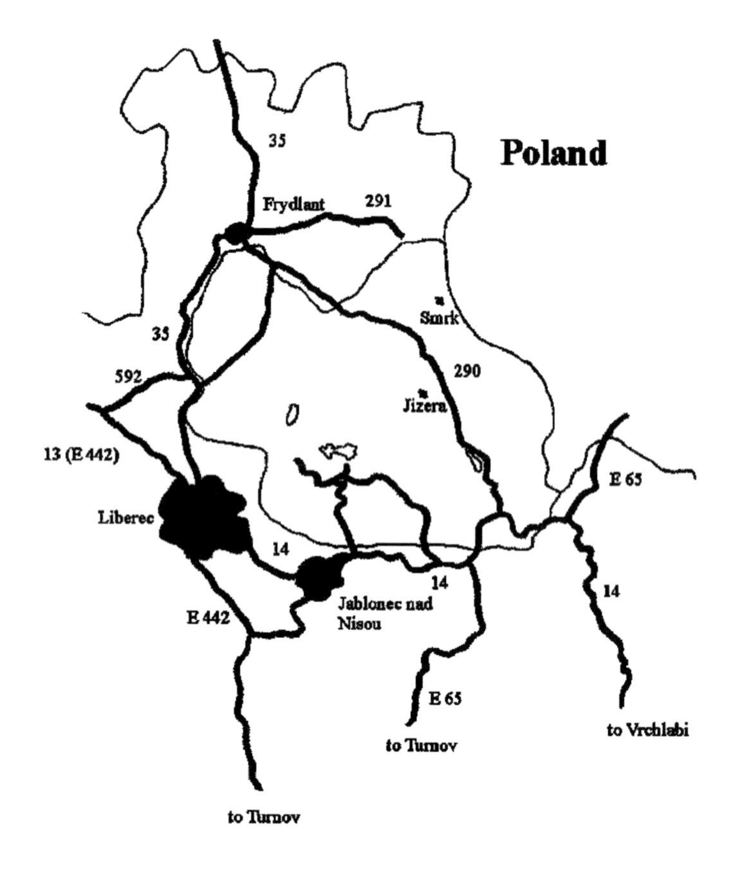

The Ohre river around Louny (LN)

General characteristics

50°20'–50°22'N 13°38'–13°48'E

Although the river Ohre is not one of the largest in the country, numerous waterfowl use it as a wintering site. Birds of course can be found at other areas of the river, but the 10-km stretch around the town of Louny hosts higher densities and a greater species diversity than elsewhere. The altitude is 175–220 m.

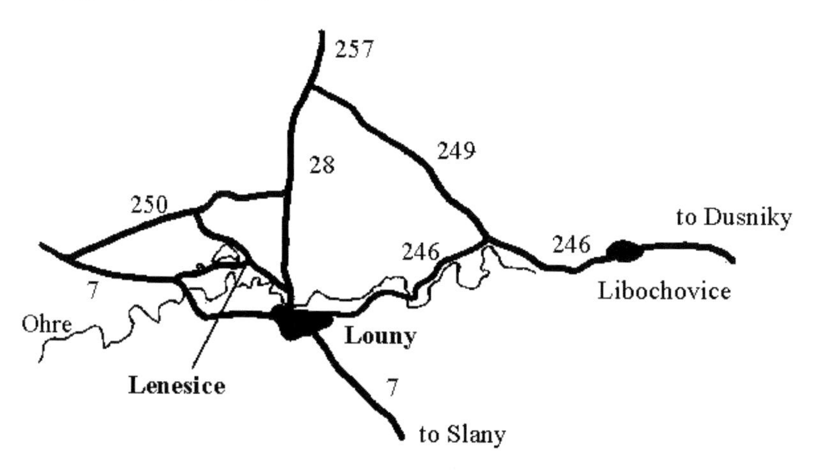

Species

Among wintering and passage species are Little Grebe, Mute Swan, Eurasian Wigeon, Gadwall, Common Teal, Common Pochard, Tufted Duck, Greater Scaup, Common Scoter, Goosander and Common Coot.

Access

From Louny, walk along the bank of the river. From Praha, highway E55 goes to the village of Dusniky (about 43 km), and from Dusniky take highway 246 to Louny (34 km).

WEST BOHEMIA

Brdy hills (RO, PB)

General characteristics

49°17'–49°44'N 13°51'–13°56'E

This is a complex of large woods between the towns of Rokycany and Pribram, with peaks called Tok (864 m) and Praha (862 m). Because the whole area has been a military training zone, there is no development. A site called Padrtske ponds is surrounded by peatbogs. The mature woods provide suitable breeding habitats for birds of prey, owls and various passerines.

Species

Among breeding species are Black Stork, Northern Goshawk, Eurasian Sparrowhawk, Common Buzzard, Woodcock, Stock Dove, Eagle Owl, Pygmy Owl, Tengmalm's Owl, European Nightjar, Common Kingfisher, Green Woodpecker, Black Woodpecker, Middle Spotted Woodpecker, Lesser Spotted Woodpecker, Grey Wagtail, Dipper, Firecrest, Common Raven, Common Redpoll and Common Crossbill.

Access

From Plzen, take highway E50 to Rokycany (14 km), and from here highway 232 to the village of Mirosov. There are county roads from Mirosov to the hills. From Mirosov, take highway 117 north to the village of Strasice (11 km) and from here county roads to the hills; also from Mirosov, highway 117 south to the village of Spalene Porici (12 km), and from here highway 19 to Rozmital pod Tremsinem (18 km). There are exits from this highway to the hills. From Pribram, take highway 18 to Rozmital pod Tremsinem (14 km) and again roads off the highway go to the hills. From Praha, take highway 4 to Pribram (60 km), or the D5 (E50) to Rokycany (65 km).

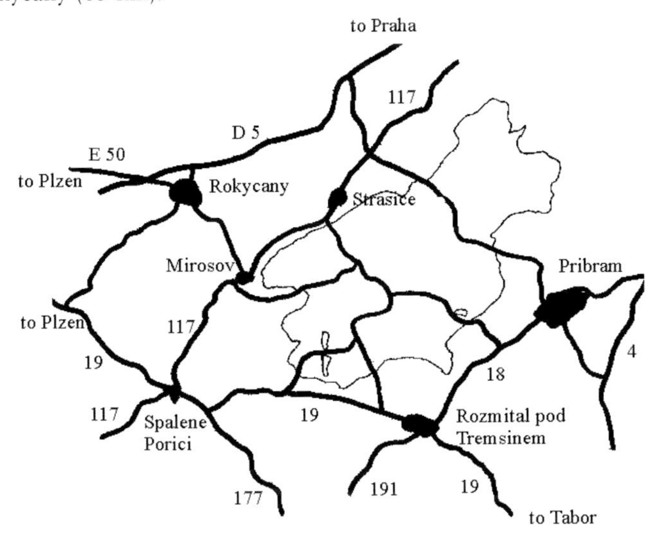

Jesenice and Skalka reservoirs (CH)

General characteristics

50°04'–50°04'N 12°18'–12°24'E

Jesenica and Skalka are large reservoirs (over 6 km^2 and 3 km^2 respectively) and are located in the west of the Czech Republic at an altitude of about 450–500 m. Even though they provide breeding habitat for several common species of waterfowl, they are better known as a site for migrating waterfowl, gulls and shorebirds.

Species

Among birds on passage are Black-throated Diver, Great Cormorant, Grey Heron, Great White Egret, White-fronted Goose, Greylag Goose, Eurasian Wigeon, Pintail, Ferruginous Duck, Common Eider (occasionally), Common Goldeneye, Goosander, Black Kite, Red Kite, Osprey, *Charadrius* spp., *Calidris* spp., *Tringa* spp., Common Gull, Herring Gull, Common Tern, Little Tern and Black Tern.

Access

From Cheb, take highway 6 to Sokolov. At the intersection with highway 21 (4.5 km from Cheb) turn right. After about 2 km, there is an exit to the reservoir. The reservoir is also accessible by a county road running directly from Cheb to its western tip (about 3 km). Skalka reservoir lies on the northwest edge of Cheb, and is also accessible from highway 6, running from Cheb to the border with Germany.

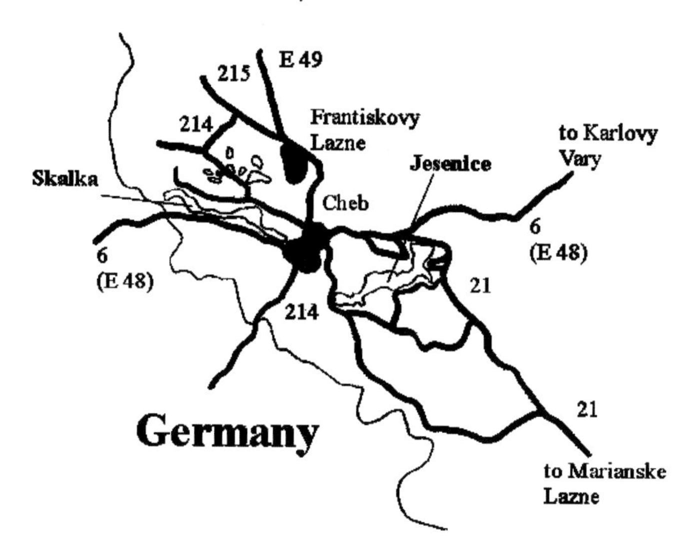

SOUTH BOHEMIA

Ponds around Blatna (ST)

General characteristics

49°38'–49°39'N 13°52'–13°54'E

There are numerous ponds of varying size within about 18 km of the village of Blatna. Located at 440 to 550 m, the ponds lie in farmland or woodland. These ponds provide breeding habitat for several species of waterfowl and a stopover site for numerous migrants.

Species

Among breeding species are Little Grebe, Great Crested Grebe, Black-necked Grebe, White Stork, Mute Swan, Gadwall, Common Teal, Garganey, Northern Shoveler, Marsh Harrier, Water Rail, Common Snipe, Black-tailed Godwit, *Locustella* and *Acrocephalus* species, and

Penduline Tit. Among non-breeding species occurring during summer or on passage are Red-throated Diver, Black-throated Diver, Red-necked Grebe, Slavonian Grebe, Great Cormorant, Little Bittern, Great White Egret, Black Stork, White-fronted Goose, Greylag Goose, Red-crested Pochard, Osprey, *Charadrius* spp., *Calidris* spp., *Tringa* spp., and Bluethroat (*L. s. cyanecula*).

Access

Take highway E49 from Blatna to Nepomuk. There are several exits from this highway leading to the ponds on the south as well as the north side. From Blatna, take highway 173 to the village of Belcice (10.5 km). Many of the ponds lie next to the highway, and are also accessible from Belcice. From Praha, take highway 4 to Pribram (45 km), stay on highway 4 until the intersection with the E49 (40 km), and from here take the E49 to Blatna (17 km).

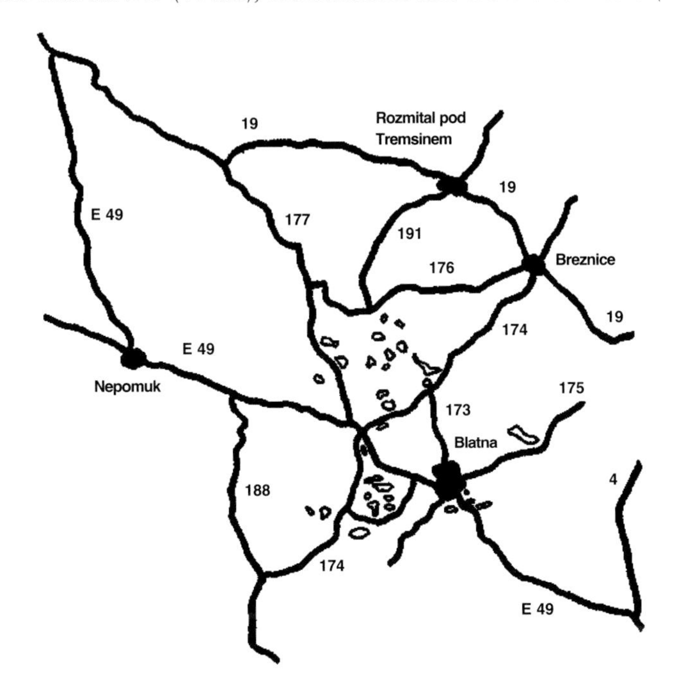

Ponds around Ceske Budejovice CB)

General characteristics

48°58'–48°58'N 14°21'–14°26'E

There are numerous ponds of varying size within 24 km of Ceske Budejovice. Many of these ponds were built more than 150 years ago, lie at 390–440 m, and are, in many cases, surrounded by farmland and meadows. Extensive reedbeds and islets at some of them provide suitable breeding habitat for numerous species of waterfowl and passerines. Avenues of mature trees, often oaks, grow around their banks or along roads running between the ponds. The ponds are, in many cases, connected by canals and brooks. Among the large ponds are Bezdrev, Blatec, Dehtar, Volesek and Vystov.

Species

Breeding species include Little Grebe, Great Crested Grebe, Black-necked Grebe, Great Cormorant, Great Bittern, Night Heron, Grey Heron, Purple Heron (occasionally), White Stork, Eurasian Spoonbill, Greylag Goose, Gadwall, Garganey, Red-crested Pochard, European Honey-buzzard, Black Kite, Red Kite, Marsh Harrier, Montagu's Harrier, Hobby, Water Rail, Spotted Crake, Little Crake, Corn Crake, Black-tailed Godwit, Common Tern, Black Tern, European Nightjar, Common Kingfisher, Grey-headed Woodpecker, Black

Woodpecker, Middle Spotted Woodpecker, Wood Lark, Yellow Wagtail, Bluethroat (*L. s. cyanecula*), *Locustella* and *Acrocephalus* species, Barred Warbler, Bearded Tit, Penduline Tit, Short-toed Treecreeper and Golden Oriole. Most of the above named passerines nest in dozens or hundreds of pairs. Among non-breeding species occurring during summer or on passage are Red-throated Diver, Black-throated Diver, Red-necked Grebe, Slavonian Grebe, Squacco Heron, Great White Egret, Glossy Ibis, Common Shelduck and Osprey.

Access

There are many ponds on both sides of highway E49 from Ceske Budejovice to Vodnany (24 km). These are easily accessibly by county roads which exit from the E49. From Ceske Budejovice, take highway 105 to Hluboka nad Vltavou (9 km). Ponds are located along the highway and around Hluboka nad Vltavou. From Praha, take highway E55 to Ceske Budejovice (140 km).

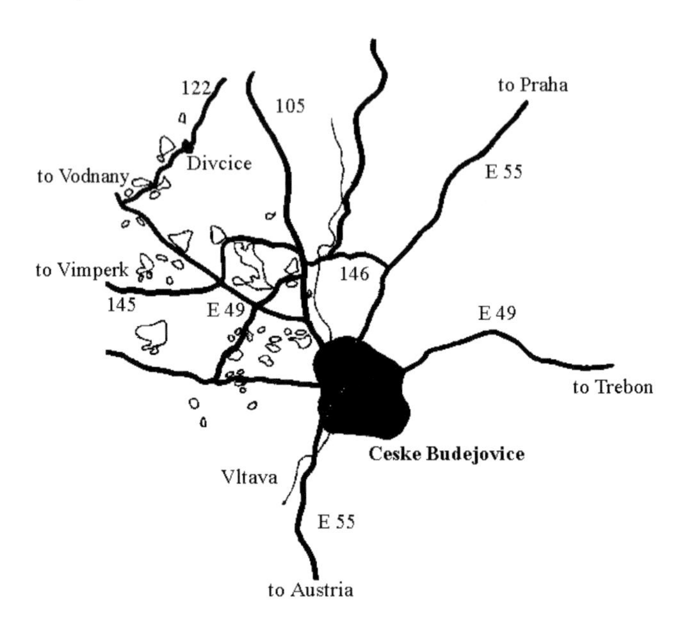

Ponds around Jindrichuv Hradec (JH)

General characteristics

49°08'–49°08'N 14°59'–15°02'E

Numerous ponds lie within 15 km of Jindrichuv Hradec. They range from the smallest, about 0.01 km^2, to the largest of more than 2 km^2 (Kaclezsky pond and Krvavy pond). Many of them are surrounded by extensive reedbeds, meadows and bushes, offering suitable breeding habitats for various species. They also host large flocks of migrating waterfowl and shorebirds, mostly on autumn passage. The altitude of the area is about 475 to 550 m.

Species

Breeding species include Little Grebe, Great Crested Grebe, Black-necked Grebe, Great Cormorant, Grey Heron, Black Stork, White Stork, Mute Swan, Gadwall, Common Teal, Garganey, Northern Shoveler, European Honey-buzzard, Marsh Harrier, Hobby, Water Rail, Spotted Crake, Corn Crake, Common Snipe, Common Redshank, Common Tern, Pygmy Owl, Little Owl, Common Kingfisher, Grey-headed Woodpecker, Black Woodpecker, Middle Spotted Woodpecker, Yellow Wagtail, Bluethroat (*L. s. cyanecula*), *Locustella* and *Acrocephalus* species and Penduline Tit. Among non-breeding species occurring during summer or on passage are Red-throated Diver, Black-throated Diver, Red-necked Grebe, Slavonian Grebe, Great White Egret, Glossy Ibis, Common Shelduck, Black Kite, Red Kite,

White-tailed Eagle, Osprey, Black-tailed Godwit, Black Tern, and numerous species of waterfowl and gulls.

Access

From Jindrichuv Hradec, 3 main highways, running in different directions, can be taken, and exits from these lead to dozens of ponds. These highways are the E551 running from the north to the southwest, the 128 running southeast to the Czech-Austria border, and the 23 running from northwest to east. From Praha, take the E55 to the intersection with highway 23 (103 km) and from here highway 23 to Jindrichuv Hradec (23 km).

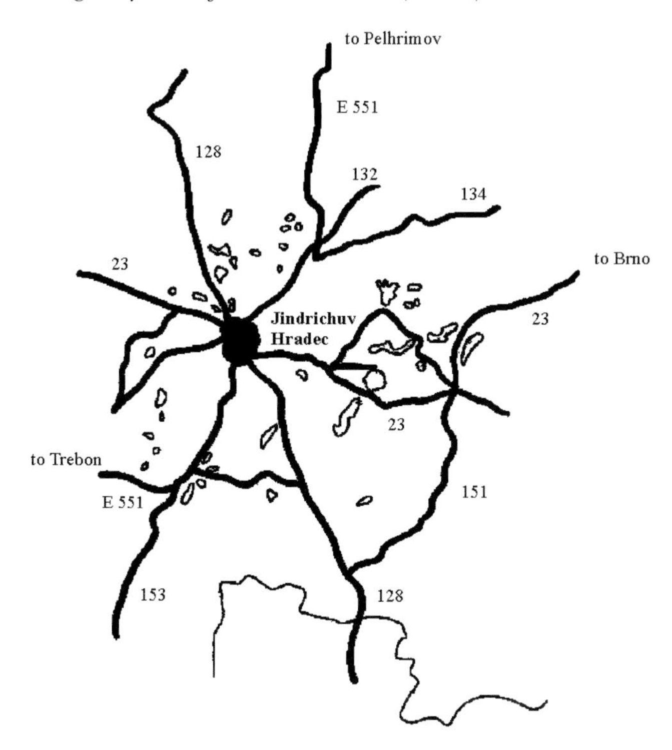

The Novohradske hory mountains (CB, JH)

General characteristics

48°39'–48°46'N 14°34'–14°42'E

These mountains cover about 200 km^2 on the Czech Republic-Austria border, with the highest peak being Kamenec (1072 m). The mountains are covered by spruce plantations and deciduous and mixed forest. The valuable habitats in the mountains include primeval forest, peatbogs, and wet meadows. At the edge of the area are several areas of open water, with the largest of them being Zarsky pond (over 1 km^2). There are numerous streams and brooks running through the mountains.

Species

Breeding species include Grey Heron, Black Stork, European Honey-buzzard, Hobby, Common Quail (common), Corn Crake (common), Common Snipe, Woodcock, Pygmy Owl, Common Kingfisher, Black Woodpecker, Lesser Spotted Woodpecker, Wood Lark, Collared Flycatcher, Red-breasted Flycatcher, Common Redpoll and Common Crossbill.

Access

There are several ways to access the mountains. From Ceske Budejovice, take the E55 to Kaplice (27 km). From Kaplice, either use highway 154, running across the northern part of the mountains, or highway 158, running across the southern part. In the mountains, there are numerous exits from both highways. From Ceske Budejovice, you can take highway 156 to Trhove Sviny (18 km), and from here the same road to Nove Hrady (12 km). The highway runs along the northern part of the area. From Praha, take the E55 to Ceske Budejovice (140 km).

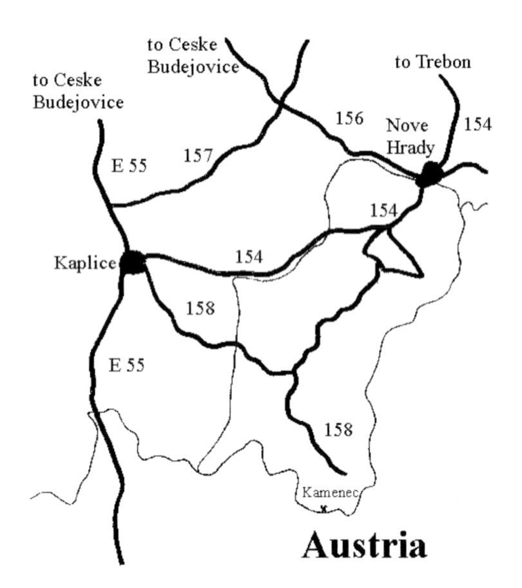

SOUTH MORAVIA

The Bile Karpaty mountains (HO, UH, ZL)

General characteristics

48°53'–49°21'N 17°17'–18°10'E

Bile Karpaty is a mountain area of about 715 km^2 on the Czech Republi-Slovak border, extending from about 200 to 970 m. The mountains are covered by spruce plantations, mixed woods, deciduous oak–hornbeam-dominated woods and, at higher elevations, by mature beech forest. A typical habitat in the Bile Karpaty mountains is hay meadows with old solitary trees, mostly oak. Another typical feature of these mountains is a mosaic-type landscape with orchards, meadows, grassland, small woods and fields. The highest mountain in the Bile Karpaty range, Velka Javorina (970 m), is covered by beech-dominated primeval forest. Annual precipitation in the mountains is 550–900 mm.

Species

Breeding species include Black Stork, European Honey-buzzard, Northern Goshawk, Eurasian Sparrowhawk, Common Buzzard, Common Kestrel, Hobby, Hazel Grouse, Common Quail, Stock Dove, Common Kingfisher, White-backed Woodpecker, Wood Lark (rare), Dipper, Barred Warbler, Common Raven and Corn Bunting. Among non-breeding species seen during the breeding season are Red Kite, Hen Harrier, Lesser Spotted Eagle, Golden Eagle and Red-footed Falcon. Breeding Eurasian Scops Owl was recorded for the first time in 1998, although individual birds have been recorded since the beginning of the 1990s.

Access

Since the mountains stretch for about 75 km along the border with Slovakia, there are many points of access. From Brno, take the E50, which crosses the middle of the Bile Karpaty range, and continues to Slovakia. However, to enter the mountains in the south, do so via towns such as Straznice and Veseli nad Moravou, in the centre Uhersky Brod, and in the north Luhacovice and Valasske Klobouky. To access the highest peak, Mt Velka Javorina, take highway 54 from Veseli nad Moravou to the village of Strani (the border with Slovakia), and about 2.5 km before entering Strani, turn left on a county road to Velka Javorina (about 8 km from the intersection).

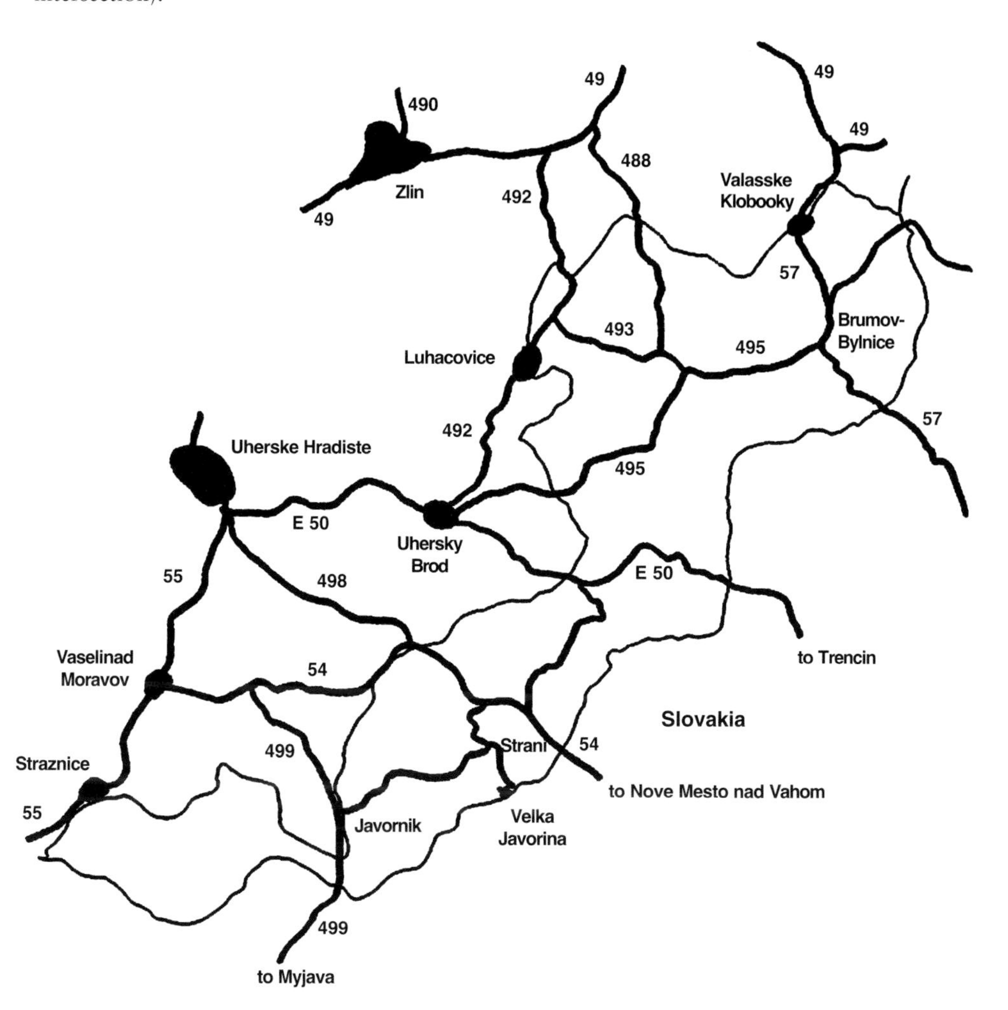

Hodoninske ponds (HO)

General characteristics

48°52'N 17°06'E

This is a system of several ponds between Hodonin and the village of Dubnany on the Kyjovka river. The size of the ponds ranges from less than 0.01 km^2 to about 0.18 km^2. The ponds, which are at about 170 m, are surrounded by farmland and woods. All of the ponds are used for fish-farming. Reeds surround most of the ponds, and trees and bushes can be found around the banks. Hodoninske ponds provide suitable breeding habitat for several endangered species, and species on passage.

Species

Breeding species include Little Grebe, Great Crested Grebe, Black-necked Grebe, Grey Heron, Marsh Harrier, Water Rail, Common Tern (occasionally), Common Kingfisher, Yellow Wagtail, and Bearded Tit. Among migrating and non-breeding species are Red-throated Diver, Black-throated Diver, Great Crested Grebe, Red-necked Grebe, Slavonian Grebe, Great Cormorant, Great Bittern, Little Bittern, Great White Egret, Ruddy Shelduck, Common Shelduck, Greater Scaup, Common Eider, Common Scoter, Velvet Scoter, Common Goldeneye, Red-breasted Merganser, Goosander, Black Kite, Red Kite, White-tailed Eagle, Montagu's Harrier, Osprey, Common Crane, Black-tailed Godwit, Grey Plover, Curlew Sandpiper, numerous *Charadrius* spp., *Calidris* spp. and *Tringa* spp., Common Gull, Herring Gull, Caspian Tern and Black Tern.

Access

From Brno, highway 51 to Hodonin crosses the area and the ponds lie on both sides. From the village of Mutenice, take the road to Dubnany, and Jarohnevicky pond lies on the north side. Other ponds lie on the south side of the same road, while several ponds lie on both sides of highway 55 running from Breclav to Hodonin.

Jaroslavicky pond (ZN)

General characteristics

48°49'N 16°05'E

This system of several fishponds covers a total area of 2.8 km^2 and lies 13 km southeast of Znojmo, about 0.5 km north of the village of Jaroslavice at an altitude of 200 m. The largest pond is 2 km^2. There are several islets in the smaller ponds. Some ponds have littoral vegetation, reeds and stands of mainly willow and poplar around their banks, others are surrounded by farmland.

Species

Breeding species include Little Grebe, Black-necked Grebe, Little Bittern, Night Heron, Red-crested Pochard, Water Rail, Avocet (accidental), Black-headed Gull (up to 2,500 pairs), Rufous Nightingale, Savi's Warbler, several *Acrocephalus* spp., Bearded Tit and Penduline Tit. Among non-breeding and migrating species are Great Cormorant, Great White Egret, Eurasian Wigeon, Pintail, Goosander, Red-breasted Merganser, Curlew Sandpiper, several

Calidris spp. and *Tringa* spp., Little Gull, Common Gull, Herring Gull, Caspian Tern, Whiskered Tern and White-winged Black Tern.

Access

From Znojmo, take highway 408 to Hradek (16 km), and from here, highway 397 to Jaroslavice. The pond lies west of highway 397. From Brno, take highway 52 to Pohorelice (24 km), and from here highway 54 to Znojmo (39 km).

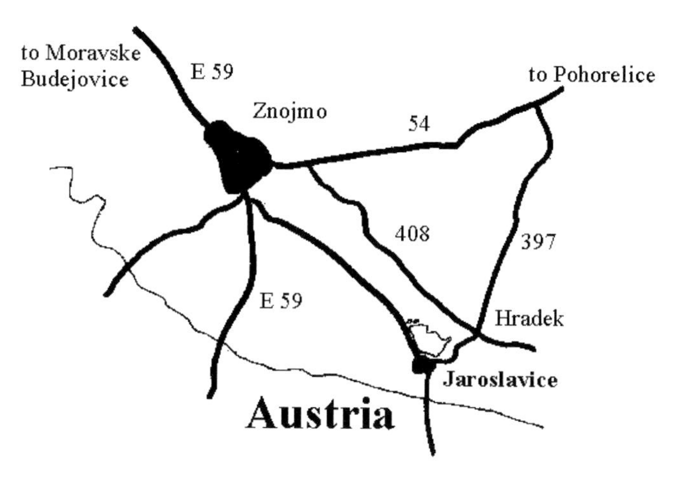

Namestske ponds (TR)

General characteristics

49°13'N 16°07'E

This is a system of fishponds located between the town of Namest nad Oslavou and the village of Vladislav at 365–450 m. The ponds vary in size, but none exceeds 1.5 km^2. Some of them are surrounded by farmland and meadows, others by woodland. They provide breeding habitat for waterfowl, and host waterfowl and shorebirds on passage.

Species

Breeding species include Little Grebe, Black-necked Grebe, Mute Swan, Gadwall, Marsh Harrier, Common Quail, Little Ringed Plover, Common Snipe (irregularly), *Acrocephalus* spp. and Penduline Tit. Among birds on passage or non-breeding birds are Great Cormorant, Great White Egret, Grey Heron, Osprey, *Anas* spp. and *Aythya* spp., shorebirds and gulls.

Access

The ponds lie along highway 23, running from Namest nad Oslavou to Trebic. They are accessed by county roads. Take highway 23, and 6.5 km fom Namest nad Oslavou, turn right

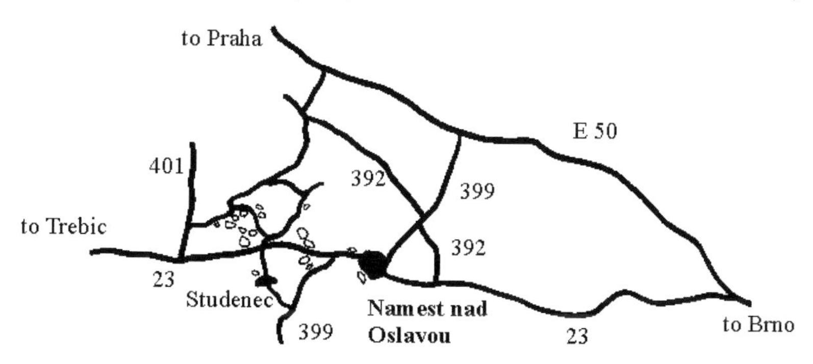

onto a county road to the village of Pozdatin. Several ponds lie along this road. From Brno, take the E50 to Rosice (15 km), and from here highway 23 to Namest nad Oslavou (26 km)

Zahlinicke ponds (KM)

General characteristics

49°16'N 17°27'E

Zahlinicke ponds comprise 4 fishponds surrounded by riverine forest, wet meadows and farmland. They lie about 2 km south of the town of Hulin, at about 190 m. The total area of water is 2.1 km^2. The fishponds (used for fish-farming) have sparse littoral vegetation. Stands of trees (mostly willow and cotton wood) are found in the meadows, and occasionally around the banks of the ponds. The riverine forest extends from the system of fishponds to the river Morava. A few oxbows can be found in the riverine forest. The average annual temperature is 8.6°C (in July 18.8°C, and in January –2.2°C), and the average annual rainfall is 599 mm. This area is important for numerous migrating waterfowl and shorebirds since some of the ponds are usually semi-drained. Surrounding woods provide favourable breeding habitats for several species. Over 270 species have been recorded in this area including about 140 breeding.

Species

Breeding species include Little Grebe, Great Crested Grebe, Little Bittern, White Stork, European Honey-buzzard, Northern Goshawk, Eurasian Sparrowhawk, Marsh Harrier, Common Quail, Water Rail, Little Ringed Plover, Black-headed Gull, 8 species of woodpecker, and numerous passerines. Among birds on passage are Red-throated Diver, Black-throated Diver, Red-necked Grebe (occasional breeding), Slavonian Grebe, Great Cormorant, Little Egret, Great White Egret, Grey Heron, Purple Heron, Glossy Ibis, Black Kite, Red Kite, White-tailed Eagle, Osprey; almost all the waterfowl, shorebirds, gulls and terns recorded in the Czech Republic; Bluethroat and Aquatic Warbler.

Access

From Prerov, take highway 55 to the village of Zahlinice. The ponds lie about 1 km west of the village and are accessible by car. However, you have to walk around the banks of the ponds. From Brno, take highway D1 to Vyskov (20 km), from Vyskov highway 47 to Popuvky (29 km), and from Popuvky highway 367 to Kromeriz (7 km). From either highway number 367 or 432 travel to Zahlinice.

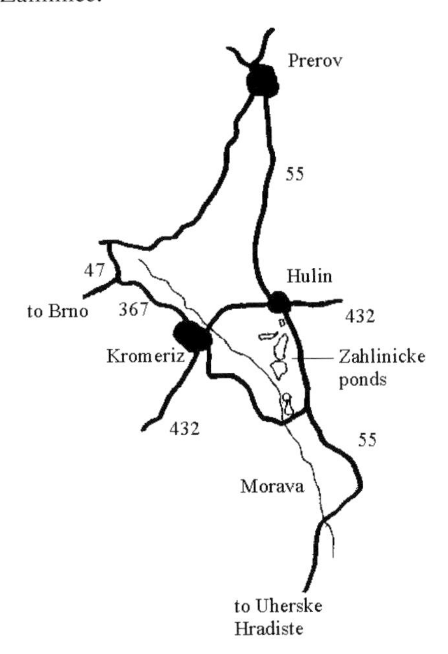

NORTH MORAVIA

Hermansky and Novy Stav ponds, Struzka (OV)

General characteristics

49°51'–49°52'N 18°19'–18°21'E

This site includes marshes, several ponds, rivers, brooks, oxbows and canals, covering about 30 km^2 in the suburbs of Ostrava, Bohumin and Rychvald. The elevation of the area is 195–230 m. The ponds have extensive reedbeds, and the total are covered by reeds is about 1 km^2. Trees, bushes, and remnant floodplain forest are scattered across the area, with woodland dominated by willow and cotton wood. Several sandpits can also be found in this area. The ponds and marshes provide an important breeding site for several endangered species, and are important for passage birds as well.

Species

Breeding species include Little Bittern, Greylag Goose (occasionally up to 5 pairs), Marsh Harrier, Water Rail, Spotted Crake, Black-tailed Godwit, Common Redshank, Little Owl, Common Kingfisher, Sand Martin (hundreds of pairs),Yellow Wagtail, Rufous Nightingale, Bluethroat (over 10 pairs), Bearded Tit (dozens of pairs) and Common Rosefinch (dozens of pairs). Among migrating and non-breeding species are Great Crested Grebe, Red-necked Grebe, Slavonian Grebe, Great Cormorant, Great Bittern, Night Heron, Great White Egret, Grey Heron, Common Scoter, Common Goldeneye, Goosander, White-tailed Eagle, Osprey, Common Crane, Grey Plover, Curlew Sandpiper, Whimbrel, numerous *Charadrius* spp., *Calidris* spp., and *Tringa* spp., Common Gull, Lesser Black-backed Gull, Herring Gull, Kittiwake, Caspian Tern, Common Tern, Little Tern and Black Tern.

Access

The whole area is encircled by highways 472 (Karvina–Ostrava), 58 (Ostrava–Bohumin) and 468 (Bohumin–Karvina). Numerous roads and pathways cross the area, which lies about 4 km from the border with Poland.

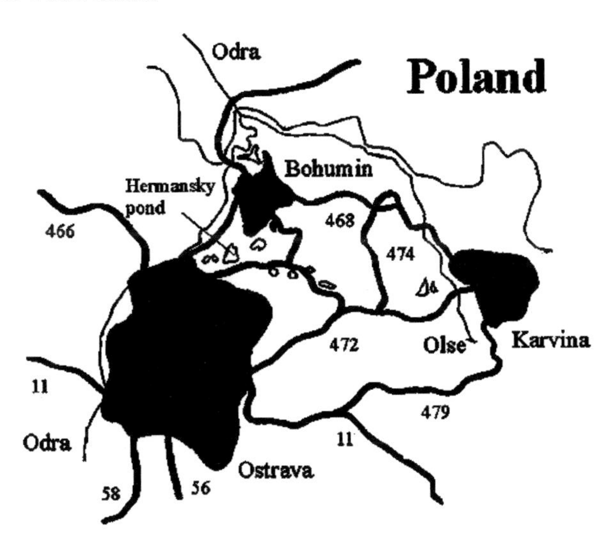

Hostynske vrchy hills (VS, ZL)

General characteristics

49°20'–49°21'N 17°39'–17°47'E

Hostynske vrchy is a hilly area, extending into 2 counties of eastern Moravia. The elevation ranges from about 500 m to 865 m, with the peak, Mt Kelcsky Javornik, at 865 m. The whole area is covered with spruce plantations, mixed woods and fragments of beech forest. Abundant brooks and streams are found in the woods throughout the area. Open areas have pastures, meadows and fields. There are several ruined castles in the woods. The woodland provides suitable breeding habitats for several endangered species.

Species

Breeding species include Black Stork, European Honey-buzzard (dozens of pairs), Northern Goshawk, Eurasian Sparrowhawk, Hobby, Hazel Grouse, Common Quail, Corn Crake, Eagle Owl, Common Kingfisher, Grey-headed Woodpecker, Green Woodpecker, Black Woodpecker, Middle Spotted Woodpecker, Grey Wagtail (dozens of pairs), Dipper, Red-breasted Flycatcher and Nutcracker. Non-breeding or passage birds include Lesser Spotted Eagle and Golden Eagle.

Access

Starting points for exploring this area can be the towns of Bystrice pod Hostynem, Valasske Mezirici, Vsetin and Zlin. Highway 437 runs from Bystrice pod Hostynem to Vsetin across the area and there are many exits to county roads which criss-cross the sites. From Brno, take the D1 to Vyskov (31 km), from here highway 47 to Prerov (50 km), and from Prerov highway 18 to Bystrice pod Hostynem (19 km).

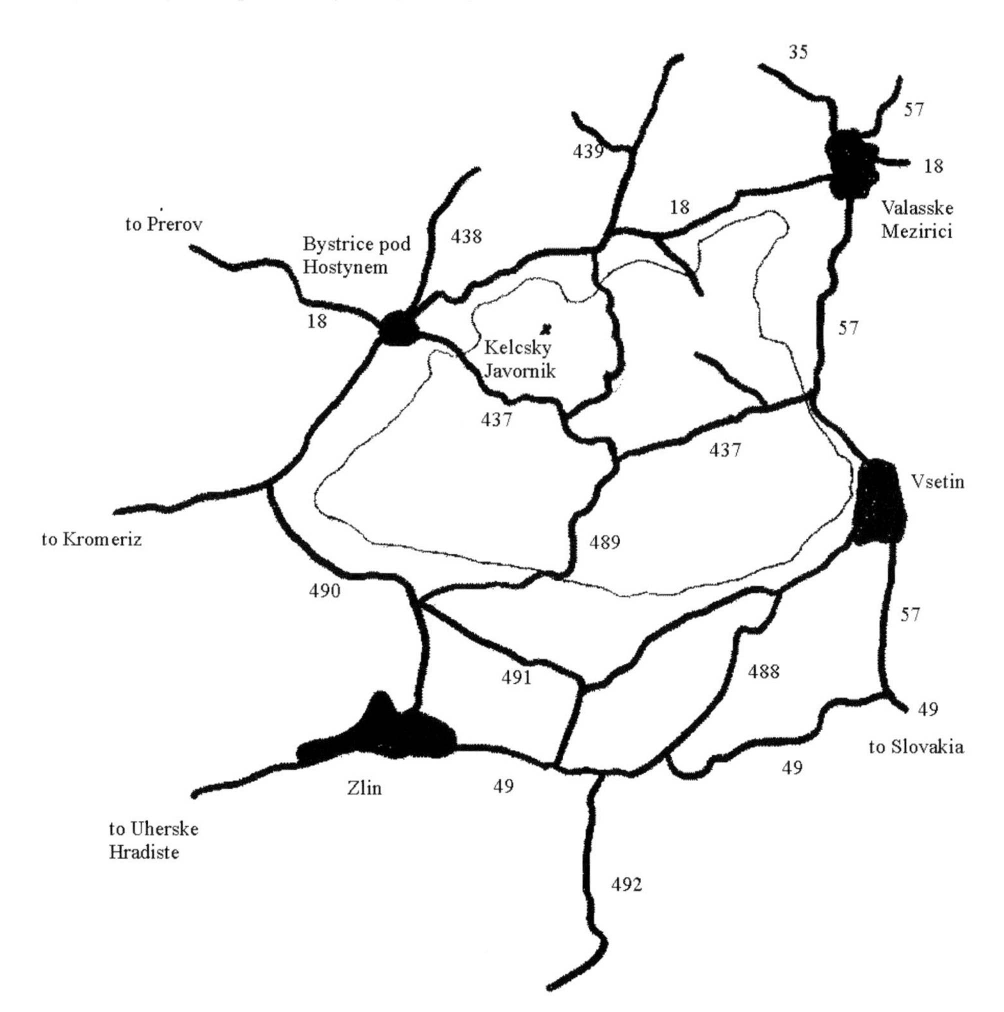

Litovelske Pomoravi (OL)

General characteristics

49°38'–49°41'N 17°07'–17°15'E

Litovelske Pomoravi is an area of flooded riverine forest along the Morava river, between the town of Mohelnice and the village of Bohunovice. The total area of about 96 km^2 comprises mature growths with rich undergrowth along the river, and oxbows and small lakes with gravel and sandy islets, numerous sandpits, and marshes with reeds. The banks of the lakes and marshes are dominated by growths of willow. At higher elevations, flooded forest is replaced by beech forest. A part of the Litovelske Pomoravi area is covered by Chomoutov gravel pit, a large area of open water with several islets hosting numerous migrants. The variety of habitat in Litovelske Pomoravi provides suitable conditions for numerous breeding and migrating species. Elevation ranges from 230 to 300 m.

Species

Breeding species include Little Grebe, Great Crested Grebe, Little Bittern, Black Stork, White Stork, European Honey-buzzard, Red Kite, Northern Goshawk, Eurasian Sparrowhawk, Marsh Harrier, Common Quail, Water Rail, Little Ringed Plover, Black-headed Gull, Stock Dove, Barn Owl, Eagle Owl, European Nightjar, Common Kingfisher, Grey-headed Woodpecker, Black Woodpecker, Sand Martin, Rufous Nightingale, Savi's Warbler, Red-breasted Flycatcher and Penduline Tit. Among birds on passage are Black-throated Diver, Great Cormorant, Great White Egret, Grey Heron, White-fronted Goose, Greylag Goose, Eurasian Wigeon, Pintail, Ferruginous Duck, Greater Scaup, Velvet Scoter, Common Goldeneye, Goosander, White-tailed Eagle, Osprey, Common Gull, Herring Gull, Caspian Tern and numerous shorebirds.

Access

The E442 runs along the southern edge of the Litovelske Pomoravi area: take this road from Olomouc to Mohelnice. Several roads exit from the E442 and cross the area. Chomoutov gravel pit is accessible from Olomouc on road 446.

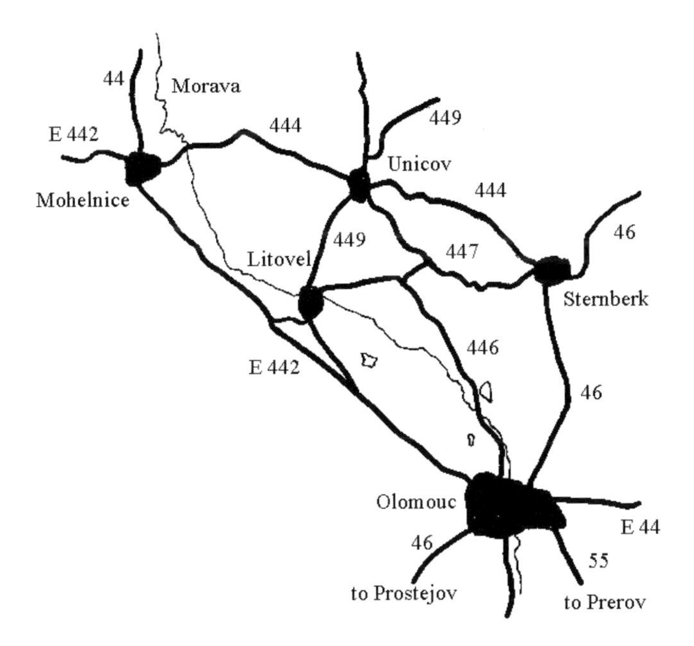

The Oderske vrchy hills (OL, PR)

General characteristics

49°36'–49°37'N 17°21'–17°24'E

The Oderske vrchy hills like the Hostynske vrchy hills offer suitable woodland for the breeding of several endangered species in north-central Moravia. These hills extend northeast of Olomouc and northwest of Hranice at an elevation of between 600 and 680 m (Fidluv kopec is the highest point). The area is covered by spruce plantations and mixed woods, with farmland and pastures. There are numerous streams and brooks.

Species

Among breeding species are Black Stork, European Honey-buzzard, Northern Goshawk, Eurasian Sparrowhawk, Corn Crake, Eagle Owl, Tawny Owl, Grey-headed Woodpecker, Green Woodpecker, Black Woodpecker, Middle Spotted Woodpecker, Lesser Spotted Woodpecker, Dipper, Firecrest, Collared Flycatcher and Corn Bunting.

Access

Because it was once a military area and closed to the public, and to development, most of the roads are closed. The best way to access the area is from the village of Velky Ujezd. From Olomouc, take highway E442 to Velky Ujezd (16 km), and from here highway 441 to the village of Boskov. The road runs through the southeasten part of the area, and also has exits to several county roads.

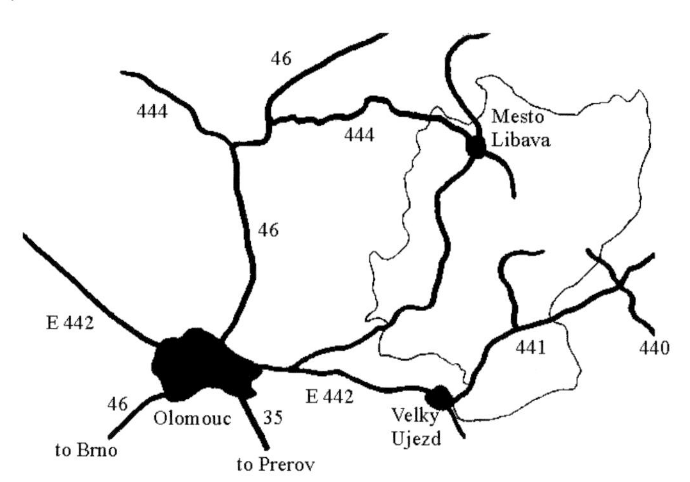

Tovacovske ponds and Donbas gravel pit (PR)

General characteristics

49°27'N 17°16'E

This is a system of 3 ponds and a gravel pit, at about 200 m, around the town of Tovacov (PR). The size of the ponds varies: 0.05 km^2 (Kolecko pond), 0.15 km^2 (Krenovsky pond), and 1.3 km^2 (Hradecky pond). The gravel pit comprises 4 reservoirs with a total area of 3.5 km^2. The Morava and Becva rivers, both with oxbows and channels, run through the area. The water is surrounded by riverine forest and patches of reed grow around the ponds. The average annual temperature is 8°C, with the maximum in July (18°C) and minimum in January (1.5°C). This area is important for many species on spring and autumn passage, as well as for those that breed. By the mid-1990s, 255 species had been recorded.

Species

Breeding species include Black-necked Grebe, Grey Heron (about 200 pairs in forest near Troubky gravel pit), Marsh Harrier, Water Rail, Little Owl, Common Kingfisher, Wryneck,

Yellow Wagtail, Great Reed Warbler and Barred Warbler. Among migrating and non-breeding species are Red-throated Diver, Black-throated Diver, Great Crested Grebe, Red-necked Grebe, Slavonian Grebe, Great Bittern, Little Bittern, Night Heron, Great White Egret, Purple Heron, Great Cormorant, Canada Goose, Common Shelduck, Greater Scaup, Common Eider, Common Scoter, Velvet Scoter, Common Goldeneye, Red-breasted Merganser, Goosander, Black Kite, Red Kite, White-tailed Eagle, Osprey, Common Crane, Oystercatcher, Black-tailed Godwit, Grey Plover, Curlew Sandpiper, Whimbrel, Turnstone, numerous *Charadrius*, *Calidris* and *Tringa* spp., Common Gull, Lesser Black-backed Gull, Herring Gull, Kittiwake, Caspian Tern, Common Tern, Little Tern, Black Tern, Citrine Wagtail and Thrush Nightingale.

Access

The area lies about 10 km west of Prerov. It is accessible from Prerov from highway 434, running from Prerov to Prostejov through Tovacov. From Brno, take the D1 to Vyskov (20 km), from Vyskov follow highway 47 to Kojetin (32 km), from Kojetin to Polkovice (5 km) on highway 367, and from Polkovice to Tovacov (5 km) on highway 435. All of the ponds and gravel pits are easily accessed from county roads.

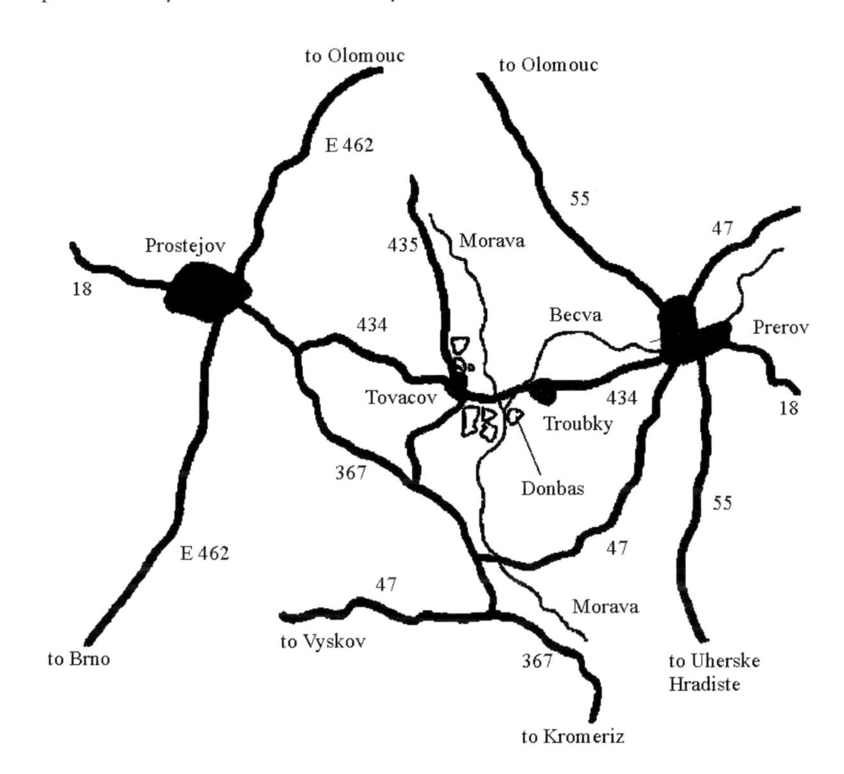

BIBLIOGRAPHY

Balat, F. 1964. Hnizdni bionomie a populacni dynamika skorce vodniho. *Zool. listy* 13: 305–320.

Beaman, M. and S. Madge. 1998. *The Handbook of Bird Identification for Europe and the Western Palearctic*. Christopher Helm. London.

Bejcek, V. and P. Tyrner. 1980. Primary succession and species diversity of avian communities on spoil banks after surface mining of lignite in the Most basin (North-Western Bohemia). *Folia zool.* 29: 67–77.

Bejcek, V., K. Stastny and K. Hudec. 1995. Atlas zimniho rozsireni ptaku v Ceske Republice 1982–1985. Nakladatelstvi a vydavatelstvi H&H.

Belka, T. 1996. Wintering of Stonechat (*Saxicola torquata*) in the Czech Republic. Zpravy CSO 43: 44–45.

Bosak, J. Ochrana volne zijicich zivocichu ve zneni zakona CNR c. 114/1992 Sb., o ochrane prirody a krajiny a predpisu souvisejicich. *Moravsky ornitolog* 2/93: 5–9.

Brandl, P. and J. Simek. 1995. Rare and uncommon records of birds in the Czech Republic (1993–1994). *Zpravy CSO* 41: 21-31.

Chytil, J. 1996. Ceska Republika a Ramsarska konvence. *Ptaci Svet* III/1: 3–4.

Chytil, J. 1997. The report of the Czech Faunistic Committee for the period 1995–1996. *Zpravy CSO* 45: 18–21.

Chytil, J. 1998. The Czech Faunistic Committee at the beginning of next millenium. *Zpravy CSO* 47: 10–12.

Chytil, J. and P. Machacek. 1991. Has Gull-billed Tern, *Gelochelidon nilotica*, nested in Czechoslovakia? *Sylvia* 28: 132–134.

Chytil, J. and M. Vavrik. 1999. Report of the Czech Rarrities Committee on the period 1997–1998. *Zpravy CSO* 49: 3–10.

Danko, S., T. Divis, J. Dvorska, M. Dvorsky, J. Chavko, D. Karaska, B. Kloubec, P. Kurka, H. Matusik, L. Peske, L. Schopfer, R. Vacik. 1994. The state of knowledge of breeding numbers of birds of prey (*Falconiformes*) and owls (*Strigiformes*) in the Czech and Slovak Republics as of 1990 and their population trends in 1970–1990. *Buteo* 6: 1–89.

Doupal, L. 1991. The first occurrence of American Wigeon, *Anas americana* Gmelin, 1789, in Czechoslovakia. *Sylvia* 28: 122–123.

Dvorska, J. and M. Dvorsky. 1999. Neobvykly tah hvizdaku eurasijskych (*Anas penelope*) na Chorynskych rybnicich u Valasskeho Mezirici. *Zpravy CSO* 48: 21–22.

Ferianc, O. 1977–1979. *Vtaky Slovenska*. Parts 1 and 2. Veda SAV. Bratislava.

Flousek, J. 1991. Activity of the Working Group for Research of the Family *Motacillidae* in 1985-1989. *Zpravy CSO* 33: 30–31.

Flousek, J. 1993. Confirmed breeding of the Greenish Warbler (*Phylloscopus trochiloides*) in the Czech Republic. *Sylvia* 29: 104–106.

Folk, C., I. Kozena, and J. Kren. 1984. International waterfowl census 1982/83 in the Czech Republic. *Vertebratologicke Zpravy* 1984: 107–115.

Folk, C. and J. Kren. 1987. International waterfowl census 1984/85 and 1986 in the Czech Republic. *Vertebratologicke Zpravy* 1987: 61–72.

Folk, C. and J. Kren. 1988. International waterfowl census 1986/87 in the Czech Republic. *Vertebratologicke Zpravy* 1988: 81–87.

Folk, C. and B. Rejman. 1983. K hnizdeni capa bileho (*Ciconia ciconia*) na elektrickych rozvodnych zarizenich v CSR. *Sylvia* XXII: 19–26.

Fric, A. 1870. *Naturgeschichte der Vögel Europas*. Prag.

Gorman, G. 1996. *The Birds of Hungary*. Christopher Helm. London.

Hagemeijer, W. J. M. and M. J. Blair (eds.). 1997. *The EBCC Atlas of European Breeding Birds. their distribution and abundance*. T & A D Poyser London.

Hajek, V. 1980. Deset let pracovni skupiny pro vyzkum bahnaku v CSSR. *Ziva* 28: 196.

Hanzak, J. 1987. Zmeny v avifaune Sumavy v poslednih 35 letech. Avifauna jiznich Cech a jeji zmeny. 1. *Sbor. predn., C. Budejovice*: 47–62.

Holan, V. 1977. Report on the activity of the Shrike Working Group in the period 1995–96. *Zpravy CSO* 44: 22–25

Hudec, K. (ed.). 1983. *Fauna CSSR*. Ptaci 3/I and 3/II. Academia Praha.
Hudec, K. (ed.). 1994. *Fauna CR a SR*. Ptaci 1. (Second ed.). Academia Praha.
Hudec, K. and W. Cerny (eds.). 1977. *Fauna CSSR*. Ptaci 2. Academia Praha.
Hudec, K., J. Chytil, K. Stastny and V. Bejcek. 1995. The birds of the Czech Republic. *Sylvia* 31: 97–149.
Hudec, K., J. Flousek and J. Chytil. 1999. Checklist of birds of the Czech Republic and relevant conservation rules. *Zpravy CSO* 48: 16 pp.
Janda, J. and P. Machacek. 1990. Cormorant, *Phalacrocorax carbo*, in Bohemia and Moravia in 1982–1988. *Sylvia* 27: 55–70.
Klejdus, J. 1980. Ptactvo Znojemska. Zpravy MOS 1980: 7–83.
Knezourek, K. 1910-12. *Velky prirodopis ptaku*. I.-II. Praha.
Kondelka, D. 1984. Hnizdeni pustika belaveho (*Strix uralensis*) v Moravskoslezskych Beskydech. *Cas. Slezs. Muz. Opava* (A) 33: 192.
Kren, J. and C. Folk. 1985. International waterfowl census 1983/84 in the Czech Republic. *Vertebratologicke Zpravy* 1985: 93–100.
Kren, J. and C. Folk. 1990. International waterfowl census 1987/88 in the Czech Republic. *Vertebratologicke Zpravy* 1990: 121–130.
Martisko, J., K. Stastny, V. Bejcek, K. Hudec, J. Pellantova, and M. Vlasin. 1994. *Hnizdni rozsireni ptaku. Jihomoravsky region*. Cast 1. Nepevci. Moravske zemske muzeum, CSOP ZO Palava, Brno.
Martisko, J. and K. Martiskova. 1996. Zvysena pocetnost rehka zahradniho (*Phoenicurus phoenicurus*) na Brnensku? *Zpravodaj Jihomoravske Pobocky* CSO 8: 14–18.
Mistera, L. 1984. *Geografie kraju CSSR*. SPN Praha.
Matousek, B. 1994. Slovenske nazvoslovie vtakov. In: Gosler, A. (ed.). *Atlas vtakov sveta*. Priroda. Bratislava.
Monroe, B. L. and C. G. Sibley. 1993. *A World Checklist of Birds*. Yale University Press. New Haven.
Mrlik, V. 1998. Spotted Eagle (*Aquila clanga*) in the Czech Republic and Lesser Spotted Eagle (*Aquila pomarina*) breeding distribution in South Bohemia, Czech Republic. *Sylvia* 34:60–72.
Murin, B., A. Kristin, A. Darolova, S. Danko, and R. Kropil. 1994. Breeding bird populations size in Slovakia. *Sylvia* 30: 97–105.
Pellantova, J. and J. Martisko. 1993. Vyvoj pocetnosti vybranych vodnich a mokradnich druhu ptaku v nivach reky Moravy a Dyje na jizni Morave. *Zpravy MOS* 51: 85–94
Pykal, J., P. Bürger, J. Hora. 1998. Report on activities of the Corncrake Research Group in 1997. *Zpravy CSO* 46: 17–19.
Rejman, B. 1977. Status of White Stork (*Ciconia ciconia*) in the Czech Republic in 1994 and 1995. *Zpravy CSO* 45: 11–15
Salek, P. 1995. The first occurrence of Spur-winged Lapwing (*Holopterus spinosus*) in the Czech Republic. *Sylvia* 31: 91–92.
Schröpfer, L. 1996. The Little owl (*Athene noctua*) in the Czech Republic – abundance and distribution in the years 1993–1995. *Buteo* 8: 23–38.
Schröpfer, L. 1999. Monitoring of the abundance and distribution of the Little Owl (*Athene noctua*) in the Czech Republic in 1998/99. Annual Report 1998. *Zpravy CSO* 48: 7–8.
Sedlacek, K. (ed.). 1988. *Cervena kniha ohrozenych a vzacnych druhu rostlin a zivocichu CSSR*. 1. Ptaci. Statni Zemedelske Nakladatelstvi Praha.
Sibley, C. G. and B. L. Monroe. *Distribution and Taxonomy of Birds of the World*. Yale University Press. New Haven.
Simecek, K. 1998. Breeding of European Bee-eater (*Merops apiaster*) in South Moravia in 1997. *Zpravodaj Jihomoravske Pobocky CSO* 11: 16–17.
Simek, J. and P. Brandl. 1996. Rare and uncommon records of birds in the Czech Republic in 1995. *Zpravy CSO* 42: 46–56.
Sirek, J. and J. Pohanka. The first record of Audouin's Gull (*Larus audouinii*) in the Czech Republic. *Sylvia* 30: 160–161.
Snow, D. W. and C. M. Perrins. 1998. *The Birds of the Western Palearctic. Concise Edition*. Oxford University Press. Oxford.
Stancl, L. and H. Stanclova. 1984–85. Anderung in der Dichte der Brutpopulation und der durchziehenden Grasmucken der Gattung *Sylvia* in Gebiet von Bohdanec. *Sylvia*

XXIII/XXIV: 13–28.
Stancl, L. and H. Stanclova. 1987. *Ptactvo Pardubicka a Bohdanecska*. Pardubice.
Stastny, K., A. Randik and K. Hudec. 1987. *Atlas hnizdniho rozsireni ptaku v CSSR 1973/1987*. Academia Praha.
Stastny, K., V. Bejcek, and K. Hudec. 1996. *Atlas hnizdniho rozsireni ptaku v Ceske Republice 1985–1989*. H & H Praha.
Statistical Yearbook of the Czech Republic 1997. Scientia. Praha
Suchy, O. 1998. Zlate navrsi bylo opravdu zlate. *Ptaci kolem nas*. 2/98: 18–19.
Tichy, H. 1993. Investigation of Coot (*Fulica atra*) breeding population an Lenesicky pond (District Louny) in 1980–1992. *Zpravy CSO* 36: 50–52.
Trnka, A., A. Kristin, S. Danko, S. Harvancik, L. Kocian, D. Karaska, and B. Murin. 1995. Checklist of the birds of Slovakia. *Tichodroma* 8: 7–21.
Tucker, G. M. and M. F. Heath 1994. *Birds in Europe: their conservation status*. (BirdLife Conservation Series no. 3.) BirdLife International. Cambridge, UK.
Viktora, L. 1997. Monitoring of the European Bee-Eater (*Merops apiaster*) breeding sites in the Czech Republic in 1995–96. *Zpravy CSO* 44: 26–29.
Vorisek, P. 1993. The winter abundance of Magpie (*Pica pica*) in the agricultural landscape in the Chocen Region. *Zpravy CSO* 37: 3–5.
Weber, H. 1976. Zajimave vysledky z akce Balt. *Prunella* 2: 16–17.

PLACE NAMES

Albrechticky (NJ), surrounding ponds
Alzbetin u Zelezne Rudy (PT), village
Anenske ponds (CH)
Bartosovice (NJ), surrounding ponds
Bartosovice v Orlickych horach (RK), village
Basta pond (CB)
Becva (PR, VS), river
Bedihost (PV), village
Bedny pond near Studenka (NJ)
Benesov (BN), town
Benesov (OP), village
Beroun (BE), town
Beskydy (FM, VS), mountains
Besov (MO), village
Bezdekov (LN), village
Bezdrev pond (CB)
Bile Karpaty mountains (HO, UH, ZL)
Biskupice (ZL), village
Blansko-Moravsky kras (BK), karst
Blatec pond (CB)
Blatenske ponds (ST)
Blatna (ST), village
Blatsky pond (JH)
Blizkovice (ZN), village
Bobrovnik (BR), village
Bohdalov (ZR), village
Bohdanecsky pond (PU)
Bohdikov (SU), village
Bohumin (OV), town
Bohunovice (OL), village
Bohuslavice (SU), village
Bolelouc (OL), village
Bolesicky pond (CB)
Bor u Tachova (TC), town
Borotice (ZN), village
Borovany (CB), surrounding ponds
Bosonohy (BM), village
Bozice (ZN), village
Branisov (CB), village
Branisovske ponds (ZN)
Branna (JH), village
Branna (SU), village
Brdy mountains (RO, PB)
Breclav (BV), town
Breclav-Lany (BV), village
Brehynsky pond (CL)
Brezi (BV), village
Breznik (TR), village
Brezova (UH), village
Brezovec pond (CB)
Brilicky pond (JH)
Brloh (CK), village
Brnenska dam (BM)
Brno (BM), town
Brno-Novy Liskovec (BO), town
Brno-Sobesice (BO), town
Brodek pond (MB)
Brodsky pond (NA)
Brumovska vrchovina highlands (NA)
Bruntal (BR), town
Budske ponds (MB)
Bukovka (PU), village
Bulanka (KO), village
Bulhary (BV), village
Bunov (ZL), village
Bustehrad (KL), village
Bystrice pod Hostynem (KM), town
Bystrice u Benesova (BN), village
Bystrovany (OL), village
Bzenec (HO), town
Bzenec-Privoz (HO), town
Cechy (PR), village
Cejc (HO), village
Cejkovice (HO), village
Cejkovicky pond (CB)
Cejkovy ponds (KT)
Cermna (UL), village
Cernicny pond (JH)
Cerny Nadymac pond (PU)
Cerny pond (SY)
Cervena Lhota (JH), village
Cervenak pond (LN)
Cerveny Kostelec (NA), surrounding ponds
Cerveny pond (RA)
Ceska Kubice (DO), surrounding ponds
Ceska Lipa (CL), surrounding ponds
Ceska Skalice (NA), town
Ceske Budejovice (CB), surrounding ponds
Ceske stredohori highlands (LN, LT, UL)
Ceskomoravska vysocina highlands (HB, JI, PE, ZR)
Cesky Brod (KO), town
Cesky Krumlov (CK), town
Cesky les mountains (DO, TC)
Cesky raj (MB), cliffs
Chabarovice (UL), village
Chalupska slat (PT), peatbogs
Cheb (CH), surrounding ponds
Chlebsky pond (BN)
Chlum pond (CB)
Chlum u Trebone (JH), town
Chlumcany (PJ), village
Chodova Plana (TC), village
Chodsky pond (TC)
Chomoutov gravel pit (OL)
Chorynske ponds (VS)
Chotelice (HK), village
Chrastany (KM), village
Chriby (KM, UH), hills
Chrlice (BO), village
Chropynsky pond (KM)
Chvalcov (KM), village
Chvalovec pond near Radomysl (ST)
Dacice (JH), village
Darkov (KI), town
Dasensky pond (CB)
Decin (DC), town
Decinske steny (DC), cliffs
Dehtar pond (CB)
Dehtare (CB), village
Dehylov (OV), village
Detmarovice (KI), village
Divcicke ponds (CB)
Dlouha Loucka (OL), village
Dlouha ves (HB), village
Dlouhopolsky pond (NB)
Dluhonice (PR), village
Dobesice (PI), village
Dobevsky pond (PI)
Dobra vule pond (JH)
Dobris (PB), surrounding ponds
Dobromerice gravel pit (LN)
Doksy (CL), surrounding ponds
Dolany nad Vltavou (PZ), village
Dolejsi pond (ST)
Dolni Benesov (OP), surrounding ponds, gravel pit
Dolni Frycovice (FM), village
Dolni Kounice (BO), village
Dolni Lutyne (KI), village
Dolni Moravice (BR), village
Dolni Pocernice gravel pit (PH)
Dolni pond (CB)
Dolni pond (SY)
Dolni Ujezd (PR), village
Dolni Ujezd (SY), village
Domazelice (PR), village
Domin pond (JH)
Donbas gravel pit (PR)
Doubrava (KI), village
Doubice (DC), in valley in the Krusne hory mountains
Doupno u Krivoklatu (RA), village
Doupovske hory (KV) mountains
Drazni pond (CK)
Dremliny pond (ST)
Drevohostice (PR), village
Drinov (ME), village
Drinov (MO), lake (non-existent today)
Drnholec (BV), village
Dubice (CL), village
Dubnanske ponds (HO)
Dubovec pond (TR)
Dubovy pond (JH)
Dvoriste pond (JH)
Dvorske ponds (JH)
Dvorsky pond (HO)
Dyjakovice (ZN), village
Dyje (BV, ZN), river
Dymokury (NB), village
Dynin (CB), village
Farsky pond (JH)
Frydlant v Cechach (LB), town
Flaje, settlement in Krusne hory mountains (MO)
Fojtuv pond (NJ)
Frantiskovy Lazne (CH), surrounding ponds
Frydlant nad Ostravici (FM), town
Frymburk (CK), village
Grygov (OL), village
Haklovy Dvory (CB), village
Halenkov (VS), village
Hanusovice (OL), village
Havran (MO), village
Havlickuv Brod (HB), town
Heclov (PR), village
Hermancie (NJ), village
Hermanek pond (SY)
Hermanicky pond (CL)
Hermansky pond (OV)
Hlasenec pond near Vlhlavy (CB)
Hlohovec (BV), village
Hluboka nad Vltavou (CB), surrounding ponds
Hlucin gravel pit (OP)
Hlusovice (OL), village

Hodkovice nad Mohelkou (LB), village
Hodonice (ZN), village
Hodonin (HO), surrounding ponds
Holice (OL), village
Holysov (DO), village
Horazdovice (ST), surrounding ponds
Horejsi pond (ST)
Horky (SY), pond
Horni Belotin pond near Hranice nad Moravou (PR)
Horni Dvorsite (CK), village
Horni Marsov (TU), village
Horni Mostenice (PR), village
Horni Petrovicky pond (BN)
Horni Pocaply (ME), village
Horni Podluzi (DC), village
Horni Polubny (SE), village
Horni pond near Bartosovice (NJ)
Horni pond near Novosedly (JH)
Horni Porici (ST), village
Horni Sucha (KI), village
Horni vytopa pond (JH)
Horusice (TA), pond
Hostin (BE), village
Hostynske vrchy hills (KM, ZL)
Houston (KL), village
Hovezi (VS), village
Hovorany (HO), village
Hrachovec (VS), village
Hradcany (NB), village
Hradec Kralove (HK), surrounding ponds
Hradec nad Moravici (OP), village
Hradecky pond near Tovacov (PR)
Hradek (ZN), village
Hranice (PR), town
Hroznetin (KV), village
Hulin gravel pit (KM)
Hurky pond (JH)
Hury (CB), village
Hustenovice (UH), village
Hustopece (BV), town
Hustopece nad Becvou, Hustopecske ponds (PR)
Hvezda pond (SY)
Ivan (BV), village
Jabkenice (MB), village
Jaderny pond (CB)
Janova Ves u Malont (CK), village
Jarohnevicky pond (HO)
Jaromer (NA), town
Jaroslavicky pond (ZN)
Javornik nad Velickou (HO), village
Javorniky (ZL, VS), hills
Jeleni-Plechy (PT), village
Jesenice (CH), dam
Jesenik nad Odrou (NJ) and Ostrava (OV), ponds between
Jeseniky mountains (BR, SU)
Jestrebi (CL), village
Jindrichuv Hradec (JH), surrounding ponds
Jistebnik nad Odrou (NJ), surrounding ponds
Jivjanske ponds near Jivjany (TC)
Jizerske hory mountains (LB, JN)
Jordan pond near Vodnany (ST)
Jordanek pond in Praha (AA)
Kaclezsky pond (JH)
Kalenicky pond (ST)
Kamenny Ujezd pond (CB)
Kanov pond (JH)
Kardas pond (JH)
Karlin (HO), village
Karvina (KI), surrounding ponds
Karvina-Stare Mesto (KI), town
Kasperske hory mountains (KT)
Katovice (ST), village
Klasterec (PT), village
Klatovy (KT), town
Klecany (PJ), village
Klentnice (BV), village
Klokocin (PI), village
Kluky (PI), village
Knizeci pond (CB)
Kobyli (BV), village
Kobylske jezero (BV), lake (non-existing today)
Koclirov pond (JH)
Kojetin, Kojetinske ponds (KM), town, surrounding ponds
Kokorinsko (ME), rocky hills
Komarovsky pond (HO)
Koneprusy (BE), village
Konice (ZN), village
Koprivnice (NJ), town
Koprnik (MB), village
Korensky pond (CB)
Kosarske meadows near Lanzhot (BV)
Kourim (KO), village
Kouty (OP), village
Kozohludky (TA), village
Kralicky Sneznik mountains (UO)
Krasny les (UL), village
Krasonice (JI), village
Krchleby-Horni Kamenice (DO), village
Krenovsky pond (PR)
Krivoklat (RA), village
Krkonose mountains (SE, TU)
Krnov (BR), town
Kromeriz (KM), town
Krusne hory mountains (CV, KV, MO, TP)
Kunovice (UH), village
Kurovice (KM), village
Kvasice gravel pit (KM)
Kyjov (HO), town
Kyjovka (HO), brook
Kytin (PB), village
Labe (DC, HK, KO, LT, ME, NB, PU, SE, TU, PU etc), river
Labska louka (TU), peatbogs in the Krkonose mountains
Labske piskovce (DC), cliffs
Ladna (BV), village
Lanskroun (UO), town
Lansky pond (SY)
Lanzhot (BV), village
Lastany (OL), village
Lazany (ST), village
Lechovice (ZN), village
Lednice, Lednicke ponds (BV), village, surrounding ponds
Lednice-Pastvisko (BV), meadows near Lednice village
Lenesicky pond (LN)
Leskovice (ST), pond nearby
Lesnik (OV), pond
Letinsky pond (JH)
Liba (CH), village
Liba (CV), village
Libejovice (ST), village
Liderovice (JH), village
Lipnice u Prahy (PH), village
Lipno, Lipno near Borkova (CK), reservoir
Lisek u Postupic (BN), village
Litava near Hrusky (VY), river
Litice (CL), village
Litomysl (SY), town
Litovicky pond near Hostivice (PZ)
Lobec (ME), village
Lobodice (PR), village
Lodenice (OP), village
Lodenicky pond (RA)
Lomnice nad Luznici (JH), town
Louny (LN), town
Lovosice (LT), town
Luby-Olovi (SO), village
Luhacovice (ZL), town
Luzec (ME), village
Luzice, Luzicke ponds (HO), village, surrounding ponds
Luznice (CB, TA), river
Lysa nad Labem (NB), village
Lysky, Lysecky pond (PR)
Majdalena (JH), village
Male Jezero pond near Klinovice (ST)
Maly Bedny (NJ), pond
Maly Bor (TR), pond
Maly Budni (NJ), pond
Maly Machovec (CB), pond
Maly Strachovicky (CB), pond
Maly Tisy (JH), pond
Marianske Lazne (CH), town
Markovec pond (ST)
Mastnik (TR), village
Matka pond (PU)
Mecichov (ST), village
Melcany (BO), village
Melcina pond near Karvina (KI)
Merklin (PJ), village
Mesice (PH), village
Metelsky pond (ST)
Metuje (NA), river
Mikulcice (HO), village
Mikulov (BV), town
Milavy pond (ST)
Miletice near Protivin (PI), village
Milevsko (TA), town
Milhostov near Frantiskovy Lazne (CH)
Milotice (HO), village
Miloticky pond (HO)
Milovice (BV), village
Milovice (MB), village
Minkovice (MO), marsh nearby
Miroslav (ZN), village
Mistek (FM), also Frydek-Mistek, town
Mistrin (HO), village
Mitrovice u Nove Bele (FM), village
Mlada (NB), village
Mlada Boleslav (MB), town
Mlada Vozice (TA), village
Mlade Buky (TU), village
Mlekovice (KO), village
Mlynec pond (JC)
Mnichovo Hradiste (MB), industrial waters nearby
Mnichovske ponds (ST)

Mnissky pond (JH)
Modrice (BO), town
Mohelno (TR), village
Morava (HO, KM, OL, PR, UH), river
Moravsky kras (BK), karst
Moravsky Krumlov (ZN), town
Moravsky Pisek (HO), town
Most (MO), surrounding ponds
Motovidlo (CB), pond
Msecke Zehrovice (RA), village
Municky pond (CB)
Musik pond near Sedlcany (BN)
Mutenice, Mutenicke ponds (HO), village, surrounding ponds
Mydlovary, Mydlovarsky pond (CB), village
Myslovice (PB), village
Mysnik pond near Namest nad Oslavou (TR)
Nadeje pond (CB)
Naklo gravel pit (OL)
Nakri (CB), village
Namest nad Oslavou (TR), surrounding ponds
Napajedla (ZL), town
Necicky (LN), village
Nedvezi (OL), village
Nepomuk (PH), village
Nestedice (UL), village
Nesvorny pond (PI)
Nesyt pond (BV), in Lednicke ponds system
Netrebsky pond (UO)
Nezvestice (PJ), village
Nizky Jesenik mountains (OL)
Nova Bystrice (JH), village
Nova Louka pond (NJ)
Nova Pec (CK), village
Nova reka (JH), river
Nova Ves u Pohorelic (BV), village
Nove Dvory (PR), village
Nove Hrady (CB), village
Nove Mesto pod Smrkem (LB), town
Nove Mlyny (BV), reservoir
Nove Straseci (RA), village
Nove Veseli (ZR), village
Novohaklovsky pond (CB)
Novohradske hory mountains (CB, CK)
Novorecke mocaly (JH), marsh
Novosedly (CB), village
Novosedly (RA), village
Novosedly u Mikulova (BV), village
Novovesky pond (BV), in the Pohorelicke ponds complex
Novovesky pond (DO)
Novozamecky pond (CL)
Novy Dvur u Lednice (BV), village
Novy Hospodar (JH), pond
Novy Jicin (NJ), town
Novy pond in Praha-Milicov (AA)
Novy pond near Branna (JH)
Novy pond near Cakov (CB)
Novy pond near Dvorce (JH)
Novy pond near Lhotka (PB)
Novy pond near Mikulov (BV)
Novy pond near Mnichovo Hradiste (MB)
Novy pond near Opatov (SY)
Novy pond near Pluhuv Zdar (JH)
Novy pond near Strpy (ST)
Novy pond near Trebon (JH)
Novy Ptacovsky pond (TR)
Novy Studenecky pond near Namest nad Oslavou (TR)
Novy Vdovec (JH), pond
Novy Vrbensky (CB), pond
Nuzov pond (CB)
Nymburk (NB), town
Obecni pond near Kardasova Recice (JH)
Oblanov pond (CB)
Ochoz u Konice (PV), village
Oderske vrchy (OL)
Odra (KI, OV), river
Odry (NJ), ponds nearby
Ohre (LN, LT, CH, SO, KV, SO), river
Okrouhlicky pond (ST)
Olbramovice (ZN), village
Olesna dam (FM)
Olesnik pond near Nakri (CB)
Olomouc (OL), town
Olsany (KT), ponds nearby
Olsany (PV), village
Olsava (UH), river
Olse (KI), river
Opatov (SY), ponds nearby
Opatov (TR), village
Opatovicky pond (JH)
Opatovske ponds (KO)
Opatsky pond (TR)
Opava (OP), town
Oplatil pond near Pardubice (PU)
Orlicke hory mountains (RK)
Ostojkovicky pond (JH)
Ostrava (OV), surrounding ponds
Ostrava-Hermanice (OV), town
Ostrava-Zabreh (OV), town
Ostrozska Nova Ves (UH), village and nearby gravel pits
Ostruzensky pond (JC)
Otice (OP), village
Padrtske ponds (PB)
Palava (BV), hills
Pancavska louka (TU), peatbogs in the Krkonose mountains
Panensky pond (JH)
Pardubice (PU), surrounding ponds
Paseka (OL), village
Pasohlavky (BV), village
Pasticky pond (ST)
Pekna na Sumave (PT), village
Petrov (HO), village
Petrovy kameny (BR), village
Pisecne ponds (HO)
Pisek (PI), surrounding ponds
Piskovy pond (TC)
Pivon (DO), village
Plana (TC), village
Plana nad Luznici (TA), village
Planice (KT), village
Plumlovska dam (PV)
Plzen (PM), town
Podebrady (NB), town
Podhradi (CR), village
Podivin (BV), village
Podkostelni pond near Putim (PI)
Podoli (UH), village
Podsedek pond (JH)
Pohorelice, Pohorelicke ponds (BV), village and surrounding ponds
Polanka nad Odrou (NJ), surrounding ponds
Polna (JI), village
Ponedrazkovsky pond (JH)
Praterske ponds (JH)
Popuvky (BO), surrounding ponds
Postovni pond near Dehylov (OP)
Postrekov (DO), village
Postrelna (CL), village
Postupice (BN), village
Potesil pond (JH)
Pouzdrany, Pouzdransky pond (BV), village and nearby pond
Prace (ZN), village
Prachen (CL), village
Pradlo pond (TC)
Praha (AA), capital of the Czech Republic
Praha-Hostavice (AA), part of town
Praha-Kunratice (PH), part of town
Praha-Litoznice (PZ), part of town
Praha-Stromovka (AA), park in Praha
Pravcice (KM), village
Prerov (KM), town
Preseka (JH), village
Proudnicky pond (KO)
Prusy (PR), village
Purkrabsky pond (JH)
Putim (PI), town
Rabsky pond (ST)
Radejov (HO), village
Radnice (RO), village
Radobytce (PI), village
Radostice (CB), village
Radov near Vrbno pond (ST)
Rajcherov (JH), village
Razicky pond (PI)
Rezabinec pond (PI)
Ricky (VY), village
Riha pond (HK)
Rimavska dam (CB)
Rod pond (JH)
Rohovladova Bela (PU), village
Rojice, Rojicky pond (ST), village and pond nearby
Rokytnice (PR), village
Roudnice nad Labem (LT), town
Rozdalovice (NB), village
Rozkos (NA), dam
Rozmberk nad Vltavou (CK), town
Rozmberk pond (JH)
Rozvadov (TC), village
Ruda near Veseli nad Luznici (JH), village
Ruda pond (JH)
Rutnik pond near Slatina (UO)
Rybnik (OV), village
Rychlebske hory mountains (SU)
Rymarov (BR), town
Sadek (DO), village
Sakvice (BV), village and surrounding ponds
Salak pond near Trebic (TR)
Sardice (HO), village
Seberov (AA), pond nearby
Sedlcanky (PH), village
Sedlcany (BN), surrounding ponds
Sedlec u Mikulova (BV), village
Semovicky pond (BN)
Silherovice (OP), village
Silnicni pond near Bor u Tachova (TC)

Siluvky (BO), village
Siroky pond (CB)
Siroky Ujezd pond (CB)
Skalsky pond (PI)
Skaly (PI), village
Skasovsky pond (PR)
Skochovice (HK), village
Skocice (ST), village
Skrin pond (PU)
Skucak pond (KI)
Slavkov (VY), town
Slezske Pavlovice (BR), village
Sluknov (DC), village
Sluzebny pond (JH)
Smetana (UO), village
Smikov pond (BN)
Smirice (HK), village
Smrciny (CH), village
Smrk (LB), village
Sobechleby (PR), village
Sobeslav (TA), village
Soprec (PU), pond
Soutok (BV), riverine forest near Lanzhot
Spalene Porici (PJ), village
Spindleruv Mlyn (TU), town
Spitalsky pond near Klenov (JH)
Srbsko (BE), village
Stablovice (OP), village
Stara Breclav (BV), town
Stara Hlina (JH), village
Stare Jezero pond (JH)
Starnov (OL), village
Stary Haklovsky pond (CB)
Stary Hospodar pond (JH)
Stary pond (BV)
Stary pond (JH)
Stary pond near Jistebnik nad Odrou (NJ)
Stary pond near Tchorovice (ST)
Stary Ptacovsky pond (TR)
Stary Trebonsky pond (JH)
Stary Vdovec pond (JH)
Steborice (OP), village
Stepankovice (OP), village
Stolarka (HO), pond
Strachotin (BV), surrounding pond
Strakonice (ST), surrounding ponds
Strani (UH), village
Straseci (PB), village
Strasnov (MB), village
Straznice (HO), town
Strelske Hostice (ST), surrounding ponds
Strizovice (KM), village
Strpsky pond (CB)
Struharov (PH), village
Struznice (CL), village
Studenec pond (NJ)
Studenec, Studenecky pond (TR)
Studenka (NJ), surrounding ponds
Suchov (HO), village
Suchovske Mlyny (HO), village
Sumava mountains (CK, KT, PT)
Sumvald pond (OL)
Svatoborice (HO), village
Svet pond near Trebon (JH)
Svital pond near Kardasova Recice (JH)
Svitavy (SY), town and ponds nearby
Svobodne Hermancie (BR), village
Svojetin (RA), village
Svratka (BO, BV), river
Tachov (TC), town and surrounding ponds
Talinsky pond (PI)
Tchorovice (ST), village
Terlicka dam (KI)
Tesany (BO), village
Tesin (KI), town
Tichy pond (PU)
Tlumacov (ZL), village
Tobolky pond near Branna (JH)
Tovacov, Tovacovske ponds (PR), town and surrounding ponds
Trebenice (LT), village
Trebon (JH), town and surrounding ponds
Tresicky pond (HK)
Trojsky ostrov islet (AA), an islet in the Vltava river in Praha
Troubky gravel pit (PR)
Tucin (PR), village
Tusimice (CV), industrial waters nearby
Tyniste nad Orlici (RK),
Uherce (PS), village
Uherske Hradiste (UH), town
Uhersky Ostroh (UH), town
Ujezdec (PR), village
Uncovice (OL), village
Upska raselina (SE), peatbogs in the Krkonose mountains
Ustek (CL), village
Usti nad Labem (UL), town
Usti nad Orlici (UO), town
Uvaly (PH), village
Valasske Mezirici (VS), town
Valtice (BV), town
Vavrinecke ponds (KH)
Velesin (CK), village
Velice (CB), village
Velichov (KV), surrounding ponds
Velicka (HO), river
Velka Cerna pond (JH)
Velka nad Velickou (HO), village
Velka Polom (OP), village
Velke Jezero pond near Klimovice (ST)
Velke Nakri pond (CB)
Velkoholsky pond (ST)
Velky Bor pond (TR)
Velky Kosir near Litomysl pond (SY)
Velky Panensky pond (JH)
Velky pond near Chlumec (HK)
Velky pond near Jesenice (RA)
Velky Tisy pond (JH)
Velky Tousny pond (JH)
Velky Ustavni pond near Vodnany (ST)Velky pond (DC)
Veltrusy (ME), village
Vernovice (KI), village
Veseli nad Luznici (JH), town and surrounding ponds
Veseli nad Moravou (HO), town
Vetrusice (PH), village
Veverska Bityska (BO), village
Veverske Kninice (BO), village
Vidlak pond (SY)
Vimperk (PT), town
Vinarsky pond (CV)
Visnova (JH), village
Vitice (ST), village
Vitkovsky pond (ST)
Vizovice (ZL), town
Vlcnov (UH), village
Vlhlavsky pond (CB)
Vlkovicky pond near Lisov (CB)
Vltava (AA, CB, CK, ME, PZ), river
Vnorovy (HO), village
Vodnany (ST), surrounding ponds
Volary (PT), town
Volesek pond (CB)
Vracov (HO), village
Vrazda pond (MB)
Vrbenske ponds (CB)
Vrbovec pond (ZN)
Vrkoc pond (BV)
Vsetin (VS), town
Vsetinske vrchy (VS), hills
Vyprachtice (PU), village
Vysatov pond (CB)
Vysluni (CV), village
Vytazniky ponds (HO)
Vytopa pond (HO)
Xaverov (PB), village
Zabakor pond (MB)
Zablatsky pond (JH)
Zabreh na Morave (SU), town and surrounding ponds
Zacler (TU), town
Zadni Zablatsky pond (CB)
Zahlinice, Zahlinicke ponds (KM), village and surrounding ponds
Zahorsky pond (ST)
Zahradka (TR), village
Zakupy (CL), village
Zamecky pond (BV), in the Lednicke ponds complex
Zarovice (PV), village
Zarsky pond (CB)
Zasova (VS), village
Zastudanci (PR), riverine forest
Zbraslav nad Vltavou (PZ), town
Zbrodsky pond (HO)
Zbudov (CB), surrounding ponds
Zbudovska Blata, Zbudovsky pond (CB)
Zbysov (KH), village
Zdar nad Sazavou (ZR), town
Zdeslav (RA), village
Zehunsky pond (NB)
Zehusice (KH), village
Zelivka (BN), dam
Zelnavske tune (PT)
Zenich pond (CB)
Zeraviny (HO), village
Zernova (PR), village
Zhejral pond (TR)
Zidlochovice (BV), town
Zizelice (KO), village
Zlata Stoka (JH), river
Zlin (ZL), town
Zliv (CB), surrounding ponds
Zlutice (ST), village
Zly pond (ST)
Znojmo (ZN), town
Zofinka pond (JH)
Zrcadlo pond (JC)
Zvikov (CB), village
Zviroticky pond near Sedlcany (BN)

CHECKLIST OF THE BIRDS OF THE CZECH REPUBLIC

GAVIIFORMES

Red-throated Diver *Gavia stellata*
Black-throated Diver *Gavia arctica*
Great Northern Diver *Gavia immer*
White-billed Diver *Gavia adamsii*

PODICIPEDIFORMES

Little Grebe *Tachybaptus ruficollis*
Great Crested Grebe *Podiceps cristatus*
Red-necked Grebe *Podiceps grisegena*
Slavonian Grebe *Podiceps auritus*
Black-necked Grebe *Podiceps nigricollis*

PROCELLARIIFORMES

Fulmar *Fulmarus glacialis*
Cory's Shearwater *Calonectris diomedea*
European Storm-petrel *Hydrobates pelagicus*

PELECANIFORMES

Northern Gannet *Morus bassanus*
Great Cormorant *Phalacrocorax carbo*
Shag *Phalacrocorax aristotelis*
Pygmy Cormorant *Phalacrocorax pygmeus*
White Pelican *Pelecanus onocrotalus*

CICONIIFORMES

Great Bittern *Botaurus stellaris*
Little Bittern *Ixobrychus minutus*
Night Heron *Nycticorax nycticorax*
Squacco Heron *Ardeola ralloides*
Cattle Egret *Bubulcus ibis*
Little Egret *Egretta garzetta*
Great White Egret *Egretta alba*
Grey Heron *Ardea cinerea*
Purple Heron *Ardea purpurea*
Black Stork *Ciconia nigra*
White Stork *Ciconia ciconia*
Glossy Ibis *Plegadis falcinellus*
Eurasian Spoonbill *Platalea leucorodia*

PHOENICOPTERIFORMES

Greater Flamingo *Phoenicopterus ruber*

ANSERIFORMES

Mute Swan *Cygnus olor*
Tundra Swan *Cygnus columbianus*
Whooper Swan *Cygnus cygnus*
Bean Goose *Anser fabalis*
Pink-footed Goose *Anser brachyrhynchos*
White-fronted Goose *Anser albifrons*
Lesser White-fronted Goose *Anser erythropus*
Greylag Goose *Anser anser*
Snow Goose *Anser caerulescens*
Canada Goose *Branta canadensis*
Barnacle Goose *Branta leucopsis*

Brent Goose	*Branta bernicla*
Red-breasted Goose	*Branta ruficollis*
Ruddy Shelduck	*Tadorna ferruginea*
Common Shelduck	*Tadorna tadorna*
Eurasian Wigeon	*Anas penelope*
American Wigeon	*Anas americana*
Gadwall	*Anas strepera*
Common Teal	*Anas crecca*
Mallard	*Anas platyrhynchos*
Pintail	*Anas acuta*
Garganey	*Anas querquedula*
Blue-winged Teal	*Anas discors*
Northern Shoveler	*Anas clypeata*
Marbled Duck	*Marmaronetta angustirostris*
Red-crested Pochard	*Netta rufina*
Common Pochard	*Aythya ferina*
Ferruginous Duck	*Aythya nyroca*
Tufted Duck	*Aythya fuligula*
Greater Scaup	*Aythya marila*
Common Eider	*Somateria mollissima*
King Eider	*Somateria spectabilis*
Long-tailed Duck	*Clangula hyemalis*
Common Scoter	*Melanitta nigra*
Surf Scoter	*Melanitta perspicillata*
Velvet Scoter	*Melanitta fusca*
Barrow's Goldeneye	*Bucephala islandica*
Common Goldeneye	*Bucephala clangula*
Smew	*Mergus albellus*
Red-breasted Merganser	*Mergus serrator*
Goosander	*Mergus merganser*
White-headed Duck	*Oxyura leucocephala*

ACCIPITRIFORMES

European Honey-buzzard	*Pernis apivorus*
Black-shouldered Kite	*Elanus caeruleus*
Black Kite	*Milvus migrans*
Red Kite	*Milvus milvus*
White-tailed Eagle	*Haliaeetus albicilla*
Egyptian Vulture	*Neophron percnopterus*
Griffon Vulture	*Gyps fulvus*
Monk Vulture	*Aegypius monachus*
Short-toed Eagle	*Circaetus gallicus*
Marsh Harrier	*Circus aeruginosus*
Hen Harrier	*Circus cyaneus*
Pallid Harrier	*Circus macrourus*
Montagu's Harrier	*Circus pygargus*
Northern Goshawk	*Accipiter gentilis*
Eurasian Sparrowhawk	*Accipiter nisus*
Levant Sparrowhawk	*Accipiter brevipes*
Common Buzzard	*Buteo buteo*
Long-legged Buzzard	*Buteo rufinus*
Rough-legged Buzzard	*Buteo lagopus*
Lesser Spotted Eagle	*Aquila pomarina*
Spotted Eagle	*Aquila clanga*
Steppe Eagle	*Aquila nipalensis*
Eastern Imperial Eagle	*Aquila heliaca*
Golden Eagle	*Aquila chrysaetos*
Booted Eagle	*Hieraaetus pennatus*

Bonelli's Eagle	*Hieraaetus fasciatus*
Osprey	*Pandion haliaetus*

FALCONIFORMES

Lesser Kestrel	*Falco naumanni*
Common Kestrel	*Falco tinnunculus*
Red-footed Falcon	*Falco vespertinus*
Merlin	*Falco columbarius*
Hobby	*Falco subbuteo*
Lanner Falcon	*Falco biarmicus*
Saker Falcon	*Falco cherrug*
Gyr Falcon	*Falco rusticolus*
Peregrine Falcon	*Falco peregrinus*

GALLIFORMES

Hazel Grouse	*Bonasa bonasia*
Black Grouse	*Tetrao tetrix*
Capercaillie	*Tetrao urogallus*
Grey Partridge	*Perdix perdix*
Common Quail	*Coturnix coturnix*
Reeve's Pheasant	*Syrmaticus reevesi*
Common Pheasant	*Phasianus colchicus*

GRUIFORMES

Water Rail	*Rallus aquaticus*
Spotted Crake	*Porzana porzana*
Little Crake	*Porzana parva*
Baillon's Crake	*Porzana pusilla*
Corn Crake	*Crex crex*
Moorhen	*Gallinula chloropus*
Purple Swamp-hen	*Porphyrio porphyrio*
Common Coot	*Fulica atra*
Common Crane	*Grus grus*
Little Bustard	*Tetrax tetrax*
Houbara Bustard	*Chlamydotis undulata*
Great Bustard	*Otis tarda*

CHARADRIIFORMES

Oystercatcher	*Haematopus ostralegus*
Black-winged Stilt	*Himantopus himantopus*
Avocet	*Recurvirostra avosetta*
Stone-curlew	*Burhinus oedicnemus*
Cream-coloured Courser	*Cursorius cursor*
Collared Pratincole	*Glareola pratincola*
Black-winged Pratincole	*Glareola nordmanni*
Little Ringed Plover	*Charadrius dubius*
Great Ringed Plover	*Charadrius hiaticula*
Kentish Plover	*Charadrius alexandrinus*
Dotterel	*Charadrius morinellus*
American Golden Plover	*Pluvialis dominica*
European Golden Plover	*Pluvialis apricaria*
Grey Plover	*Pluvialis squatarola*
Spur-winged Plover	*Hoplopterus spinosus*
Sociable Plover	*Vanellus gregaria*
Northern Lapwing	*Vanellus vanellus*
Red Knot	*Calidris canutus*
Sanderling	*Calidris alba*
Little Stint	*Calidris minuta*

Temminck's Stint	*Calidris temminckii*
White-rumped Sandpiper	*Calidris fuscicollis*
Baird's Sandpiper	*Calidris bairdii*
Pectoral Sandpiper	*Calidris melanotos*
Curlew Sandpiper	*Calidris ferruginea*
Purple Sandpiper	*Calidris maritima*
Dunlin	*Calidris alpina*
Broad-billed Sandpiper	*Limicola falcinellus*
Buff-breasted Sandpiper	*Tryngites subruficollis*
Ruff	*Philomachus pugnax*
Jack Snipe	*Lymnocryptes minimus*
Common Snipe	*Gallinago gallinago*
Great Snipe	*Gallinago media*
Woodcock	*Scolopax rusticola*
Black-tailed Godwit	*Limosa limosa*
Bar-tailed Godwit	*Limosa lapponica*
Whimbrel	*Numenius phaeopus*
Slender-billed Curlew	*Numenius tenuirostris*
Eurasian Curlew	*Numenius arquata*
Spotted Redshank	*Tringa erythropus*
Common Redshank	*Tringa totanus*
Marsh Sandpiper	*Tringa stagnatilis*
Greenshank	*Tringa nebularia*
Greater Yellowlegs	*Tringa melanoleuca*
Green Sandpiper	*Tringa ochropus*
Wood Sandpiper	*Tringa glareola*
Terek Sandpiper	*Xenus cinereus*
Common Sandpiper	*Actitis hypoleucos*
Turnstone	*Arenaria interpres*
Red-necked Phalarope	*Phalaropus lobatus*
Grey Phalarope	*Phalaropus fulicarius*
Pomarine Skua	*Stercorarius pomarinus*
Arctic Skua	*Stercorarius parasiticus*
Long-tailed Skua	*Stercorarius longicaudus*
Great Skua	*Catharacta skua*
Great Black-headed Gull	*Larus ichthyaetus*
Mediterranean Gull	*Larus melanocephalus*
Little Gull	*Larus minutus*
Sabine's Gull	*Larus sabini*
Bonaparte's Gull	*Larus philadelphia*
Black-headed Gull	*Larus ridibundus*
Audouin's Gull	*Larus audouinii*
Ring-billed Gull	*Larus delawarensis*
Common Gull	*Larus canus*
Lesser Black-backed Gull	*Larus fuscus*
Herring Gull	*Larus argentatus*
Yellow-legged Gull	*Larus cachinnans*
Iceland Gull	*Larus glaucoides*
Glaucous Gull	*Larus hyperboreus*
Great Black-backed Gull	*Larus marinus*
Kittiwake	*Rissa tridactyla*
Gull-billed Tern	*Sterna nilotica*
Caspian Tern	*Sterna caspia*
Sandwich Tern	*Sterna sandvicensis*
Common Tern	*Sterna hirundo*
Arctic Tern	*Sterna paradisaea*
Little Tern	*Sterna albifrons*
Whiskered Tern	*Chlidonias hybridus*

Black Tern	*Chlidonias niger*
White-winged Black Tern	*Chlidonias leucopterus*
Common Guillemot	*Uria aalge*
Razorbill	*Alca torda*
Black Guillemot	*Cepphus grylle*
Little Auk	*Alle alle*
PTEROCLIDIFORMES	
Pallas's Sandgrouse	*Syrrhaptes paradoxus*
COLUMBIFORMES	
Rock Dove	*Columba livia*
Stock Dove	*Columba oenas*
Wood Pigeon	*Columba palumbus*
Collared Dove	*Streptopelia decaocto*
Turtle Dove	*Streptopelia turtur*
CUCULIFORMES	
Common Cuckoo	*Cuculus canorus*
STRIGIFORMES	
Barn Owl	*Tyto alba*
Eurasian Scops Owl	*Otus scops*
Eagle Owl	*Bubo bubo*
Snowy Owl	*Nyctea scandiaca*
Hawk Owl	*Surnia ulula*
Pygmy Owl	*Glaucidium passerinum*
Little Owl	*Athene noctua*
Tawny Owl	*Strix aluco*
Ural Owl	*Strix uralensis*
Long-eared Owl	*Asio otus*
Short-eared Owl	*Asio flammeus*
Tengmalm's Owl	*Aegolius funereus*
CAPRIMULGIFORMES	
European Nightjar	*Caprimulgus europaeus*
APODIFORMES	
Alpine Swift	*Tachymarptis melba*
Common Swift	*Apus apus*
CORACIIFORMES	
Common Kingfisher	*Alcedo atthis*
European Bee-eater	*Merops apiaster*
European Roller	*Coracias garrulus*
Hoopoe	*Upupa epops*
PICIFORMES	
Wryneck	*Jynx torquilla*
Grey-headed Woodpecker	*Picus canus*
Green Woodpecker	*Picus viridis*
Black Woodpecker	*Dryocopus martius*
Great Spotted Woodpecker	*Dendrocopos major*
Syrian Woodpecker	*Dendrocopos syriacus*
Middle Spotted Woodpecker	*Dendrocopos medius*
White-backed Woodpecker	*Dendrocopos leucotos*
Lesser Spotted Woodpecker	*Dendrocopos minor*
Three-toed Woodpecker	*Picoides tridactylus*

PASSERIFORMES

Calandra Lark	*Melanocorypha calandra*
Black Lark	*Melanocorypha yeltoniensis*
Crested Lark	*Galerida cristata*
Wood Lark	*Lullula arborea*
Sky Lark	*Alauda arvensis*
Horned Lark	*Eremophila alpestris*
Sand Martin	*Riparia riparia*
Barn Swallow	*Hirundo rustica*
House Martin	*Delichon urbica*
Richard's Pipit	*Anthus novaeseelandiae*
Tawny Pipit	*Anthus campestris*
Tree Pipit	*Anthus trivialis*
Meadow Pipit	*Anthus pratensis*
Red-throated Pipit	*Anthus cervinus*
Rock Pipit	*Anthus petrosus*
Water Pipit	*Anthus spinoletta*
Yellow Wagtail	*Motacilla flava*
Citrine Wagtail	*Motacilla citreola*
Grey Wagtail	*Motacilla cinerea*
White Wagtail	*Motacilla alba*
Bohemian Waxwing	*Bombycilla garrulus*
Dipper	*Cinclus cinclus*
Wren	*Troglodytes troglodytes*
Hedge Accentor	*Prunella modularis*
Siberian Accentor	*Prunella montanella*
Alpine Accentor	*Prunella collaris*
Robin	*Erithacus rubecula*
Thrush Nightingale	*Luscinia luscinia*
Rufous Nightingale	*Luscinia megarhynchos*
Bluethroat	*Luscinia svecica*
Black Redstart	*Phoenicurus ochruros*
Common Redstart	*Phoenicurus phoenicurus*
Whinchat	*Saxicola rubetra*
Common Stonechat	*Saxicola torquata*
Northern Wheatear	*Oenanthe oenanthe*
Black-eared Wheatear	*Oenanthe hispanica*
Rock Thrush	*Monticola saxatilis*
Ring Ouzel	*Turdus torquatus*
Blackbird	*Turdus merula*
Eyebrowed Thrush	*Turdus obscurus*
Dusky Thrush	*Turdus naumanni*
Dark-throated Thrush	*Turdus ruficollis*
Fieldfare	*Turdus pilaris*
Song Thrush	*Turdus philomelos*
Redwing	*Turdus iliacus*
Mistle Thrush	*Turdus viscivorus*
American Robin	*Turdus migratorius*
Grasshopper Warbler	*Locustella naevia*
River Warbler	*Locustella fluviatilis*
Savi's Warbler	*Locustella luscinioides*
Moustached Warbler	*Acrocephalus melanopogon*
Aquatic Warbler	*Acrocephalus paludicola*
Sedge Warbler	*Acrocephalus schoenobaenus*
Marsh Warbler	*Acrocephalus palustris*
Reed Warbler	*Acrocephalus scirpaceus*
Great Reed Warbler	*Acrocephalus arundinaceus*
Olivaceous Warbler	*Hippolais pallida*

Icterine Warbler	*Hippolais icterina*
Melodious Warbler	*Hippolais polyglotta*
Dartford Warbler	*Sylvia undata*
Sardinian Warbler	*Sylvia melanocephala*
Orphean Warbler	*Sylvia hortensis*
Barred Warbler	*Sylvia nisoria*
Lesser Whitethroat	*Sylvia curruca*
Common Whitethroat	*Sylvia communis*
Garden Warbler	*Sylvia borin*
Blackcap	*Sylvia atricapilla*
Greenish Warbler	*Phylloscopus trochiloides*
Pallas's Leaf Warbler	*Phylloscopus proregulus*
Yellow-browed Warbler	*Phylloscopus inornatus*
Radde's Warbler	*Phylloscopus schwarzi*
Western Bonelli's Warbler	*Phylloscopus bonelli*
Wood Warbler	*Phylloscopus sibilatrix*
Common Chiffchaff	*Phylloscopus collybita*
Iberian Chiffchaff	*Phylloscopus brehmii*
Willow Warbler	*Phylloscopus trochilus*
Goldcrest	*Regulus regulus*
Firecrest	*Regulus ignicapillus*
Spotted Flycatcher	*Muscicapa striata*
Red-breasted Flycatcher	*Ficedula parva*
Collared Flycatcher	*Ficedula albicollis*
Pied Flycatcher	*Ficedula hypoleuca*
Bearded Tit	*Panurus biarmicus*
Long-tailed Tit	*Aegithalos caudatus*
Marsh Tit	*Parus palustris*
Willow Tit	*Parus montanus*
Crested Tit	*Parus cristatus*
Coal Tit	*Parus ater*
Blue Tit	*Parus caeruleus*
Azure Tit	*Parus cyanus*
Great Tit	*Parus major*
European Nuthatch	*Sitta europaea*
Wallcreeper	*Tichodroma muraria*
Eurasian Treecreeper	*Certhia familiaris*
Short-toed Treecreeper	*Certhia brachydactyla*
Penduline Tit	*Remiz pendulinus*
Golden Oriole	*Oriolus oriolus*
Red-backed Shrike	*Lanius collurio*
Lesser Grey Shrike	*Lanius minor*
Great Grey Shrike	*Lanius excubitor*
Woodchat Shrike	*Lanius senator*
Eurasian Jay	*Garrulus glandarius*
Magpie	*Pica pica*
Nutcracker	*Nucifraga caryocatactes*
Yellow-billed Chough	*Pyrrhocorax graculus*
Jackdaw	*Corvus monedula*
Rook	*Corvus frugilegus*
Crow	*Corvus corone*
Common Raven	*Corvus corax*
Common Starling	*Sturnus vulgaris*
Rosy Starling	*Sturnus roseus*
House Sparrow	*Passer domesticus*
Tree Sparrow	*Passer montanus*
Snowfinch	*Montifringilla nivalis*
Common Chaffinch	*Fringilla coelebs*

Brambling	*Fringilla montifringilla*
European Serin	*Serinus serinus*
Citril Finch	*Serinus citrinella*
Greenfinch	*Carduelis chloris*
Goldfinch	*Carduelis carduelis*
Siskin	*Carduelis spinus*
Linnet	*Carduelis cannabina*
Twite	*Carduelis flavirostris*
Common Redpoll	*Carduelis flammea*
Arctic Redpoll	*Carduelis hornemanni*
Two-barred Crossbill	*Loxia leucoptera*
Common Crossbill	*Loxia curvirostra*
Parrot Crossbill	*Loxia pytopsittacus*
Common Rosefinch	*Carpodacus erythrinus*
Pine Grosbeak	*Pinicola enucleator*
Common Bullfinch	*Pyrrhula pyrrhula*
Hawfinch	*Coccothraustes coccothraustes*
Lapland Longspur	*Calcarius lapponicus*
Snow Bunting	*Plectophrenax nivalis*
Pine Bunting	*Emberiza leucocephalos*
Yellowhammer	*Emberiza citrinella*
Cirl Bunting	*Emberiza cirlus*
Rock Bunting	*Emberiza cia*
Ortolan Bunting	*Emberiza hortulana*
Rustic Bunting	*Emberiza rustica*
Little Bunting	*Emberiza pusilla*
Yellow-breasted Bunting	*Emberiza aureola*
Reed Bunting	*Emberiza schoeniclus*
Red-headed Bunting	*Emberiza bruniceps*
Black-headed Bunting	*Emberiza melanocephala*
Corn Bunting	*Emberiza calandra*

CHECKLIST OF THE BIRDS OF THE SLOVAK REPUBLIC

RB = regularly breeding species; IB = irregularly breeding species; RNO = regularly occurring non-breeding species (usually refers to migrants); INO = irregularly occurring non-breeding species (usually refers to migrants); RR = rarely occurring species (fewer than 10 records since 1980)

GAVIIFORMES

Red-throated Diver	RNO
Black-throated Diver	RNO
Great Northern Diver	INO
White-billed Diver	RR

PODICIPEDIFORMES

Little Grebe	RB
Great Crested Grebe	RB
Red-necked Grebe	RB
Slavonian Grebe	INO
Black-necked Grebe	RB

PELECANIFORMES

Great Cormorant	RB
Pygmy Cormorant	INO
White Pelican	RR

CICONIIFORMES

Great Bittern	RB
Little Bittern	RB
Night Heron	RB
Squacco Heron	RNO
Little Egret	IB, RNO
Great White Egret	RB
Grey Heron	RB
Purple Heron	RB
Black Stork	RB
White Stork	RB
Glossy Ibis	RNO
Eurasian Spoonbill	IB, RNO

ANSERIFORMES

Mute Swan	RB
Tundra Swan	RR
Whooper Swan	RNO
Bean Goose	RNO
Pink-footed Goose	RR
White-fronted Goose	RNO
Lesser White-fronted Goose	INO
Greylag Goose	RB
Canada Goose	RR
Barnacle Goose	RR
Brent Goose	RR
Red-breasted Goose	RR
Ruddy Shelduck	RR
Common Shelduck	INO
Eurasian Wigeon	RNO
Gadwall	RB
Common Teal	RB
Mallard	RB
Pintail	IB, RNO
Garganey	RB
Northern Shoveler	RB
Red-crested Pochard	RB
Common Pochard	RB
Ferruginous Duck	RB
Tufted Duck	RB
Greater Scaup	RNO
Common Eider	RNO
Long-tailed Duck	INO
Common Scoter	RNO
Velvet Scoter	RNO
Common Goldeneye	RNO
Smew	RNO
Red-breasted Merganser	RNO
Goosander	RNO
White-headed Duck	RR

ACCIPITRIFORMES

European Honey-buzzard	RB
Black Kite	RB
Red Kite	RB
White-tailed Eagle	RNO
Egyptian Vulture	RR
Griffon Vulture	RR
Black Vulture	RR
Short-toed Eagle	RB
Marsh Harrier	RB
Hen Harrier	RNO
Pallid Harrier	INO
Montagu's Harrier	RB
Northern Goshawk	RB
Eurasian Sparrowhawk	RB
Common Buzzard	RB
Long-legged Buzzard	INO
Rough-legged Buzzard	RNO
Lesser Spotted Eagle	RB
Spotted Eagle	INO
Steppe Eagle	RR
Eastern Imperial Eagle	RB
Golden Eagle	RB
Booted Eagle	RB
Osprey	RNO

FALCONIFORMES

Lesser Kestrel	RR
Common Kestrel	RB
Red-footed Falcon	IB, RNO
Merlin	RNO
Hobby	RB
Saker Falcon	RB
Peregrine Falcon	IB, RNO

GALLIFORMES

Hazel Grouse	RB
Black Grouse	RB
Capercaillie	RB
Grey Partridge	RB
Common Quail	RB
Common Pheasant	RB

GRUIFORMES

Water Rail	RB
Spotted Crake	RB
Little Crake	RB
Baillon's Crake	RR
Corn Crake	RB
Moorhen	RB
Common Coot	RB
Common Crane	RNO
Demoiselle Crane	RR
Little Bustard	RR
Great Bustard	RB

CHARADRIIFORMES

Oystercatcher	INO
Black-winged Stilt	IB, INO
Avocet	RB
Stone-curlew	INO
Collared Pratincole	RR
Black-winged Pratincole	RR
Little Ringed Plover	RB
Great Ringed Plover	RNO
Kentish Plover	RNO
Dotterel	RR
European Golden Plover	RNO
Grey Plover	RNO
Sociable Plover	RR
Northern Lapwing	RB
Red Knot	INO
Sanderling	INO
Little Stint	RNO
Temminck's Stint	RNO
Pectoral Sandpiper	RR
Curlew Sandpiper	RNO
Purple Sandpiper	RR
Dunlin	RNO
Broad-billed Sandpiper	RNO
Ruff	RNO
Jack Snipe	RNO
Common Snipe	RB
Great Snipe	INO
Woodcock	RB
Black-tailed Godwit	RB
Bar-tailed Godwit	INO
Whimbrel	RNO
Slender-billed Curlew	RR
Eurasian Curlew	RB
Spotted Redshank	RNO
Common Redshank	RB
Marsh Sandpiper	RNO
Greenshank	RNO
Green Sandpiper	RNO
Wood Sandpiper	RNO
Terek Sandpiper	INO
Common Sandpiper	RB
Turnstone	RNO
Red-necked Phalarope	RNO
Grey Phalarope	RR
Pomarine Skua	INO
Arctic Skua	INO
Long-tailed Skua	RR
Mediterranean Gull	INO
Little Gull	RNO
Black-headed Gull	RB
Common Gull	RB
Lesser Black-backed Gull	INO
Herring Gull	RNO
Yellow-legged Gull	RNO
Great Black-backed Gull	INO
Kittiwake	INO
Gull-billed Tern	RR
Caspian Tern	RNO
Sandwich Tern	RR
Common Tern	RB
Arctic Tern	RR
Little Tern	IB, RNO
Whiskered Tern	RB
Black Tern	RB
White-winged Black Tern	RNO

PTEROCLIDIFORMES

Pallas's Sandgrouse	INO

COLUMBIFORMES

Rock Dove	RB
Stock Dove	RB
Wood Pigeon	RB
Collared Dove	RB
Turtle Dove	RB

CUCULIFORMES

Great Spotted Cuckoo	RR
Common Cuckoo	RB

STRIGIFORMES

Barn Owl	RB
Eurasian Scops Owl	RB
Eagle Owl	RB
Snowy Owl	RR
Hawk Owl	RR
Pygmy Owl	RB
Little Owl	RB
Tawny Owl	RB
Ural Owl	RB
Long-eared Owl	RB
Short-eared Owl	IB, RNO
Tengmalm's Owl	RB

CAPRIMULGIFORMES

European Nightjar	RB

APODIFORMES

Alpine Swift	RB
Common Swift	RR

CORACIIFORMES

Common Kingfisher	RB
European Bee-eater	RB
European Roller	RB
Hoopoe	RB

PICIFORMES

Wryneck	RB
Grey-headed Woodpecker	RB
Green Woodpecker	RB
Black Woodpecker	RB
Great Spotted Woodpecker	RB
Syrian Woodpecker	RB
Middle Spotted Woodpecker	RB
White-backed Woodpecker	RB
Lesser Spotted Woodpecker	RB
Three-toed Woodpecker	RB

PASSERIFORMES

Short-toed Lark	RR
Crested Lark	RB
Wood Lark	RB
Sky Lark	RB
Horned Lark	INO
Sand Martin	RB
Barn Swallow	RB
House Martin	RB
Tawny Pipit	RB
Tree Pipit	RB
Meadow Pipit	RB
Red-throated Pipit	RNO
Water Pipit	RB
Yellow Wagtail	RB
Citrine Wagtail	RR
Grey Wagtail	RB
White Wagtail	RB
Bohemian Waxwing	RNO
Dipper	RB
Wren	RB
Hedge Accentor	RB
Siberian Accentor	RR
Alpine Accentor	RB
Robin	RB
Thrush Nightingale	RB
Rufous Nightingale	RB
Bluethroat	RB
Black Redstart	RB
Common Redstart	RB
Whinchat	RB
Common Stonechat	RB
Northern Wheatear	RB
Rock Thrush	RB
Blue Rock Thrush	RR
Ring Ouzel	RB
Blackbird	RB
Fieldfare	RB
Song Thrush	RB
Redwing	IB, RNO
Mistle Thrush	RB
Grasshopper Warbler	RB
River Warbler	RB
Savi's Warbler	RB
Moustached Warbler	RB
Aquatic Warbler	INO
Sedge Warbler	RB
Marsh Warbler	RB
Reed Warbler	RB
Great Reed Warbler	RB
Olivaceous Warbler	RR
Icterine Warbler	RB
Barred Warbler	RB
Lesser Whitethroat	RB
Common Whitethroat	RB
Garden Warbler	RB
Blackcap	RB
Greenish Warbler	INO
Western Bonelli's Warbler	RR
Wood Warbler	RB
Common Chiffchaff	RB
Willow Warbler	RB
Goldcrest	RB
Firecrest	RB
Spotted Flycatcher	RB
Red-breasted Flycatcher	RB
Collared Flycatcher	RB
Pied Flycatcher	RB
Bearded Tit	RB
Long-tailed Tit	RB
Marsh Tit	RB
Willow Tit	RB
Crested Tit	RB
Coal Tit	RB
Blue Tit	RB
Azure Tit	RR
Great Tit	RB
European Nuthatch	RB
Wallcreeper	RB
Eurasian Treecreeper	RB
Short-toed Treecreeper	RB
Penduline Tit	RB
Golden Oriole	RB
Red-backed Shrike	RB
Lesser Grey Shrike	RB
Great Grey Shrike	RB
Woodchat Shrike	INO
Eurasian Jay	RB
Magpie	RB
Nutcracker	RB
Yellow-billed Chough	RR

Eurasian Jackdaw	RB
Rook	RB
Crow	RB
Common Raven	RB
Common Starling	RB
Rosy Starling	INO
House Sparrow	RB
Tree Sparrow	RB
Snowfinch	RR
Common Chaffinch	RB
Brambling	RNO
European Serin	RB
Greenfinch	RB
Goldfinch	RB
Siskin	RB
Linnet	RB
Twite	RNO
Common Redpoll	RB
Arctic Redpoll	RR
Two-barred Crossbill	RR
Common Crossbill	RB
Common Rosefinch	RB
Pine Grosbeak	RR
Common Bullfinch	RB
Hawfinch	RB
Lapland Longspur	RR
Snow Bunting	RNO
Yellowhammer	RB
Rock Bunting	RB
Ortolan Bunting	INO
Reed Bunting	RB
Black-headed Bunting	RR
Corn Bunting	RB

APPENDIX A: SPECIES WHICH MAY BE HUNTED IN THE CZECH REPUBLIC

The Czech National Council Act No.114/1992 on the Protection of Nature and Landscape, and the Decrees of the Ministry of Agriculture of the Czech Republic No. 512/1992 and No. 134/1996 allow hunting of the following species.

Great Cormorant
All year round. There are exceptions given by conservation authorities for certain sites.
Grey Heron
May be hunted from 16 August untill 30 November at specified fish hatcheries.
Anser **spp.**
From 1 September till 28 February.
Mallard
From 1 September till 30 November.
Common Pochard
From 1 September till 30 November.
Tufted Duck
From 1 September till 30 November.
Northern Goshawk
All year round. There are exceptions given by conservation authorities for certain sites.
Common Buzzard
Under certain conditions, and at certain sites, may be hunted all year round.
Rough-legged Buzzard
May be hunted under certain conditions, and at certain sites.
Black Grouse
From 16 April till 15 May.
Grey Partridge
From 1 September till 30 September.
Reeves's Pheasant
Male may be hunted from 16 October till 15 March, females in pheasantries only from 16 October till 31 January.
Common Pheasant
Both male and female may be hunted from 16 October till 31 December, in pheasantries till 31 January.
Common Coot
From 1 September till 15 December.
Woodcock
From 16 March till 15 April.
Black-headed Gull
May be hunted all year round in pheasantries, and sites with Hazel Grouse, Black Grouse, Capercaillie or Great Bustard. May also be hunted at fish hatcheries.
Wood Pigeon
From 16 August till 31 October.
Collared Dove
From 1 August till 15 February.
Eagle Owl
Only clutches of eggs may be taken or destroyed; shooting is illegal.
Eurasian Jay
From 1 October till 31 March.
Magpie
All year round.
Rook
From 16 October till 28 February.
Crow (both races)
All year round.

APPENDIX B: PLANT NAMES

acacia	*Acacia* spp.
alder	*Alnus* spp.
apple	*Malus* spp.
ash	*Fraxinus* spp.
aspen	*Populus tremula*
beech	*Fagus* spp.
birch	*Betula* spp.
blackberry	*Rubus* spp.
blackthorn	*Prunus spinosa*
buckthorn	*Rhamnus catharticus*
cherry	*Prunus* spp.
currant	*Ribes* spp.
dwarf (mountain) pine	*Pinus mugo*
elm	*Ulmus* spp.
european elder	*Sambucus nigra*
fir	*Abies* spp.
goosebery	*Ribes uva-crispa*
guelder rose	*Viburnum opulus*
hawthorn	*Crataegus monogyna*
hazel	*Corylus avellana*
hornbeam	*Carpinus betulus*
horse chestnut	*Aesculus hippocastanum*
juniper	*Juniperus* spp.
European larch	*Larix decidua*
lime	*Tilia* spp.
maple	*Acer* spp.
mountain-ash	*Fraxinus excelsior*
nettle	*Urtica* spp.
oak	*Quercus* spp.
pear	*Pyrus* spp.
pine	*Pinus* spp.
poplar	*Populus* spp.
ragwort	*Senecio jacobaea*
raspberry	*Rubus ideaus*
reed	*Phragmites communis*
reedmace	*Typha* spp.
sedge	*Carex, Scirpus*
spruce	*Picea* spp.
thistle	*Carduus* spp.
cypress	*Cupressus* spp.
vine	*Vitis vinifera*
rose	*Rosa* spp.
willow	*Salix* spp.

APPENDIX C: USEFUL ADDRESSES

Krivoklatsko (BE, KL, RA).
Sprava Chranene krajinne oblasti Krivoklatsko
Zbecno 5
270 24 Zbecno
Czech Republic
Telephone: 0313/98834; fax: 0313/98810
E-mail: chko-kri@orfinet.cz

Krkonose mountains (SE,TU).
Krkonose National Park Administration
Dobrovskeho 3
543 11 Vrchlabi
Czech Republic
Telephone: [420] (438) 456 212/456 224
Fax: [420] (438) 422 095
E-mail: jflousek@krnap.cz
Web site: http://www.krnap.cz/

Sumava mountains (CK, KT, PT).
Administration of the Sumava National Park and Landscape Protected Area
ulice l. MAJE 260
385 01 Vimperk
Czech Republic
Telephone: [420] (339) 450 111/450 227
Fax: [420] (339) 413 019
E-mail: vladimir.zatloukal@npsumava.cz
Web site: http://www.npsumava.cz

Trebonsko (CB, JH, TA).
The Trebonsko Protected Landscape Area and Biosphere Reserve Administration
Valy 121
379 01 Trebon
Czech Republic
Telephone: [420] (333) 721 248/721 400
Fax: [420] (333) 721 400
E-mail: chkot@envi.cz
Web site: http://chkot.envi.cz

Lednicke ponds (BV), and Nove Mlyny reservoir (BV).
See Palava hills.

Palava hills (BV).
Palava Protected Landscape Area and Biosphere Reserve
Namesti 32
692 01 Mikulov
Czech Republic
Telephone: [42] (625) 2585; fax: [42] (625) 3130
E-mail: chko@palava.cz
Web site: http://www.ihost.cz/chko/

Beskydy mountains (FM, VS).
Sprava CHKO Beskydy
Nadrazni 36
756 61 Roznov pod Radhostem
Czech Republic
Telephone: 0651/654293; fax: 065/57407
E-mail: beskydy@schkocr.cz

Jeseniky mountains (BR, SU).
Sprava CHKO Jeseniky
790 01 Jesenik – Bukovice 93
Czech Republic
Telephone: 0645/402228; tel./fax: 0645/403050
E-mail: jeseniky@schkocr.cz
chkojs@ova.pvtnet.cz

Poodri (FM, NJ, OV).
Sprava CHKO Poodri
Trocnovska 2
702 00 Ostrava- Privoz
Czech Republic
Telephone: 069/6133014, 069/6134658
Fax: 069/6133337
E-mail: poodri@schkocr.cz, poodri@prfl.osu.cz
Web site: www.osu.cz/prf/bi/poodri/begin.htm

Jizerske hory mountains (LB).
Správa CHKO Jizerské hory
U Jezu 10
460 01 Liberec 4
Czech Republic
Telephone/fax: [420] 48 5104771
E-mail: schkojh@mbox.vol.cz

Bile Karpaty mountains (HO, UH, ZL)
Správa Chránené krajinné oblasti (CHKO) Bílé Karpaty
Bartolomejské nam. 47
CZ-69801 Veseli n.Mor.
Czech Republic
Telephone [420] (631) 322 545; fax [420] (631) 324 792
E-mail visbk@es-servis.cz

Litovelske Pomoravi (OL).
Sprava CHKO Litovelske Pomoravi
Lazecka 6
772 00 Olomouc
Czech Republic
Telephone: 068/522 49 34
Fax: 068/522 63 44
E-mail: litpom@schkocr.cz

National Contact for Czech Biosphere Reserves
Eva JELINKOVA, Secretary
Czech MAB National Committee
Academy of Sciences of the Czech Republic
Narodni 3
CZ-117 42 Prague 1
Czech Republic
Telephone: [420] (2) 24 22 03 84 ext. 420
Fax: [420] (2) 24240531
E-mail: mab@kav.cas.cz
Web site: http://mab.kav.cas.cz/

Information about other sites mentioned in this book can be obtained at the following addresses:

MOS (Moravian Ornithological Society)
P.O.Box 65
750 65 Prerov 2
Czech Republic
e-mail: mos@iweb.cz
Web site: http://www.iweb.cz/mos

Czech Society for Ornithology
Hornomìcholupská 34
CZ-102 00 Praha 10
Czech Republic
Telephone/fax (+420 2)7866700

INDEX OF SPECIES

Numbers in bold refer to the main species accounts.

ENGLISH NAMES

Accentor, Alpine 27, 41, **190**
Hedge **189-190**
Siberian **276**
Auk, Little **274**
Avocet 29, 31, 34, 35, **123**, 302

Bee-eater, European 39, **167**
Bittern, Great 9, 25, 27, 28, 29, 31, 33, 36, **68**, 289, 297, 302, 305, 309
Little 9, 27, 28, 33, 36, 42, **68-69**, 289, 297, 302, 304, 305, 307, 309
Blackbird **198-199**, 200, 202
Blackcap 156, **212-213**
Bluethroat 27, 29, 30, 32, 33, 34, 35, **193**, 297, 298, 304, 305
Brambling 30, **244**, 255
Bullfinch, Common **253-254**
Bunting, Black-headed **285**
Cirl **283**
Corn 29, 39, **258-259**, 300, 308
Little **284**
Ortolan 29, **256-257**
Pine **283**
Red-headed **285**
Reed 25, 27, 28, 39, **257-258**, 286
Rock **283-284**
Rustic **284**
Snow 26, **255**
Yellow-breasted **284**
Bustard, Great 39, **121-122**
Houbara **266**
Little **120-121**
Buzzard, Common 25, 36, **102-103**, 287, 288, 295, 299, 300
European-honey 25, 27, 29, 30, 33, 36, 38, 40, 41, **94-95**, 291, 297, 298, 300, 304, 306, 307, 308
Long-legged **103**
Rough-legged 102, **103**

Capercaillie 9, 27, 30, 33, 40, 41, **113**
Chaffinch, Common **243-244**, 255
Chiffchaff, Common **215-216**
Iberian **280-281**
Chough, Yellow-billed **282**
Cormorant, Great 25, 27, 28, 31, 33, 34, 35, **66-67**, 288, 289, 289, 291, 292, 293, 296, 297, 298, 302, 303, 304, 305, 307, 309
Pygmy **261-262**
Coot, Common **119-120**, 288, 292, 295
Crake, Baillon's **266**
Corn 9, 25, 27, 30, 33, 34, 38, 40, 41, **118**, 291, 297, 298, 299, 306, 308
Little 25, 33, **117**, 297
Spotted 25, 27, 31, 33, 36, 42, **116-117**, 297, 298, 305
Crane, Common 27, 28, 29, 31, 42, **120**, 286, 302, 305, 309
Crossbill, Common 27, 30, 40, 41, **251**, 295, 299
Parrot **251-252**
Two-barred **250**
Crow 11, **238-239**
Cuckoo, Common **156**
Curlew, Eurasian 26, 31, **135-136**
Slender-billed **270**
Courser, Cream-coloured **267**

Dipper **188**, 295, 300, 306, 308
Diver, Black-throated 25, 28, 31, 33, 34, 35, **61-62**, 288, 289, 291, 296, 297, 298, 302, 304, 307, 309
Great Northern **62**
Red-throated 25, 31, 33, 34, 35, **61**, 289, 291, 297, 298, 302, 304, 309
White-billed **260**
Dotterel 27, 41, **125-126**
Dove, Collared **154**
Rock **152**
Stock 25, 29, 40, 41, **152-153**, 291, 293, 295, 300, 307
Turtle 20, **155**, 286, 287
Duck, Ferruginous 29, **88-89**, 288, 296, 307
Long-tailed **90-91**, 288, 292, 293
Marbled **263**
Tufted **89**, 286, 288, 289, 292, 293, 295
White-headed 9, 34, 35, **94**, 293
Dunlin **130**

Eagle, Bonnelli's 9, **265**
Booted **105-106**
Eastern Imperial 9, 36, 38, **105**
Golden **105**, 300, 306
Lesser Spotted 27, 29, 30, 33, **104**, 300, 306
Short-toed **98**
Spotted **104**
Steppe **265**
White-tailed 7, 25, 27, 28, 29, 31, 33, 34, 35, 36, 38, **96**, 291, 292, 299, 302, 304, 305, 307, 309
Egret, Cattle **262**
Great White 25, 31, 33, 34, 35, 42, **70-71**, 289, 291, 293, 296, 297, 298, 302, 303, 304, 305, 307, 309
Little 34, 35, **70**, 304
Eider, Common **90**, 288, 291, 296, 302, 309
King **263**

Falcon, Gyr **266**
Lanner **265**
Peregrine 27, 30, 31, 41, **110-111**
Red-footed 31, **108**, 300
Saker 9, 36, 38, 39, **109-110**
Fieldfare **199-200**, 201
Finch, Citril **283**
Firecrest 40, 41, **217-218**, 295, 308
Flamingo, Greater **75**
Flycatcher, Collared 25, 33, 34, 36, 38, 40, 41, 42, **220**, 299, 308
Pied 25, **220-221**, 291, 293
Red-breasted 25, 27, 29, 30, 33, 40, 41, **219**, 291, 293, 299, 306, 307
Spotted 25, **218-219**, 287, 291
Fulmar **260**

Gadwall **83**, 286, 288, 293, 295, 296, 297, 298, 303
Gannet, Northern **261**
Garganey 42, **85-86**, 286, 296, 297, 298
Godwit, Bar-tailed 31, **134-135**
Black-tailed 31, 33, 42, **134**, 291, 296, 297, 299, 302, 305, 309
Goldcrest **216-217**
Goldeneye, Barrow's 9, **264**
Common 25, 33, 42, **92**, 288, 289, 291, 292, 293, 296, 302, 305, 307, 309
Goldfinch **246-247**
Goosander 25, **93-94**, 288, 289, 291, 292, 293, 295, 296, 302, 305, 307, 309
Goose, Barnacle 31, 36, **80**
Bean 20, 25, 27, 36, **77**
Brent **80-81**
Canada **80**, 309
Greylag 9, 20, 25, 27, 31, 33, 35, 36, **79**, 291, 296, 297, 305, 307
Lesser White-fronted **78-79**
Pink-footed **78**
Red-breasted 36, **81**
Snow **262**
White-fronted 25, 31, 36, **78**, 296, 297, 307
Goshawk, Northern 25, 36, **100-101**, 295, 300, 304, 306, 307, 308
Grebe, Black-necked 25, 33, 34, 35, 42, **65-66**, 286, 293, 296, 297, 298, 302, 303
Great Crested **63-64**, 286, 288, 289, 291, 292, 293, 296, 297, 298, 302, 302, 304, 305, 307, 308, 309
Little **63**, 286, 288, 289, 292, 293, 295, 296, 297, 298, 302, 303, 304, 307
Red-necked 31, 33, 42, **64-65**, 288, 289, 289, 291, 293, 297, 298, 302, 304, 305, 309

Slavonian 25, 33, 34, 35, **65**, 291, 292, 297, 298, 302, 304, 305, 309
Greenfinch **245-246**, 255
Greenshank **137-138**
Grosbeak, Pine **252-253**
Grouse, Black 9, 27, 29, 30, 33, 41, **112**, 293
Hazel 9, 30, 33, 40, 41, **111**, 300, 306
Guillemot, Black **274**
Common **273-274**
Gull, Audouin's **272**
Black-headed 31, **143-144**, 272, 288, 291, 292, 302, 304, 30
Bonaparte's **271**
Common 32, 35, **144-145**, 272, 288, 289, 291, 296, 302, 303, 305, 307, 309
Glaucous **273**
Great Black-backed **146-147**
Great Black-headed Gull **271**
Herring **145-146**, 272, 288, 291, 296, 302, 303, 305, 307, 309
Iceland **272**
Lesser Black-backed **145**, 305, 309
Little 26, 32, **143**, 288, 289, 303
Mediterranean 31, 35, **142**
Ring-billed **272**
Sabine's **271**
Yellow-legged 35, **146**, 272

Harrier, Hen 26, 30, 33, 41, **99**, 300
Marsh 25, 27, 28, 31, 33, 35, 36, 42, **98-99**, 289, 291, 296, 297, 298, 302, 303, 304, 305, 307, 308
Montagu's 9, 25, 29, 31, 33, **100**, 286, 297, 302
Pallid 9, **99-100**
Hawfinch **254**
Heron, Grey 31, 33, 38, 42, **71**, 242, 288, 291, 292, 293, 296, 297, 298, 299, 302, 303, 304, 305, 307, 308
Night 9, 33, **69**, 289, 291, 297, 302, 305, 309
Purple 9, 31, 33, 35, 36, **72**, 297, 304, 309
Squacco 33, 34, 35, 36, **69-70**, 298
Hobby 29, 33, 40, **109**, 291, 297, 298, 299, 300, 306
Hoopoe 25, 29, 36, **168-169**

Ibis, Glossy 33, 34, 35, **74**, 298, 304

Jackdaw, Eurasian 20, **237**, 238, 239
Jay, Eurasian **235**

Kestrel, Common **107-108**, 287, 288, 300
Lesser **107**
Kingfisher, Common 25, 27, 30, 33, 34, 36, 38, 40, 41, **166-167**, 287, 288, 291, 295, 297, 298, 299, 300, 302, 305, 306, 308,307
Kite, Black 25, 29, 33, 36, 38, **95**, 296, 297, 298, 302, 304, 309
Black-shouldered **264**
Red 9, 25, 29, 33, 36, 38, 39, **95-96**, 296, 297, 298, 300, 302, 304, 307, 309
Kittiwake **147**, 305, 309
Knot, Red 31, **128**

Lapwing, Northern 20, **127**
Sociable **268-269**
Spur-winged **268**
Lark, Black **275**
Calandra **275**
Crested **177-178**
Horned 38, **179**
Sky 20, 39, **178-179**,
Wood 27, 29, 30, 33, 34, **178**, 298, 299, 300
Linnet **248-249**, 255
Longspur, Lapland **254-255**

Magpie 162, **235-236**
Mallard **84**, 292
Martin, House **181**
Sand 39, 305, 307, 109, **180**
Merganser, Red-breasted **93**, 289, 289, 291, 302, 309
Merlin 27, **108-109**
Moorhen **118-119**, 288, 292

Nightingale, Rufous 29, 36, **192-193**, 286, 287, 288, 293, 302, 305, 307
Thrush 32, 38, **191-192**,309
Nightjar, European 29, 33, 34, 40, 41, **164-165**, 295, 297, 307
Nutcracker 25, 27, 30, 40, 41, **236-237**, 293, 306
Nuthatch, European **228-229**

Oriole, Golden 7, 29, 33, 34, 36, 38, **232-233**, 286, 287, 288, 291, 298
Osprey 26, 27, 28, 31, 33, 34, 35, 42, **106**, 286, 289, 289, 291, 293, 296, 297, 298, 299, 302, 303, 304, 305, 307, 309
Ouzel, Ring 27, 30, 40, 41, **198**
Owl, Barn 20, 25, 29, **157**, 307
Eagle 25, 27, 29, 30, 33, 36, 40, 41, **158**, 291, 295, 306, 307, 308
Eurasian Scops **157-158**, 300
Hawk **159**
Little 29, **160-161**, 298, 305, 308
Long-eared **162-163**, 286, 287, 288
Pygmy 9, 25, 27, 30, 33, 40, **159-160**, 295, 298, 299
Short-eared 26, 33, **163**
Snowy **158-159**
Tawny 25, **161**, 286, 287, 288, 308
Tengmalm's 9, 25, 27, 30, 33, 40, 41, **163-164**, 291, 293, 295
Ural 7, 30, 40, **162**
Oystercatcher 26, **122**, 309

Partridge, Grey 20, **113-114**, 288
Pelican,White **67**
Phalarope, Grey **141**
Red-necked **140**
Pheasant, Common 20, **115**
Reeve's **114-115**,
Pigeon, Wood **153-154**, 286, 287
Pipit, Meadow 40, **183**, 291
Rock 11, 14
Red-throated 27, 31, **183-184**
Richard's **276**
Tawny 29, 39, **181-182**
Tree **182-183**
Water 27, 32, 41, **184**, 291
Pintail 25, 31, 38, **85**, 288, 289, 296, 302, 307
Plover, American Golden **268**
European Golden 26, 31, **126**, 289
Great Ringed 31, **125**
Grey 26, 31, **126-127**, 289, 291, 302, 305, 309
Kentish **125**
Little Ringed 34, 35, **124**, 303, 304, 307
Pochard, Common **87-88**, 286, 289, 292, 293, 295
Red-crested 25, 31, 33, 35, 36, **86-87**, 288, 297, 302
Pratincole, Black-winged **268**
Collared **267**

Quail, Common 25, 29, **114**, 287, 288, 299, 300, 303, 304, 306, 307

Rail, Water 33, 36, 42, **115-116**, 286, 289, 296, 297, 298, 302, 304, 305, 307, 308
Raven, Common 25, 27, 29, **239-240**, 295, 300
Razorbill **274**
Redpoll, Arctic **250**
Common 27, 30, 41, **249-250**, 291, 295, 299
Redshank, Common 34, 42, **136-137**, 298, 305
Spotted **136**
Redstart, Common 156, **194-195**, 286
Black **194**
Redwing 30, 40, 200, **201**
Robin 156, **190-191**
American **278**
Roller, European **168**
Rook 20, 23, 39, 40, 41, **238**, 239
Rosefinch, Common 26, 27, 29, 30, 40, 41, **252**, 291, 293, 305
Ruff **131**

Sanderling **128**
Sandgrouse, Pallas' **151-152**
Sandpiper, Baird's **269**
Broad-billed **130-131**
Buff-breasted **270**
Common **139-140**
Curlew 31, **129-130**, 302, 305, 309
Green **138-139**
Marsh **137**
Pectoral **269**
Purple **270**
Slender-billed **270**
Terek **271**
White-rumped **269**
Wood 32, **139**

Scaup, Greater 25, **89-90**, 288, 289, 291, 292, 295, 302, 307, 309
Scoter, Common **91**, 288, 291, 292, 295, 302, 305, 309
Surf **263**
Velvet **91**, 288, 293, 302, 307
Serin, European **244-245**
Shag **261**
Shearwater, Cory's **260**
Shelduck, Common 25, 31, 33, 34, 35, **81-82**, 288, 298, 302, 309
Ruddy 31, **81**, 302
Shoveler, Northern 42, **86**, 286, 289, 296, 298
Shrike, Great Grey 25, **234-235**
Lesser Grey **281**
Red-backed 27, 29, 30, 36, 39, 40, 41, 156, **233-234**
Woodchat **281-282**
Siskin **247-248**
Skua, Arctic **141**
Great **142**
Long-tailed **141-142**
Pomarine **141**
Smew 25, **92-93**, 288, 292
Snipe, Common 42, **132**, 293, 296, 298, 299, 303
Great **132-133**
Jack 26, 289
Snowfinch **243**
Sparrow, House **241-242**
Tree **242**
Sparrowhawk, Eurasian 25, **101-102**, 287, 288, 293, 295, 300, 304, 306, 307, 308
Levant **264**
Spoonbill, Eurasian 9, 31, 33, 34, 35, **74**, 297
Starling, Common **240-241**
Rosy **241**
Stilt, Black-winged 34, 35, **122-123**
Stint, Little 31, **128-129**
Temminck's 31, **129**
Stonechat, Common 20, 23, **196-197**
Stone-curlew 39, **123-124**
Stork, Black 25, 27, 28, 29, 30, 33, 36, 38, 40, 41, 42, **72-73**, 291, 293, 295, 297, 298, 299, 300, 306, 307, 308
White 20, 33, 36, 38, 42, **73-74**, 242, 296, 297, 298, 304, 307
Storm-petrel, European **261**
Swallow, Barn 109, **180-181**
Swamp-hen, Purple **266**
Swan, Mute 28, **76**, 288, 292, 293, 295, 296, 298, 303
Tundra **76-77**
Whooper **77**
Swift, Common **165-166**
Alpine **274-275**
Teal, Blue-winged 11, **262**
Common 42, **83-84**, 286, 295, 296, 298
Tern, Arctic **149**
Black 9, 26, 27, 28, 31, 33, 35, **150-151**, 289, 291, 293, 296, 297, 299, 302, 305, 309
Caspian 26, 32, **147-148**, 289, 302, 303, 305, 307, 309
Common 27, 31, 33, 35, 36, **148-149**, 289, 291, 296, 297, 298, 302, 305, 309
Gull-billed 26, **147**
Little 26, **149**, 296, 305, 309
Sandwich **273**
Whiskered 26, **150**, 289, 303
White-winged Black 26, **151**, 289, 303
Thrush, Dark-throated **277**
Dusky **277**
Eyebrowed **277**
Mistle **201-202**
Rock **276-277**
Song **200-201**, 202
Tit, Azure **227**
Bearded 7, 25, 31, 33, 34, 35, 36, **221-222**, 289, 298, 302, 302, 305
Blue 222, **226-227**, 228
Coal 222, **225-226**, 227
Crested 27, 30, 40, 41, **224-225**
Great 222, **227-228**
Long-tailed **222-223**
Marsh **223**
Penduline 27, 28, 33, 34, 35, 36, 42, **231-232**, 286, 288, 289, 297, 298, 302, 303, 307
Willow **223-224**
Treecreeper, Eurasian **229-230**
Short-toed 33, 34, 38, **230-231**, 287, 288, 291, 298
Turnstone **140**, 291, 309
Twite 26, 31, **249**

Vulture, Monk **97-98**
Egyptian **264**
Griffon **97**

Wagtail, Citrine **185-186**, 309
Grey 25, **186**, 287, 295, 306
Yellow 25, 29, 33, 34, **185**, 286, 298, 302, 305, 309
White 156, **186-187**
Wallcreeper 36, **229**
Warbler, Aquatic 9, 26, **205**, 304
Barred 7, 25, 29, 33, 34, 36, 38, 39, 40, 42, **209-210**, 298, 300, 309
Dartford **278**
Garden 156, **212**
Grasshopper **202-203**, 286, 287
Great Reed 156, **208-209**, 309
Greenish 27, 30, **213-214**
Icterine **209**, 287
Marsh **207**, 287
Melodious **278**
Moustached **205**
Olivaceous **278**,
Orphean **279**
Pallas's Leaf **280**
Radde's **280**
Reed 156, **207-208**, 287
River **203-204**, 286, 287
Sardinian **279**
Savi's **204**, 302, 307
Sedge **205-206**
Western Bonelli's **214**
Willow 156, **216**
Wood 156, **214-215**
Yellow-browed **280**
Waxwing, Bohemian **187-188**
Wheatear, Northern 25, 36, 39, **197**, 291, 293
Black-eared **276**
Whimbrel 32, **135**, 291, 305, 309
Whinchat 29, **195-196**
Whitethroat, Common 156, **211-212**
Lesser 156, **210-211**
Wigeon, American **262**
Eurasian 25, 31, 38, **82**, 288, 289, 289, 295, 296, 302, 307
Woodcock 25, 29, **133**, 295, 299
Woodpecker, Black 25, 27, 30, 33, 34, 36, 38, 40, 41, 42, 153, 163, **171-172**, 287, 288, 295, 297, 298, 299, 306, 307, 308
Great Spotted **172-173**, 291
Green 34, 36, 38, 42, **170-171**, 286, 287, 288, 291, 295, 306, 308
Grey-headed 25, 27, 30, 33, 34, 36, 38, 40, 41, 42, **170**, 286, 287, 288, 297, 298, 306, 307, 308
Lesser Spotted 25, 34, 38, 42, **175**, 288, 295, 299, 308
Middle Spotted 25, 33, 34, 36, 38, 42, **174**, 295, 298, 306, 308
Syrian 7, 34, 36, 38, 39, **173**
Three-toed 27, 30, 40, 41, **176**
White-backed 7, 9, 30, 40, **174-175**, 300
Wren **188-189**
Wryneck 25, 29, 38, **169-170**, 308

Yellowhammer 156, 244, **255-256**, 257
Yellowlegs, Greater **270**

SCIENTIFIC NAMES

Accipiter brevipes **264**
Accipiter gentiles **100-101**
Accipiter nisus **101-102**
Acrocephalus arundinaceus **208-209**
Acrocephalus melanopogon **205**
Acrocephalus paludicola **205**
Acrocephalus palustris **207**
Acrocephalus schoenobaenus **205-206**
Acrocephalus scirpaceus **207-208**
Actitis hypoleucos **139-140**
Aegithalos caudatus **222-223**
Aegolius funereus **163-164**
Aegypius monachus **97-98**
Alauda arvensis **178-179**
Alca torda **274**
Alcedo atthis **166-167**
Alle alle **274**

Anas discors **262-263**
Anas acuta **85**
Anas americana **262**
Anas clypeata **86**
Anas crecca **83-84**
Anas penelope **82**
Anas platyrhynchos **84**
Anas querquedula **85-86**
Anas strepera **83**
Anser albifrons **78**
Anser anser **79**
Anser brachyrhynchos **78**
Anser caerulescens **262**
Anser erythropus **78-79**
Anser fabalis **77**
Anthus campestris **181-182**
Anthus cervinus **183-184**
Anthus novaeseelandiae **276**
Anthus petrosus *11*
Anthus pratensis **183**
Anthus spinoletta **184**
Anthus trivialis **182-183**
Apus apus **165-166**
Aquila chrysaetos **105**
Aquila clanga **104**
Aquila heliaca **105**
Aquila nipalensis **265**
Aquila pomarina **104**
Ardea cinerea **71**
Ardea purpurea **72**
Ardeola ralloides **69-70**
Arenaria interpres **140**
Asio flammeus **163**
Asio otus **162-163**
Athene noctua **160-161**
Aythya ferina **87-88**
Aythya fuligula **89**
Aythya marila **89-90**
Aythya nyroca **88-89**

Bombycilla garrulus **187-188**
Bonasa bonasia **111**
Botaurus stellaris **68**
Branta bernicla **80-81**
Branta canadensis **80**
Branta leucopsis **80**
Branta ruficollis **81**
Bubo bubo **158**
Bubulcus ibis **262**
Bucephala clangula **92**
Bucephala islandica **264**
Burhinus oedicnemus **123-124**
Buteo buteo **102-103**
Buteo lagopus **103**
Buteo rufinus **103**

Calcarius lapponicus **254-255**
Calidris alba **128**
Calidris alpina **130**
Calidris bairdii **269**
Calidris canutus **128**
Calidris ferruginea **129-130**
Calidris fuscicollis **269**
Calidris maritima **270**
Calidris melanotos **269**
Calidris minuta **128-129**
Calidris temminckii **129**
Calonectris diomedea **260**
Caprimulgus europaeus **164-165**
Carduelis cannabina **248-249**
Carduelis carduelis **246-247**
Carduelis chloris **245-246**
Carduelis flammea **249-250**
Carduelis flavirostris **249**
Carduelis hornemanni **250**
Carduelis spinus **247-248**
Carpodacus erythrinus **252**
Catharacta skua **142**
Cepphus grylle **274**
Certhia brachydactyla **230-231**
Certhia familiaris **229-230**
Charadrius alexandrinus **125**
Charadrius dubius **124**
Charadrius hiaticula **125**
Charadrius morinellus **125-126**
Chlamydotis undulata **266**
Chlidonias hybridus **150**
Chlidonias leucopterus **151**
Chlidonias niger **150-151**
Ciconia ciconia **73-74**
Ciconia nigra **72-73**
Cinclus cinclus **188**
Circaetus gallicus **98**
Circus aeruginosus **98-99**
Circus cyaneus **99**
Circus macrourus **99-100**
Circus pygargus **100**
Clangula hyemalis **90-91**
Coccothraustes coccothraustes **254**
Columba livia domestica **152**
Columba oenas **152-153**
Columba palumbus **153-154**
Coracias garrulus **168**
Corvus corax **239-240**
Corvus corone **238-239**
Corvus frugilegus **238**
Corvus monedula **237**
Coturnix coturnix **114**
Crex crex **118**
Cuculus canorus **156**
Cursorius cursor **267**
Cygnus columbianus **76-77**
Cygnus Cygnus **77**
Cygnus olor **76**

Delichon urbica **181**
Dendrocopos major **172-173**
Dendrocopos syriacus **173**
Dendrocopus leucotos **174-175**
Dendrocopus medius **174**
Dendrocopus minor **175**
Dryocopus martius **171-172**

Egretta alba **70-71**
Egretta garzetta **70**
Elanus caeruleus **264**
Emberiza aureola **284**
Emberiza brunniceps **285**
Emberiza calandra **258-259**
Emberiza cia **283-284**
Emberiza cirlus **283**
Emberiza citrinella **255-256**
Emberiza hortulana **256-257**
Emberiza leucocephalos **283**
Emberiza melanocephala **285**
Emberiza pusilla **284**
Emberiza rustica **284**
Emberiza schoeniclus **257-258**
Eremophila alpestris **179-180**
Erithacus rubecula **190-191**

Falco biarmicus **265**
Falco cherrug **109-110**
Falco columbarius **108-109**
Falco naumanni **107**
Falco peregrinus **110-111**
Falco rusticolus **266**
Falco subbuteo **109**
Falco tinnunculus **107-108**
Falco vespertinus **108**
Ficedula albicollis **220**
Ficedula hypoleuca **220-221**
Ficedula parva **219**
Fringilla coelebs **243-244**
Fringilla montifringilla **244**
Fulica atra **119-120**
Fulmarus glacialis **260**

Galerida cristata **177-178**
Gallinago gallinago **132**
Gallinago media **132-133**
Gallinula chloropus **118-119**
Garrulus glandarius **235**
Gavia arctica **61-62**
Gavia immer **62**
Gavia stellata **61**
Gavia adamsi **260**
Glareola nordmanni **268**
Glareola pratincola **267**
Glaucidium passerinum **159-160**
Grus grus **120**
Gyps fulvus **97**

Haematopus ostralegus **122**
Haliaeetus albicilla **96**
Hieraaetus fasciatus **265**
Hieraaetus pennatus **105-106**
Himantopus himantopus **122-123**
Hippolais icterina **209**
Hippolais pallida **278**
Hippolais polyglotta **278**
Hirundo rustica **180-181**
Hoplopterus spinosus **268**
Hydrobates pelagicus **261**

Ixobrychus minutus **68-69**

Jynx torquilla **169-170**

Lanius collurio **233-234**
Lanius excubitor **234-235**
Lanius minor **281**
Lanius senator **281-282**
Larus argentatus **145-146**
Larus audouinii **272**
Larus cachinnans **146**
Larus canus **144-145**
Larus delawarensis **272**
Larus fuscus **145**
Larus glaucoides **272-273**
Larus hyperboreus **273**
Larus ichthyaetus **271**
Larus marinus **146-147**
Larus melanocephalus **142**
Larus minutus **143**
Larus philadelphia **271**
Larus ridibundus **143-144**
Larus sabini **271**
Limicola falcinellus **130-131**
Limosa lapponica **134-135**
Limosa limosa **134**
Locustella fluviatilis **203-204**

Locustella luscinioides **204**
Locustella naevia **202-203**
Loxia curvirostra **251**
Loxia leucoptera **250**
Loxia pytyopsittacus **251-252**
Lullula arborea **178**
Luscinia luscinia **191-192**
Luscinia megarhynchos **192-193**
Luscinia svecica 27, 29, 30, 33, 34, 35, **193**, 297, 298
Lymnocryptes minimus **131-132**

Marmaronetta angustirostris **263**
Melanitta fusca **91**
Melanitta nigra **91**
Melanitta perspicillata **263**
Melanocorypha calandra **275**
Melanocorypha yeltoniensis **275**
Mergus albellus **92-93**
Mergus merganser **93-94**
Mergus serrator **93**
Merops apiaster **167**
Milvus migrans **95**
Milvus milvus **95-96**
Monticola saxatilis **276-277**
Montifringilla nivalis **243**
Morus bassanus **261**
Motacilla alba **186-187**
Motacilla cinerea **186**
Motacilla citreola **185-186**
Motacilla flava **185**
Muscicapa striata **218-219**

Neophron percnopterus **264**
Netta rufina **86-87**
Nucifraga caryocatactes **236-237**
Numenius arquata **135-136**
Numenius phaeopus **135**
Numenius tenuirostris **270**
Nyctea scandiaca **158-159**
Nycticorax nycticorax **69**

Oenanthe hispanica **276**
Oenanthe oenanthe **197**
Oriolus oriolus **232-233**
Otis tarda **121-122**
Otus scops **157-158**
Oxyura leucocephala **94**

Pandion haliaetus **106**
Panurus biarmicus **221-222**
Parus ater **225-226**
Parus caeruleus **226-227**
Parus cristatus **224-225**
Parus cyanus **227**
Parus major **227-228**
Parus montanus **223-224**
Parus palustris **223**
Passer domesticus **241-242**
Passer montanus **242**
Pelecanus onocrotalus **67**
Perdix perdix **113-114**
Pernis apivorus **94-95**
Phalacrocorax carbo **66-67**
Phalacrocorax aristotelis **261**
Phalacrocorax pygmeus **261-262**
Phalaropus fulicarius **141**
Phalaropus lobatus **140**
Phasianus colchicus **115**
Philomachus pugnax **131**
Phoenicopterus ruber **75**
Phoenicurus ochruros **194**
Phoenicurus phoenicurus **194-195**
Phylloscopus bonelli **214**
Phylloscopus collybita **215-216**
Phylloscopus inornatus **280**
Phylloscopus proregulus **280**
Phylloscopus schwarzi **280**
Phylloscopus sibilatrix **214-215**
Phylloscopus trochiloides **213-214**
Phylloscopus trochilus **216**
Pica pica **235-236**
Picoides tridactylus **176**
Picus canus **170**
Picus viridis **170-171**
Pinicola enucleator **252-253**
Platalea leucorodia **74**
Plectrophenax nivalis **255**
Plegadis falcinellus **74**
Pluvialis apricaria **126**
Pluvialis dominica **268**
Pluvialis squatarola **126-127**
Podiceps auritus **65**
Podiceps cristatus **63-64**
Podiceps grisegena **64-65**
Podiceps nigricollis **65-66**
Porphyrio porphyrio **266**
Porzana parva **117**
Porzana porzana **116-117**
Porzana pusilla **266**
Prunella collaris **190**
Prunella modularis **189-190**
Prunella montanella **276**
Pyrrhocorax graculus **282**
Pyrrhula pyrrhula **253-254**

Rallus aquaticus **115-116**
Recurvirostra avosetta **123**
Regulus ignicapillus **217-218**
Regulus regulus **216-217**
Remiz pendulinus **231-232**
Riparia riparia **180**
Rissa tridactyla **147**

Saxicola rubetra **195-196**
Saxicola torquata **196-197**
Scolopax rusticola **133**
Serinus citrinella **283**
Serinus serinus **244-245**
Sitta europaea **228-229**
Somateria spectabilis **263**
Somateria mollissima **90**
Stercorarius longicaudus **141-142**
Stercorarius parasiticus **141**
Stercorarius pomarinus **141**
Sterna albifrons **149**
Sterna caspia **147-148**
Sterna hirundo **148-149**
Sterna nilotica **147**
Sterna paradisaea **149**
Sterna sandvicensis **273**
Streptopelia decaocto **154**
Streptopelia turtur **155**
Strix aluco **161**
Strix uralensis **162**
Sturnus roseus **241**
Sturnus vulgaris **240-241**
Surnia ulula **159**
Sylvia atricapilla **212-213**
Sylvia borin **212**
Sylvia communis **211-212**
Sylvia curruca **210-211**
Sylvia hortensis **279**
Sylvia melanocephala **279**
Sylvia nisoria **209-210**
Sylvia undata **278**
Syrmaticus reevesi **114-115**
Syrrhaptes paradoxus **151-152**

Tachybaptus ruficollis **63**
Tachymarptis melba **274-275**
Tadorna ferruginea **81**
Tadorna tadorna **81-82**
Tetrao tetrix **112**
Tetrao urogallus **113**
Tetrax tetrax **120-121**
Tichodroma muraria **229**
Tringa erythropus **136**
Tringa glareola **139**
Tringa melanoleuca **270**
Tringa nebularia **137-138**
Tringa ochropus **138-139**
Tringa stagnatilis **137**
Tringa tetanus **136-137**
Troglodytes troglodytes **188-189**
Tryngites subruficollis **270**
Turdus iliacus **201**
Turdus merula **198-199**
Turdus migratorius **278**
Turdus naumanni **277**
Turdus obscurus **277**
Turdus philomelos **200-201**
Turdus pilaris **199-200**
Turdus ruficollis **277**
Turdus torquatus **198**
Turdus viscivorus **201-202**
Tyto alba **157**

Upupa epops **168-169**
Uria aalge **273-274**

Vanellus gregarius **268-269**
Vanellus vanellus **127**

Xenus cinereus **271**

Anas spp. 31, 32, 303
Acrocephalus spp. 25, 27, 28, 33, 34, 35, 36, 42, 286, 289, 296, 298, 302, 303
Aythya spp. 31, 32, 303
Calidris spp. 289, 291, 296, 297, 302, 303, 305, 309
Charadrius spp. 291, 296, 297, 302, 305, 309
Locustella spp. 25, 27, 28, 33, 34, 35, 36, 42, 286, 289, 296, 298
Parus spp. 291
Phylloscopus spp. 291
Sylvia spp. 291
Tringa spp. 289, 291, 296, 297, 302, 303, 305, 309